12
Edition

CORRELATIVE
NEUROANATOMY

and

FUNCTIONAL
NEUROLOGY

JOSEPH G. CHUSID, MD

Clinical Associate Professor of Medicine (Neurology)
Seton Hall College of Medicine and Dentistry
Jersey City, New Jersey
Attending Neurologist and Associate Director
Department of Neurology and Neurosurgery
St. Vincent's Hospital, New York

JOSEPH J. McDONALD, MD

Dean of the School of Medicine
American University of Beirut
Beirut, Lebanon

1964

Lange Medical Publications

LOS ALTOS, CALIFORNIA

A Concise Medical Library for Practitioner and Student

Physician's Handbook, 13th Edition, 1964 M. A. Krupp, N. J. Sweet, E. Jawetz, E. G. Biglieri	$4.50
Handbook of Medical Treatment, 9th Edition, 1964 M. J. Chatton, S. Margen, H. Brainerd, Editors	$5.00
Handbook of Pediatrics, 5th Edition, 1963 H. K. Silver, C. H. Kempe, H. B. Bruyn	$4.00
Handbook of Poisoning: Diagnosis & Treatment, 4th Edition, 1963 R. H. Dreisbach	$4.00
Current Medical References, 3rd Edition, 1963 M. J. Chatton, P. J. Sanazaro, Editors	$5.00
Handbook of Surgery, 2nd Edition, 1963 J. L. Wilson, J. J. McDonald, Editors	$4.50

Correlative Neuroanatomy and Functional Neurology,
  12th Edition, 1964
  J. G. Chusid, J. J. McDonald
	$6.00

Review of Physiological Chemistry, 9th Edition, 1963 H. A. Harper	$6.00
Review of Medical Microbiology, 6th Edition, 1964 E. Jawetz, J. L. Melnick, E. A. Adelberg	$6.00
Principles of Clinical Electrocardiography, 5th Edition, 1964 M. J. Goldman	$5.50
General Urology, 4th Edition, 1963 D. R. Smith	$6.00
General Ophthalmology, 3rd Edition, 1962 D. Vaughan, R. Cook, T. Asbury	$5.50
Current Diagnosis & Treatment, 1964 H. Brainerd, S. Margen, M. J. Chatton, Editors	$9.50
Review of Medical Physiology, 1963 W. F. Ganong	$6.50

Preface

This volume is intended for the beginner in neurology and will serve
him best if used as an aid or supplement to standard neurologic texts and
literature. Over the years it has become popular with practitioners,
residents, and graduate physicians preparing for specialty board examinations as a review of neurology. Our primary objective has been to present
simply and clearly some of the structural and functional features of the
nervous system related to problems encountered in clinical neurology.
Concise format, charts, diagrams, and photographs have been prepared
with this purpose in mind. Efforts have been made to include recent important advances in neurology; for the Twelfth Edition, the sections on
clinical neurology have been extensively revised and amplified, and new
chapters on muscle and psychiatric disorders have been added.

We again acknowledge our gratitude and indebtedness to Dr. C.G.
de Gutiérrez-Mahoney, Director of the Department of Neurology and
Neurosurgery of St. Vincent's Hospital, New York, for the use of the
facilities of the Department, and for his continued kind interest in this
book. We extend our sincere thanks also to those authors, publishers,
and editors who graciously permitted the reproduction of various items.

Joseph G. Chusid
Joseph J. McDonald

New York, August, 1964

Table of Contents

SECTION I - CENTRAL NERVOUS SYSTEM

Chapter   1 The Brain   1
            The Cerebral Hemispheres 1
                Physiology and Function 7
            The Basal Ganglia 15
            Extrapyramidal System 17
            Diencephalon 17
                The Thalamus 19
                The Subthalamus 21
                The Epithalamus 21
                The Hypothalamus 23
            The Midbrain (Mesencephalon) 24
            The Brain Stem (Pons and Medulla Oblongata) 29
            The Cerebellum 37
            The Ventricles 41
            Brain Circulation 43
            Blood-Brain Barrier 55
            Composition of Neural Tissue 55
            Cellular Neurochemistry 56
            Brain Metabolism 59
            Embryology 59
Chapter   2 The Spinal Cord   62
            Anatomy 62
            Physiology 68

SECTION II - PERIPHERAL NERVES AND AUTONOMIC SYSTEM

Chapter   3 Introduction   75
Chapter   4 The Cranial Nerves   76
            I - Olfactory Nerve and Tract 81
            II - Optic Nerve and Tract 82
            III, IV, and VI - Oculomotor, Trochlear, Abducens 85
            V - Trigeminal 91
            VII - Facial 93
            VIII - Acoustic 95
            IX - Glossopharyngeal 97
            X - Vagus 99
            XI - Accessory 101
            XII - Hypoglossal 102
            Syndromes Due to Lesions of Last Four Cranial Nerves 104
Chapter   5 The Spinal Nerves   106
            The Cervical Nerves 109
            The Cervical Plexus 109
            The Brachial Plexus 111
            The Musculocutaneous Nerve 115
            The Axillary (Circumflex) Nerve 117
            The Radial (Musculospiral) Nerve 117
            The Median Nerve 119
            The Ulnar Nerve 121
            Combined Median and Ulnar Nerve Lesions 123

Chapter 5 The Spinal Nerves (Cont'd.)
        The Thoracic Nerves 123
        The Lumbar Nerves 124
        The Lumbar Plexus 125
        The Femoral (Anterior Crural) Nerve 127
        The Obturator Nerve 128
        The Sacral Nerves 128
        The Sacral Plexus 129
        The Sciatic Nerve 131
        The Common Peroneal (External Popliteal) Nerve 133
        The Tibial (Internal Popliteal) Nerve 135
        The Pudendal and Coccygeal Plexuses 135
Chapter 6 **The Autonomic Nervous System** 138
        Autonomic Nerves to the Head 141
        Autonomic Nerves to the Urogenital Organs and Rectum 143
          Urinary Bladder 143
          Defecation 145
          Sexual Function 146
        Physiology of the Autonomic System 146
        Pharmacology of the Autonomic System 147
        Disorders of the Autonomic System 147
Chapter 7 **Muscle** 151
        Composition of Muscle 151
        Structure of Muscle 151
        Function of Muscle 153
        Metabolism of Muscle 153
        Muscle Receptors 154

SECTION III - PRINCIPLES OF NEURODIAGNOSIS

Chapter 8 **Motion** 156
        Disturbances in Motor Power 156
        Patterns of Neuronal Assemblies in the Neuraxis 157
        Increased Movements and Disturbances in Tonus 159
        Disturbances in Synergy 163
        Gaits 164
        Deformities and Postures 165
Chapter 9 **Muscle Innervation and Testing** 166
        Segmental Motor Innervation 166
        Muscle Innervation Listed by Individual Nerves 168
        Motor Function Chart 169
        Functional Tests for the Principal Muscles 172
        Muscle Examination Charts 184
        Range of Motion Chart 185
        Superficial Muscles of Head and Neck 186
        Superficial Muscles of Trunk 187
        Superficial Muscles of Right Extremities 188
Chapter 10 **Sensation** 189
        Diseases Characterized by Marked Sensory Disturbances 194
Chapter 11 **Cutaneous Innervation** 197
Chapter 12 **Reflexes** 204
        Anatomy of Reflexes (The Reflex Arc) 204
        Types of Reflexes 204
        Summary of Reflexes 206
Chapter 13 **Aphasia, Apraxia, and Agnosia** 210
Chapter 14 **Trophic Changes** 215
        Diseases Showing Marked Trophic Changes 216
        Sweating 216
Chapter 15 **The Cerebrospinal Fluid** 219
        Cerebrospinal Fluid Findings 222

Chapter 16 Electroencephalography 223
            Representative Electroencephalograms 228
Chapter 17 Electromyography 232
Chapter 18 Electrodiagnostic Examinations 235
Chapter 19 Radiologic Examination. 241
            Roentgenography of the Skull 241
            Intracranial pneumography 247
            Pneumoencephalography 247
            Angiography 251
            Radioisotopic Encephalography 253
            Echoencephalography 253
            Roentgenography of the Spine 254
            Myelography 254
Chapter 20 Cystometry 258
Chapter 21 Audiometry 262
Chapter 22 Psychometric Tests 264

SECTION IV – CENTRAL NERVOUS SYSTEM DISORDERS

Chapter 23 Congenital Defects 266
            Spina Bifida Group 267
            Cranium Bifidum 269
            Congenital Hydrocephalus 269
            Cerebral Palsy (Little's Disease) 270
            Mental Retardation 271
            Mongolism (Mongolian Idiocy) 272
            Tuberous Sclerosis (Epiloia, Bourneville's Disease) 272
            Craniostenosis (Craniosynostosis) 272
            Klippel-Feil Syndrome 272
            Neurofibromatosis (Von Recklinghausen's Disease) 272
            Arnold-Chiari Malformation 273
            Syringomyelia 273
            Platybasia (Basilar Impression) 274
            Cervical Rib Syndrome 274
Chapter 24 Disorders Due to Vascular Disease of the Central Nervous System 275
            Arteriosclerosis of the Brain 275
            Hypertensive Encephalopathy 276
            Cerebrovascular Accidents 276
            Intracranial Aneurysm 283
Chapter 25 Infectious Diseases of the Central Nervous System 289
            Pyogenic Leptomeningitis 289
            Brain Abscess 290
            Less Common Pyogenic Infections 292
            Acute Infantile Hemiplegia 293
            Cytomegalic Inclusion Body Disease 293
            Neurosyphilis 293
            Tuberculous Meningitis 295
            Yeast Meningitis 297
            Epidemic Encephalitis (Von Economo's Disease) 297
            Acute Anterior Poliomyelitis (Heine-Medin Disease) 299
            Rabies 300
            Chorea (Sydenham's Chorea) 300
            Bacterial Neurotoxins 301
Chapter 26 Trauma to the Central Nervous System 302
            Head Injury 302
            Birth Injuries 307
            Spinal Cord Injuries 308
            Herniation of Intervertebral Disk 308
            Low Back Pain 310
            Cervical Spondylosis 311

Chapter 27 Tumors of the Central Nervous System 313
        Intracranial Tumors 313
        Pseudotumor Cerebri 321
        Tumors Within the Spinal Canal 321
Chapter 28 Degenerative Diseases of the Central Nervous System 323
        Multiple Sclerosis 323
        Presenile Dementia (Pick's Disease and Alzheimer's
          Disease) 324
        Senile Degeneration 324
        Paralysis Agitans (Parkinson's Syndrome) 324
        Chronic Progressive Chorea (Huntington's Chorea,
          Adult Chorea) 327
        Hepatolenticular Degeneration (Wilson's Disease) 327
        Friedreich's Ataxia 328
        Familial Spastic Paraplegia 328
        Olivocerebellar and Olivopontocerebellar Atrophy 328
        Hereditary Cerebellar Ataxia With Spasticity
          (Sanger Brown and Marie) 328
        Parenchymatous Cerebellar Degeneration 329
        Hereditary Ataxia With Muscular Atrophy
          (Levy-Roussy Syndrome) 329
        Ataxia Telangiectasia 329
        Acute Cerebellar Ataxia of Children 329
        Schilder's Disease (Encephalitis Periaxialis Diffusa) 329
        Neuromyelitis Optica (Devic's Disease) 329
        Leukodystrophy 329
        Diffuse Sclerosis (Merzbacher-Pelizaeus Type) 329
        Metachromatic Leukoencephalopathy (Greenfield's
          Disease) 329
        Multifocal Leukoencephalopathy 330
        Progressive Subcortical Encephalopathy (Binswanger's
          Disease) 330
        Marchiafava-Bignami Disease (Primary Degeneration of
          Corpus Callosum) 330
        Hereditary Optic Atrophy (Leber's Disease) 330
        Status Marmoratus (Vogt's Disease) 331
        Status Dysmyelinatus 331
        Spastic Pseudosclerosis (Creutzfeldt and Jakob Syndrome) 331
        Hallervorden-Spatz Disease (Pigmentary Degeneration of
          Globus Pallidus) 331
        Dystonia Musculorum Deformans (Torsion Spasm) 331
        Spasmodic Torticollis (Wryneck) 331
Chapter 29 Metabolic and Toxic Disorders of the Nervous System 332
        Blood Diseases 332
          Posterolateral Sclerosis (Subacute Combined System
            Disease) 332
          Neurologic Complications of Other Blood Diseases 333
        Disorders of Lipoid Metabolism (Lipoidoses) 333
        Disorders of Amino Acid Metabolism 334
        Disorders of Carbohydrate Metabolism 336
        Neuroendocrine Disorders 336
          Pituitary Syndromes 336
          Adrenal Syndromes 336
          Thyroid Syndromes 337
          Other Neuroendocrine Disorders 337
        Diseases of Collagen Tissues 338
        Miscellaneous Metabolic Disorders 339
        Neurologic Complications of Drug and Chemical
          Intoxications 340
        Neuropathies 342

Chapter 30 Epilepsy 345
        Epilepsy 345
        Narcolepsy 351
        Breath-Holding Attacks 352
Chapter 31 Syncope and Coma 353
        Vasodepressor Syncope 353
        Carotid Sinus Syncope 353
        Orthostatic Hypotension 355
        Cardiac Functional Change 355
        Impaired Brain Metabolism 356
        Impaired Brain Circulation 356
        Syncope in Hysteria 356
        Coma 356
        Ménière's Syndrome (Paroxysmal Labyrinthine Vertigo) 358
Chapter 32 Headache 359
        Migraine 362
        Histaminic Cephalalgia (Horton's Syndrome) 363
        Tension Headaches 364
        Headaches Due to Meningeal Involvement 364
Chapter 33 Neuromuscular Disorders 366
        Clinical Features 366
        Progressive Muscular (or Nuclear) Atrophies 368
        Progressive Muscular Dystrophy 369
        McArdle's Syndrome 371
        Familial Periodic Paralysis 371
        Central Core Disease 372
        Polymyositis 372
        Myohemoglobinuria 372
        Myasthenia Gravis 372
        Amyotonia Congenita (Oppenheim's Disease) 374
        Myotonia Congenita (Thomsen's Disease) 375
        Myotonia Atrophica (Dystrophia Myotonica) 375
        "Stiff Man" Syndrome 375
        Generalized Myositis Ossificans 375
        Congenital Neuromuscular Disorders 376
Chapter 34 Psychiatric Disorders 378
        Acute Brain Syndrome 378
        Chronic Brain Syndrome 378
        The Psychoses 379
          Affective Reactions 379
          Schizophrenic Reactions 380
        The Neuroses 380
          Anxiety Reaction 381
          Phobic Reaction 381
          Conversion Reaction (Conversion Hysteria) 381
          Obsessive-Compulsive Reaction 381
        Personality Disorders 381
          Personality Trait Disturbances 382
          Personality Pattern Disturbances 382
          Sociopathic Personality 382
        Glossary of Psychologic Terms 383

Appendix 385
        The Neurologic Examination 385
        Visual Field Charts 391
        Neonatal Neurologic Examination 391
        Developmental Screening 393
        Average Development Chart 394
        Rehabilitation Charts 395
Index 397
Selected Reference Textbooks . . . . Back Endsheets

Section I: Central Nervous System

1...

The Brain

The brain is the greatly modified and enlarged anterior portion of the CNS. It is surrounded by 3 protective membranes (meninges) and enclosed within the cranial cavity of the skull. Division into cerebral cortex, basal ganglia, thalamus and hypothalamus, midbrain, brain stem, and cerebellum provides a useful basis for the study of brain localization.

THE CEREBRAL HEMISPHERES

The 2 cerebral hemispheres, which make up the largest portion of the brain, are separated by the deep **longitudinal cerebral fissure.** The **falx cerebri,** a crescent-shaped extension of dura mater, projects into the longitudinal cerebral fissure. The **corpus callosum** is the great white central commissure which crosses the longitudinal cerebral fissure. The body of the corpus callosum is arched; its anterior curved portion, the genu, continues anteroventrally as the rostrum. The thick posterior portion terminates in the curved splenium, which overlaps the midbrain.

The surfaces of the cerebral hemispheres are dorsolateral, medial, and basal. They contain many grooves or furrows, known as fissures and sulci. The portions of brain lying between these grooves are called convolutions or gyri. Some gyri are relatively constant in location and contour, whereas others show considerable variation. The **lateral cerebral fissure** (fissure of Sylvius) separates the temporal from the frontal lobe. Starting at the base of the brain as a deep cleft lateral to the anterior perforated substance, it divides into 3 branches: the anterior horizontal ramus, which ascends into the inferior frontal gyrus; the anterior ascending ramus, which also ascends into the inferior frontal gyrus farther posteriorly; and the posterior ramus, which continues backward and upward to terminate in the parietal lobe.

The **central sulcus** (fissure of Rolando) arises about the middle of the hemisphere, beginning near the longitudinal cerebral fissure and extending downward and forward to about an inch above the lateral cerebral fissure. The **parieto-occipital fissure** passes along the medial surface of the posterior portion of the cerebral hemisphere, runs downward and forward as a deep cleft with much buried cortex, and joins the calcarine fissure. The **calcarine fissure** begins on the medial surface, near the occipital pole, and extends forward to an area slightly below the splenium of the corpus callosum. The rostral portion is deeper and more constant in location and structure. The **cingulate sulcus** begins below the anterior end of the corpus callosum on the medial surface of the hemisphere, continues parallel to the corpus callosum, and finally curves up to the superior medial border a short distance behind the upper end of the central sulcus. The **circular sulcus** (circuminsular fissure) surrounds the insula, or island of Reil, and separates it from the adjacent frontal, parietal, and temporal lobes.

Main Divisions of the Cerebrum.

The cerebral hemisphere may be divided into the frontal, parietal, occipital, and temporal lobes, the insula, and the rhinencephalon.

A. Frontal Lobe: The frontal lobe extends from the frontal pole to the central sulcus behind and the lateral fissure at the side. The **precentral sulcus** passes anterior and parallel to the central sulcus. It is subdivided into the superior and inferior precentral sulci. The **superior and inferior frontal sulci** extend forward and downward from the precentral sulcus, dividing the lateral surface of the frontal lobe into 3 parallel gyri: the **superior, middle, and inferior frontal gyri.** The inferior frontal gyrus is divided into 3 parts by the anterior horizontal and ascending rami of the lateral cerebral fissure: The orbital part lies rostral to the anterior horizontal ramus; the triangular part is the wedge-shaped portion between the

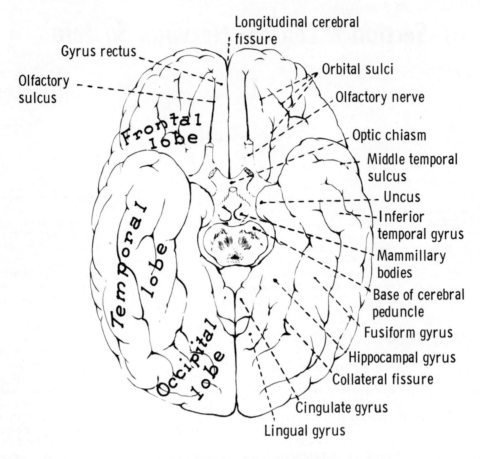

Longitudinal cerebral
fissure

Gyrus rectus

Olfactory
sulcus

Orbital sulci

Olfactory nerve

Optic chiasm

Middle temporal
sulcus

Uncus

Inferior
temporal gyrus

Mammillary
bodies

Base of cerebral
peduncle

Fusiform gyrus

Hippocampal gyrus

Collateral fissure

Cingulate gyrus

Lingual gyrus

Frontal
lobe

Temporal
lobe

Occipital
lobe

Basal View of Cerebrum

anterior horizontal and anterior ascending
rami; the opercular part is between the ascending ramus and the precentral sulcus.

The **orbital sulci and gyri** are irregular in
contour and location. The **olfactory sulcus**
lies beneath the olfactory tract on the orbital
surface; lying medial to it is the gyrus rectus
or **straight gyrus**. The **cingulate gyrus** is the
crescentic or arched convolution on the medial
surface between the cingulate sulcus and the
corpus callosum. The **paracentral lobule** is
the quadrilateral gyrus around the end of the
central sulcus on the medial surface of the
hemisphere.

B. Parietal Lobe: The parietal lobe extends from the central sulcus to the parieto-
occipital fissure and laterally to the level of
the lateral cerebral fissure. The **postcentral
sulcus** extends behind and parallel to the lateral
(Rolandic) fissure, and consists of a superior
and inferior portion. The **intraparietal sulcus**
is a horizontal groove which sometimes unites
with the postcentral sulcus. The **superior pa-**

rietal lobule lies above the horizontal portion
of the intraparietal sulcus, and the **inferior
parietal lobule** lies below.

The **supramarginal gyrus** is that portion of
the inferior parietal lobule which arches above
the ascending end of the posterior ramus of the
lateral cerebral fissure. The **angular gyrus** is
that part which arches above the end of the superior temporal sulcus and becomes continuous
with the middle temporal gyrus. The **posterior
central gyrus** lies between the central and postcentral sulci. The **precuneus** is the posterior
portion of the medial surface between the
parieto-occipital fissure and the ascending end
of the cingulate sulcus.

C. Occipital Lobe: The occipital lobe is
the pyramid-shaped posterior lobe situated behind the parieto-occipital fissure. The **lateral
occipital sulcus** extends transversely along the
lateral surface, dividing the occipital lobe into
a **superior** and **inferior gyrus**. The **calcarine
fissure** divides the medial surface of the occipital lobe into the cuneus and the lingual gyrus.

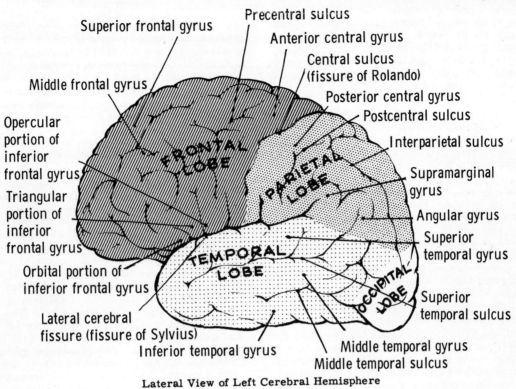

Superior frontal gyrus

Precentral sulcus

Anterior central gyrus

Central sulcus
(fissure of Rolando)

Middle frontal gyrus

Posterior central gyrus

Postcentral sulcus

Opercular
portion of
inferior
frontal gyrus

Interparietal sulcus

Supramarginal
gyrus

Triangular
portion of
inferior
frontal gyrus

Angular gyrus

Superior
temporal gyrus

Orbital portion of
inferior frontal gyrus

Superior
temporal sulcus

Lateral cerebral
fissure (fissure of Sylvius)

Inferior temporal gyrus

Middle temporal gyrus

Middle temporal sulcus

FRONTAL LOBE

PARIETAL LOBE

TEMPORAL LOBE

OCCIPITAL LOBE

Lateral View of Left Cerebral Hemisphere

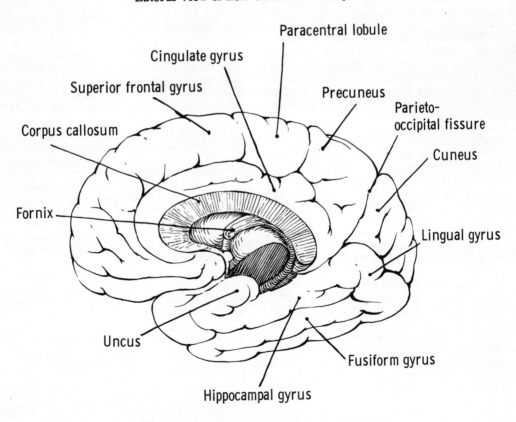

Paracentral lobule

Cingulate gyrus

Precuneus

Superior frontal gyrus

Parieto-
occipital fissure

Corpus callosum

Cuneus

Fornix

Lingual gyrus

Uncus

Fusiform gyrus

Hippocampal gyrus

Medial View of Right Cerebral Hemisphere

The wedge-shaped **cuneus** lies between the calcarine and parieto-occipital fissures. The **lingual gyrus** is between the calcarine fissure and the posterior part of the collateral fissure. The posterior part of the **fusiform gyrus** is on the central or basal surface of the occipital lobe.

D. Temporal Lobe: The temporal lobe portion of the cerebral hemisphere lies inferior to the lateral cerebral (sylvian) fissure and extends back to the level of the parieto-occipital fissure. The **superior temporal sulcus** extends across the temporal lobe parallel to the sylvian fissure. The **middle temporal sulcus** runs parallel to the superior temporal sulcus at a lower level. The **superior temporal gyrus** is the part of the lateral surface of the temporal lobe between the sylvian fissure and the superior temporal sulcus. The **middle temporal gyrus** lies between the superior and middle temporal sulci. The **inferior temporal gyrus** is below the middle temporal sulcus and extends posteriorly to connect with the inferior occipital gyrus. The **transverse temporal gyrus** (Heschl's gyrus) occupies the posterior part of the superior temporal surface (the inferior border of the lateral cerebral fissure). The **inferior temporal sulcus** extends along the inferior surface of the temporal lobe from the temporal pole in front to the occipital pole behind. The **fusiform gyrus** is medial and the **inferior temporal gyrus** lateral to the inferior temporal sulcus. The **hippocampal fissure** extends along the inferomedian aspect of the temporal lobe from the area of the splenium of the corpus callosum to the uncus. The **hippocampal gyrus** lies between the hippocampal fissure and the anterior part of the collateral fissure. Its anterior part curves in the form of a hook and is known as the uncus.

E. Insula: The insula (island of Reil) lies deep within the fissure of Sylvius and can be exposed by separating the upper and lower lips of the fissure. The deep **circular sulcus** bounds the insula. Several **short gyri**, formed by shallow sulci, occupy the anterior portion of the insula; a **long gyrus** occupies the posterior part.

The **opercula** of the insula are portions of the lips of the lateral cerebral fissure. The orbital operculum is anterior and inferior to the anterior horizontal ramus. The frontal operculum lies between the orbital operculum and the anterior ascending ramus. The parietal operculum lies between the frontal operculum and the end of the posterior ramus. The temporal operculum lies below the posterior ramus.

F. Rhinencephalon: The rhinencephalon, a phylogenetically old portion of the cerebral hemisphere, includes the portions associated with the perception of olfactory sensation. The **olfactory bulb**, an oval structure, lies on the cribriform plate of the ethmoid bone and receives the olfactory nerves which have passed upward through the cribriform plate from the olfactory zone of the nasal cavity. The **olfactory tract** lies in the olfactory sulcus on the orbital surface of the frontal lobe. As it passes posteriorly, it divides into the **lateral olfactory stria,** which passes laterally, then medially, to enter the uncus; and the **medial olfactory stria,** which passes medially and up toward the subcallosal gyrus near the inferior aspect of the corpus callosum. The **olfactory trigone** is the small triangular attachment between the medial and lateral olfactory striae, just anterior to the anterior perforated substance. The **anterior perforated substance,** a depressed area of gray matter, extends from the olfactory striae to the optic tract. The **pyriform area** includes the anterior portion of the hippocampal gyrus, the uncus, and the lateral olfactory gyrus. The **subcallosal gyrus** is the portion of gray matter which covers the under aspect of the rostrum of the corpus callosum and is continuous about the genu of the corpus callosum with the supracallosal gyrus. The **supracallosal gyrus** (indusium griseum) is the thin layer of gray matter that extends from the subcallosal gyrus and covers the upper surface of the corpus callosum. The **medial and lateral longitudinal striae** are delicate longitudinal strands which extend along the upper surface of the corpus callosum. The **dentate fascia,** a thin crenated strip of cortex, lies on the upper surface of the hippocampal gyrus. The **hippocampus,** composed chiefly of gray substance, extends the length of the floor of the temporal horn of the lateral ventricle and becomes continuous with the supracallosal gyrus at the splenium of the corpus callosum. The **paraterminal body** is a triangular area of cortex lying just anterior to the lamina terminalis.

The **fornix** is an arched white fiber tract extending from the hippocampal formation. The **alveus** is the white layer on the ventricular surface of the hippocampus containing fibers from the dentate fascia and hippocampus. From the alveus fibers lead to the medial aspect of the hippocampus and form the fimbria, a flat band of white fibers which ascends below the splenium of the corpus callosum and bends forward above the thalamus, forming the crus of the fornix. The **hippocampal commissure** is the collection of transverse fibers connecting the 2 crura of the fornix. The 2 **crura** lie close to the under surface of the corpus callosum and join anteriorly to form the body of the fornix. The **2 columns of the fornix** bend downward and backward from the body to enter the anterior part of the lateral wall of the third ventricle and terminate in the **mammillary bodies of the hypothalamus.**

The **anterior commissure** is a band of white fibers that crosses the midline to join both cerebral hemispheres. It is believed to contain 2 parts: a rostral portion that joins both olfactory bulbs, and a remainder that connects the pyriform areas of both cerebral hemispheres. The **septum pellucidum,** a thin-walled structure separating the lateral ventricles, is situated between the fornix and the corpus callosum. It is composed of 2 thin vertical sheets of tissue, which are sometimes separated by a space, the cavity of the septum pellucidum (cavum septi pellucidi).

White Substance.

The white substance of the cerebral hemisphere contains medullated nerve fibers of many sizes as well as neuroglia. Three types of myelinated nerve make up the center of the cerebral hemisphere: transverse fibers, projection fibers, and association fibers.

Transverse (commissural) fibers interconnect the 2 cerebral hemispheres. The **corpus callosum** is the largest, and most of its fibers arise from various parts of one cerebral hemisphere and terminate in the symmetric area of the opposite cerebral hemisphere. It is a broad transverse structure which forms the roof of the lateral and third ventricles. The **anterior commissure** connects the 2 olfactory bulbs at its rostral part and the 2 pyriform areas at its caudal portion. The **hippocampal commissure** joins the 2 hippocampi.

Projection fibers, some of which pass through the corona radiata to the internal capsule, connect the cerebral cortex with the lower portions of the brain and spinal cord. The **afferent** or **corticipetal fibers** include the geniculocalcarine tract from the lateral geniculate body to the calcarine cortex; the auditory radiation from the medial geniculate body to the auditory cortex (Heschl's gyrus); and thalamic radiations from the thalamic nuclei to specific cerebrocortical areas. **Efferent** or **corticifugal fibers** proceed from the cerebral cortex to the thalamus, brain stem, and spinal cord. The corticospinal and corticobulbar tracts, making up the pyramidal motor system, originate in the motor cortex and proceed inferiorly via the internal capsule. Corticopontile tracts from cerebral cortex to pons include a frontopontile tract, which originates in the frontal lobe cortex and goes to the pontine nuclei; and a temporopontile tract, which terminates sim-

ilarly but originates in the temporal lobe cortex. Corticothalamic fibers pass from the cerebral cortex to the thalamic nuclei. A corticorubral tract extends from the frontal lobe to the red nucleus of the midbrain. The fornix projects in part to the midbrain after originating in the hippocampus.

Association fibers connect the various portions of the same cerebral hemisphere. Short association fibers connect adjacent gyri; those located in the deeper portion of the cortex are known as intracortical fibers, whereas those just beneath the cortex are called subcortical fibers. **Long association fibers** connect more widely separated areas: The **uncinate fasciculus** crosses the bottom of the lateral cerebral fissure and connects the inferior frontal lobe gyri with the anterior temporal lobe. The **cingulum,** a white band lying within the cingulate gyrus, connects the anterior perforated substance and the hippocampal gyrus. The **superior longitudinal fasciculus** connects portions of the frontal lobe with occipital and temporal areas. The **inferior longitudinal fasciculus,** extending parallel to the lateral border of the inferior and posterior horns of the lateral ventricle, connects the temporal and occipital lobes. The **occipito-frontal fasciculus** extends backward from the frontal lobe, radiating into the temporal and occipital lobes. The **fornix** for the most part connects the hippocampus with the mammillary body.

Microscopic Structure of Cortex.

The cortex of the cerebrum may be conveniently considered as being of 2 types: allocortex and isocortex. The **allocortex** is found predominately in the rhinencephalon, or portions concerned with olfaction. The **isocortex** (neocortex) is the more commonly found type of most of the cerebral hemispheres. It is composed of 6 layers of cells which have their embryologic origin in the mass of gray matter surrounding the ventricles: The outermost **molecular layer (I)** contains fibers which come from within the cortex. The **external granular layer (II)** is a rather dense layer composed of small cells. The **external pyramidal layer (III)** contains pyramidal cells, frequently in row formation. The **internal granular layer (IV)** is usually a thin layer with cells similar to those in the external granular layer (II). The **ganglionic layer (V)** in most areas contains pyramidal cells which are fewer but larger than in the external pyramidal layer (III). The **fusiform layer (VI)** is composed of fusiform irregular cells whose axons enter adjacent white matter.

Medullated fiber layers between the cortical layers give the appearance of white lines. The **line of Gennari** in the striate area of the occipital lobe is quite prominent, visible to the naked eye, and forms the outer portion of the internal granular layer (IV). The same line present elsewhere in the cortex is thinner and is known as the **external line of Baillarger.** The **internal line of Baillarger** is formed by the inner portion of the ganglionic layer (V).

Division and classification of the cortex has been attempted by many investigators on the basis of cyto-architecture, and inferences concerning its structure and function are drawn largely from observations on animals, especially monkeys and chimpanzees. The most commonly employed systems are those of Von Economo and Brodmann. Von Economo differentiated 5 main types of isocortex based on the characteristics of lamination or layering. Brodmann labeled individual areas which he believed were different from others with numbers (see p. 12). The areas have been used as a reference base for the localization of physiologic and pathologic processes.

Ablation and stimulation, electrically and with various chemicals, have led to functional localizations. Some of the principal areas are as follows:

(1) Frontal lobe: Area 4 is the principal motor area. Area 6 is a part of the extra-pyramidal tract circuit. Area 8 is concerned with eye movements and pupillary changes. Areas 9, 10, 11, and 12 are frontal association areas.

(2) Parietal lobe: Areas 3, 1, and 2 constitute the postcentral principal sensory area. Areas 5 and 7 are sensory association areas.

(3) Temporal lobe: Area 41 is the primary auditory cortex. Area 42 is the secondary or associative auditory cortex. Areas 38, 40, 20, 21, and 22 are association areas.

(4) Occipital lobe: Area 17 is the striate cortex, the principal visual cortex. Areas 18 and 19 are visual association areas.

Flechsig used the myelogenetic method to make a detailed subdivision of the cerebral cortex by studying the time and pattern of myelination of fibers in white substance immediately beneath the cortex. Initially, Flechsig described 40 cortical fields; this number was later increased.

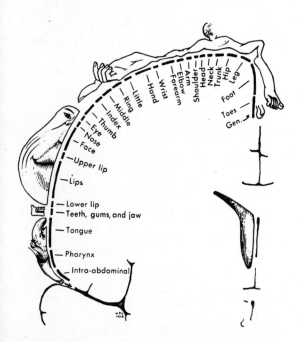

Sensory Homunculus, Drawn Overlying a Coronal Section Through the Postcentral Gyrus.

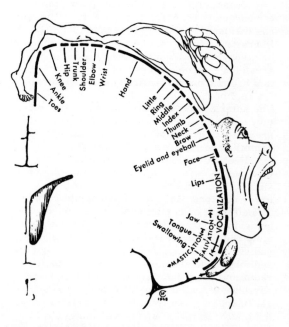

Motor Homunculus, Drawn Overlying a Coronal Section Through the Precentral Gyrus.

The above figures represent the location of cortical representation of the various parts. The size of the various parts is proportionate to the amount of cortical area devoted to them. (Reproduced, with permission, from Penfield & Rasmussen: The Cerebral Cortex of Man: A Clinical Study of Localization of Function. Macmillan, 1950.)

Bailey and Von Bonin have made a tentative sectoral map of the human cerebral cortex (see pp. 10 and 11); they feel that the subdivision into sectors is more logical than the customary division into lobes. The map is based principally on the distribution of corticothalamic afferents. The boundaries of the sectors are only roughly approximate, and density of radiation is not uniform throughout the sectors. The authors feel that the microscopic appearance of cortical sections from parietal, temporal, and large areas of frontal cortex are indistinguishable from each other. Their vivid color map of the cerebral cortex of man, based on cortical cyto-architecture, supports their statement that, "The human isocortex is more remarkable for its uniformity than for multifarious differentiations."

PHYSIOLOGY AND FUNCTION*

The Primary Motor Projection Cortex (Area 4).

The primary motor projection cortex is located on the anterior wall of the central sulcus and the adjacent portion of the precentral gyrus, corresponding generally to the distribution of the giant pyramidal (Betz) cells. These cells control voluntary movements of skeletal muscle on the opposite side of the body, the impulses traveling over their axons in the corticobulbar and corticospinal tracts to the nuclei of the cerebrospinal nerves. The inverted arrangement within the motor areas appears in the diagrams on p. 12. Conjugate deviation of the head and eyes occurs upon stimulation of the posterior part of the middle frontal gyrus (areas 6 and 8). Irritative lesions of the motor centers may cause convulsive seizures, beginning as focal twitchings and spreading to involve large muscle groups (jacksonian epilepsy), modification of consciousness, and postconvulsive weakness or paralysis.

Destructive lesions of the motor cortex (area 4) produce contralateral flaccid paresis or paralysis of affected muscle groups. Spasticity is more apt to occur if area 6 and the intermediate cortex is also ablated. The paralysis following ablation of area 4 is more pronounced in the distal portions of the extremities. Section of the pyramidal tract in the medulla oblongata produces a flaccid paralysis similar to that from cortical ablation of area 4. Therefore, the presence of spasticity is believed to indicate interruption of extrapyramidal pathways.

---

*Numbers in the text refers to Brodmann areas. See p. 12.

The most excitable portion of the cerebral cortex to motor stimulation is area 4. It is believed that the ganglionic layer (V), which contains the Betz cells, significantly affects the excitable characteristics of this area. Transient reduction in excitability occurs in the motor cortex on continuous stimulation; after about 15 seconds, "extinction" may occur in which the motor cortex becomes temporarily unexcitable. **Facilitation** is that phenomenon by which a subthreshold stimulus becomes adequate for stimulation (as through serial repetition). **Suppression** refers to the phenomenon associated with inhibition of striated muscle responses following cerebral cortical or subcortical stimulation.

Stimulation of the "premotor area" (area 6) produces movements similar to those of the motor area (area 4). However, after ablation of area 4 or interruption of fibers between areas 4 and 6, stimulation then produces stereotyped movements accompanied by head turning and torsion of the body. Following premotor (area 6) ablations in monkeys, forced grasping may become evident, best demonstrated with the subject in the lateral position and the affected side uppermost.

The Primary Sensory Projection Cortex (Areas 3, 1, 2).

The primary sensory projection cortex for the reception of general sensations is located in the postcentral gyrus and is called the somesthetic area. It receives fibers from the thalamic radiations conveying skin, muscle, joint, and tendon sense from the opposite side of the body. Irritative lesions of this area produce paresthesias, e. g., numbness, formication, "electric shock," and "pins-and-needles" on the opposite side of the body. Destructive lesions produce objective impairment in sensibility, e. g., an inability to localize or measure the intensity of painful stimuli and a diminution in the various forms of cutaneous sensation. However, complete anesthesia on a cortical basis is rare.

Experimental studies indicate that a relatively wide portion of the adjacent frontal lobe (areas 4 and 6) may also receive sensory stimuli; conversely, motor responses can be achieved by stimulation of the primary sensory areas (3, 1, 2). The primary sensorimotor area may therefore be considered capable of functioning both as motor or sensory cortex, with the portion of the cortex anterior to the central (Rolandic) sulcus predominantly motor and that behind this sulcus predominantly sensory.

Topographic organization exists both in the sensory and motor areas (see p. 6). Recent findings indicate that the primary motor and

Classification of Human Cerebral Cortex by Bailey and Von Bonin	Terminology of Map	Legend
Allocortex	Allocortex	

Isocortex
A. Eulaminate variants
   1. Inferior parietal
   2. Superior parietal
   3. Preoccipital
   4. Inferior frontal
   5. Inferior temporal
	Homotypical isocortex
	   ,, ,,
	   ,, ,,
	   ,, ,,
	   ,, ,,	

B. Agranular variants 1. Simple precentral	Agranular cortex	
2. Gigantopyramidal precentral	Agranular giganto- pyramidal cortex	
3. Limbic juxtallocortical	Mesocortex	

C. Koniose variants
   1. Occipital striate
   2. Postcentral
   3. Supratemporal
	Koniocortex
	   ,,
	   ,,	

D. Limitrophic variants
   1. Occipital, postcentral, and
      supratemporal parakonio-
      cortical
	Parakoniocortex	

2. Temporal juxtallocortical	Juxtallocortex	
3. Frontal dysgranular	Dysgranular cortex	

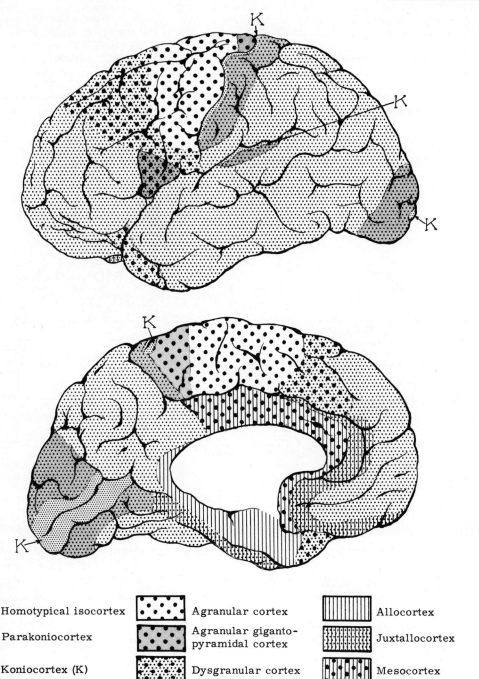

	Homotypical isocortex		Agranular cortex		Allocortex
	Parakoniocortex		Agranular giganto-pyramidal cortex		Juxtallocortex
	Koniocortex (K)		Dysgranular cortex		Mesocortex

Map of Human Cerebral Cortex Based Upon the Original Color Maps of Bailey and Von Bonin. Transitions from one field to another, as well as the lack of sharp boundaries, are indicated in the original maps by blending and shading of colors. See table at left. (Redrawn, modified, and reproduced, with permission, from Bailey and Von Bonin: The Isocortex of Man. University of Illinois, 1951.)

primary sensory areas are arranged topographically on the cerebral cortex as contiguous mirror images.

The cortical taste area is located in the facial sensory area and extends onto the opercular surface of the sylvian fissure.

The Primary Visual Receptive Cortex (Area 17).

The primary visual receptive cortex is located in the occipital lobe in the cortex of the calcarine fissure and adjacent portions of the cuneus and the lingual gyri. Irritative lesions may produce visual hallucinations, e.g., flashes of light, rainbows, brilliant stars, or bright lines. Destructive lesions may cause contralateral homonymous defects in the visual fields without destruction of macular vision. Cortex containing macular representation receives overlapping blood supply from the middle and posterior cerebral arteries.

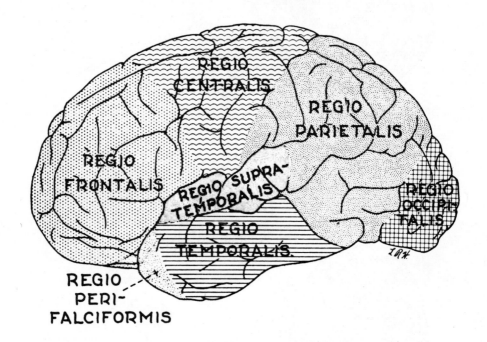

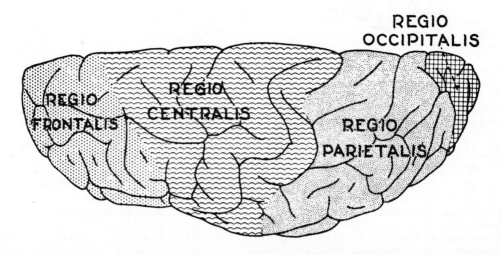

Sectoral Map of the Left Cerebral Cortex Based Upon Distribution of Fibers From Thalamus to Cortex. (Reproduced, with permission, from Bailey and Von Bonin: Ibid.)

The posterior portion of the occipital pole of primates is primarily concerned with macular vision, whereas the more anterior parts of the calcarine fissure are concerned with peripheral vision. Visual association is a function of areas 18 and 19, and injury to these areas may produce visual disorganization with defective spatial orientation in the homonymous halves of the visual field. Area 19 can receive stimuli from the entire cerebral cortex; area 18 receives stimuli mainly from area 17.

Field defects may also be caused by lesions of the parietal or temporal lobes by interference with the optic pathways. Visual hallucinations from temporal lobe lesions may be of formed objects, people, buildings, etc.

The Primary Auditory Receptive Area (Area 41).

The primary auditory receptive area is located in the transverse temporal gyrus (Heschl's gyrus), which lies buried in the floor

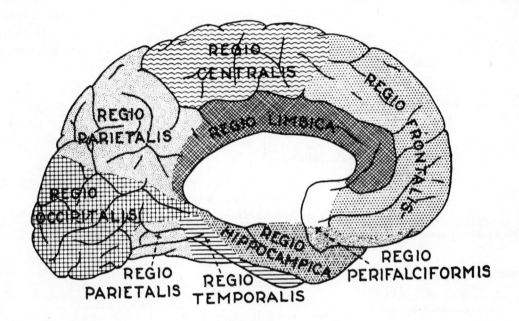

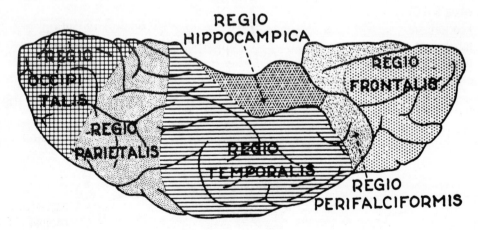

Sectoral Map of the Left Cerebral Cortex Based Upon Distribution of Fibers From Thalamus to Cortex. (Reproduced, with permission, from Bailey and Von Bonin: Ibid.)

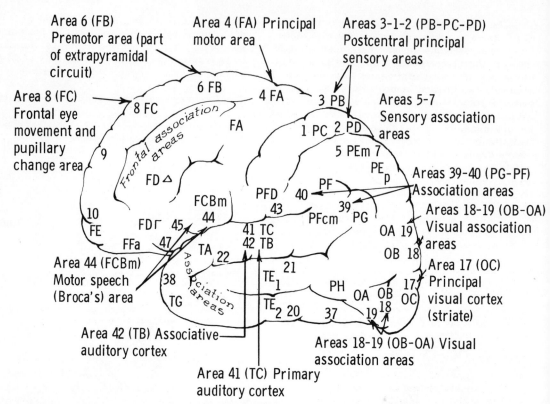

The Lateral Aspect of the Cerebrum. The cortical areas are shown according to Brodmann (numbers) and Von Economo (letters), with functional localizations.

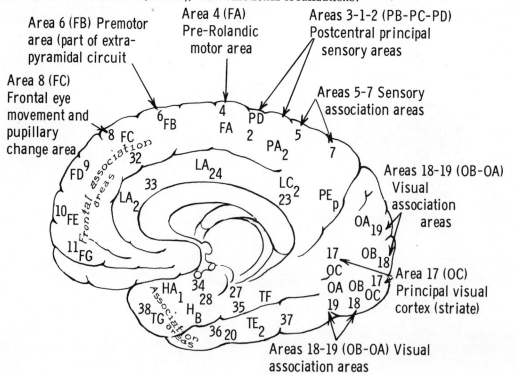

The Medial Aspect of the Cerebrum. The cortical areas are shown according to Brodmann (numbers) and Von Economo (letters), with functional localizations.

of the lateral cerebral fissure (fissure of Sylvius). It receives the auditory radiation from the medial geniculate body, which conveys impulses from the cochlea of each ear; lesions of this area cause dnly mild deafness except when bilateral. Point to point projection of the cochlea upon the acoustic area occurs; in man the low tones are in the frontolateral portion and the high tones in the occipitomedial portion of area 41. In the cochlea, low tones are detected near the apex and high tones near the base.

Stimulation of the region near the primary auditory receptive area in humans causes buzzing and roaring sensations.

The Olfactory Receptive Area.

The olfactory receptive area is located in the uncus and adjacent portions of the hippocampal gyrus of the temporal lobe. Destruction of the olfactory pathways or cortex produces anosmia. Irritative lesions may cause olfactory hallucinations known as "uncinate fits" characterized by sensations of peculiar odors and tastes and often associated with a dreamy state. These may occur as an epileptic aura.

The Association Areas.

The association areas are connected with the various sensory and motor areas by association fibers. They are of importance in the maintenance of higher mental activities in man, although it is not possible to localize any specific mental faculty or fraction of conscious experience. Aphasias or speech defects resulting from cortical lesions illustrate the significance of association areas. In right-handed individuals these are produced by lesions in the left hemisphere (the dominant hemisphere). Motor aphasia may result from destruction of the triangular and opercular portions of the inferior frontal gyrus (area 44). The individual can move his lips and tongue but is unable to carry out the coordinated movements required in speaking. Agraphia (inability to write words) is often associated with motor aphasia. Sensory aphasia results from lesions in the posterior part of the left superior temporal gyrus (area 39). The patient may hear the spoken word but cannot comprehend its meaning. Word blindness, the inability to understand written words although vision is unimpaired, may result from lesions of the angular gyrus (areas 39 and 40).

The frontal lobe, in its portions anterior to the precentral motor area, has long been known as an area concerned with higher intellectual and psychic functions. Classically, destructive lesions of this area may produce facetiousness ("Witzelsucht"), change in moral and social attributes, disinterest in environment and former interests, intellectual deterioration, and distractibility. The orbitofrontal area (areas 9, 10, 11, and 12) receives projections from the dorsomedial nuclei of the thalamus, which in turn has connections with the hypothalamus. Surgical procedures which affect the connections between this portion of the frontal cortex and the thalamus have been used. In general, when used they are most successful in surgical treatment of obsessions, anxiety, schizophrenic psychoses, and intractable pain. Frontal leukotomy and lobotomy sever the cortical-subcortical connections in the frontal lobe usually at about the level of the anterior limit of the lateral ventricles. Topectomy, as the term is generally used, refers to the removal of cortical areas of the brain, usually areas 9 and 10 on both sides. Cortical undercutting is less commonly used; it consists of interrupting the connections just below the cortex. Thalamotomy creates a lesion usually in the dorsomedial nucleus of the thalamus by means of stereotaxic devices. Other methods have also been used to produce uniform subcortical destructive lesions. For the purposes of frontal leukotomy, radiofrequency waves have been applied to stereotactically placed electrodes. In the hope of avoiding the dangers of hemorrhage and sepsis, the Bragg peak of a proton beam has been used to produce precise intracerebral lesions.

The posterior portion of the orbital surface (area 47) and the contiguous portion of the anterior half of the insula produce pronounced autonomic effects upon electric stimulation; inhibition of respiration and alteration of blood pressure may also be readily induced. Upon stimulation of the anterior cingulate area (area 24), which lies on the medial aspect of the cerebral hemisphere, pronounced autonomic effects and inhibition of skeletal muscle tone may occur. Following ablation of this area, aggressive male monkeys become relatively tame, manageable, and less fearful and anxious.

Parietal lobe (areas 5 and 7) association centers are necessary for the correlation of cutaneous sensations, thus enabling an individual to recognize familiar objects placed in his hand (with his eyes closed), a function referred to as stereognostic sense. In lesions of the parietal cortex this ability may be lost (astereognosis).

Secondary or Second Motor and Sensory Areas.

These have been demonstrated in the opercular cortex (parietal lobe) forming the superior wall of the lateral cerebral fissure. These areas have extensive communications with the primary motor and sensory areas.

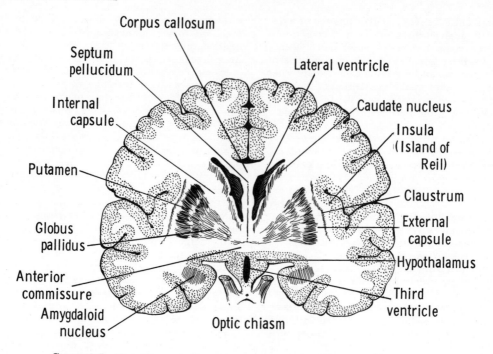

Corpus callosum

Septum pellucidum

Lateral ventricle

Internal capsule

Caudate nucleus

Insula (Island of Reil)

Putamen

Claustrum

External capsule

Globus pallidus

Hypothalamus

Anterior commissure

Third ventricle

Amygdaloid nucleus

Optic chiasm

Coronal Section Through Cerebrum at Level of Anterior Commissure

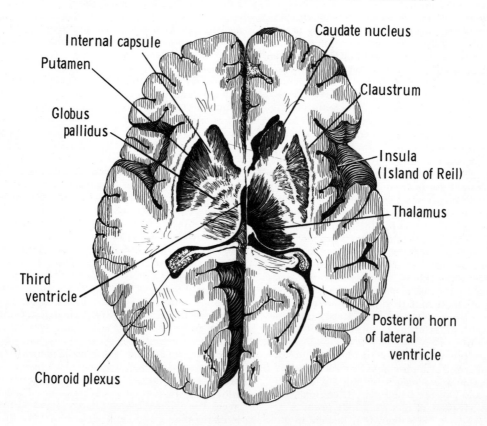

Internal capsule

Caudate nucleus

Putamen

Claustrum

Globus pallidus

Insula (Island of Reil)

Thalamus

Third ventricle

Posterior horn of lateral ventricle

Choroid plexus

Horizontal Sections Through Cerebrum at Two Levels
to Show Basal Ganglia

Supplemental Motor and Sensory Area.

Electric stimulation of a circumscribed zone of cerebral cortex situated on the mesial aspect of the cerebral hemisphere, just anterior to the principal motor area for the foot, is capable of producing characteristic motor responses and occasionally sensory responses.

Rhinencephalon.

Clinical observations and animal experiments indicate that rhinencephalic structures have important functions other than those concerned with olfaction. In primates a variety of autonomic, somatomotor, and somatosensory responses may be produced by electric stimulation of the anterior limbic, subcallosal, and posterior orbital regions of the frontal lobes; the anterior insula, anterior hippocampal gyri, and anterior temporal cortex; and the amygdaloid nuclei. Electric stimulation may inhibit respiratory movements, spontaneous movements such as shivering and swallowing, and motor discharges initiated from the precentral motor cortex; or may produce chewing, swallowing, licking, facio-vocal movements, tonic movements of the trunk and extremities, pupillary changes, pilo-erection, salivation, and involuntary micturition and defecation. The electric activity of the greater part of the cerebral cortex may be altered in various ways by electric stimulation of these structures.

Rhinencephalic structures (such as the anterior limbic area and the posterior orbital surface) may exert an inhibitory effect on brain stem mechanisms concerned in the expression of emotions such as anger. Restlessness and hyperactivity result from lesions affecting these structures.

The term "visceral brain" has been used to designate the limbic system, which includes the limbic lobe and infolded hippocampus, and subcortical cell stations: amygdala, septal nuclei, hypothalamus, anterior thalamic nuclei, parts of the basal ganglia, and probably the epithalamus. The terms limbic lobe, limbic system, and rhinencephalon are used interchangeably. The rhinencephalon has many connections with the hypothalamus and is also concerned with biologic rhythms, sexual behavior, emotions of rage and fear, and motivation. According to MacLean, the medial forebrain bundle is the major afferent and efferent communication between the limbic lobe and brain stem, with 3 major branches to the amygdala, septum, and anterior hypothalamus.

Loss of recent memory may occur following extensive bilateral hippocampal lesions in man.

Electric stimulation of the cortex of the anterolateral or lateral surface of the temporal lobe of man may produce responses which have led Penfield to label this area as "interpretive cortex." He has reported that stimulation of interpretive cortex in man, "(1) may cause the stream of former consciousness to flow again or (2) may give him an interpretation of the present that is unexpected or involuntary." (Science 129:1719, 1959.)

BASAL GANGLIA

Anatomy.

The basal ganglia are masses of gray matter situated deep within the cerebral hemispheres. The corpus striatum presents a striped appearance because of the white fascicles of the internal capsule which are situated between the gray putamen and the caudate nuclei. The caudate nucleus, an elongated gray mass whose pear-shaped head is continuous with the anterior perforated substance, lies adjacent to the inferior border of the anterior horn of the lateral ventricle. The slender end continues backward and downward as the tail, entering the roof of the temporal horn of the lateral ventricle to end at the level of the amygdala. The lenticular or lentiform nucleus is situated between the insula, the caudate nucleus, and the thalamus, and is divided into 2 parts by the external medullary lamina. The putamen is the larger, convex gray mass lying lateral and just beneath the insular cortex. The globus pallidus is the smaller, median triangular zone, whose numerous myelinated fibers make it appear lighter in color. The caudate nucleus sends many fibers to the putamen, which in turn sends short fibers to the globus pallidus. The putamen and globus pallidus receive some fibers from the substantia nigra, and the thalamus sends fibers to caudate nucleus.

Efferent fibers from corpus striatum leave via the globus pallidus. Some fibers pass through the internal capsule and on reaching the medial side form a bundle, the fasciculus lenticularis. Other fibers sweep the mesial border of the internal capsule to form a loop, the ansa lenticularis. Both of these sets of fibers give off some terminals to the subthalamic nucleus; others continue upwards to the thalamus via the fasciculus thalamicus.

The amygdaloid nucleus is a small, spherical gray mass located in the roof of the terminal part of the inferior horn of the lateral ventricle. The amygdala of both cerebral hemispheres are interconnected by white commissural fibers in the anterior commissure. The claustrum is a thin layer of gray substance situated just beneath the insular cortex and separated from the more median putamen by the thin lamina of white matter known as the external capsule.

The **internal capsule** is a broad band of white substance separating the lenticular nucleus from the medial caudate nucleus and thalamus. In horizontal section, it presents a "V" appearance with the apex or genu pointing medially. The anterior limb separates the lenticular from the caudate nucleus and contains thalamocortical and corticothalamic fibers, joining the lateral thalamic nucleus with the frontal lobe cortex; frontopontile tracts from the frontal lobe to the pontine nuclei; and fibers from the caudate nucleus to the putamen.

The posterior limb of the internal capsule, located between the thalamus and the lenticular nucleus, may be divided into 3 parts: lenticulothalamic, retrolenticular, and sublenticular. The anterior two-thirds of the lenticulothalamic part contains the corticospinal tract with the fibers to the arm anterior to the fibers to the leg; corticorubral fibers from the frontal lobe cortex to the red nucleus accompany the corticospinal tract. The retrolenticular part contains fibers from the lateral nucleus of the thalamus to the postcentral gyrus. The sublenticular part, lying below the lenticular nucleus, contains parietotemporopontile fibers

from the temporal and parietal lobe cortex to the pontine nuclei; auditory radiations from the medial geniculate body to Heschl's gyrus (the transverse temporal gyrus); and optic fibers from the geniculate body to the calcarine cortex.

Physiology.

The caudate and lentiform nuclei, together with the fascicles of the internal capsule which separate them, constitute the corpus striatum, an important unit of the extrapyramidal system. The corpus striatum sends efferent projections to the globus pallidus and receives fibers from the frontal lobe, thalamus, and hypothalamus. A major efferent route is from the globus pallidus via the ansa lenticularis to the cerebral nuclei and brain stem nuclei. Upon electric stimulation of the basal ganglia, inhibition of skeletal muscle tone and cortically induced motor responses may occur. The globus pallidus and lateral nuclear groups of the thalamus appear to be focal structures upon which many pathways concerned with motor function converge. These nuclei exert important regulating and controlling influences on motor integration, in addition to relaying afferent systems to the cerebral cortex. The extrapyramidal system

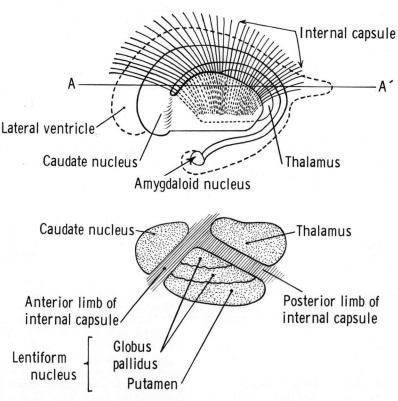

Lateral View of Basal Ganglia and Adjacent Structures With Horizontal Cross Section at Level AA. (Reproduced, with permission, from Buchanan: Functional Neuroanatomy, 2nd Ed. Lea & Febiger, 1951.)

is a functional unit dependent upon an intact lateral corticospinal or pyramidal system.

Primary motor movements are not obtained in most animals following electric stimulation of portions of the basal ganglia, but somatic reactions initiated by the cerebral cortex may be inhibited. In the absence of injury to the cerebral cortex, isolated lesions of the basal ganglia in primates usually give little evidence of positive symptomatology beyond a transient spasticity. When lesions of precentral motor cortical areas coexist with basal ganglia lesions, tremor and choreo-athetosis or a marked increase in rigidity may occur in higher primates.

In man, therapeutic production of lesions of the globus pallidus may reduce tremor and rigidity of patients with parkinsonism or dystonia musculorum deformans.

Secondary lesions made in the region of the globus pallidus and internal capsule may abolish tremors and alter tone of an experimental parkinsonism-like syndrome of monkeys produced by lesions made in reticular substance near the red nucleus and substantia nigra.

EXTRAPYRAMIDAL SYSTEM

The extrapyramidal system has in the past usually been assumed to consist of motor mechanisms of the CNS excluding those of the pyramidal tract. However, anatomic and physiologic separation of the extrapyramidal from the pyramidal tract system has become increasingly more difficult. The extrapyramidal system has come to be considered as a functional rather than an anatomic unit and, as such, may be said to be composed of extrapyramidal portions of cerebral cortex, thalamic nuclei connected with striatum, corpus striatum, subthalamus, rubral, and reticular systems. The extrapyramidal system, in contrast to the more direct pyramidal system, reaches segmental levels of distribution after many detours with neuronal chains synaptically interrupted in basal ganglia, subcortical ganglia, and reticular areas.

The extrapyramidal system may be regarded as a functional system with 3 layers of integration: cortical, striatal (basal ganglia), and tegmental (midbrain). The bulboreticular inhibitory and facilitatory area receives fibers from cerebral cortical areas, the striatum, and the anterior cerebellum. The principal functions of the extrapyramidal system are concerned with associated movements, postural adjustments, and autonomic integration. Le-

sions at any level may obscure or abolish voluntary movements and replace them with involuntary movements.

Clinically important syndromes caused by dysfunction of the extrapyramidal system include the following:

(1) Parkinsonism, in which resting tremors and rigidity occur. The primary destruction is frequently in the globus pallidus, its cortical projection, the substantia nigra, or the reticular substance of the midbrain.

(2) Involuntary movements: Athetosis, chorea, and torsion spasms are frequently associated with lesions of the caudate nucleus and putamen of the striate bodies and the midbrain nuclei.

(3) Involvement of the internal capsule, as frequently occurs with cerebral vascular accidents (e.g., thrombosis or hemorrhage of the lenticulostriate artery), results in a spastic hemiplegia of the opposite side of the body.

The pathophysiology of diseases of the extrapyramidal system is obscure. In general, it is felt that release from suppressor circuit action may occur. Operative measures aimed at interfering with an unsuppressed, relatively overactive circuit (Brodmann area 6 and the extrapyramidal system) or the precentral motor area which this circuit in turn affects may be helpful in overcoming annoying clinical symptoms. Thus, removal of area 6 or 4 and of area 4 alone has overcome severe hemiballism (one-sided jerking and twitching), athetosis, or tremor. Surgical or chemical destruction of the globus pallidus or the ventrolateral nucleus of the thalamus may ameliorate involuntary movements in patients with dystonias or parkinsonism.

Connection between the gamma loop (see p. 160) and the extrapyramidal system seems quite likely since extrapyramidal system disease may result in hypokinetic or rigid syndromes, as well as hyperkinetic, dystonic syndrome including choreic, athetoid, ballistic, myotonic and dystonic syndromes. Muscle innervation may be considered to be directed by either alpha or gamma fiber routes and alterations between these systems may feature extrapyramidal system disease.

DIENCEPHALON

Enclosing the third ventricle is the diencephalon, which includes the thalamus with the geniculate bodies, epithalamus, subthalamus, and hypothalamus.

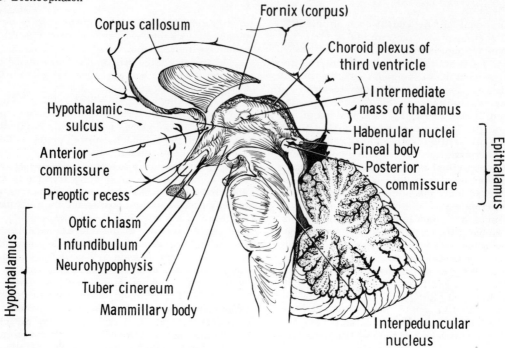

Sagittal Section Through Brain Showing the Diencephalon

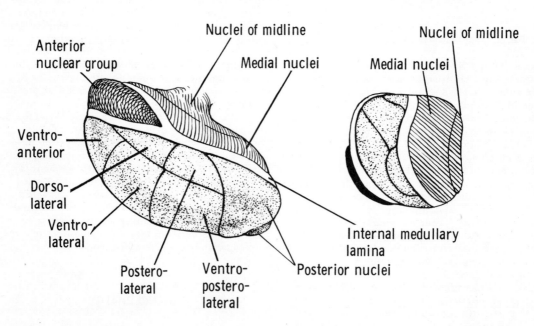

Diagrams of Thalamus (Modified After Netter). Superior surface view and coronal section through posterior third.

THALAMUS

Anatomy.

Each cerebral hemisphere contains a thalamus, a large, ovoid gray mass located on either side of the third ventricle and placed obliquely across the rostral end of the cerebral peduncle. The rostral end (the anterior tubercle) of the thalamus is rather narrow, lies close to the midline, and forms the posterior limit of the interventricular foramen. The posterior end is broader; its prominent medial portion is known as the **pulvinar**, whereas the lateral oval swelling is called the **lateral geniculate body**. The dorsal surface is separated from the more laterally placed caudate nucleus by the **stria terminalis** and the **terminal vein**. The medial surface forms the lateral wall of the third ventricle and is connected with the corresponding surface of the opposite thalamus by the **massa intermedia**, a short communicating bar of gray matter. The **thalamic radiation** refers to the tracts emerging from the lateral surface of the thalamus which then enter the internal capsule and terminate in the cerebral cortex. The **external medullary lamina** is the layer of myelinated fibers on the lateral surface of the thalamus next to the internal capsule. The **internal medullary lamina** is a vertical sheet of white matter which bifurcates in its anterior portion and thus divides the gray matter of the thalamus into a lateral, medial, and anterior portion.

Five groups of thalamic nuclei have been described by A. E. Walker:

(1) Anterior nuclear group. This makes up the tubercle of the thalamus and is separated from the rest of the thalamus by the limbs of the internal medullary lamina. It receives fibers from the mammillary bodies by way of the mammillothalamic tract and projects to the cingulate cortex of the cerebrum.

(2) Nuclei of the midline. Groups of cells located just beneath the lining of the third ventricle and in the massa intermedia which are believed to connect with the hypothalamus and central periaqueductal gray matter.

(3) Medial nuclei: These include most gray substance medial to the internal medullary lamina (intralaminar nuclei) as well as the dorsal medial nucleus, which projects to the frontal cortex of the frontal pole anterior to the motor cortex; and the nucleus of the central medianum, which is believed to connect with the corpus striatum.

(4) Lateral nuclear mass: A large part of the thalamus anterior to the pulvinar between the internal and external medullary lamina. This mass includes (a) a reticular nucleus between the external medullary lamina and the internal capsule; (b) an anterior ventral nucleus which connects with the corpus striatum; (c) a lateral ventral nucleus which projects to the cerebral motor cortex; (d) a posterolateral ventral nucleus which projects to the postcentral gyrus and receives fibers from the medial lemniscus and from the spinothalamic and trigeminal tracts, and (e) a dorsolateral nucleus and a posterolateral nucleus which project to the parietal lobe cortex.

(5) Posterior nuclei: The pulvinar and the medial and lateral geniculate bodies, including (a) the pulvinar nucleus, a large nucleus which connects with the parietal and temporal lobe cortices; (b) the **medial geniculate body**, which lies lateral to the midbrain under the pulvinar and receives acoustic fibers from the lateral lemniscus and inferior colliculus and projects fibers via the acoustic radiation to the temporal lobe cortex (Heschl's gyrus), and (c) the **lateral geniculate body**, which receives most of the fibers of the optic tract and projects via the geniculocalcarine radiation to the visual cortex around the calcarine fissure. It appears as an oval elevation on the lateral portion of the posterior end of the thalamus.

Depending upon anatomic connections, the thalamic nuclei may be considered as nuclei with subcortical connections restricted to the thalamus, hypothalamus, basal ganglia, and subthalamus; cortical relay nuclei, which, after receiving the major sensory system fibers, send projections to the cerebral cortex primary sensory areas; or association nuclei, which project to association areas of the cerebral cortex, receive no fibers from the major sensory systems, and have connections with other diencephalic nuclei.

Function.

The thalamus rather than the sensory cortex may be the crucial structure for the perception of some types of sensation, and the sensory cortex may function to give finer detail to the sensation.

The "thalamic syndrome" (thalamic apoplexy, Déjerine-Roussy syndrome) is characterized by immediate hemianesthesia. Later, the threshold to pinprick, heat, and cold is raised; when sensation is felt, it is a disagreeable and unpleasant one, sometimes referred to as thalamic hyperpathia. The syndrome usually appears during the phase of recovery from a thalamic infarct. The pains are persistent and greatly aggravated by emotional stress and fatigue and are described as distressing, burning, drawing, pulling, swelling, or "tension."

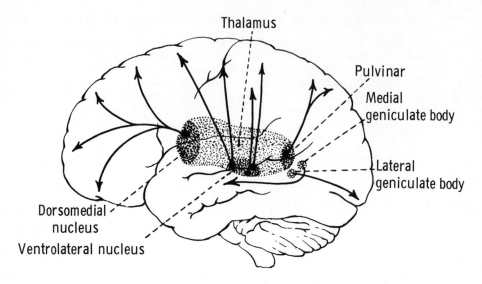

Diagram of Principal Thalamocortical Projections

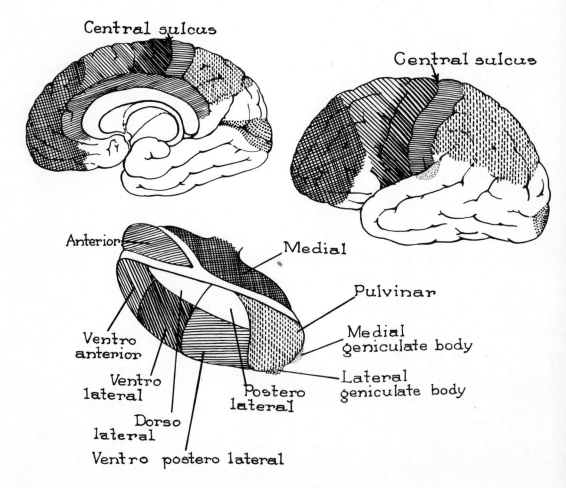

Diagrams of Principal Thalamocortical Projections Showing Relation of Cortical Areas to Thalamic Nuclei. (Redrawn from original drawings by Frank H. Netter, M.D., which first appeared in Ciba Clinical Symposia, copyright 1950. Reproduced with permission.)

The dorsomedial nucleus of the anterior portion of the thalamus and its projections to the frontal lobe are usually the site of surgical attack in frontal lobotomy and leukotomy. If the frontal pole of the cerebral hemisphere is removed, degeneration of the dorsomedial nucleus subsequently occurs. The ventrolateral nucleus of the anterior portion of the thalamus projects to the primary motor and sensory areas of the cerebral hemispheres (areas 1, 3, 4, 6). This nucleus is a relay on the path from the red nucleus. Thalamotomy by interruption of the ventrolateral nucleus of the thalamus has been used in the treatment of patients with parkinsonism as well as in patients with dystonia musculorum deformans. The pulvinar, a large nuclear mass in the posterior portion of the thalamus, sends projection fibers to the parietal cerebral cortex; it may serve to integrate auditory, visual, and somatic impulses. The medial geniculate body is a thalamic nucleus which has been displaced downward. It projects to the primary auditory area of the temporal lobe (Brodmann area 41) and receives fibers from the lateral lemniscus. The lateral geniculate body lies lateral to the medial geniculate body and projects via the geniculocalcarine tract to the visual cortex of the occipital lobe.

Stimulation of the ventrolateral nucleus of the thalamus produces inhibition of contralateral muscle spindle discharge if the sensorimotor cortex remains intact. The muscle spindle which is innervated by the slow, small motor fibers of the ventral motor root (gamma efferents) is believed to register differences between the main muscle mass and itself. Muscle innervation from cortical levels may be considered to be effected by either the alpha or gamma route. The alpha route is direct or through relays to alpha anterior horn cells and thence to muscle. The gamma route is to the gamma cells of the anterior horn of the spinal cord and thence to muscle spindle. Alterations of the balance between alpha and gamma systems may produce altered muscle tone.

Thalamocortical interrelations: The spontaneous electric activity of the cerebral cortex may be affected by stimulation of the midline nuclei of the thalamus, and a thalamic reticular system has been described in this area which is believed to be a continuation of the reticular systems of the brain stem. The "nonspecific" projection fibers from the thalamic reticular system play an important role in sustaining and regulating the normal resting rhythms of the cortex. Stimulation of the thalamic reticular system in animals via implanted electrodes may result in transient maintenance of the posture at the time of stimulation. Although thalamocortical circuits which influence the electric activity of the thalamus and cortex are believed to exist, it must be borne in mind that both the thalamus and the cerebral cortex may show rhythmic electric activity after interruption of the interconnecting fibers; however, this activity is usually depressed or of abnormal form. Corticifugal projections to the thalamus also assist in regulation of the thalamic reticular system activity. Local self-sustained epileptic discharges of the thalamus may be projected to the local cortical area, simulating focal cortical epilepsy.

SUBTHALAMUS

The subthalamus is the zone of brain tissue which lies between the tegmentum of the midbrain and the dorsal thalamus. The hypothalamus lies medial and rostral to it; lateral to it lies the internal capsule. The **red nucleus** and **substantia nigra** extend into its caudal part from the midbrain. The **subthalamic nucleus** or body of Luys is a cylindric mass of gray substance dorsolateral to the upper end of the substantia nigra which extends posteriorly as far as the lateral aspect of the red nucleus. It receives fibers from the globus pallidus, forming a part of the efferent descending path from the corpus striatum.

Anterior to the red nucleus are the **fields of Forel,** containing cells which may be a rostral extension of reticular nuclei. Fibers from the globus pallidus occupy these fields. The ventromedial portion is usually designated as field H. The dorsomedial portion is designated as field H_1. The ventrolateral portion is designated as field H_2. From the globus pallidus, the **fasciculus lenticularis** (field H_2) runs medially. It is joined by the **ansa lenticularis** bending acutely in field H. The thalamic fasciculus extends through field H_1 to the anterior ventral nucleus of the thalamus. The **zona incerta** is a thin zone of gray substance above the fasciculus lenticularis.

EPITHALAMUS

The epithalamus consists of the pineal body, the posterior commissure, and the habenular trigone. The **habenular trigone,** a small depressed triangular area anterior to the superior colliculus, contains the **habenular nuclei,** which receive fibers from the stria medullaris and are joined together via the ha-

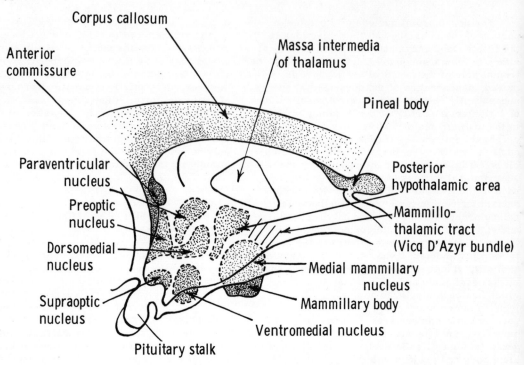

Diagram Showing the Hypothalamic Nuclei Projected onto the Lateral Wall of the Third Ventricle. (Reproduced, with permission, from W. E. Le Gros Clark, The Topography and Homologies of the Hypothalamic Nuclei in Man, J. Anat. **70**:204, 1936.)

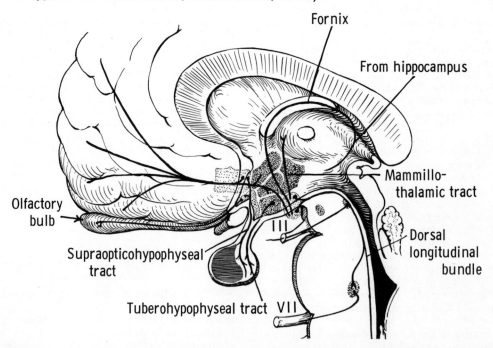

Diagram to Illustrate Chief Hypothalamic Connections. (Redrawn from original drawings by Frank H. Netter, M.D., which first appeared in Ciba Clinical Symposia, copyright 1950. Reproduced with permission.)

benular commissure; and the **habenulopeduncu-lar tract** (retroflex tract of Meynert), which extends from the habenular nucleus to the interpeduncular ganglion in the midbrain.

The **pineal body** is a small mass lying in the depression between the superior colliculi. Its base is attached by a stalk. The ventral lamina of the stalk is continuous with the posterior commissure and the dorsal lamina with the habenular commissure. At their proximal end the laminas of the stalk are separated, forming the **pineal recess** of the third ventricle.

The **posterior commissure** is a cylindric band of white fibers which crosses the median plane on the dorsal aspect of the rostral end of the cerebral aqueduct (aqueduct of Sylvius). Some of its fibers connect the 2 superior colliculi.

HYPOTHALAMUS

The hypothalamus lies below or ventral to the thalamus and forms the floor and part of the inferior lateral walls of the third ventricle. It includes the following: (1) the **mammillary bodies,** 2 adjacent pea-sized white masses inferior to the gray matter of the floor of the third ventricle and rostral to the posterior perforated space; (2) the **tuber cinereum,** an eminence rostral to the mammillary bodies; (3) the **infundibulum,** a hollow process extending downward from the under surface of the tuber cinereum to the posterior lobe of the hypophysis; and (4) the **optic chiasm.**

The lower portion of the infundibulum is continuous with the neural lobe of the hypophysis. The enlarged upper portion of the infundibulum, the median eminence, the infundibular stem, and the neural lobe of the hypophysis constitute the **neurohypophysis.**

Each half of the hypothalamus may be divided into a supraoptic, a tuberal, and a mammillary portion. The **supraoptic** portion is farthest anterior; the **tuberal** portion lies immediately behind the supraoptic portion; and the **mammillary** portion is farthest posterior. Anterior to the hypothalamus, between the optic chiasm and the anterior commissure, is a region referred to as the **preoptic area.**

The nuclei of the hypothalamus may be classified as follows:

(1) Anterior: The **paraventricular nucleus** is a flat sheet of cells lying close to the lining of the third ventricle. The **supraoptic nucleus** lies above the optic chiasm and extends along the anterior part of the tuber cinereum. It contains an especially rich network of capillaries.

The supraoptic nucleus gives rise to the supraopticohypophysial tract, which extends to the neurohypophysis by way of the pituitary stalk.

(2) Lateral: The lateral nucleus includes the lateral part of the tuber cinereum.

(3) Middle: The **ventromedial hypothalamic nucleus** is an oval mass of cells anterior to the mammillary bodies and posterior to the supraoptic nucleus. The dorsomedial hypothalamic nucleus is a mass lying above the ventromedial hypothalamic nucleus.

(4) Posterior: The cells of the posterior hypothalamic area lie above and immediately anterior to the mammillary bodies. Nuclei of the mammillary body include the **medial mammillary nucleus,** which makes up the protuberance of the mammillary body; and the **lateral mammillary nucleus,** located between the lateral border of the medial nucleus and the base of the brain. The nucleus intercalatus lies in the dorsal portion.

Afferent connections to the hypothalamus which have been described include (1) the **medial forebrain bundle,** which sends fibers to the hypothalamus from nuclei in the parolfactory area and corpus striatum; (2) **thalamohypothalamic fibers** from the medial and midline thalamic nuclei; (3) the fornix, which brings fibers from the hippocampus to the mammillary bodies; (4) the **stria terminalis,** which brings fibers from the amygdala; (5) **pallido-hypothalamic fibers,** which lead from the lenticular nucleus to the ventromedial hypothalamic nucleus; and (6) the **inferior mammillary peduncle,** which sends fibers from the tegmentum of the midbrain.

Efferent tracts from the hypothalamus include (1) the **hypothalamico-hypophysial tract,** from the supraoptic nuclei to the neurohypophysis; (2) the **mammillotegmental tract** to the tegmentum; (3) **hypothalamic-thalamic tracts,** including the tract of Vicq d'Azyr from the mammillary nuclei to the anterior thalamic nuclei; (4) the **periventricular system,** including the dorsal fasciculus of Schütz to lower brain levels; and (5) the **tubero-hypophysial tract,** from the tuberal portion of the hypothalamus to the posterior pituitary.

Function.

The hypothalamus is believed to have diversified activities. Lesions of the hypothalamic region may produce a variety of symptoms, including diabetes insipidus, obesity, sexual dystrophy, somnolence, loss of sexual appetite, and loss of temperature control. A visual defect such as bitemporal hemianopsia frequently is associated due to involvement of the nearby optic chiasm.

Animals whose cerebral hemispheres have been removed may exhibit "sham rage," in which struggling, pilo-erection, dilatation of pupils, and increase in blood pressure occur on slight provocation. If only the posterior hypothalamus is removed, this reaction does not appear. Studies indicate that removal of the neocortex may produce placidity. If the amygdaloid nuclear complex and the pyriform lobe are removed bilaterally from a placid animal, a state of ferocity follows.

Somnolence may be caused regularly by bilateral lesions of the lateral hypothalamic area. Temperature regulation disorders may be associated with hypothalamic lesions. Experimental lesions of the anterior hypothalamus may cause hyperthermia; lesions of the posterior nuclei are associated with hypothermia.

Diabetes insipidus may be caused by destruction of the neurohypophysis, the supraoptic nuclei, or the tract connecting these structures. Production of antidiuretic hormone ceases, and the patient passes excessive quantities of sugar-free urine of low specific gravity. Specialized vesicular bodies in the supraoptic nuclei have been described. These are believed to be sensitive to small changes in the osmotic pressure of blood from the internal carotid artery.

Disturbances of fat metabolism as a result of hypothalamic lesions are known to occur in rats and probably occur in other animals as well as man.

Proposed mechanism of emotion: J. W. Papez has suggested that the hypothalamus, the anterior thalamic nuclei, the cingulate gyrus, the hippocampus, and their interconnections may serve as a structural and functional unit for emotion.

THE MIDBRAIN
(Mesencephalon)

Anatomy.

The midbrain is the short portion of the brain between the pons and the cerebral hemispheres. The dorsal portion of the midbrain (the tectum) contains the 4 corpora quadrigemina; the ventrolateral portions contain the 2 cerebral peduncles. The **corpora quadrigemina** consist of 4 rounded eminences arranged in pairs, the superior and inferior colliculi, which are separated from each other by a cruciate sulcus. The **superior colliculi** are larger and darker than the inferior colliculi and are associated with the optic system. The superior quadrigeminal brachium extends laterally from them and connects with the **lateral geniculate body.** The **inferior colliculi** are more prominent than the superior colliculi and are associated with the auditory system. The inferior quadrigeminal brachium extends laterally to the medial geniculate body.

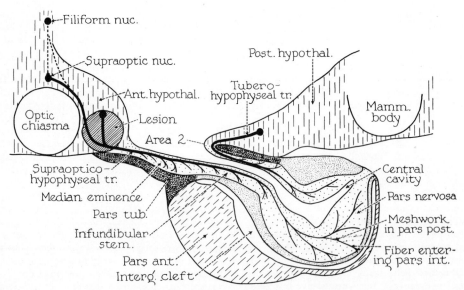

Diagram of a Midsagittal Section Through the Hypothalamus of the Cat, Showing the Supraoptico-hypophysial Tract, Whose Interruption Causes Diabetes Insipidus. (Reproduced, with permission, from Fisher, Ingram, and Ranson: Diabetes Insipidus and the Neurohormonal Control of Water Balance. Edwards, 1938.)

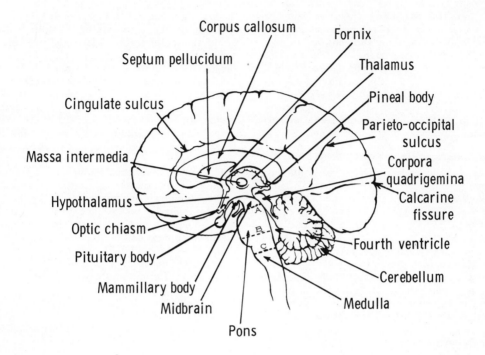

Corpus callosum
Fornix
Septum pellucidum
Thalamus
Cingulate sulcus
Pineal body
Parieto-occipital sulcus
Massa intermedia
Corpora quadrigemina
Calcarine fissure
Hypothalamus
Optic chiasm
Fourth ventricle
Pituitary body
Cerebellum
Mammillary body
Medulla
Midbrain
Pons

Midsagittal Section of the Brain. (Dotted lines do not indicate lines of demarcation of divisions of the brain but the levels at which sections are cut as shown below and on p. 27.)

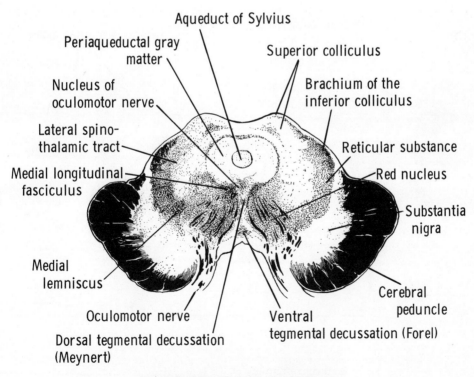

Aqueduct of Sylvius
Periaqueductal gray matter
Superior colliculus
Nucleus of oculomotor nerve
Brachium of the inferior colliculus
Lateral spino-thalamic tract
Reticular substance
Medial longitudinal fasciculus
Red nucleus
Substantia nigra
Medial lemniscus
Cerebral peduncle
Oculomotor nerve
Ventral tegmental decussation (Forel)
Dorsal tegmental decussation (Meynert)

Cross Section Through the Midbrain
at the Level of the Superior Colliculus (Dotted Line A, Above)

The **cerebral peduncles** converge from the lower surface of the cerebral hemispheres toward the midline, entering the pons on its upper surface. The interpeduncular fossa is the depressed area between the peduncles which contains in its lower portion the **interpeduncular ganglion,** the terminus for the retroflex bundle of Meynert from the habenular ganglion. The ventral portion of each peduncle is known as the **base,** a broad, compact crescentic structure. The corticospinal tract occupies the middle three-fifths of the base, the frontopontile tract is located in the medial fifth, and the temporopontile tract is in the lateral fifth. Corticobulbar fibers accompany the corticospinal tract. The **substantia nigra** is a broad layer of pigmented gray substance separating the ventral portion or base from the tegmentum and extending from the upper surface of the pons to the hypothalamus. It is believed to receive fibers from the corpus striatum via the strionigral tract; other connections with cerebral peduncles, subthalamic nucleus superior colliculi, and reticular substance may also exist.

The **tegmentum** is the dorsal portion of the cerebral peduncle. It contains the lateral lemniscus, whose fibers turn laterally and lead to the inferior colliculus and the medial geniculate body. Just ventral to the lateral lemniscus is a group of fibers containing the **spinothalamic** and **spinotectal tracts.** The **medial lemniscus** forms, with the trigeminal lemniscus, a triangular bundle medial to the spinothalamic tract. The **medial longitudinal fasciculus** is in the dorsomedian part close to the central gray substance. The **red nucleus** is a large oval mass of gray substance located in the rostral part of the tegmentum on the path of the superior cerebellar peduncle. The **rubrospinal tract** arises in the posterior portion of the red nucleus and decussates early in the ventral tegmental decussation (decussation of Forel). The **superior cerebellar peduncles** enter the tegmentum and decussate beneath the central gray matter at the level of the inferior colliculus. The **tectospinal** and **tectobulbar tracts** decussate ventral to the oculomotor nucleus in the dorsal tegmental decussation (fountain decussation of Meynert). **Reticulothalamic bundles** run lateral to the medial lemniscus.

The **nucleus of the trochlear nerve** is situated in the ventral part of the central gray substance at the level of the inferior colliculus. The **nucleus of the oculomotor nerve** lies rostral to the nucleus of the trochlear nerve in the ventral part of the central gray substance beneath the superior colliculus. The **nucleus of**

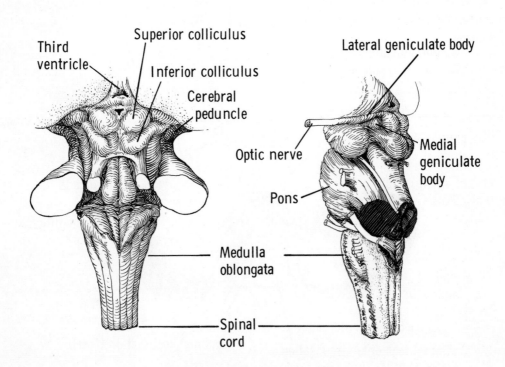

External Anatomy of the Midbrain

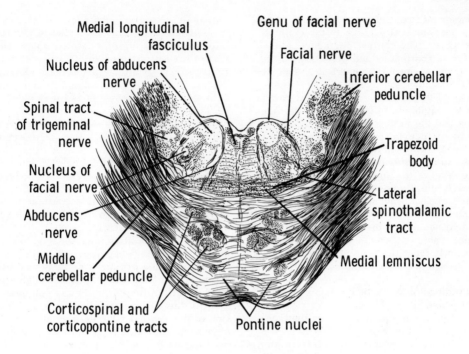

Medial longitudinal fasciculus

Nucleus of abducens nerve

Spinal tract of trigeminal nerve

Nucleus of facial nerve

Abducens nerve

Middle cerebellar peduncle

Corticospinal and corticopontine tracts

Genu of facial nerve

Facial nerve

Inferior cerebellar peduncle

Trapezoid body

Lateral spinothalamic tract

Medial lemniscus

Pontine nuclei

**Cross Section Through the Pons
at the Level of the Facial Colliculus (Dotted Line B, p. 25)**

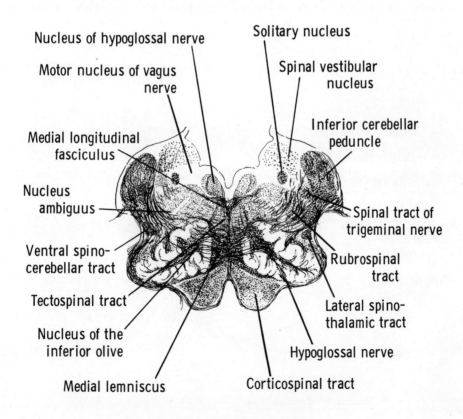

Nucleus of hypoglossal nerve

Motor nucleus of vagus nerve

Medial longitudinal fasciculus

Nucleus ambiguus

Ventral spino-cerebellar tract

Tectospinal tract

Nucleus of the inferior olive

Medial lemniscus

Solitary nucleus

Spinal vestibular nucleus

Inferior cerebellar peduncle

Spinal tract of trigeminal nerve

Rubrospinal tract

Lateral spino-thalamic tract

Hypoglossal nerve

Corticospinal tract

**Cross Section Through Medulla
at the Level of the Inferior Olive (Dotted Line C, p. 25)**

the mesencephalic root of the trigeminal nerve lies in the dorsolateral surface of the central gray substance. The central periaqueductal gray matter is continuous posteriorly with the gray substance of the third ventricle. The nucleus of Darkschewitsch lies in the ventrolateral section of this area. The reticular formation of the midbrain is continuous with that of the pons and the reticular nucleus of the thalamus (zona incerta) and the lateral hypothalamic area. The red nucleus, an ovoid large mass in the anterior part of the tegmentum at the level of the superior colliculus, extends upward into the posterior portion of the subthalamic area. Fibers leave this nucleus to go to the reticular formation nuclei, the lateroventral nucleus of the thalamus, and the rubrospinal tract. Afferents to the nucleus proceed chiefly from the superior cerebellar peduncle, globus pallidus, and frontal cortex.

Clinical Findings of Disturbed Mesencephalic Function.

Symptoms which may arise from destructive lesions of the midbrain are usually a reflection of the structure involved. Destruction of the corpora quadrigemina causes paralysis of upward movements of the eyes. Destruction of the third and fourth cranial nerve nuclei gives rise to the classical syndromes of paralysis of these nerves (see pp. 89 and 90). Destruction of the red nucleus, the substantia

nigra, or reticular substance (as occurs in encephalitic states) may give rise to involuntary movements and rigidity (see p. 156). Destruction of the cerebral peduncle gives rise to spastic paralysis of the contralateral side due to destruction of the corticospinal tract. Cats with experimentally produced lesions of the periaqueductal gray substance resemble in behavior humans with akinetic mutism. A cataleptic state comparable to flexibilitas cerea may occur following destruction of portions of the tegmentum of the midbrain in cats. A syndrome of "obstinate progression" occurs in cats with destructive lesions of the interpeduncular area. These animals continue to push and attempt to walk against interposed resistance, such as a restraint or wall.

Irritative lesions may conceivably occur but are not well recognized. In animals, electric stimulation produces definite reactions: Stimulation of the quadrigeminal region may produce dilatation of pupils and conjugate movement of the eyes to the opposite side. Stimulation of the ventral surface may give rise to slow tonic movements of the extremities. Stimulation of the red nucleus may cause involuntary movements of the extremities in decorticate primates. Clinical syndromes may be correlated to the portions of the midbrain involved. Lesions of the ventral portion of the midbrain may produce clinical features of Weber's syndrome; lesions of tegmentum may

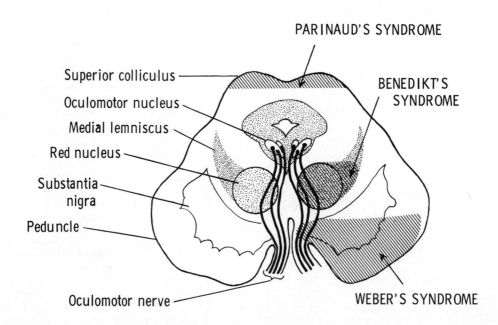

PARINAUD'S SYNDROME

Superior colliculus

Oculomotor nucleus

Medial lemniscus

Red nucleus

Substantia nigra

Peduncle

Oculomotor nerve

BENEDIKT'S SYNDROME

WEBER'S SYNDROME

Clinical Syndromes Associated With Midbrain Lesions

produce clinical picture of Benedikt's syndrome. Disorders or lesions involving the superior colliculi of the tectum or roof of the midbrain may produce Parinaud's syndrome.

Weber's syndrome is characterized by ipsilateral ophthalmoplegia and contralateral hemiplegia. The ophthalmoplegia results from oculomotor nerve or nucleus interruption and the hemiparesis from involvement of the cerebral peduncle with its corticospinal tract.

Benedikt's syndrome is characterized by ipsilateral ophthalmoplegia and contralateral hyperkinesia such as tremor, chorea, athetosis. It results from a lesion of tegmentum which destroys oculomotor nerve and red nucleus of one side of the midbrain.

Parinaud's syndrome refers to conjugate ocular paralysis in the vertical plane so that there is paralysis of upward gaze. It is associated with lesions or disorders of the quadrigeminal plate of the midbrain, especially the superior colliculi, as occurs when this area is compressed by tumor of the pineal body.

THE BRAIN STEM
(Pons and Medulla Oblongata)

Anatomy of the Pons.

The pons lies ventral to the cerebellum and anterior to the medulla, from which it is separated by a groove through which the abducens, facial, and acoustic nerves emerge.

A. External Structure: The anterior limits of the pons are marked by the 2 cerebral peduncles which appear on both sides of the midline. The **brachium pontis,** also known as the **middle cerebellar peduncle,** connects the bulging ventral portion with the cerebellum. The triangular posterior or dorsal surface is concealed by the cerebellum.

B. Internal Structure: The basilar or ventral portion of the pons contains a thick superficial layer, the **superficial transverse fibers,** which give rise to the brachium pontis; **deep transverse fibers,** which lie dorsal to the corticospinal tract and also contribute to the brachium pontis; and **longitudinal fasciculi,** which lead from the cerebral peduncles into the pons.

The longitudinal fasciculi consist of (1) the **corticospinal tract,** which occupies the middle three-fifths of the cerebral peduncle, enters the pons and breaks up into small bundles, and then becomes relatively compact again as it leaves the pons; (2) the **corticobulbar fibers,** which originate in the medial portion of the cerebral peduncle, enter the pons, and pass dorsally toward the cranial nerve nuclei; (3) the **frontopontine tract** (Arnold's bundle), which originates from Brodmann area 6 of the cerebral cortex and then traverses the anterior limb of the internal capsule and the medial fifth of the cerebral peduncle to terminate in ipsilateral pontine nuclei; and (4) the **parietotemporopontine tract** (Türck's bundle), which leads from the parietal and temporal cortex through the posterior limb of the internal capsule and the lateral fifth of the cerebral peduncle, terminating in the ipsilateral pontine nuclei.

The pontine nuclei are small collections of nerve cells profusely scattered among the transverse fiber bundles.

The dorsal or tegmental portion of the pons consists mainly of the rostral continuation of the gray substance and the reticular formation of the medulla. The **trapezoid body** is the group of transverse fibers in the caudal portion of the tegmentum pons, continuous with the lateral lemniscus. The **medial lemniscus** lies along the midline of the medulla and shifts ventrally and then laterally in the pons, where it courses through the ventral portion of the reticular formation and then crosses the trapezoid body at right angles.

The **ventral spinocerebellar tract** turns dorsolaterally near the rostral end of the pons, winds about the superior cerebellar peduncle, and enters the vermis of the cerebellum. The **medial longitudinal fasciculus** receives many of its fibers from vestibular nuclei and lies in the mid-dorsal portion of the reticular formation.

Cranial nerve nuclei in the pons: The **nucleus of the abducens nerve** lies in the dorsomedial area just beneath the floor of the fourth ventricle. Its fibers pass ventrally between lateral bundles of the corticospinal fibers to exit at the groove separating the pons and the medulla. The **nucleus of the facial nerve** is dorsal to the superior olivary nucleus. Its fibers run dorsomedially toward the floor of the fourth ventricle, make an acute compact bend at the medial side of the abducens nucleus, then turn laterally through the pons to exit at the lower border between the olive and the inferior cerebellar peduncle. The **motor nucleus of the trigeminal nerve** and the **main sensory nucleus of the trigeminal nerve** are located close together in the dorsolateral portion of the reticular formation. The sensory nucleus is located more laterally, and the tracts which arise from it are functionally comparable to the posterior columns of the spinal cord. The **nucleus of the descending spinal tract of the trigeminal nerve** is a continuation of the substantia gelatinosa

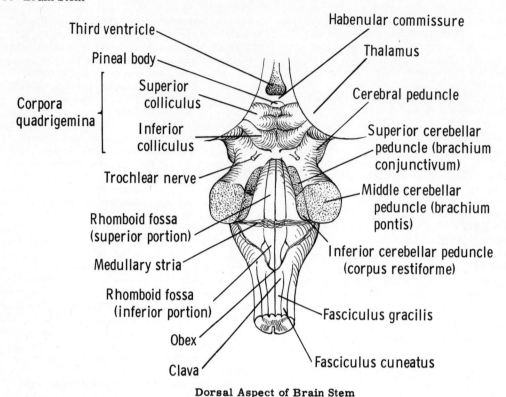

Third ventricle
Habenular commissure
Pineal body
Thalamus
Superior colliculus
Cerebral peduncle
Corpora quadrigemina
Inferior colliculus
Superior cerebellar peduncle (brachium conjunctivum)
Trochlear nerve
Middle cerebellar peduncle (brachium pontis)
Rhomboid fossa (superior portion)
Inferior cerebellar peduncle (corpus restiforme)
Medullary stria
Rhomboid fossa (inferior portion)
Fasciculus gracilis
Obex
Clava
Fasciculus cuneatus

Dorsal Aspect of Brain Stem

PONTOCEREBELLAR ANGLE SYNDROME
Medial longitudinal fasciculus
Sup. vestibular nucleus
Spinal tract V
Nucleus of spinal tract V
VIII
VII
Corticospinal and corticobulbar tracts
VI
ALTERNATING ABDUCENT HEMIPLEGIA

Clinical Syndromes Associated With Pontile Lesions

rolandi of the spinal cord, and the spinal tract is functionally similar to the spinothalamic tract.

The **nuclei of the vestibular nerve** make up a diamond-shaped mass of gray matter in the floor and lateral wall of the fourth ventricle in the pons and the medulla. The **superior vestibular nucleus** (nucleus of Bechterew) is situated in the angle of the floor and lateral wall of the fourth ventricle just behind the trigeminal motor nucleus. The **medial vestibular nucleus** (nucleus of Schwalbe), the largest of the vestibular nuclei, occupies part of the area acoustica of the rhomboid fossa. Fibers pass from it to the medial longitudinal fasciculus, cranial nerve nuclei, and cerebellum. The **lateral vestibular nucleus** (nucleus of Deiters) is next to the inferior cerebellar peduncle at the level of the vestibular nerve entrance and gives rise to the fibers of the vestibulo-spinal tract. The **inferior vestibular nucleus**, or nucleus of the descending tract of the vestibular nerve, extends from the lateral nucleus to the cuneate nucleus in the medulla and lies medial to the inferior cerebellar peduncle and dorsal to the spinal trigeminal tract.

Nuclei of the cochlear nerve (acoustic nuclei) include the **dorsal cochlear nucleus**, located on the dorsolateral surface of the inferior cerebellar peduncle; and the **ventral cochlear nucleus**, located in the ventrolateral region of the inferior cerebellar peduncle at the level of the entrance of the auditory fibers

The **reticular formation** of the pons is similar to that of the medulla.

Clinical Syndromes of the Pons.

Certain clinical syndromes may be characteristically associated with lesions of the pons. Lesions of the more ventral portion of the inferior pons may produce alternating abducent hemiplegia, Millard-Gubler syndrome, or Foville's syndrome. Lesions of the lateral pons, so often associated with tumors growing in the pontocerebellar angle, may produce a characteristic clinical picture. Lesions of the ventral portion of the mid pons may produce alternating trigeminal hemiplegia. More extensive lesions of the inferior pons may produce clinical features of Raymond-Cestan syndrome.

Alternating abducent hemiplegia is featured by ipsilateral lateral rectus paresis and contralateral hemiplegia. It may occur with softening of the paramedian area of pons due to involvement of the abducens nerve and corticospinal tract.

A. Millard-Gubler Syndrome: A form of crossed paralysis (facial hemiplegia alternans) produced by a pontile lesion and characterized by contralateral hemiplegia and ipsilateral facial palsy. In many cases the sixth serve is also involved, producing an internal strabismus.

B. Foville's Syndrome: A form of crossed hemiplegia from a pontile lesion. Consists of contralateral hemiplegia with ipsilateral palsies of the sixth and seventh cranial nerves, internal strabismus with diplopia, and paralysis of the muscles of facial expression.

C. Raymond-Cestan or Cestan-Chenais Syndrome: Quadriplegia, anesthesia, and nystagmus due to softening in the pons resulting from thrombosis of twigs of the basilar artery supplying this region and involving the pyramidal tracts, medial lemnisci, and medial longitudinal fasciculus.

D. Pontocerebellar Angle Tumor Syndrome: Caused by acoustic neurinomas involving primarily the fifth and eighth cranial nerves but may also affect cranial nerves VI, VII, IX, X, and XII.

1. Cranial nerve symptoms - VIII, persistent tinnitus, progressive deafness, and vertigo; V, ipsilateral facial anesthesia with loss of corneal and sneeze reflexes; VI, internal squint; IX, dysphagia; X, syncope; XII, ipsilateral paralysis of the tongue with thick speech.

2. Cerebellar and peduncular symptoms - Ipsilateral ataxia with staggering, vertigo, and hypotonia of the leg and arm.

3. Motor and sensory symptoms - Contralateral hemiplegia and slight hemianesthesia from pressure on the pathways in the pons.

4. General symptoms of brain tumor - Signs of increased intracranial pressure (papilledema, etc.) develop sooner or later.

E. Alternating trigeminal hemiplegia may result from a lesion of ventral pons involving corticospinal tract and fibers of the adjacent trigeminal nerve. Clinically there may be contralateral hemiplegia and ipsilateral paralysis of jaw muscles and loss of sensation over ipsilateral face in the trigeminal nerve distribution.

Anatomy of the Medulla Oblongata.

The medulla oblongata is the pyramid-shaped portion of the brain stem between the spinal cord and pons. The lower half contains a central canal; the dorsal portion of the upper half forms the floor of the body of the fourth ventricle.

A. External Structure: The **anterior median fissure** extends along the ventral surface to terminate at the pontine border in the **foramen cecum.** In its lower portion, the anterior median fissure is crossed by the obliquely decussating pyramidal tracts. The **posterior median fissure**, a shallow groove along the dorsal lower half of the medulla, ends at the posterior limit of the fourth ventricle. The **median sulcus** is a longitudinal groove in the midsagittal portion of the floor of the fourth ventricle. The **anterior lateral sulcus** is a shallow furrow on the anterolateral surface; the fibers of the hypoglossal nerve emerge from the medulla in this furrow. The **posterior lateral sulcus** is a furrow on the posterolateral surface; the spinal accessory, vagus, and glossopharyngeal nerves emerge from the medulla in this furrow.

The following subdivisions of the medulla may be made: (1) The anterior (ventral) section (between the anterior median fissure and the anterior lateral sulcus) contains the pyramid, formed by the corticospinal tract. The pyramidal decussation is the area where the majority of the fibers from one pyramid cross to the opposite side. The medial longitudinal fasciculus lies anteriorly in the lower portion of the medulla. (2) The lateral (middle) section (between the anterior and posterior lateral sulci) contains a prominent mass, the olive, in its upper portion. (3) The posterior (dorsal) section (between the posterior lateral sulcus and posterior median fissure or median sulcus) contains, in its lower portion, the **funiculus gracilis** and **funiculus cuneatus**. At the lower end of the fourth ventricle, these columns diverge from the midline and present elongated swellings; that on the funiculus gracilis is the **clava**, and that on the funiculus cuneatus is the **cuneate tubercle**. The upper portion of the posterior section is occupied by the inferior cerebellar peduncle (restiform body), which forms the floor of the lateral recess of the fourth ventricle. The striae medullares cross the floor of the fourth ventricle transversely, extending across the inferior peduncle.

B. Internal Structure: Within the substance of the medulla are situated certain gray nuclear areas. The **hypoglossal nucleus** is located near the ventrolateral portion of the central canal in the lower half of the medulla; its upper part lies a short distance from the midline under an eminence called the hypoglossal trigone. The nerve roots of the hypoglossal nerve pass ventrally to emerge at the anterior lateral sulcus. The **nucleus ambiguus**, the somatic motor nucleus of the glossopharyngeal, vagus, and spinal accessory nerves, lies in the reticular formation ventromedial to the nucleus of the spinal tract of the trigeminal nerve. Fibers from it pass toward the floor of the fourth ventricle and then turn sharply ventrolaterally to join the

fibers of the dorsal nucleus of the vagus nerve. The **dorsal motor nucleus of the vagus** lies dorsolateral to the hypoglossal nucleus and gives rise to fibers which join the motor roots of the vagus and spinal accessory nerves. The **nucleus salivatorius** is said to be located in reticular formation near the junction of the medulla oblongata and the pons. The **nucleus of the tractus solitarius** lies ventrolateral to the dorsal motor nucleus of the vagus and extends the length of the medulla. The **sensory nucleus of the vagus** is dorsomedial to the nucleus of the tractus solitarius and lateral to the dorsal motor nucleus of the vagus. The **dorsal and ventral cochlear nuclei** are located at the dorsal and ventral borders of the inferior cerebellar peduncle near the pontine border.

The **reticular substance**, containing scattered groups of cells, is a continuation of the reticular substance of the spinal cord which extends upward through the midbrain and thalamus. The **inferior olivary nucleus** is located within the olive; olivocerebellar fibers extend through the hilum of the olive, decussate, and enter the opposite inferior cerebellar peduncle as the **internal arcuate fibers**. The **medial accessory olivary nucleus** lies between the inferior olivary nucleus and the pyramid. The **dorsal accessory olivary nucleus** is a small nucleus dorsal to the inferior olivary nucleus. The **nucleus gracilis** and **nucleus cuneatus** are large masses of gray substance located in the posterior funiculi of the posterior portion of the medulla. Within the brain stem, a central system called the centrencephalic system has been postulated which may be involved in integration of the functions of both cerebral hemispheres or of different functions from various portions of the same hemisphere.

Fiber tracts: Fibers from the nucleus gracilis and nucleus cuneatus, known as **internal arcuate fibers**, cross in the **decussation of the lemniscus** and continue thereafter in the **medial lemniscus**, which is identified as a broad band dorsomedial to the pyramids. The **dorsal spinocerebellar tract** and the more ventromedial **ventral spinocerebellar tract** lie close to the lateral surface. The **spinal tract of the trigeminal nerve**, superficial and lateral to the **nucleus of the spinal tract of the trigeminal nerve**, lies in the dorsolateral portion of the medulla.

Clinical Findings in Lesions of Medulla.

Lesions of the brain stem produce symptoms referable to involvement of the motor and sensory pathways passing through it and particularly to involvement of the nuclei of the cranial nerves which lie within it. The symp-

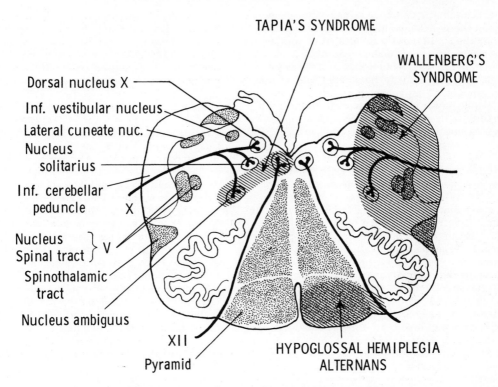

TAPIA'S SYNDROME

WALLENBERG'S SYNDROME

Dorsal nucleus X

Inf. vestibular nucleus

Lateral cuneate nuc.

Nucleus solitarius

Inf. cerebellar peduncle   X

Nucleus
Spinal tract } V

Spinothalamic tract

Nucleus ambiguus

XII

Pyramid

HYPOGLOSSAL HEMIPLEGIA ALTERNANS

Clinical Syndromes Associated With Medullary Lesions

toms are discussed under the heading of the individual cranial nerves in Chapter 4 and under bulbar syndromes on p. 105.

Clinical syndromes may be related to the portion of the medulla oblongata involved. Lesions of the ventral portion of the upper medulla may produce hypoglossal hemiplegia alternans (alternating hypoglossal hemiplegia), while lesions of the dorsolateral area of the upper medulla may produce Wallenberg's syndrome, so often associated with posterior inferior cerebellar artery disease. Involvement of the more central area of the upper medulla may produce a variety of clinical pictures depending upon the cranial nuclei and other structures involved, such as the syndrome of Jackson, Avellis, Schmidt, etc. (See p. 105 for details of bulbar syndromes involving the last 4 cranial nerves.)

A. **Decerebrate rigidity**, in which there is an exaggerated posture with continuous spasm of muscles, especially the extensors, was first produced by Sherrington in animals by transection of the brain at a prepontile level. Since it was shown that intact vestibular nuclei were necessary for decerebrate rigidity to persist, the disorder was believed to be caused by re-

lease of vestibular nuclei from higher extrapyramidal control. Experimental studies have suggested the presence of a **facilitatory and inhibitory center** in the reticular substance extending from the medulla to the midbrain. The interplay of various pathways on these centers is considered to play an important part in reflex postural mechanisms. Experimental destruction of the inhibitory center causes decerebrate rigidity, which implies that an exaggeration or abundance of stimuli from the cortex and higher levels reaches the spinal cord and produces hyperactive extension reflexes and spasticity. In contrast, experimental destruction of the facilitatory center produces an opposite effect: decreased tone and limp, relaxed muscles.

In decerebrate rigidity the extensor muscles exhibit **lengthening** and **shortening reactions**. These reactions require intact posterior roots. The **shortening reaction** refers to the behavior of an extensor muscle which, after its ends have been passively approximated, resists subsequent attempts at lengthening. It is believed to depend upon the stretch reflex. The **lengthening reaction** is a phenomenon in which there is first great resistance to passive lengthening of an extensor muscle, then sudden overcoming of resistance (clasp-knife phenomenon); the lengthened muscle then remains lengthened. **Plasticity** results from combined shortening and lengthening reactions.

In primates, decerebration produced at a high level (cortical) is associated with strong semiflexion of the upper extremities, whereas in low decerebrations the typical decerebrate rigidity is produced with extension of upper as well as lower extremities.

B. Integration of reflexes concerned with swallowing, vomiting, respiration, and cardiovascular control occurs in the medulla oblongata. The respiratory center in the medulla is composed of an inspiratory and expiratory portion. Electric stimulation of the ventral reticular portion of the medulla in animals produces forced, fixed deep inspiration. Similar stimulation of the reticular formation lying more dorsally and rostrally may produce expiration. Cardiovascular reflexes essential for maintenance of blood pressure, vasopressor and vasodilator reflexes, and some cardiac reflexes require an intact medulla. Cheyne-Stokes respiration, with periodic breathing characterized by intense hyperventilation alternating with apnea, is believed due to increased respiratory sensitivity to carbon dioxide resulting from bilateral descending motor system dysfunction at higher levels, and moderate arterial oxygen desaturation.

Animal studies indicate that the integrating mechanism for vomiting lies in the lateral reticular formation of the medulla. Two anatomically close but functionally distinct units are recognized: (1) an **emetic center** in the region of the fasciculus solitarius and the underlying reticular formation, which may be activated directly by visceral afferent stimulation from the gastrointestinal tract and which is close to areas concerned in spasmodic respiration, salivation, inspiration and expiration, vasomotor control, postural tone control, and the vestibular nuclei; and (2) a **chemoreceptor trigger zone**, which lies superficially in the floor of the fourth ventricle and is sensitive to drugs like apomorphine and intravenous copper sulfate but requires an intact emetic center to produce vomiting.

The medulla is concerned functionally with the eighth, ninth, tenth, eleventh, and twelfth cranial nerves, whose nuclei lie therein (see Chapter 4).

C. Some basic **postural reactions** require an intact medulla (vestibular nuclei). **Postural reflexes** of several types are recognized: (1) Local static reflexes affect single extremities and are exemplified by the positive and negative

supporting reactions. In the **positive supporting reaction**, stimulation of the animal's foot causes the toes to separate and the limb to become rigidly fixed to support weight. The **negative supporting reaction** refers to the inhibition of the weight-supporting posture by flexion of distal parts of the extremity. (2) Segmental static reflexes are those in which a stimulus in one extremity affects the homologous opposite extremity. (3) General static reflexes originate in one segment and affect motor responses in other segments.

D. Tonic Neck Reflexes (Magnus–de Kleijn): After destruction of both labyrinths, the following reactions may be obtained in decerebrate dogs and cats (sectioned at the level of the medulla) and in primates (sectioned at the level of the midbrain): (1) Rotation of the head causes extension of the extremities on the jaw side and flexion of the opposite extremities. (2) Deviation of the head without rotation also causes extension of extremities on the jaw side and contralateral extremity flexion. (3) Dorsiflexion of the head produces extension of the upper extremities and relaxation of the lower extremities. (4) Ventroflexion of the head produces flexion of the upper extremities and extension of the lower extremities.

E. **Tonic labyrinthine reflexes** can be elicited in decerebrate animals in whom posterior root section of the upper cervical nerves (to exclude tonic neck reflexes) has been done. **Acceleratory reflexes** follow stimulation of the semicircular canals with production of nystagmus. **Positional reflexes** arise from stimulation of the otolithic maculae of the labyrinths and are concerned with the righting reflexes.

F. The **righting reflexes** function to maintain the top side uppermost: (1) Labyrinthine righting reflexes maintain the head's orientation in space and require an intact midbrain. (2) Body righting reflexes acting upon the head keep the head orientated with respect to the body and require an intact midbrain. (3) Body righting reflexes acting upon the body, arising from receptors on the body surfaces, tend to keep the body orientated in space and require an intact midbrain. (4) Neck righting reflexes arising in the neck keep the body orientated with respect to the head and require an intact medulla. (5) Optical righting reflexes keep the head in proper orientation and depend upon an intact occipital cortex.

The Reticular Activating System.

A portion of the central cephalic brain stem and adjacent areas composed of reticular

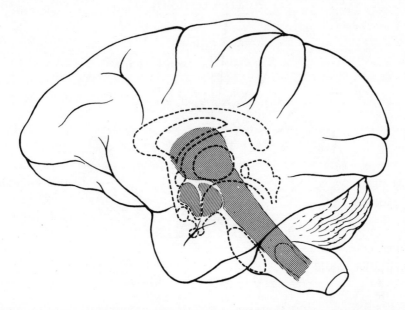

Phantom Drawing of the Monkey Brain With the Brain Stem and Hypothalamic Structures Indicated by Hatching. A bulbar zone which yields generalized inhibition of motor responses throughout the neuraxis is indicated by the lines at right angles to the axis of the brain stem. The more cephalad parts of the brain stem augment motor responses generally. An anterior (mainly parasympathetic) zone of the hypothalamus and a posterior (mainly sympathetic) zone are suggested as being in intimate relation with the anterior brainstem, in fact, their anatomic separation is artificial. Jointly, these regions constitute an ascending reticular activating system which provides the background of neuronal activity essential to movement visceral or somatic. (Reproduced, with permission, from Livingston: Some brain stem mechanisms relating to psychosomatic function. Psychosom. Med 17.347-54, 1955)

formation, subthalamus, hypothalamus, and medial thalamus has been shown in animal experiments to be essential for initiation and maintenance of alert wakefulness. The reticular activating system may be considered to be essential for arousal from sleep, wakefulness, alerting or focusing of attention, perceptual association, and directed introspection; its impaired function may be associated with anesthesia and comatose states. This system can be stimulated en masse by stimulation of all peripheral sense organs. Upon excitation, a sleeping animal arouses, and electrocortical tracings change from a sleeping to a waking pattern. Corticifugal impulses of wide range, especially those from orbital, cingulate, sensorimotor, and cortical eye fields (Brodmann areas 8 and 18) may similarly excite the reticular activating system.

Hypnotic drugs selectively block transmission of impulses in the reticular activating system; awakening from the induced anesthetic state is associated with normal conductivity. Electrolytic destruction of the area containing the reticular activating system results in a state similar to that encountered in permanent coma in man. In human patients rendered permanently unconscious by injury to or disease of the brain, the lesions responsible may be so situated as to destroy the functional capacity of the reticular activating system.

The **reticular formation** of the tegmentum of the medulla and pons refers to the diffuse primitive system of interlacing fibers and nerve cells forming the central core of the brain stem. It is bordered by the nuclei of origin or termination of the fifth to twelfth cranial nerves, whose many connections add to its reticular structure. According to Papez, ascending paths from this reticular formation of the brain stem include the reticulothalamic tract, the tegmentothalamic tract, and the tectothalamic tract, which terminate in thalamic intralaminar nuclei (along the internal medullary lamina of the dorsal thalamus). Intralaminar nuclei include parafascicular, limitans, centrum medianum, central, paracentral, and central lateral nuclei. Fibers from these nuclei go to the reticular nucleus on the outer surface of the thalamus From the reticular nucleus of the

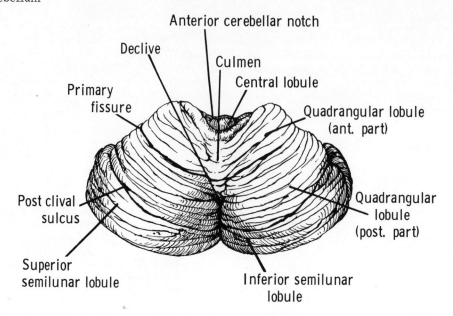

Anterior cerebellar notch

Declive

Culmen

Central lobule

Primary
fissure

Quadrangular lobule
(ant. part)

Post clival
sulcus

Quadrangular
lobule
(post. part)

Superior
semilunar lobule

Inferior semilunar
lobule

Superior Surface of Cerebellum

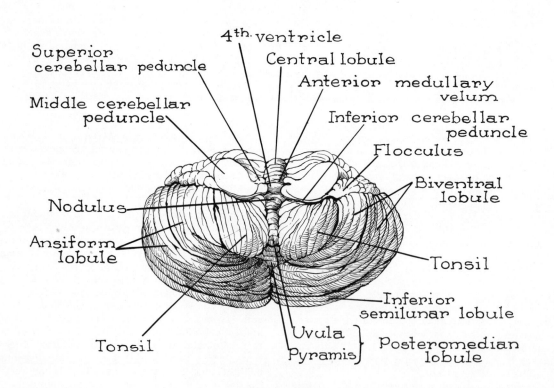

4th ventricle

Superior
cerebellar peduncle

Central lobule

Anterior medullary
velum

Middle cerebellar
peduncle

Inferior cerebellar
peduncle

Flocculus

Nodulus

Biventral
lobule

Ansiform
lobule

Tonsil

Inferior
semilunar lobule

Tonsil

Uvula
Pyramis

Posteromedian
lobule

Inferior Surface of Cerebellum

thalamus "nonspecific" fibers project to all parts of the cerebral cortex. These fibers and pathways from the reticular nucleus of the thalamus can activate the cerebral cortex independently of the specific sensory or other neural systems which can activate cortex.

THE CEREBELLUM

The cerebellum, located in the posterior fossa of the skull behind the pons and medulla, is separated from the overlying cerebrum by an extension of dura mater, the **tentorium cerebelli.** It is oval in form, with its widest diameter along the transverse axis.

Anatomy.

A. Surface: The surface of the cerebellum contains many sulci and furrows, giving it a laminated appearance which is accentuated by several deep fissures which divide the cerebellum into several lobes. The numerous shallower sulci within each lobe separate the individual folia from each other.

B. Lobes: The cerebellum is composed of a small unpaired median portion, the vermis, and two large lateral masses, the cerebellar hemispheres. The **flocculonodular lobe** includes the nodulus of the posterior vermis and the attached flocculi and is sometimes referred to as the **archicerebellum.**

The body of the cerebellum or corpus cerebelli is anterior to the flocculonodular lobe and separated from it by the **posterolateral fissure.** The body may be subdivided into an **anterior lobe** and a **posterior lobe** with respect to the deepest fissure, the **primary fissure** or fissura prima. The anterior lobe, which contains the **lingula, central lobule,** and **culmen monticuli,** is part of the paleocerebellum.

The posterior lobe makes up the greater part of the cerebellum. It may be considered part **neocerebellum** and part **paleocerebellum.** The neocerebellum includes the **simplex lobe** just behind primary fissure; the **medial lobe,** made up of the tuber and folium of the vermis; and the **ansiform lobules,** which include the remainder of the cerebellar hemispheres and the tonsil. The **paleocerebellum** includes the **posteromedian lobule,** the midline structure composed of the pyramis and uvula of the vermis;

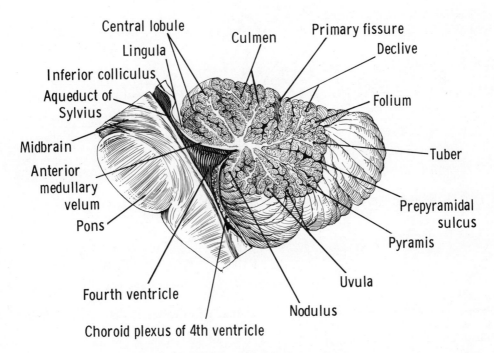

Midsagittal Section Through Cerebellum

and the **paraflocculus**, which is rudimentary in man.

C. Internal Structure: The internal structure of the cerebellum is characterized by a layer of cortex and an internal mass of white matter in which are located a group of nuclei. The **dentate nucleus** is located slightly medial to the center of the white substance of each cerebellar hemisphere. It is a serrated, purse-like lamina with an open anteromedian hilus. It receives fibers from the neocerebellar portion of the posterior lobe and some from the anterior lobe. It sends fibers by the superior cerebellar peduncles to the red nucleus

and the ventrolateral nucleus of the thalamus. The **emboliform nucleus** is an elongated mass just anteromedian to the hilus of the dentate nucleus. It receives fibers from the paleocerebellum and sends fibers by way of the superior cerebellar peduncle to the red nucleus. The **globose nucleus** is composed of small groups of cells between the emboliform and fastigial nuclei. Its connections are similar to those of the emboliform nucleus, and these two nuclei are referred to together as the **nucleus interpositus**. The **fastigial nucleus** lies close to the midline just over the roof of the fourth ventricle in the anterior portion of the vermis and is larger than the globose or emboliform nuclei. It re-

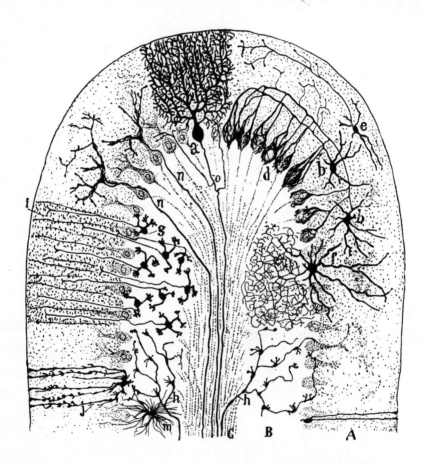

Semidiagrammatic Transverse Section of a Cerebellar Convolution of a Mammal. A = molecular zone, B = granular zone, C = zone of the white substances, a = Purkinje cell seen from the side, b = small stellate cells of the molecular zone, d = final descending arborizations which surround the cells of Purkinje, e = superficial stellate cells, g = pyramidal cells with their ascending axis-cylinders bifurcating, h = mossy fibers, j = neuroglia cell with a tuft, n = climbing fibers, m = neuroglia cell in the nuclear zone, f = large stellate cells of the nuclear zone. (Reproduced, with permission, from Cajal: Recollections of My Life. Memoirs of the American Philosophical Society, Vol. 8, 1937.)

ceives fibers from the flocculonodular lobe and sends fibers to the vestibular nuclei via the hook bundle of Russell (uncinate fasciculus).

D. Microscopic Appearance: The cortex of the cerebellum has a rather characteristic appearance. Microscopic examination reveals an outermost molecular layer and an innermost granular layer. The molecular layer contains few nerve cells and, in transverse section,

presents a finely punctate appearance. The cells are small and arranged in an outer and inner section. Basket cells in the inner section run through the molecular layer in a plane at right angles to the long axis of the folium, giving off many collaterals with arborizations about the Purkinje cells. The cells of Purkinje form a single layer of large cells at the junction of the molecular and granular layers. Climbing fibers are afferent nerve fibers which ter-

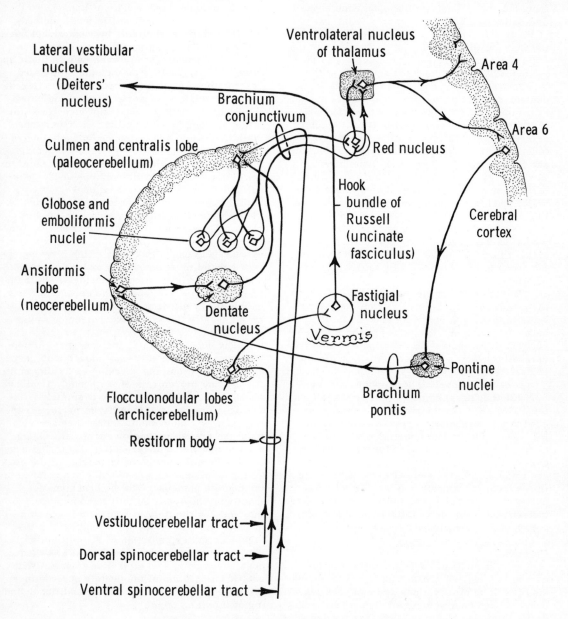

Diagram of Principal Cerebellar Connections

minate in the molecular layer near the Purkinje cells. The granular layer is characterized by many small granule cells. Mossy fibers are afferent fibers with moss-like appendages which terminate in the granular layer.

E. White Matter: The cerebellum contains 3 pairs of major projection bundles, the cerebellar peduncles. The **superior cerebellar peduncle** (brachium conjunctivum) proceeds from the upper medial white substance of the cerebellar hemisphere to enter the lateral wall of the fourth ventricle. Thereafter, most of the fiber bundle ascends, going deeper into the tegmentum and decussating completely in the midbrain below the cerebral aqueduct at the level of the inferior colliculi. It contains (1) **dentato-rubral fibers**, from the dentate nucleus to the opposite red nucleus and the thalamus; (2) the **ventral spinocerebellar tract**, which enters the cerebellum from the spinal cord to terminate in the cortex of the paleocerebellum; and (3) the **uncinate fasciculus** (hook bundle of Russell), by means of which fibers from the fastigial nucleus wind about the superior cerebellar peduncle to terminate in the lateral vestibular nucleus.

The **middle cerebellar peduncle** (brachium pontis) is the largest of the cerebellar peduncles. Fibers from the pontine nuclei pass to the opposite neocerebellum by means of this peduncle.

The **inferior cerebellar peduncle** (restiform body) ascends laterally from the lateral walls of the fourth ventricle and enters the cerebellum between the superior and middle cerebellar peduncles. It contains (1) the **olivo-cerebellar tract**, with fibers mostly from the contralateral inferior olivary nucleus to the cortex of the cerebellar hemisphere and vermis; (2) the **dorsal spinocerebellar tract**, containing fibers from the spinal cord which proceed to the cerebellar cortex of the anterior lobe and to the pyramis portion of the paleocerebellum; (3) the **dorsal external arcuate fibers** from the nuclei of the funiculus gracilis and cuneatus; (4) the **ventral external arcuate fibers** from the arcuate and lateral reticular nuclei of the medulla; and (5) the **vestibulocerebellar tract** from the vestibular nuclei to the cortex of the flocculonodular lobe.

Function.

The functions of various portions of the cerebellum may be grossly localized on the basis of clinical observations and comparative anatomic and embryologic studies. The **archicerebellum**, the oldest portion, has the function of keeping the individual oriented in space. Lesions in this area cause trunk ataxia, swaying

and staggering which are not made worse by closing the eyes, and diminished or absent response on thermal or rotational stimulation of the labyrinths. Ablation of the nodulus produces protection against induced motion sickness in animals. Impulses from the labyrinths arrive via the vestibulocerebellar pathways to the flocculonodular lobe cerebellar cortex, pass to the roof nuclei (fastigial nucleus) of the cerebellum, and finally emerge by way of the uncinate fasciculus (hook bundle of Russell) to the lateral vestibular nucleus (Deiters' nucleus).

The **paleocerebellum**, the next oldest portion, controls the antigravity muscles of the body. In animals, stimulation causes inhibition of antigravity posture on the side stimulated; destruction causes increased stretch reflexes of the muscles of support. Studies indicate that when higher frequencies of electric stimulation are employed, facilitation rather than inhibition of cortically induced muscle contractions may occur. Impulses from antigravity muscles pass via the spinocerebellar tracts to the culmen and centralis portions of the cerebellar cortex, thence to the globose and emboliform nuclei of the cerebellum, and finally via the brachium conjunctivum to the red nucleus. Topographic orientation is believed to occur in the ipsilateral portion of the anterior cerebellum, caudal portions of the body being represented most anteriorly and the cephalic portion of the body most posteriorly. Stimulation of the anterior lobe of the cerebellum has an inhibitory effect on the blood pressure rise which usually follows sensory nerve stimulation.

The **neocerebellum**, the youngest portion, acts as a brake on volitional movements, especially those requiring checking or halting activity and fine movements of the hands. Lesions of the neocerebellum produce dysmetrias, intention tremors, and inability to perform rapidly changing movements. Impulses arrive from the precentral motor cortex (Brodmann area 6) via the pontocerebellar tracts and reach the ansiformis portion of the cortex of the cerebellar hemisphere, whence they are relayed to the dentate nucleus. Via the brachium conjunctivum they pass on to the red nucleus and thalamus, ultimately to return to Brodmann areas 4 and 6 of the cerebral cortex. In the higher primates, ablation of the cerebellar cortex causes transient ipsilateral awkwardness, hypotonia, and alteration in gait. With additional ablation of the dentate nucleus more prolonged signs result, with the additional finding of intention tremor.

THE VENTRICLES

Within the brain substance is a communicating system of 4 cavities filled with CSF. These are designated as the 2 lateral, the third, and the fourth ventricles.

The Lateral Ventricles.

The 2 lateral ventricles are the largest of the ventricles. They are irregular in shape and are lined with ependyma, which is continuous with the ependyma of the third ventricle. The **anterior horn** is anterior to the interventricular foramen. Its roof and anterior border are formed by the corpus callosum, its vertical medial wall by the septum pellucidum; the floor and lateral wall are formed by the bulging head of the caudate nucleus. The central part or body is the long, narrow portion extending from the interventricular foramen to a point opposite the splenium of the corpus callosum. Its roof is formed by the corpus callosum and the medial wall by the septum pellucidum. The floor contains (from medial to lateral side) the following structures: the fornix, the choroid plexus, the lateral part of the dorsal surface of the thalamus, the stria terminalis, the vena terminalis, and the caudate nucleus. The **posterior horn** extends into the occipital lobe. Its roof is formed by fibers of the corpus callosum. On its medial wall is an elevation of the ventricular wall produced by the calcarine fissure known as the calcar avis. A more dorsally situated longitudinal elevation of the medial wall formed by the occipital portion of the corpus callosum radiation is known as the bulb of the posterior horn. The **inferior horn** (temporal horn) traverses the temporal lobe. Its roof is formed by the white substance of the cerebral hemisphere. Along the medial border are the stria terminalis and the tail of the caudate nucleus. The amygdaloid nucleus bulges into the terminal part of the inferior horn. The floor and medial wall are formed by the fimbria, the hippocampus, and the collateral eminence.

The **interventricular foramen** is an oval aperture between the column of the fornix and the anterior end of the thalamus through which the lateral ventricle communicates with the third ventricle. It is frequently referred to as the **foramen of Monro.**

The **choroid plexus of the lateral ventricle** is a vascular, fringe-like process of pia mater projecting into the ventricular cavity and covered by an epithelial layer of ependymal origin. A triangular process of pia mater projecting upward into the body of the lateral ventricle covers the lateral edge of the fornix and is known as the **tela choroidea.** The choroid plexus extends from the interventricular foramen (where it is joined with the plexus of the opposite lateral ventricle) to the end of the inferior horn. The arteries to the plexus consist of the **anterior choroidal artery,** a branch of the internal carotid artery, which enters the plexus at the inferior horn of the ventricle; and the **posterior choroidal artery,** a branch of the posterior cerebral artery.

The Third Ventricle.

The third ventricle is a narrow vertical cleft between the 2 lateral ventricles. The roof of the third ventricle is formed by a thin layer of ependyma. The lateral walls are formed mainly by the medial surfaces of the 2 thalami. The lower lateral wall and the floor of the ventricle are formed by the hypothalamus and subthalamus. The anterior commissure and the lamina terminalis form the rostral limit of the third ventricle. The optic recess is an extension of the third ventricle between the lamina terminalis and the optic chiasm. A small **pineal recess** projects into the stalk of the pineal body. The funnel-shaped infundibular recess is a downward extension at whose apex the hypophysis is attached. The **massa intermedia** is a band of gray matter which crosses the cavity of the ventricle joining the external walls. The following structures may be found in the floor of the third ventricle (from anterior to posterior end): optic chiasm, infundibulum, tuber cinereum, mammillary bodies, and subthalamus.

Three openings communicate with the third ventricle: The 2 interventricular foramens at the anterior end communicate with the lateral ventricles, and the cerebral aqueduct (aqueduct of Sylvius) opens into the caudal end of the third ventricle.

Two choroid plexuses extend side by side from the tela choroidea in the roof of the third ventricle from the interventricular foramens to the caudal extremity of the roof.

The Fourth Ventricle.

The fourth ventricle is a cavity bounded ventrally by the pons and medulla oblongata and dorsally by the cerebellum. It is continuous with the cerebral aqueduct (aqueduct of Sylvius) above and the central canal of the medulla below. The lateral recess extends as a narrow, curved extension of the cavity on the dorsal surface of the inferior cerebellar peduncle. The floor of the fourth ventricle, also known as the **rhomboid fossa,** is formed by the dorsal surfaces of the pons and medulla oblongata. The lateral boundaries of the floor of the fourth ventricle are formed by the superior

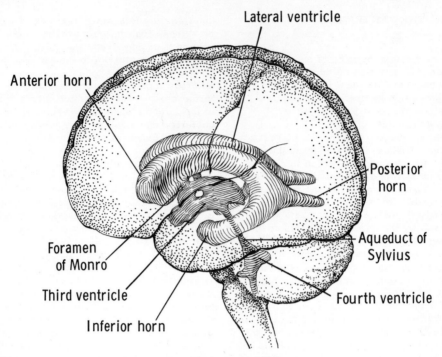

The Ventricular System

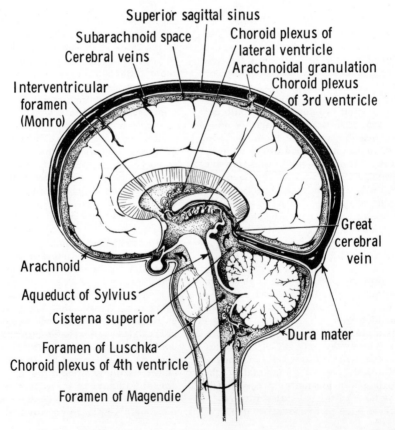

Circulation of Cerebrospinal Fluid. (Redrawn from original drawings by Frank H. Netter M.D., which first appeared in Ciba Clinical Symposia, copyright 1950. Reproduced with permission.)

cerebellar peduncles, the middle cerebellar peduncles, the inferior cerebellar peduncles, the cuneate tubercles, and the clava. The **calamus scriptorius** is the inferior portion of the rhomboid fossa.

The **roof of the fourth ventricle** is formed by the anterior and posterior medullary vela. The **anterior medullary velum** extends between the dorsomedial borders of the superior cerebellar peduncles from the quadrigeminal plate to the middle of the cerebellum. Its dorsal surface is covered by the adherent lingula of the cerebellum. The **posterior medullary velum** extends caudally from the cerebellum. The point at which the fourth ventricle passes up into the cerebellum is called the apex or peak.

The communications of the fourth ventricle include the cerebral aqueduct, the lateral aperture, and the medial aperture. The **cerebral aqueduct** (aqueduct of Sylvius) is a narrow canal in the midline connecting the third and fourth ventricles. It is about 1.5 cm. long and 1-2 mm. in diameter. Its floor is formed by the tegmentum of the midbrain. Its roof consists of the quadrigeminal plate of the midbrain and the posterior commissure. The **lateral aperture** (foramen of Luschka) is the opening of the lateral recess into the subarachnoid space near the flocculus of the cerebellum. The **medial aperture** (foramen of Magendie) is an opening in the caudal portion of the roof of the ventricle.

The **tela choroidea** is a layer of pia mater of great vascularity which invaginates close to the median plane into the davity of the fourth ventricle to form the **choroid plexus of the fourth ventricle.** The right and left halves of the choroid plexus diverge at right angles and run toward the lateral recesses. Modern anatomic findings indicate that the average normal ventricular system has a capacity of less than 20 ml., probably about 16 ml. There would appear to be no lower limit; but in practice about 7 ml. is the smallest volume, and about 30 ml. may be considered the upper limit of normal.

BRAIN CIRCULATION

The blood transports oxygen, nutrients, and other substances which are necessary for proper functioning of living tissue. The needs of the brain are critical and vital, and a constant flow of blood must be maintained.

Arterial Circulation.

The **circle of Willis** at the base of the brain is the principal arterial anastomotic trunk of the brain. Blood reaches it mainly via the vertebral and internal carotid arteries (see p. 48). Some anastomoses occur between arteriolar branches of the circle of Willis in the subcortical white matter.

Venous Circulation.

The venous drainage from the brain is chiefly into the **dural sinuses,** vascular channels lying within the tough structure of the dura. The dural sinuses contain no valves and, for the most part, are triangular in shape.

Superficial cortical veins drain largely into the medially situated superior longitudinal sinus. The 2 major cortical veins are the **great anastomotic vein** (vein of Trolard), which drains into the superior longitudinal sinus; and the **small anastomotic vein** (vein of Labbé), which drains into the transverse sinus. The deep cerebral veins drain the basal ganglia. The **internal cerebral vein** drains the **basal vein** of Rosenthal. The junction of the two internal cerebral veins forms the **great cerebral vein** of Galen, a short midline vein that enters the straight sinus.

In the falx cerebri is the **superior longitudinal sinus.** The **straight sinus,** a posterior continuation of the great cerebral vein, joins the superior longitudinal sinus to form the **confluence of sinuses.** The **transverse sinuses** conduct blood received from the superior longitudinal sinus and straight sinus to the internal jugular veins. The two **cavernous sinuses** receive blood from the middle cerebral veins and drain into the internal jugular veins and the transverse sinuses. The cavernous sinuses are joined across the midline by two **intercavernous sinuses,** one of which is anterior and the other posterior to the hypophysis, thus forming a venous circle about the hypophysis, the **circular sinus.** The **inferior petrosal sinus** drains from the cavernous sinus into the internal jugular vein. The **superior petrosal sinus** drains from the cavernous sinus into the transverse sinus. **Emissary veins** connecting extracranial veins with the venous sinuses are common.

Physiology of Cerebral Circulation.

The vital need of brain tissue for oxygen is reflected in the experimental findings of workers who found severe permanent lesions in the cortex of the cat after the circulation was stopped for almost 3 minutes. It has been estimated that brain metabolism accounts for about 8% of the total oxygen consumption of the body. In a large measure the oxygen is used for the oxidation of glucose; and in the brain, carbohydrate metabolism is the chief source of energy. It can be demonstrated that protein and fat metabolism play little, if any, part in energy production. The rate at which oxygen is used is controlled to some degree by the level of high energy phosphate derived from glucose. In man, at any one time, the brain probably contains about 7 cc. total oxygen, which at normal rates of utilization would last about 10 seconds. It is not surprising, therefore, that the survival time of CNS tissue in the face of oxygen deficit is quite short.

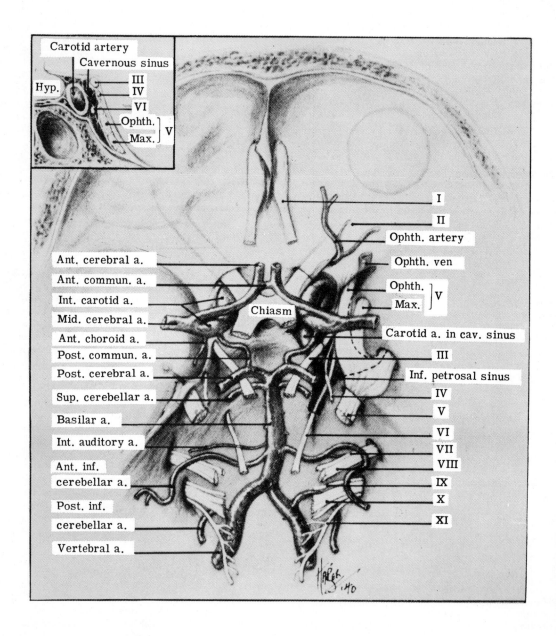

The Usual Relationship of the Cranial Nerves to the Cranial Arteries at the Base of the Brain and in the Cavernous Sinus. Composite drawing of the regional anatomy of the base of the skull, cranial nerves, circle of Willis, and cavernous sinus. (Reproduced, with permission, from Walsh, Arch. Ophth. 27:1, 1942.)

The oxygen supply is maintained by means of controls upon the cerebral circulation. In general, all factors which affect systemic blood pressure indirectly affect the cerebral circulation. The well-recognized role of the carotid sinus receptors, the aortic receptors, and the vasomotor centers in the reflex regulation of blood flow depends upon cortical sensitivity to blood pressure and metabolic changes. Relatively local circulatory changes may occur within the brain as a result of metabolic or autonomic nervous stimulation. Vasoconstriction, when it can be achieved experimentally, is more prominent in pial vessels. Relatively little vasoconstriction of intracerebral arteries occurs. Vasodilatation of more pronounced degree can be obtained experimentally by stimulation of vasodilator autonomic fibers. Clinically, carbon dioxide inhalations, glyceryl tri-nitrate, and ingestion of alcohol are believed to induce vasodilatation within the brain.

It is believed that under normal circumstances each internal carotid artery supplies the ipsilateral cerebral hemisphere, whereas the basilar artery carries blood to structures within the posterior fossa. The circle of Willis may function as an anastomotic pathway when occlusion of a major artery occurs. In arteries distal to an occluded internal carotid artery, a pressure of about half that of normal can be maintained through collaterals. Immediately following ligation of an internal carotid artery, no significant change in the electroencephalogram may occur provided there is no pronounced drop in systemic blood pressure.

Circulation of the brain has been studied by various technics, including: observations of retinal circulation, determination of difference

[Cont'd. on p. 51.]

Circle of Willis and Principal Arteries of the Brain

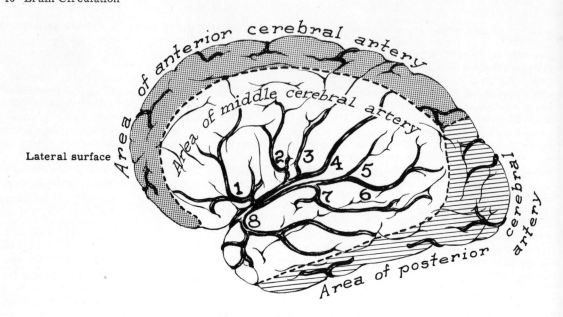

Lateral surface

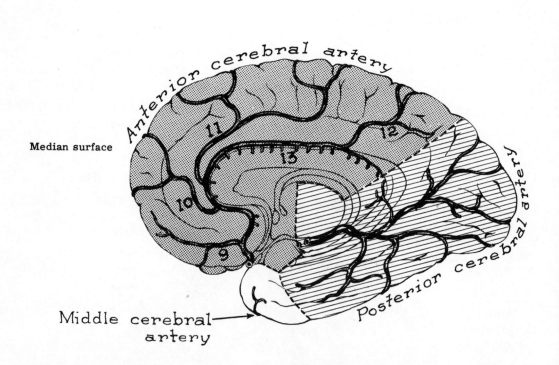

Median surface

Middle cerebral artery

Scheme of the Arterial Supply of the Cerebral Cortex

1. Orbitofrontal artery
2. Prerolandic artery
3. Rolandic artery
4. Anterior parietal artery
5. Posterior parietal artery
6. Angular artery
7. Posterior temporal artery
8. Anterior temporal artery
9. Orbital artery
10. Frontopolar artery
11. Callosomarginal artery
12. Posterior internal frontal artery
13. Pericallosal artery

(Redrawn and reproduced, with permission, from Bailey: Intracranial Tumors, 2nd Ed. Thomas, 1948.)

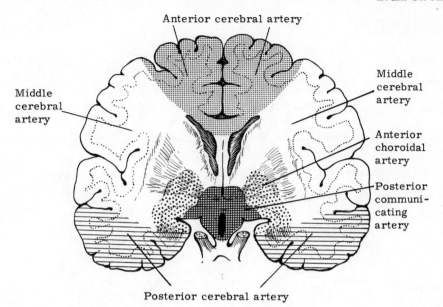

Anterior cerebral artery

Middle cerebral artery

Middle cerebral artery

Anterior choroidal artery

Posterior communi- cating artery

Posterior cerebral artery

Coronal Section Through Cerebrum at Level of Anterior Commissure to Show Major Arterial Supply.

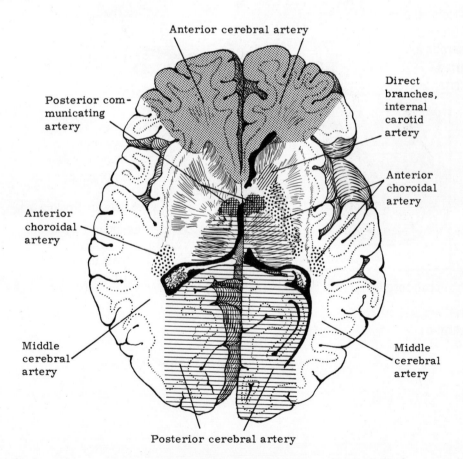

Anterior cerebral artery

Posterior com- municating artery

Direct branches, internal carotid artery

Anterior choroidal artery

Anterior choroidal artery

Middle cerebral artery

Middle cerebral artery

Posterior cerebral artery

Horizontal Sections Through Cerebrum at Two Levels to Show Arterial Supply

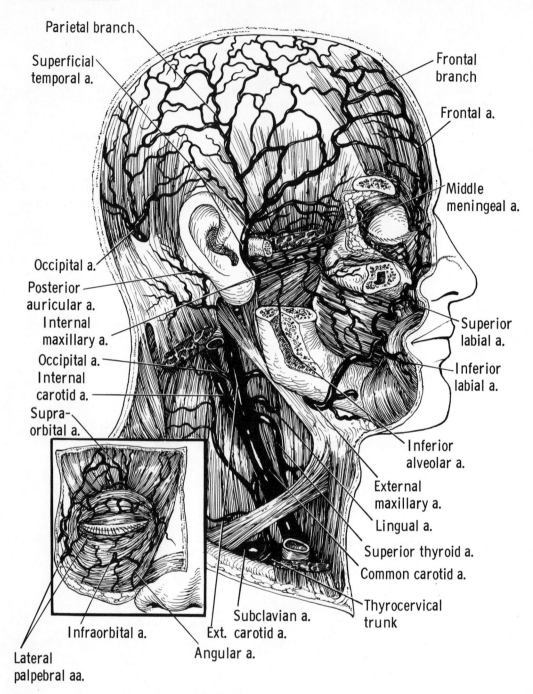

Parietal branch

Superficial
temporal a.

Frontal
branch

Frontal a.

Middle
meningeal a.

Occipital a.

Posterior
auricular a.

Internal
maxillary a.

Occipital a.

Internal
carotid a.

Supra-
orbital a.

Superior
labial a.

Inferior
labial a.

Inferior
alveolar a.

External
maxillary a.

Lingual a.

Superior thyroid a.

Common carotid a.

Thyrocervical
trunk

Infraorbital a.

Lateral
palpebral aa.

Subclavian a.

Ext. carotid a.

Angular a.

Principal Arteries of the Head and Neck

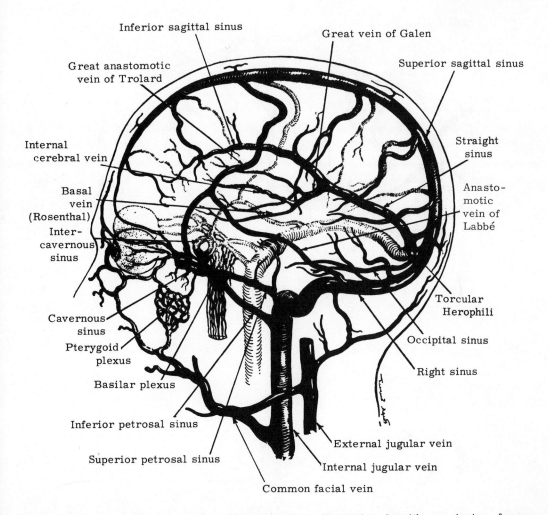

Inferior sagittal sinus

Great vein of Galen

Great anastomotic
vein of Trolard

Superior sagittal sinus

Internal
cerebral vein

Straight
sinus

Basal
vein
(Rosenthal)

Anasto-
motic
vein of
Labbé

Inter-
cavernous
sinus

Cavernous
sinus

Torcular
Herophili

Pterygoid
plexus

Occipital sinus

Basilar plexus

Right sinus

Inferior petrosal sinus

External jugular vein

Superior petrosal sinus

Internal jugular vein

Common facial vein

The Venous Drainage of the Brain (Semidiagrammatic). (Reproduced, with permission, from Shenkin, Harmel, and Kety, Arch. Neurol. & Psychiat. **60**:245, 1948.)

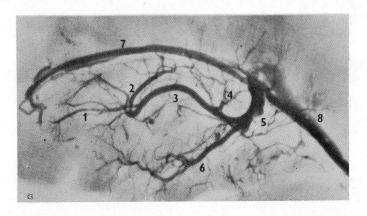

Deep Cerebral Veins (Autopsy Specimen, Lateral View). 1. Septal vein. 2. Thalamostriate vein. 3. Internal cerebral vein. 4. Vein of the posterior horn. 5. Great cerebral vein (Galen). 6. Basal vein (Rosenthal). 7. Inferior longitudinal sinus. 8. Straight sinus. (Reproduced, with permission, from Johanson, Acta Radiol. Suppl. **107**:54, 1954.)

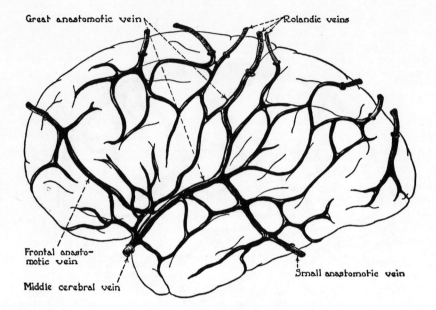

Lateral
surface

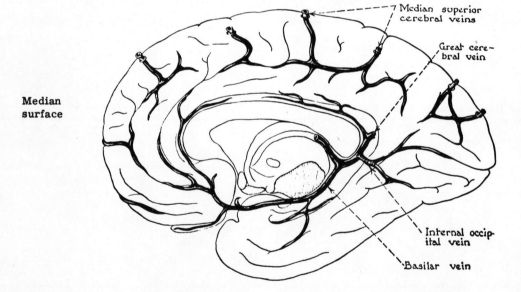

Median
surface

Scheme of the Venous Drainage of the Cerebral Cortex. (Reproduced, with permission, from
Bailey: Intracranial Tumors, 2nd Ed. Thomas, 1948.)

in oxygen content of internal jugular and carotid blood, thermoelectric studies upon exposed brain surface, cerebrospinal fluid displacement upon occlusion of both internal jugular veins, and the nitrous oxide method (in which difference in arteriovenous concentration is inversely related to rate of blood flow). The nitrous oxide method, developed and applied by Kety and Schmidt and their co-workers, has provided quantitative data on human brain circulation. This method is based on the Fick principle, which states essentially that the quantity of a given substance taken up by an organ in a given time from arterial blood equals the amount of the substance carried to the organ by the arterial blood minus the amount removed by the venous blood during the same time.

The nitrous oxide method has its limitations, however. Localized changes in blood flow or in oxygen consumption are not identified as such, since the method measures over-all blood flow and over-all oxygen consumption. Furthermore, blood flow or metabolic changes which occur in a short period of time cannot be measured since the nitrous oxide method requires blood sampling through a period of 10 minutes. Although relatively few studies of local brain area circulation by other technics have been reported, estimates of local blood flow in various areas indicate less flow in white matter than in gray matter. Anesthesia tends to reduce differences in blood flow between various areas of gray matter in the brain. Determination of rapid changes in cerebral blood flow has been reported feasible by use of gamma emitting I^{131} labeled iodoantipyrine. A steady intravenous infusion over periods of 5-25 minutes allows direct estimation of brain antipyrine content in a sensitive and instantly responsive manner; this, coupled with cerebral arteriovenous antipyrine difference, permits the determination of rapid cerebral blood flow changes.

Dye dilution technics using injection of radioactive diatrizoate (Hypaque®) into the internal carotid arteries bilaterally with collection at both jugular bulbs have also been recently used. In normal controls, cerebral blood flow by this method averages 750 ml./minute, with a mean circulation time averaging 8 seconds time from internal carotid artery to jugular bulb.

The use of the electromagnetic flowmeter method allows a selective study of the blood flow through a particular artery. The amount of blood flowing through the different branches of the carotid system in man may be calculated after measurements made on exposed but intact neck vessels. The values reported are claimed to be in good agreement with those obtained by the nitrous oxide method for total cerebral circulation. Blood flow through the common carotid artery by this method is reported to be about 500 ml./minute with about 350 ml. passing through the internal carotid artery and 150 ml. through the external carotid artery.

The appearance of substances such as radioactive hippuric acid in each cerebral hemisphere may be monitored by 2 scintillation detector units following its intravenous injection. The amount of isotope in each hemisphere as a function of time is plotted; as the isotope arrives in the head, the curve rises rapidly for 5-10 seconds beginning about 10 seconds after its release from a mechanically obstructed arm vein. The relative rates of rise represent the relative blood flow within the 2 cerebral hemispheres. Average brain transit time is usually 6-8 seconds for the most active portion of the bolus. Because of rapid urinary excretion within an hour, patient radiation is negligible.

Alterations in flow through the vertebral and carotid arteries may occur with different head positions. Studies on cadavers indicated that a great reduction of flow could occur in simultaneously perfused carotid and vertebral arteries in certain positions. At operation it has been found that turning the head may reduce carotid blood flow significantly.

According to the nitrous oxide method, blood flow in healthy young men is 54 ml./100 Gm. of brain/minute. A brain of average weight has 740 ml. of blood circulating through it/minute. A normal brain consumes approximately 3.3 ml. of oxygen/100 Gm. of brain/minute. It would therefore consume about 46 ml. of oxygen/minute. In advanced age, circulation and oxygen consumption are reduced to as much as 30% below average levels in young adults. In sleep, blood flow through the brain is said to increase, whereas oxygen consumption is essentially unchanged. Considerably higher values are obtained in normal children: blood flow of 104 ml./100 Gm. of brain/minute and oxygen consumption of 5.1 ml./100 Gm. of brain/minute. Continuous quantitative measurements of local changes in cortical pH, oxygen and carbon dioxide tensions, cortical blood flow, alveolar oxygen and carbon dioxide concentrations, and arterial oxygen saturation have been made. Increased local cerebral metabolism results in increased local blood flow, since oxygen tension becomes reduced and carbon dioxide tension becomes increased in areas of increased cerebral metabolism. When cerebral metabolism becomes reduced, local oxygen utilization and carbon dioxide production also becomes reduced. Severe ischemia and anoxia produce cerebral metabolic paralysis with reduction of carbon dioxide and oxygen metabolism before infarction. This state may be reversible if severe anoxia is not prolonged. Milder ischemic anoxia may result in a state of metabolic paralysis for prolonged periods which is

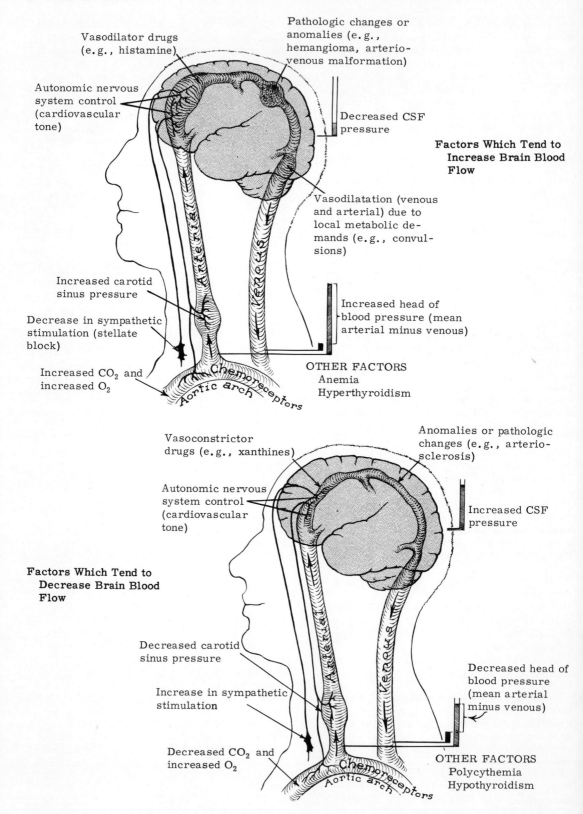

Vasodilator drugs
(e.g., histamine)

Pathologic changes or
anomalies (e.g.,
hemangioma, arterio-
venous malformation)

Autonomic nervous
system control
(cardiovascular
tone)

Decreased CSF
pressure

**Factors Which Tend to
Increase Brain Blood
Flow**

Vasodilatation (venous
and arterial) due to
local metabolic de-
mands (e.g., convul-
sions)

Increased carotid
sinus pressure

Decrease in sympathetic
stimulation (stellate
block)

Increased head of
blood pressure (mean
arterial minus venous)

Increased CO_2 and
increased O_2

Arterial

Venous

Chemoreceptors

Aortic arch

OTHER FACTORS
Anemia
Hyperthyroidism

Vasoconstrictor
drugs (e.g., xanthines)

Anomalies or pathologic
changes (e.g., arterio-
sclerosis)

Autonomic nervous
system control
(cardiovascular
tone)

Increased CSF
pressure

**Factors Which Tend to
Decrease Brain Blood
Flow**

Decreased carotid
sinus pressure

Increase in sympathetic
stimulation

Decreased head of
blood pressure
(mean arterial
minus venous)

Decreased CO_2 and
increased O_2

Arterial

Venous

Chemoreceptors

Aortic arch

OTHER FACTORS
Polycythemia
Hypothyroidism

(Modified from drawings in the Pfizer Spectrum. Reproduced with permission.)

reversible if normal circulation and tissue oxygen are restored.

Brain circulation may be affected by various factors:

(1) Blood pressure head (difference between arterial and venous pressures at the level of the brain): Homeostatic mechanisms (such as the carotid sinus reflex and central control of peripheral vascular tone) tend to maintain a normal arterial blood pressure. A mean arterial blood pressure of about 70 mm. Hg is believed to be critical or essential; below this level serious limitation in brain circulation may occur. The hypersensitive carotid sinus syndrome, surgical shock, and orthostatic hypotension represent clinical states of impaired brain circulation on such a basis. On assuming an erect posture, effective arterial pressure at the level of the head may be significantly reduced without a compensatory reduction in brain blood flow. Venous pressure presumably tends to combat the influence of gravity upon brain circulation, and, in the preceding situation, an appropriate head of pressure could be maintained by a concomitant drop in venous pressure.

(2) Cerebrovascular resistance, the resistance to flow of arterial blood through the brain, may be affected by such factors as the following:

(a) Intracranial cerebrospinal fluid pressure: A parallel increase in resistance to blood flow occurs with increased intracranial cerebrospinal fluid pressure; at pressures of over 500 mm. water, a moderate to severe restriction in circulation occurs.

(b) Viscosity of blood: Circulation may be reduced over 50% in polycythemia, whereas a significant increase in brain circulation may occur in severe anemia.

(c) Status of cerebral vessels, especially arterioles: Stellate ganglion block may fail to influence ''cerebrovascular tone'' or brain blood flow in pathologic conditions. Animal experiments (cerebral embolization) and human angiographic studies suggest the possibility of brain vascular spasm. Cerebrovascular tone is believed to correlate well with the carbon dioxide tension of arterial blood as well as with the degree of anoxemia.

Significant changes in brain blood flow may, however, occur without much change in oxygen consumption, as in the case of hyperventilation, cerebral angioma, and inhalation of 10% oxygen. Conversely, significant changes in oxygen uptake may occur without much change in blood flow. In vitro studies show the oxygen uptake tends to decrease with increasing size of animal species; for many species, the oxygen use of the brain is of the same order as that of other organs (or even less).

Regional cerebral blood flow has been measured in operatively exposed brain areas following intracarotid injection of Kr^{85} based on its disappearance from the blood. Relatively easy measurement of local cerebral blood flow through the intact skull has been recently reported when Xe^{133} was substituted.

Estimates of retinal arterial pressure may be made by application of a measurable amount of external force to the sclera. Obstruction of an internal carotid artery proximal to the ophthalmic artery may lower the ipsilateral diastolic and systolic retinal arterial pressure, although the finding of normal retinal arterial pressure does not necessarily exclude impairment of internal carotid artery flow. While the ophthalmodynamometer applies pressure to the lateral sclera, the retinal arteries are observed with an ophthalmoscope. At diastolic pressure, main retinal arteries pulsate; with additional increase in pressure, retinal arterial systolic pressure is determined by blanching of the arteries.

A mechanical device using the principle of the plethysmograph may also be used to give repeated information. The ophthalmic artery ''pulsensor'' closes the anterior aspect of the orbit with a rigid artificial wall containing a sensitive pressure transducer. By applying sufficient pressure, systolic and diastolic pressure may be read from a manometer.

Determination of retinal artery pressure by ophthalmodynamometry with the patient in the reclining and upright positions indicate that a large majority of those with unilateral stenosis or occlusion of the carotid arterial system show an increased difference between the 2 eyes when the patient is upright.

Arm-to-retina circulation time has been measured following antecubital intravenous injection of fluorescein with the end-point being the appearance of greenish-yellow fluorescence detected in the retina by an ophthalmoscope with a blue filter. Circulation time in normal persons ranges from 8-18 seconds, with difference between the 2 sides usually less than 0.5 second. Compression, thrombosis, or ligation of a carotid artery causes delay in appearance of fluorescence in the ipsilateral eye.

Clinical studies with the nitrous oxide method have demonstrated that certain pathologic states have definite effects upon the cerebral vascular system. Studies of patients with cerebral arteriosclerosis suggest that a decrease in brain circulation of up to 30% may occur with aging. In essential hypertension, circulation through the brain is maintained within normal limits by increased tone of the brain vessels in the face of an elevated mean arterial blood pressure. It is believed that the narrowing of vessels of the brain in essential hypertension unassociated with cerebral arteriosclerosis is capable of reversal (relaxation) by measures which bring blood pressure nearer to that of normal vessels. Angioma of the brain is associated with increased blood flow (2-3 times normal) with no change in oxygen consumption. In general paresis there is more marked reduction in the oxygen consumption than in the brain blood flow. In meningovascular lues there is increased vascular resistance with significant reduction in the brain blood flow and lesser reduction in the oxygen consumption. No change in the oxygen consumption or brain blood flow is noted in asymptomatic neurosyphilis. In multiple sclerosis and epilepsy (between attacks) there is no significant alteration in brain blood flow or oxygen consumption.

Therapeutic agents have been evaluated by means of the nitrous oxide method in man. Carbon dioxide (5 to 7%) inhalations produce up to 75% increase in brain blood flow in young adults; a lesser but significant increase also occurs in elderly patients. Oxygen (85 to 100%) produces a moderate constriction of brain vessels with decrease in brain blood flow (about 12%). Papaverine intravenously produces moderate relaxation of brain vessels and slight increase in brain circulation. Xanthine drugs consistently produce a significant brain vasoconstriction. Aminophylline and caffeine intravenously are usually followed by marked reduction in blood flow on the basis of increased brain vascular resistance. Histamine intravenously dilates brain vessels and produces a decrease in blood pressure with no great change in brain blood flow. Ethyl alcohol, intravenously injected to the point of mild intoxication, produces no significant change in brain blood flow or brain vascular resistance. In patients with self-induced, profound acute alcoholism, depression of oxygen consumption occurs despite a significant increase in brain blood flow. Norepinephrine and epinephrine intravenously increase mean arterial blood pressure about 20%. Hexamethonium and tetraethylammonium, while producing a fall in elevated blood pressure to nearly normal levels, simultaneously produce comparable relaxation of brain blood vessels so that brain circulation remains essentially unchanged. Volatile anesthetic agents may affect the cerebral metabolic rate of oxygen consumption. Recent studies using krypton-85 instead of nitrous oxide disclosed that at surgical depths of ether anesthesia reduction in cerebral metabolic rate to 60-75% of normal may occur. The onset of reduction in cerebral metabolic rate of oxygen consumption appeared to be correlated with the solubility coefficient of the volatile anesthetic.

Recurrent hemodynamic crises within the area supplied by a stenosed or occluded cerebral artery may depend upon extraneural factors such as lowered blood pressure, anemia, and increased blood viscosity. Recovery from transient insufficiency requires adequate systolic tension and arterial blood oxygenation; failure of compensation may be due to stenosis of multiple arteries, hypertensive effects on anastomotic vessels, vascular anomalies, or unsuspected damage to other blood vessels. Denny-Brown suggests that effects similar to those of cerebral vascular insufficiency may result from repeated embolization of cerebral vessels from platelet thrombi formed in diseased vessels. In monkeys' brains whose oxygen content was studied by polarographic electrodes and circulation by stereoscopic microscopy, occlusion of carotid or cerebral arteries caused an immediate drop in blood supplies to the area, with resulting decrease in oxygen levels. Although oxygen loss in normal animals was great at first, it tended to rise slowly and to reach a high or moderate recovery level. Following carotid occlusion, when the monkey's blood pressure was lowered by withdrawal of blood, small collateral vessels at first dilated but quickly became constricted. The slow flow of blood resulted in "venous microstasis," characterized by red cell clumping and stoppage of blood (stasis) in very small venules. Although venous microstasis could be reversed by an increase in blood pressure, it resulted, if untreated, in microscopic intracortical hemorrhages with a related death of affected nerve tissues.

Experimental animals after a fatty meal show increased aggregation of red blood cells in pial vessels, beginning in small arterioles and venules and proceeding to slowing of blood flow and segmentation of blood columns. These effects are greater in areas of relative ischemia or after occlusion of a cerebral vessel. In the presence of endothelial damage, localized hemoconcentration, erythremia, and hyperproteinemia tend to produce local aggregation, segmentation, and stasis of red blood cells. Intravenous injection of high molecular weight substances may result in aggregation of red blood cells in small pial blood vessels, especially in areas of ischemia where segmentation and stasis of blood may lead to infarction. These changes appear to be unrelated to increase in blood coagulability.

Cerebral vessels of various species may differ in their reactions to intra-arterial noxious agents; in the same species, the same noxious agent may produce increased permeability to one substance but not to another. Thus, whereas healthy cerebral vessels of cats and rabbits are not permeable to radioactive iodinated bovine albumin and trypan blue, air embolism may produce a transient effect on cerebrovascular permeability. In the cat, following air embolization, increased permeability of the affected vessel area reaches its maximum within the first hour, declines rapidly thereafter, and disappears almost entirely after 24 hours.

BLOOD-BRAIN BARRIER

The **blood-brain barrier** may influence brain function by determining the level of metabolism and the ionic composition of tissue fluids. Certain types of abnormal brain function could conceivably result from an abnormal blood-brain barrier. The function of the blood-brain barrier may be influenced by the metabolism of brain cells as well as by the composition of the circulating blood, and it may hinder the free passage of many metabolites into the brain, thus protecting the brain from variations of blood composition and from the entry of toxic compounds. As the brain matures, changes occur in the relative ease with which substances can enter it. Thus the brain of the premature human infant is quite permeable to bilirubin; kernicterus develops readily in these infants, but not at all in adults with greatly increased blood bilirubin levels. Trypan blue, an azo dye, and ferricyanide both penetrate freely into the brain of very young but not of mature laboratory animals following I.V. injection. Radioactive phosphorus (P^{32}) enters more readily and in greater amounts into the brains of newborn and very young animals.

The rate of uptake of dyes, anions, and cations from the circulating blood by the intact adult CNS is slow compared with the uptake by other organs. This applies for inorganic substances (potassium, sodium, etc.) as well as organic substances (e.g., glutamic acid). There is a relatively rapid gas exchange and uptake of lipid-soluble compounds and of glucose. Glutamic acid and its amide, glutamine, are present in the brain in large amounts, comprising almost half of the nonprotein nitrogen. The blood-brain barrier appears to prevent glutamic acid from penetrating into the intact brain, but glutamine enters readily.

Following repeated electroshocks, increased cerebrovascular permeability of brain occurs in rabbits and cats, which does not occur in anesthetized animals. "Water intoxication" in rabbits produced by I.V. infusion of hypotonic glucose and vasopressin, results in reduced responsiveness and impaired reflex activity. Convulsive seizures occur in about one-fourth of animals. During induction of water intoxication, progressive reduction in concentration of serum sodium, chloride, bicarbonate, and total effective solute occurs with expansion of intracellular and extracellular volumes. Water intoxication relates more directly to reduction of serum osmolality than to decrease in serum sodium and chloride, since recovery follows I.V. infusion of mannitol and urea, which further lower the concentration of serum sodium and chloride.

There is little space between the various cellular components of the CNS. Electron microscopy suggests that in adult CNS tissue all cellular processes and vascular elements are tightly packed, leaving very little real extracellular space. Within the CNS, the capillaries are completely invested by glial or neural processes so that no perivascular space is present. In cerebral edema there is definite and often rapid increase in the bulk of the brain. Electron micrographs reveal massive expansion of glial processes surrounding capillaries, and cytoplasm. Alteration in volume of the brain in cerebral edema may not be a change in the interstitial fluid but a change in volume of cells and their processes - an intracellular alteration. In experiments leading to increase of general extracellular space of other tissues and in water intoxication, the CNS water content and structure may remain unaltered. A relationship of the blood-brain barrier to the membrane of the astrocyte or oligodendroglia has been suggested by swelling of the glia when the membrane is altered or other parts of the cell surface are exposed to fluid medium. Oligodendroglia are engaged in formation of myelin as well as in its disposal in some pathologic conditions that lead to degeneration of nerve fibers so that synthesis, maintenance, and disposal of myelin may be considered a function of oligodendroglia.

The immature CNS, in comparison with the adult, has incomplete glial development, so that myelin formation is scant or incomplete, neurons may contact the capillary surface, direct neuron-to-neuron contact is common, and spaces may occasionally occur between cells and around capillaries. The lack of glial development in the immature CNS may be related to the incomplete blood-brain barrier of the newborn animal. The glial investment becomes complete at about the time the blood-brain barrier develops.

COMPOSITION OF NEURAL TISSUE

There is a high percentage of **water** in neural tissue. The adult brain is about 78% water; the spinal cord, about 75%. Gray matter has a higher water content than white matter. The water, most of which is intra-cellular (about 15% is extracellular), appears to be freely and rapidly diffusible, serving as a solvent for metabolites and nutrients and contributing to the osmotic and hydraulic regulation of the nervous system.

The **solids** of neural tissue are made up for the most part of proteins and lipids, with smaller fractions of inorganic salts and organic extractives. **Proteins** constitute up to 40% of the total solids. Most brain protein is linked with lipids in the form of lipoproteins, compounds which resemble living protoplasm much more closely than either free proteins or free lipids. Water-soluble liponucleo-proteins (nucleoproteins combined with lipids) are present in brain. The trypsin-resistant and pepsin-resistant protein fraction is known as neurokeratin. Globulin and albumin are present. A large fraction of brain protein is insoluble in water or saline solution but (unlike neurokeratin) is digestible by proteolytic enzyme.

Lipids make up a large part of the solid content of neural tissue (variously estimated at 40-75%). Very little simple lipid is found. The lipids of the CNS are highly complex and different from lipids of the remainder of the body. Neutral fats and cholesterol esters, common to most body tissues, do not normally occur in the CNS; in general, CNS lipids are units built upon glycerol, sphingosine, or inositol, with added phosphate or hexose groups plus fatty acids and, frequently, amino acids. Compound lipids are abundant and include phospholipids (lecithins, cephalins, and sphingomyelin), cholesterol, cerebrosides or galactolipids (glycolipids), sulfur-containing lipids, and amino lipids. Lipids present in brain are synthesized there rather than transported to the brain from other sources. The white matter contains more cholesterol, sphingomyelin, and cerebrosides than the gray matter. Neural tissue lipids may be unique in that certain of their important component fatty acids (e. g., 24-carbon fatty acids) have not been demonstrated elsewhere in the body. Lipids are metabolized faster during early development of brain than later; in adult brain there is a slow turnover of fatty acids which penetrate into the brain very slowly if at all. The rate of exchange of brain lipids is slow compared with that of liver lipids.

Inorganic salts are found in the combustion products (1% ash) of neural tissue. The principal inorganic salts found are potassium phosphate and chloride. Sodium and other alkaline elements are found in lesser amounts. There are high potassium and magnesium concentrations intracellularly but little or no sodium or chloride, which are found extracellularly.

CELLULAR NEUROCHEMISTRY

The **Nissl bodies** of cytoplasm are considered to be centers of protein production. Portions of the endoplasmic reticulum supply various enzymes and substrates, and the fine granular component of the cytoplasm supplies some of the requirements for protein synthesis. Oxidative and synthetic activities of the mitochondria and glycolytic activities of the fluid matrix may be coordinated by structural alterations within the cytoplasm (mitochondrial movements, cytoplasmic streaming, and sol-gel changes in the matrix). Microsomes (particulates obtained from nerve cytoplasm by differential centrifugation) are rich in phospholipids and contain most of the ribonucleic acid of the cytoplasm.

The **nuclei** of nerve cells are rich in nucleic acids. Two general types of nucleotides are found in nucleic acids: ribonucleic acid (RNA) and deoxyribonucleic acid (DNA). The tissue of the CNS contains about twice as much RNA as DNA. The DNA is confined to the nuclei of nerve and glial cells, with a considerable part of the nuclear DNA in the chromosomes. RNA is found in both the nucleus (mainly in the nucleolus) and in the cytoplasm. RNA may be identified histologically by the orcinol green reactions for pentoses; DNA by the color reaction of Feulgen. Quantitative spectrophotometry can be performed on various cellular constituents with the use of the quartz microscope, which is capable of transmitting ultraviolet light. Nucleic acids absorb ultraviolet light strongly at a wavelength of 2600 Å.

Histologic studies of neural tissue may permit the identification of various pigments and substances. **Melanin** is the deep black pigment found in the nerve cells of the substantia nigra, of the locus caeruleus, in some of the cerebrospinal and sympathetic ganglion cells, and in the chromatophore cells of the leptomeninges. Melanin is usually not present in the newborn but appears toward the end of the first year, increases in amount until puberty, and remains more or less constant thereafter. Depigmentation of the substantia nigra is a frequent finding in postencephalitic parkinsonism. **Lipochrome** or **lipofuscin**, a yellow pigment, appears in spinal ganglia neurons about the sixth year; a few years later it appears in the spinal cord, and after the twentieth year is found in cerebral cortical neurons. It increases with advancing age and is quite marked in old age. It appears as droplets around the nerve cell nucleus, stains deeply with osmic acid and Sudan III, and is insoluble in the usual fat solvents.

Fine Chemical Anatomy of Neurons*

Subdivision	Ultrastructure	% Water	Solids		
			% Lipid	% Prot.	% N.A.†
1. Nucleolus	Chains or threads of 10-30 mµ diam. granules.	25	?	(96)	3.5(P)
2. Nucleolus assoc. chromatin	(a) Nucleolar caps 0.5-2µ diam., numbering 2-4.	...	...	...	...(D)
	(b) Satellite (sex chromatin) 1µ diam. in females.	...	...	...	...(D)
	(c) Chromocenter area—? more prominent in females.	...	...	...	...(P)
3. Nucleus	Possesses double membrane, outer showing cytoplasmic projections and discontinuities up to 30 mµ wide.	77	25	74	0.5 {P/D 2/1
4. Cytoplasm (perikaryon)	(a) Nissl bodies: (1) "Endoplasmic reticulum" of parallel tubules or vesicles 100-200 mµ in diam. with walls 7-8 mµ thick in continuous system of lacunae. (2) Fine granules 10-30 mµ in diam. in patterned rows and clusters along tubules (?microsomal fraction—no succinoxidase, 50% of P.N.A.) (b) Fibrillar network: 6-10 mµ in diam. and 200+ mµ long, separating Nissl bodies. (c) Mitochondria: 80% succinoxidase activity; 20% P.N.A. (d) Lipid droplets and yellow pigment. (e) Cell membrane: single, smooth.	60	25	73	1.5(P)
5. Dendrites	Similar appearance to perikaryon. Synaptic bulbs or end-feet on dendrites resemble simplified version of motor end-plate of Couteaux.	...	...	...	...
6. Axon hillock		85	?	±100	0
7. Axon: Axoplasm	(a) Extension of Nissl "endoplasmic reticulum." (b) Fibrillar network. (c) Axoplasmic migration or flow.	90	0(?)	±100	0
Sheath	Complex of concentric layers of protein interspersed with radially oriented bimolecular layers of lipid, each lamella separated by water spaces.	65	55	45	?

*Reproduced, with permission, from Harlow and Woolsey: Biological and Biochemical Bases of Behavior. University of Wisconsin, 1958.
†Nucleic acids: P = pentose type, D = desoxypentose type.

Hemoglobin derivatives are sometimes found in the CNS. Yellow-brown granules of **hemosiderin**, an iron-containing pigment, appear following extravasations of blood and in hemochromatosis. **Hemofuscin**, a light yellow granular substance containing no iron, is found in excessive quantities in hemochromatosis. **Hematoidin**, a decomposition product of heme, forms biliverdin, a green pigment which imparts a light green color to white matter surrounding a hemorrhagic site.

Calcification occurs normally within the pineal body during adult life. Small granules or large masses of calcium phosphate and carbonate occur pathologically in the CNS. Calcification of the cerebral cortex occurs in the Sturge-Weber syndrome; within the vascular tree, meninges, and the choroid plexuses as a degenerative process; and in some brain tumors such as meningiomas, oligodendro-

gliomas, and craniopharyngiomas. **Iron compounds** are normally present in the globus pallidus and substantia nigra. Some of the brain iron has been identified as ferritin, a crystallizable protein containing 23% iron. The tissue iron of brain probably is a product of iron metabolism, although it can also arise from extravasated red blood cells.

BRAIN METABOLISM

Embryonic Brain.

The metabolism of the embryonic brain is characterized by a great capacity to synthesize the proteins and lipids needed for growth. Oxidative mechanisms are deficient, but the brain is highly capable of utilizing carbohydrates by glycolysis. During fetal life glucose oxidation systems become more active, extending progressively from the lower to the higher centers and continuing after birth. As development proceeds successive changes in the activity of individual enzymes take place, with new enzymes appearing, increasing in activity, and then declining.

Among the studies made in an attempt to correlate functional brain status and enzymatic findings are those of Flexner on the guinea pig. In early fetal life, the cerebral cortex of the guinea pig has been found to contain low, constant concentrations of respiratory enzymes, cytochrome C, succinic dehydrogenase, and adenylpyrophosphatase (apyrase). The concentrations of these enzymes increase sharply at the time of morphologic differentiation and the onset of electric activity in nerve cells. The adult level is reached or approximated at birth. A similar close relationship in other vertebrate species has been noted between functional development and brain enzyme concentrations of cholinesterase and carbonic anhydrase.

Increased knowledge of the metabolic characteristics of mammalian embryonal tissues has resulted from the studies of Hicks and others on experimental induction of brain malformations of small laboratory animals. Developing cells change their response to metabolic injury as they grow, and the organism changes metabolically as it develops. Although developmental patterns are primarily genetically determined and latent genetic abnormalities may be precipitated by injurious agents, different agents may produce different types of malformation at the same stage of development. In general the rat embryo is resistant to anoxia and hypoglycemia, but interference with nucleic acid metabolism of primitive differentiating cells causes their destruction. In late fetal and neonatal life resistance to anoxia persists, but the interruption of some phases of glucose metabolism has serious consequences. At this stage, the brain is able to utilize glucose either aerobically or anaerobically for sustained periods. The capacity for anaerobic survival is lost at about the second or third week, when embryonal cells have generally grown to their mature forms. The cerebrum becomes dependent upon an immediate supply of glucose and oxygen, although parts of the brain stem and midbrain may be less dependent than other tissues. Some drugs (cyanide, azide, and malononitrile) can now cause damage to the neurons of cortex and striatum similar to that caused by anoxia, and may also damage white matter. Certain parts of the hypothalamus, brain stem, and peripheral ganglia may be damaged by acetylpyridine, and this effect can be prevented by its analogue, nicotinamide. Adult neurons of the brain are relatively radioresistant.

Different types of metabolic toxins or inhibitors can selectively damage primitive, differentiating embryonal cells. Radiation attacks such primitive cells in stages at which they are apparently engaged in the synthesis of nucleic acid and protein, and growing rapidly from an embryonal stage to a more adult phase. Oxidizing compounds produced in water by radiation seem to affect enzymes with sulfhydryl groups, and this type of enzyme seems to be important at this early stage of cell differentiation. Effects similar to those produced by ionizing radiation may be produced by chemicals which react with sulfhydryl groups (nitrogen mustard, iodosobenzoate) or interfere with certain phases of nucleic acid metabolism (aminopterin and certain steroids).

Adult Brain.

In the adult brain the ability to synthesize certain proteins and lipids is greatly reduced, but the dependence upon carbohydrate as its main fuel persists. The brain is characterized by a high over-all oxygen consumption, with metabolic activity generally highest in the cortex and cerebellum. The high energy requirement of most portions of the brain is related to the transport of ions, the synthesis of acetylcholine, and the metabolism of glutamic acid. Concomitant changes affecting phospholipids and nucleoproteins occur, but the metabolic processes associated with functional activity of the brain are poorly understood.

Carbohydrate, in the form of glucose, is the principal source of energy for tissue cells of the CNS; it serves as a major contributor in the building of amino and fatty acids and is a source of CO_2 which helps regulate pH. Carbohydrate metabolism of nerve tissue is similar to that of muscle. Lactic acid and pyruvic acid appear under anaerobic conditions; they disappear very slowly, and oxygen does not accelerate this process. Very little storage of glycogen occurs in neural tissue, and brain extracts react more readily with glucose than with glycogen. The respiratory quotient of neural tissue is 1.0, which suggests that ordinarily the tissues of the CNS utilize carbohydrate almost exclusively; burning sugar with oxygen and introducing energy into cells via high-energy phosphate esters. In some circumstances, however, the brain can apparently remain active without the use of extrinsic or intrinsic carbohydrates.

There is no evidence that high blood glucose levels affect nervous system function directly. The effects of low blood glucose, however, are better established. Prolonged hypoglycemia depresses total brain metabolism. Patients may show confusion, excitement, combativeness, automatism, drowsiness, ataxia, incoordination, dysarthria, and diplopia. Symptoms often are preceded by marked sweating and sometimes by hunger, and some patients pass rapidly into coma and convulsions.

A constant rather than a rich supply of oxygen is considered essential for normal brain function. Quantitatively, the most important substance utilized in brain for oxygen activation is probably cytochrome oxidase. Brain has a markedly high anaerobic glycolytic rate, but its rate of aerobic glycolysis is small. Energy for the metabolic activities of the brain presumably comes largely from oxidative breakdown of glucose. Two enzymes of major importance in degradation of glucose in brain are (1) hexokinase, probably responsible for initiating the metabolic reactions of glucose; and (2) triosephosphate dehydrogenase, which controls rate of energy production from glucose-6-phosphate.

Glutamate, aspartate, gamma-aminobutyric acid, and glutamine form about 70% of **brain amino acid nitrogen.** These substances are normally formed by transaminases in the brain acting on alpha-ketoglutaric acid and oxalacetic acid, formed during carbohydrate breakdown. Subsequent enzymatic operations on glutamate produce glutamine (in the presence of adenosinetriphosphate) or gamma-aminobutyric acid. Unlike glutamate, glutamine passes readily into the brain from blood and may be important in peptide synthesis or as a means of transporting ammonia. Amino acids are taken up by brain in vitro, as is easily shown by the use of radioactive compounds. However, free entry of amino acids into the brain in vivo is often hindered by the blood-brain barrier.

Serotonin (5-hydroxytryptamine) may be one of the important regulatory amines of the body, similar in this respect to histamine, epinephrine, and norepinephrine. It is present in high concentration in the hypothalamus, midbrain, and caudate nucleus. It is probably synthesized from the amino acid, tryptophan, although by a different metabolic pathway from that which leads to nicotinic acid, and is disposed of through deamination to 5-hydroxyindoleacetic acid. It has vasoconstrictor and pressor effects and may also be found in the mammalian gastrointestinal tract and blood platelets. Some tranquilizing drugs, such as reserpine, may act by releasing bound serotonin in the brain. A structural analogue of serotonin is d-lysergic acid diethylamide (LSD), which in small doses is capable of evoking mental symptoms similar to those of schizophrenia. The vasoconstrictive action of LSD is inhibited by serotonin.

The tissue enzyme monoamine oxidase (MAO) is responsible for the metabolism of serotonin and its excretion as 5-hydroxyindoleacetic acid. Iproniazid and phenelzine increase the stores of serotonin by inhibiting MAO, while reserpine decreases storage of serotonin by inactivating binding sites and allowing free serotonin to be metabolized by MAO. An enzyme capable of attaching methyl groups to the amine nitrogen of tryptamine and serotonin has been found in mammalian tissues. A number of indolic substances which occur in plants are known to produce depersonalization, delusions, and hallucinations. Abnormalities of indole metabolism have been reported in schizophrenia, and some investigators believe that mammalian tissues can produce indolic hallucinogens. Serotonin injected into newly hatched chicks with incompletely developed blood-brain barriers has produced ataxia, decreased muscle tone and motor activity, and stupor. After high doses, 14/sec. and 6/sec. positive spike potentials were noted in the EEG; in sufficiently high doses, clonic convulsions occurred, followed by death.

GABA (gamma-aminobutyric acid) is present in relatively large amounts in the gray matter of brain and may regulate portions of available energy, thereby influencing the functional activity of the brain. GABA and the enzyme which forms it from ʟ-glutamic acid, glutamic acid decarboxylase (GAD), occur uniquely in the CNS. GABA-alpha-ketoglutarate (GABA-T) catalyzes the reversible transamination of GABA with alpha-ketoglutarate. Convulsant hydrazides can lower GABA in brain by preferential inhibition of GAD, and hydroxylamine can increase the content of GABA by preferential inhibition of GABA-T.

EMBRYOLOGY

Early Differentiation.

A thickened plate of ectoderm, the **neural plate**, develops along the middorsal line of the embryo and is transformed by invagination into a neural tube. The **neural tube** detaches from the overlying ectoderm and thickens to develop into the spinal cord and brain. The rostral end of the neural tube, which ultimately forms the brain, differentiates into 3 primary brain vesicles: (1) the **prosencephalon**, or forebrain, which lies closest to the rostrum; (2) the **mesencephalon**, or midbrain, which lies behind the prosencephalon; and (3) the **rhombencephalon,** or hindbrain, which lies most caudad.

Development of the Brain.

From the prosencephalon are formed the telencephalon and diencephalon. The telencephalon forms the cerebral cortex, the striate bodies, the rhinencephalon, the lateral ventricles, and the anterior portion of the third ventricle. The diencephalon gives rise to the epithalamus, thalamus, metathalamus, hypothalamus, optic chiasm, tuber cinereum, posterior lobe of the hypophysis, mammillary bodies, and most of the third ventricle.

From the mesencephalon develop the quadrigeminal plate, the cerebral peduncles, and the aqueduct of Sylvius.

The rhombencephalon gives rise to the metencephalon and the myelencephalon. The metencephalon forms the cerebellum, pons, and part of the fourth ventricle. The myelencephalon forms the medulla oblongata and part of the fourth ventricle.

Development of the Spinal Cord.

The spinal cord develops from the caudal portion of the neural tube. The earliest tracts of nerve fibers appear in the marginal zone at about the second month. Long association tracts appear about the third month and pyramidal tracts about the fifth month of fetal life. Myelination of nerve fibers of the spinal cord begins about the middle of fetal life and is not completed in some tracts for 20 years. The oldest tracts myelinate first; pyramidal tracts later, largely during the first and second postnatal years.

Cellular Developmental Changes.

Initially, the neural plate consists of a single layer of cells. These divide and proliferate and their cell bodies become indistinct, so that by the time of the formation of the neural tube the wall is formed of several layers of cells with a syncytial appearance. Three layers may be differentiated early: (1) a marginal or nonnuclear outer layer, which in the spinal cord develops into the white substance; (2) a mantle layer with many nuclei, which in the spinal cord differentiates into the gray matter; and (3) an innermost ependymal layer in which may be found large mitotic nuclei of germinal cells. Neuroblasts form, which differentiate into neurons; and spongioblasts, which differentiate into neuroglial and ependymal cells.

The neural crest, a ridge of ectodermal cells at the junction of the neural groove and the overlying superficial ectoderm, gives rise to the neuroblasts which form the sensory (afferent) fibers and the sensory ganglia. Some ectodermal cells migrate from the neural tube and neural crest along the course of the ventral or dorsal roots. From these is derived the neurilemma or nucleated sheath of the peripheral nerve fiber. Ectodermal cells of similar origin give rise to sympathetic ganglia. The chromaffin tissue (carotid bodies, aortic bodies, adrenal medulla, etc.) and all of the nerve cells outside of the CNS, with the exception of those arising from the neural placodes, come from the neural tube and neural crests. The placodes (ectodermal thickenings) give rise to olfactory neuroepithelium, epithelium of the otocyst, and the lens of the eye, and contribute to formation of the trigeminal, facial, glossopharyngeal, and vagus nerves.

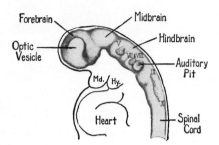

At 20 somites - based on the Davis embryo - probable F.A. of 3 1/2 weeks.

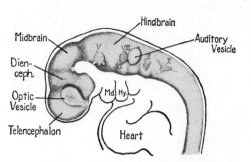

At 4 mm., F.A. of about 4 weeks.

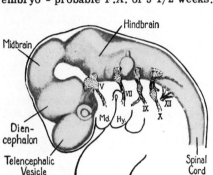

At 8 mm., F.A. of about 5 1/3 weeks.

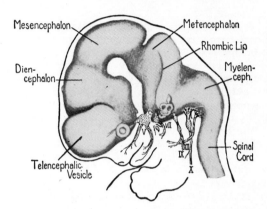

At 17 mm., F.A. of about 7 weeks.

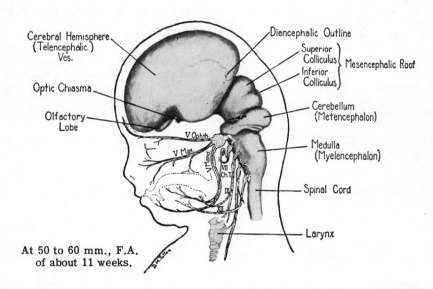

At 50 to 60 mm., F.A. of about 11 weeks.

Five Stages in Early Development of Brain and Cranial Nerves. (Adapted from various sources, primarily figures by Streeter and reconstructions in the Carnegie Collection.) The cranial nerves shown are indicated by the appropriate roman numerals: V, trigeminal; VII, facial; VIII, acoustic; IX, glossopharyngeal; X, vagus; XI, accessory; XII, hypoglossal.

Abbreviations: F.A. = fertilization age; Ch. T. = chorda tympani branch of seventh nerve; Hy. = hyoid arch; Md. = mandibular arch; V Mand. = mandibular branch of trigeminal nerve; V Max. = maxillary branch; V Ophth. = ophthalmic branch. (Reproduced, with permission, from Patten: Human Embryology, 2nd Ed. Blakiston, 1953.)

2...

The Spinal Cord

ANATOMY

The spinal cord is an elongated cylindric mass of nerve tissue which occupies the upper two-thirds of the vertebral canal and usually measures 42-45 cm. in length in adults. It extends from the superior border of the atlas (first cervical vertebra) to the upper border of the second lumbar vertebra. It is continuous with the medulla oblongata at its rostral end.

The conus medullaris is the conical distal or inferior end of the spinal cord from the apex of which a delicate filament, the filum terminale, extends and attaches to the first segment of the coccyx.

Until the third month of fetal life, the spinal cord is as long as the vertebral canal. Thereafter the vertebral column elongates faster than the spinal cord, until by the end of the fifth month of fetal life the end of the cord is at the level of the base of the sacrum. At about the time of birth the cord extends to about the third lumbar level.

Investing Membranes.

Three membranes surround the spinal cord: dura mater, arachnoid, and pia mater. The **dura mater**, the outermost membrane, is a tough, fibrous tubular sheath which extends downward to the level of the second sacral vertebra, where it ends as a blind sac. The **epidural space** separates the dura mater from the bony vertebral column and contains loose areolar tissue and venous plexuses. The **subdural space** is a thin space between the dura mater and the underlying arachnoid.

The **arachnoid** is a thin, transparent sheath separated from the underlying pia mater by the **subarachnoid space**, which contains collections of CSF. The **pia mater** closely surrounds the spinal cord and sends septa into the substance of the cord.

The **filum terminale** is composed mainly of fibrous tissue and is continuous with the pia mater. The proximal three-quarters of the filum terminale, which is surrounded by the cauda equina, is known as the internal filum terminale. The remaining portion, which is closely invested by dura mater, is known as the external filum terminale and is attached to the back of the first segment of the coccyx.

The denticulate ligament extends from each lateral surface of the pia mater and is attached by a series of processes to the inner surface of the dura mater.

Divisions of the Spinal Cord.

The spinal cord contains an **anterior median fissure** and a **posterior median sulcus**, which may be considered to divide the cord into symmetric right and left halves which are joined in the central midportions. The anterior median fissure is relatively deep and contains a fold of pia mater; its floor is formed by white matter, the **anterior white commissure.** The posterior median sulcus is a shallow groove. In the cervical and upper thoracic regions, the **posterior intermediate sulcus** appears on the dorsal surface of the spinal cord between the posterior median sulcus and the posterolateral sulcus. The posterior nerve roots are attached to the spinal cord along a vertical furrow, the **posterolateral sulcus**, which lies a short distance anterior to the posterior median sulcus.

Each lateral half of the spinal cord may be divided into **columns or funiculi.** The posterior column or funiculus lies between the posterior median sulcus and the posterolateral sulcus. In the cervical and upper thoracic region, the posterior column is divided by the posterior intermediate sulcus into a medial portion, the **fasciculus gracilis**, and a lateral portion, the **fasciculus cuneatus.** The lateral column lies between the posterolateral sulcus and the anterolateral sulcus, the line of origin of the anterior roots. The anterior column lies between the anterolateral sulcus and the anterior median fissure.

The **central canal** extends the length of the spinal cord. It is lined with ependymal cells, filled with CSF, and continues upward to open into the posterior portion of the fourth ventricle in the medulla oblongata.

Segments of the Spinal Cord.

The spinal cord segments are referred to as cervical, thoracic, lumbar, or sacral to

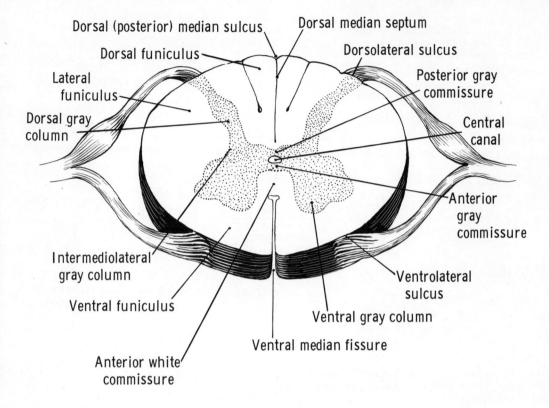

Dorsal (posterior) median sulcus

Dorsal median septum

Dorsal funiculus

Dorsolateral sulcus

Lateral funiculus

Posterior gray commissure

Dorsal gray column

Central canal

Intermediolateral gray column

Anterior gray commissure

Ventral funiculus

Ventrolateral sulcus

Anterior white commissure

Ventral gray column

Ventral median fissure

Anatomy of the Spinal Cord

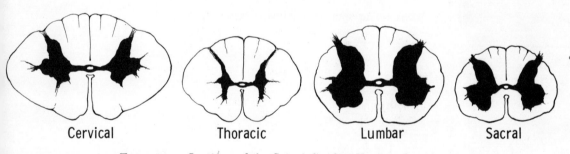

Cervical Thoracic Lumbar Sacral

Transverse Sections of the Spinal Cord at Various Levels

correspond with attachments of groups of nerves. Individual segments vary in length, being about twice as long in the midthoracic region as in the cervical or upper lumbar areas.

The spinal cord is considerably enlarged in 2 regions: The **cervical** enlargement corresponds to the area of the nerves to the upper limbs and extends from about the third cervical to the second thoracic vertebral level. The **lumbar** enlargement extends from about the level of the ninth thoracic to the twelfth thoracic vertebra and tapers thereafter to form the

conus medullaris. The 2 enlargements of the cord correspond to the origin of the nerves of the upper and lower extremities. The cervical enlargement gives origin to the nerves of the brachial plexus; the lumbar enlargement, which is not as extensive, corresponds to the origin of the nerves of the lumbosacral plexus.

Because of the different growth rates of the cord and spine, the cord segments are displaced upward from their corresponding vertebrae, the discrepancy becoming greater as one passes downward along the cord. Thus the

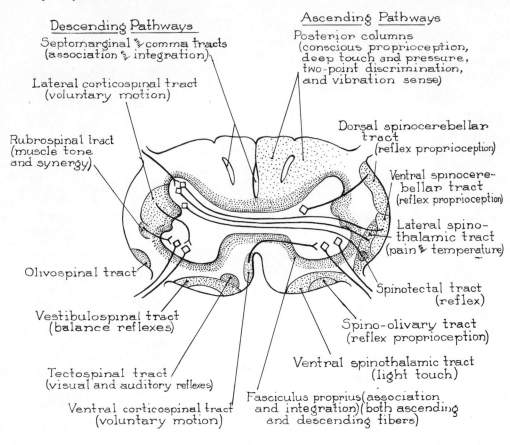

<u>Descending Pathways</u>

Septomarginal & comma tracts
(association & integration)

Lateral corticospinal tract
(voluntary motion)

Rubrospinal tract
(muscle tone
and synergy)

Olivospinal tract

Vestibulospinal tract
(balance reflexes)

Tectospinal tract
(visual and auditory reflexes)

Ventral corticospinal tract
(voluntary motion)

<u>Ascending Pathways</u>

Posterior columns
(conscious proprioception,
deep touch and pressure,
two-point discrimination,
and vibration sense)

Dorsal spinocerebellar
tract
(reflex proprioception)

Ventral spinocere-
bellar tract
(reflex proprioception)

Lateral spino-
thalamic tract
(pain & temperature)

Spinotectal tract
(reflex)

Spino-olivary tract
(reflex proprioception)

Ventral spinothalamic tract
(light touch)

Fasciculus proprius (association
and integration)(both ascending
and descending fibers)

Pathways in Spinal Cord (Lower Cervical Region)

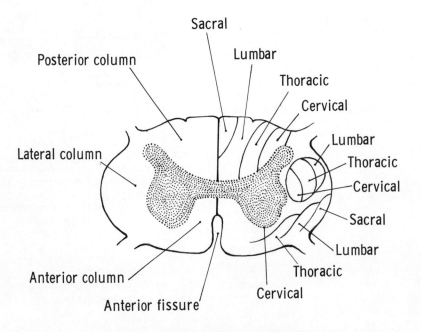

Sacral

Lumbar

Posterior column

Thoracic

Cervical

Lumbar

Thoracic

Lateral column

Cervical

Sacral

Lumbar

Anterior column

Thoracic

Anterior fissure

Cervical

Segmental Arrangement in the Spinal Cord (Modified After Walker)

lower the nerve root, the greater the distance between its origin in the segment of the cord and its point of exit from the spinal canal. This relationship between cord segments and the vertebral bodies and spines is of clinical importance in locating the level of a lesion of the cord and in approaching it surgically. (See also p. 108.)

Anatomic Relationships of Spinal Cord and Bony Spine in Adults

Cord Segments	Vertebral Bodies	Spinous Process
C8	Lower C6 and upper C7	C6
T6	Lower T3 and upper T4	T3
T12	T9	T8
L5	T11	T10
S	T12 and L1	T12 and L1

Gray Matter.

In transverse section the spinal cord is seen to contain an "H"-shaped internal mass of gray substance surrounded by white matter. The gray matter is made up of 2 symmetric halves joined across the midline by a transverse connection (commissure) of gray substance through which runs the minute central canal. The **anterior gray column** (anterior horn) is anterior to the central canal. It contains the cells of origin of the fibers of the ventral roots. The **lateral column** is the lateral triangular projection of gray matter which is prominent in the upper cervical, thoracic, and midsacral regions. It contains preganglionic cells for the autonomic nervous system. The **posterior gray column** (posterior horn) is a long slender column which reaches almost to the posterolateral sulcus. It is capped by a crescentic mass of translucent tissue containing nerve cells, the **substantia gelatinosa** of Rolando. The **reticular formation** is a network of processes extending into the lateral funiculus between the anterior and posterior columns. The central canal divides the transverse commissure into anterior and posterior gray commissures.

The form, quantity, and appearance of the gray substance varies at different levels of the spinal cord. The greatest proportion of gray matter to white matter is in the lumbar and cervical enlargements. In the cervical region, the posterior gray column is comparatively narrow and the anterior column is broad and expansive. In the thoracic region, the posterior and anterior columns are narrow and a lateral column is evident. In the lumbar region, the posterior and anterior columns are broad and expanded. In the conus medullaris, the gray matter looks like 2 oval masses, one in each half of the cord, connected by a wide gray commissure.

The gray substance of the spinal cord may be divided into 2 major components: motor and receptor. The motor part consists of the anterior and lateral columns and gives rise to the anterior roots. It contains the anterior horn or motor cells which supply voluntary striated muscle. The lateral column cells give rise to the preganglionic fibers of the thoracic and lumbosacral autonomic systems, which leave the spinal cord via the anterior roots. Cell groups within the anterior columns may be named, according to their location, as anteromedian, posteromedian, anterolateral, posterolateral, post-posterolateral, and central.

The receptor part of the spinal cord consists of posterior columns. Most of the fibers from the cells of this column divide in the shape of a "T" in entering the white matter, giving rise to ascending and descending branches which in turn give off branches to reenter the gray matter. The cells within the posterior column are generally not arranged in definite groups except for the **nucleus dorsalis** (Clarke's column). The medial part of the base of the posterior column is occupied by the nucleus dorsalis, which sends fibers to the ipsilateral dorsal spinocerebellar tract.

White Matter.

The white matter of the spinal cord consists of nerve fibers in a network of neuroglia. These nerve fibers are myelinated or nonmyelinated and serve to link different segments of the spinal cord and to connect the spinal cord with the brain. The fasciculi proprii immediately surrounding the gray columns contain short ascending and descending fibers which terminate within the spinal cord. Three white columns are formed by the posterior roots and the most lateral of the anterior nerve roots.

A. The anterior white column extends between the anteromedian fissure and the anterolateral sulcus.

1. Descending tracts: The **ventral corticospinal tract** (direct pyramidal tract or anterior cerebrospinal tract) lies close to the anterior median fissure and ends in the midthoracic region. Its cells of origin are in the larger pyramidal cells of the ipsilateral pre-Rolandic motor cortex. The **vestibulospinal tract** is located in the marginal portion and extends from the vestibular nerve nuclei to the sacral segments. The **tectospinal tract** lies immediately posterior to the vestibulospinal tract and takes its origin from the contralateral superior col-

Important Ascending and Descending Tracts of Spinal Cord

Anterior Column	Lateral Column	Posterior Column
ASCENDING TRACTS		
Ventral spinothalamic (light touch) Spino-olivary (reflex proprioception)	Dorsal and ventral spinocerebellar (reflex proprioception) Lateral spinothalamic (pain and temperature) Spinotectal (reflex)	Fasciculus gracilis and fasciculus cuneatus (vibration, passive motion, joint and two-point discrimination)
DESCENDING TRACTS		
Ventral corticospinal (voluntary motion) Vestibulospinal (balance reflex) Tectospinal (audiovisual reflex) Reticulospinal (muscle tone)	Lateral corticospinal (voluntary motion) Rubrospinal (muscle tone and synergy) Olivospinal (reflex)	Fasciculus interfascicularis and septomarginal fasciculus (association and integration)

liculus of the midbrain, crossing in the fountain decussation of Meynert in the midbrain. The **reticulospinal tract** in the sulcomarginal zone comes from reticular substance of medulla and midbrain.

2. Ascending tracts: The **ventral spinothalamic tract** is located in the marginal portion of the anterior column and is derived from cells of the opposite posterior column. The **spino-olivary tract** is located in the anterior marginal zone and contains fibers going to the inferior olivary nucleus of the medulla oblongata.

B. The lateral white column extends between the anterolateral and posterolateral sulci.

1. Descending tracts: The **lateral corticospinal tract** (crossed pyramidal tract, lateral cerebrospinal tract) extends throughout the length of the spinal cord between the dorsal spinocerebellar tract and the fasciculus proprius. Its fibers arise from the large pyramidal cells of the contralateral precentral motor cortex and are so arranged that the fibers to the upper extremity are situated medially and those to the lower extremity peripherally. The

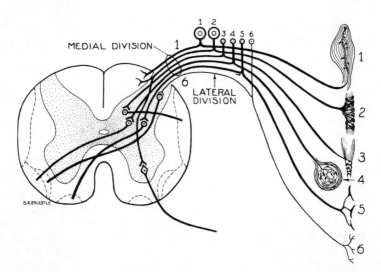

Diagrammatic Cross Section of Spinal Cord Showing Principal Sites of Termination of Dorsal Root Fibers. 1 and 2 represent large medullated fibers having large dorsal root ganglion cells and passing to the dorsal columns; they arise from Pacinian (1) and muscle spindle (2) endings. 3 and 4 terminate on dorsal horn cells that cross and give rise to spinothalamic and spinocerebellar tracts. 5, a similar cell terminating on a neuron that gives rise to ventral spinothalamic tract. 6, a small fibered neuron (pain) terminating in substantia gelatinosa of Rolando giving rise to fiber of ascending spinothalamic tract of opposite side. (Reproduced, with permission, from Fulton: Physiology of the Nervous System, 3rd Ed. Oxford, 1949.)

rubrospinal tract (tract of Monakow) is situated just anterior to the lateral corticospinal tract and is small in man. Its fibers originate in the red nucleus of the midbrain, cross the median plane, and then descend in the spinal cord. The olivospinal tract (Helwig's bundle) lies close to the most lateral of the anterior nerve roots in the cervical cord region and takes its origin in the medulla oblongata in the vicinity of the inferior olivary nucleus.

2. Ascending tracts: The dorsal spinocerebellar tract (tract of Flechsig, cerebellospinal tract) lies at the periphery of the posterior part of the lateral column just ventral to the posterior lateral sulcus. Its fibers arise from cells of the ipsilateral dorsal nucleus (Clarke's column) and proceed to the cerebellum via the inferior cerebellar peduncle. The ventral spinocerebellar tract (tract of Gowers) is located at the periphery of the lateral column anterior to the dorsal spinocerebellar tract. Its fibers arise from cells of the posterior gray column and intermediate gray substance of both sides and enter the cerebellum via the superior cerebellar peduncle. The lateral spinothalamic tract lies on the medial and anterior side of the ventral spinocerebellar tract. Its fibers arise from cells of the opposite dorsal column, which crosses via the anterior white commissure shortly after their origin to end in the thalamus. The spinotectal tract passes ventrally to the lateral spinothalamic tract; its fibers arise from the opposite posterior gray column to end in the tectum or roof of the midbrain.

C. The posterior white column extends between the posterolateral and posteromedian sulci.

1. Descending tracts: The fasciculus interfascicularis (comma tract of Schultze) is situated between the fasciculus gracilis and fasciculus cuneatus. Its fibers are of intraspinal and dorsal root origin. The septomarginal fasciculus is located near the posteromedian septum.

2. Ascending tracts: The fasciculus gracilis (tract of Goll) is located next to the posteromedian septum, beginning in the lowest portion of the spinal cord and increasing in size from below upward. It receives fibers from the medial group of nerve fibers of the posterior roots and terminates in the nucleus of the funiculus gracilis in the medulla. The fasciculus cuneatus (tract of Burdach) lies between the fasciculus gracilis and the posterior gray column and is similarly derived from the posterior nerve roots of the thoracocervical region. It terminates in the nucleus of the funiculus cuneatus in the medulla.

The fasciculus proprius (juxtogriseal area), located immediately adjacent to the gray matter, is composed of a mixture of fiber pathways: short fibers running in both directions and serving to integrate the functions of the cord through intersegmental and intrasegmental association connections; fibers of the medial longitudinal fasciculus, descending from the medulla in the anterior portion of the fasciculus proprius and conveying impulses from the vestibular, oculomotor, trochlear; and abducens nuclei concerned with equilibratory reflexes; and fibers of the reticulospinal tract, conveying part of the extrapyramidal flow for the regulation of muscle tone.

Spinal Roots and Nerves.

Thirty-one pairs of spinal nerves arise from the spinal cord. Each nerve has an anterior or ventral root and a posterior or dorsal root. The spinal ganglion or dorsal root ganglion is a swelling containing cells in the dorsal root of each nerve. Each root contains bundles of nerve fibers. The groups of spinal nerves are divided into 8 cervical, 12 thoracic, 5 lumbar, 5 sacral, and one coccygeal nerve. The nerve roots become increasingly more oblique in direction at progressively lower levels of the spinal cord. In the lumbosacral region, the nerve roots descend almost vertically to exit from the bony vertebral canal. Because of their length and appearance, the collection of lumbosacral nerve roots is referred to as the cauda equina.

The anterior nerve root consists of efferent fibers originating in the ventral and lateral gray columns. These become medullated shortly after their origin and emerge from the spinal cord in 2 or 3 irregular rows over an area about 3 mm. wide. The posterior nerve root, made up of 6-8 rootlets attached in the posterolateral sulcus in a linear series, contains afferent fibers from the nerve cells in the spinal ganglion. In general, the most medial fibers pass to the fasciculus cuneatus; most of the remaining fibers terminate in the substantia gelatinosa of Rolando and the dorsal gray column.

Spinal Cord Circulation.

The anterior spinal artery, formed by the midline union of paired branches of the vertebral arteries, extends along the anterior surface of the cervical spinal cord, narrowing somewhat near the upper (fourth) thoracic segments.

The lateral spinal arteries arise as a single set of branches from the vertebral arteries and pass through the lower cervical and upper thoracic intervertebral foramens to supply the spinal cord segments from C7 to Th2.

The anterior medial spinal artery is the prolongation of the anterior spinal artery below the fourth thoracic cord segment. Intercostal arteries from the aorta supply segmental branches to the spinal cord to the level of the first lumbar cord segment; and the largest of these branches, the great ventral radicular artery, enters the spinal cord between the eighth thoracic and fourth lumbar cord segments.

In the lumbosacral area, **radicular arteries** are derived from the lumbar, iliolumbar, and lateral sacral arteries. The major such vessel appears to enter the intervertebral foramens at the second lumbar vertebra to form the lowermost portion of the anterior spinal artery, called the **terminal artery**, which runs along the filum terminale.

The **posterior spinal arteries**, also known as posterolateral spinal arteries, receive branches from the posterolateral arterial plexus at various levels; they are paired and are considerably smaller than the single large anterior spinal artery.

Anterior sulcal arteries arise from the anterior spinal artery at various levels along the cervical and thoracic cord within the anterior sulcus and supply the anterior and lateral columns on either side of the spinal cord. At any given cord segment, only one side of the cord is supplied by this vessel. The posterior spinal arteries supply the posterior white columns and the more posterior part of the posterior gray columns.

Segmentally, arteries are given off from the intercostal vessels and lateral spinal arteries, which enter the intervertebral foramens; and from the dorsal and ventral radicular arteries, which accompany the posterior and anterior nerve roots, respectively. These unite directly with the posterior and anterior spinal arteries and then are joined together segmentally along the periphery of the spinal cord as the **arteriae coronae**.

PHYSIOLOGY

Three types of nerve fibers have been described according to their fiber diameters, conduction velocities, and physiologic characteristics (see table on p. 69). **A fibers** are large, somatic, myelinated, and conduct rapidly. They are most susceptible to injury by

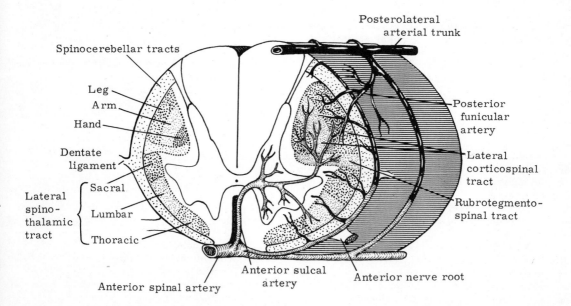

Cross Section of Cervical Spinal Cord. The diagram shows the anterior spinal artery with its anterior sulcal branch, which supplies the anteromedial two-thirds of one-half of the cervical spinal cord at any given segment. The peripheral branches from the arteriae coronae supply the region of the lateral spinothalamic tract of the anterolateral portion of the spinal cord. The leg area in the lateral corticospinal tract is supplied by the posterior funicular artery. The arm and hand portion of this tract and the rubrotegmentospinal tract are supplied by the anterior sulcal vessel. The lateral spinothalamic tract receives much of its blood supply by the arteriae coronae. There are numerous variations in this vascular supply. (Redrawn and reproduced, with permission, from Schneider and Crosby: Vascular insufficiency of brain stem and spinal cord in spinal trauma. Neurology 9:643-56, 1959.)

Nerve Fiber Types in Mammalian Nerve*

Fiber Type		Function	Fiber Diameter (μ)	Conduction Velocity (m/sec)	Spike Duration (msec)	Absolute Refractory Period (msec)
A	α	Proprioception; somatic motor sense	12-20	70-120		
	β	Touch, pressure	5-12	30-70		
	γ				0.4-0.5	0.4-1
	δ	Pain, temperature	2-5	12-30		
B		Preganglionic sympathetics	< 3	3-15	1.2	1.2
C	d.r.†	Pain	0.4-1.2	0.5-2	2	2
	S.‡	Postganglionic sympathetics	0.3-1.3	0.7-2.3	2	2

*Reproduced, with permission, from Ganong: Review of Medical Physiology, Lange, 1963.
†Dorsal root fibers.
‡Sympathetic C fibers.

mechanical pressure or oxygen lack. **B fibers** are smaller, autonomic, myelinated, and conduct slowly. **C fibers** are the smallest, autonomic, nonmyelinated, and slowest in conduction.

A nerve fiber may be excited from its own cell body or by a variety of mechanical, thermal, chemical, or electric stimuli applied anywhere along its course; the energy for transmission is derived from the substance of the nerve fiber or its ensheathing tissue. The current generated is not continuous, but appears to be built up in successive waves by each segment of nerve fiber acting as a metabolic unit. In a nerve trunk, the number of stimulated fibers will increase with the size of the stimulus, but in the single nerve fiber the only gradation with intensity is the frequency of the recurrent impulses in the fiber. The velocity at which a nerve impulse is conducted is independent of the strength of stimulus, and the impulse set up by a strong stimulus travels no faster than that from a weak stimulus. The all-or-none principle refers to the fact that if the impulse is strong enough to be propagated, the size of the response and the spread of its conduction will be independent of the size of the stimulus so that the response obtained is all that the nerve can give at that moment.

A great deal of data on voltage, conduction velocity, frequency, refractoriness, spike potentials, negative and positive after-potentials is now available. During the resting state, the interior of the nerve fiber remains electrically negative with respect to the outer surface, and this gives rise to a membrane potential. The nerve impulse itself is associated with a characteristic action potential, the intact longitudinal nerve surface becoming less positive as the impulse passes. The spread of action potential along the surface of the nerve fiber is associated with the local passage of sodium ions into the fiber during the rising phase of the action potential. The primary function of a nerve cell or neuron is to conduct an impulse. When a living neuron is at rest, there is a membrane potential or resting potential consisting of the difference in potential between the outer and inner surfaces of the cell membrane. The outside of the membrane at rest is normally positively charged, whereas the inside is negatively charged, and because of this disposition of electric charges the membrane is said to be polarized. Depolarization refers to a diminution of the difference in charge, whereas hyperpolarization refers to an increase in the charges normally present at the membrane surface. The conduction of the nerve impulse is associated with a characteristic electric change known as the action potential. The passage of the nerve impulse is associated with a transient reversible depolarization of the membrane associated with membrane permeability changes. Sodium ions enter the nerve fiber during the rise of the action potential, and potassium ions leave.

Although a definite threshold must be exceeded before a nerve impulse can be initiated by electric current stimulation, the impulse, once started, is independent of the stimulus needed for its evocation. The current of intensity just sufficient to excite the nerve is called **rheobasic**, and the time required by twice the rheobasic current to excite a nerve fiber is known as the **chronaxie**. The excitability of a nerve may be considered to be the reciprocal of its stimulation threshold. The absolute refractory period is the period during which no stimulus, however strong, will excite the fiber, while the relative refractory period is the pe-

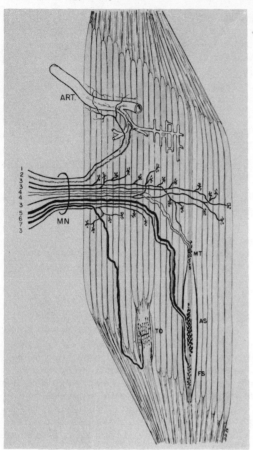

Distribution of Nerve Fibers to a Striped Muscle.
← MN = muscular nerve. 1 = small sensory fibers, often nonmedullated in peripheral portion, to perivascular tissue. 2 = fibers from sympathetic nervous system to arteriolar muscle coats. 3 = medium sized fibers to motor end plates. 4 = small fibers to end plates of muscle spindles. 5, 6, 7 = large sensory nerve fibers to muscle spindles. AS = annulo-spiral ending. FS = flower-spray ending. TO = tendon organ. ART = arteriole. (Original drawing by Professor Derek Denny-Brown, M.D., Professor of Neurology, Harvard University. Reproduced, with permission, from Adams, Denny-Brown, and Pearson: Diseases of Muscle. Hoeber, 1953.)

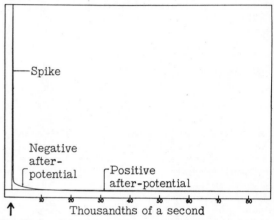

Diagram of the Potentials in a Mammalian Nerve Fiber in Their Normal Relationship in a Single Response.
(Reproduced, with permission, from Gasser: The Control of Excitation in the Nervous System. Harvey Lectures, 1936-1937.)

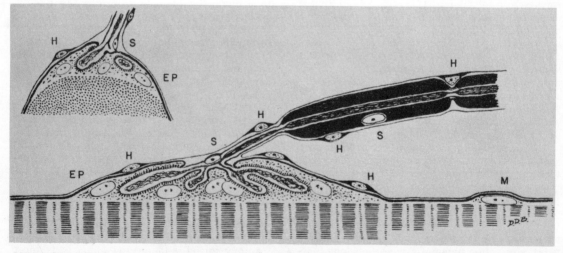

Motor End Plate, Showing the Relationship Between the Various Structures in Nerve and Muscle.
EP = end plate nuclei. H = nuclei of Henle's sheath. M = sarcolemmal nuclei. S = nuclei of Schwann's sheath. (Original drawing by Professor D. Denny-Brown. Reproduced, with permission, from Adams, Denny-Brown, and Pearson: Diseases of Muscle. Hoeber, 1953.)

riod when the nerve can be excited only if the stimulus is of more than normal threshold strength. The period of absolute refractoriness coincides approximately with the rise of the spike potential and with its decline to the point where the negative after-potential distorts its falling curve, at which point the nerve becomes relatively refractory, coincident with the period of transition from the spike potential to the negative after-potential. When the relative refractory period dies out, the nerve next enters the supernormal period when it is more excitable than normally. Following this there is a period of less excitability of the nerve fiber, referred to as the subnormal period. The supernormal period corresponds to the period of the negative after-potential, and the subnormal period to the period of the positive after-potential.

The action potential in mammalian nerve fibers (A type) characteristically consists of 3 components: (1) the spike potential, (2) the negative after-potential, and (3) the positive after-potential. The spike potential has by far the greatest magnitude and shortest duration, and follows the "all or none" principle. The negative after-potential, a period of heightened excitability, is quite variable; its greatest size is only $1/20$ that of the spike potential, and it lasts only for about 0.015 second. The positive after-potential which follows is of very low amplitude, but it lasts the longest (about 0.07 second).

Nerve Function.

Electrolytes may influence nerve function. High external potassium and low external calcium concentrations decrease the resting potential of peripheral nerve, presumably increasing its excitability. Nerves lose calcium in low-calcium solutions and gain potassium when exposed to high concentrations of external potassium. Excessive magnesium has a general depressant effect on nervous system function.

Neural activity, such as occurs in nerve conduction, may lead to altered inorganic ion concentrations. A loss of potassium due to activity has been demonstrated in ganglia and unmyelinated nerve. According to the membrane theory of nerve action, the surface of a nerve is permeable to potassium but relatively impermeable to sodium; upon excitation there is an alteration in permeability of the membrane, permitting sodium and perhaps other ions to enter. When a nerve conducts an impulse following stimulation, a small amount of heat is produced. The rapidly released initial heat may represent energy associated with transmission of the impulse; the recovery or delayed heat (up to 45 minutes) may be related to the mechanisms of energy restoration.

Under anaerobic conditions (nitrogen atmosphere), a nerve may conduct impulses and develop heat; recovery, however, depends upon oxygen utilization.

Chemical mediators may be elaborated at the myoneural junction in association with the action of a nerve impulse. **Acetylcholine** is produced in parasympathetic and voluntary nerves to skeletal muscles. **Sympathin** results from sympathetic nerve stimulation, and its effects are opposite to those of acetylcholine. Sympathin may have an excitatory (sympathin E) or an inhibitory effect (sympathin I). Sympathin resembles epinephrine in its activity; sympathetic nerve stimulation may cause release of epinephrine from the adrenal medulla.

The adrenal medulla is a derivative of the sympathetic portion of the autonomic nervous system; in general, the hormone of the adrenal medulla (epinephrine) duplicates the effect of sympathetic stimulation of an organ. About 80% of the hormonal activity of the adrenal medulla is due to epinephrine and the remainder to norepinephrine (arterenol), a closely related hormone which is a precursor of epinephrine. Epinephrine produces vasodilatation of the blood vessels of the skeletal muscle and vasoconstriction of the arterioles of the skin, mucosa, and splanchnic viscera; norepinephrine exerts an over-all vasoconstrictor effect. Both epinephrine and norepinephrine produce elevation of blood pressure, which is more marked in the case of norepinephrine.

Acetylcholine esterase (cholinesterase), found within nerve fibers and at nerve endings, readily hydrolyzes acetylcholine to choline and acetic acid. The inactivating hydrolyzing effect of acetylcholine esterase is believed to control the action of acetylcholine in the body. This substance must be distinguished from pseudocholinesterase, found in blood serum, which hydrolyzes other esters. For resynthesis of acetylcholine, energy is required. Active acetate (coenzyme A acetate) serves as acetate donor for acetylation of choline. Choline acetylase, activated by potassium and magnesium ions, catalyzes the transfer of acetyl from coenzyme A acetate to choline. Regeneration of adenosinetriphosphate (ATP) from adenosinediphosphate (ADP) is accomplished by phosphocreatine, which is resynthesized from creatine and free phosphate with the aid of energy produced in glycolysis.

+ Water
(Acetylcholine esterase)

Acetylcholine $\xrightleftharpoons{}$ Choline + Acetic acid

(Choline acetylase + Coenzyme A acetate)
(ATP $\rightarrow$ ADP)

Physostigmine inhibits acetylcholine esterase, thus prolonging parasympathetic activity. Neostigmine (Prostigmin®), an alkaloid, is believed to act similarly. Diisopropyl-fluorophosphate (DFP) is a synthetic substance which irreversibly inhibits acetylcholine esterase. This compound is believed to be one of the most powerful and specific enzyme inhibitors known. The toxic properties of some "nerve gases" and some insecticides (such as Parathion®) depend upon their action as anticholine esterases. A highly effective antidote for certain nerve gases and insecticides is pyridine-2-aldoxime methiodide (PAM), which is especially effective with atropine.

Synaptic Transmission.

Individual nerve cells are in close contact at synapses, where functional connections occur. Synaptic characteristics such as synaptic delay, facilitation, fatigue, and blockage are well recognized. With microelectrode technics, an excitatory or inhibitory postsynaptic potential can be detected by the depolarization or hyperpolarization of the postsynaptic membrane. This potential can be clearly differentiated from the signal reaching the synapse and the all-or-none impulse originating in the postsynaptic element and thence conducted through the axon.

In the neuromuscular junction, spontaneous miniature end-plate potentials exist, possibly related to the emission of units of acetylcholine. In this special type of synapse, the postsynaptic membrane is electrically unexcitable. The 2 essential types of synaptic actions, the excitatory and inhibitory, are believed to be produced by a flux of ions across the synaptic cleft which leads, respectively, to depolarization or hyperpolarization of the postsynaptic membrane. This ionic flux is preceded by discharge of a chemical transmitter at the synaptic cleft. It has been hypothesized that the synaptic vesicles, special vesicular submicroscopic structure in synapses at presynaptic endings, may represent the quantal unit of transmitter substance. Acetylcholine or other chemical mediators may be synthesized at the endings and segregated into packets surrounded by a membrane. It has been suggested that these vesicles can flow toward the presynaptic membrane, perforate it, and discharge their contents into the intermembranal cleft of the synapse.

Dendrites of neurons are believed to produce graded electric responses, in contrast to the all-or-none responses of the axon or cell body. Such graded responses characteristically have no absolute refractory period, so that a second response may overlie the first. The intensity and time course of such graded responses of dendrites are directly related to the stimulus, and the graded response is essentially a local response of postsynaptic membrane.

In contrast to peripheral nerve and muscle, CNS synapses appear to be chemically but not electrically excitable. Depending upon the type or nature of the synaptic membrane, depolarizing or hyperpolarizing electrogenesis may occur. Postsynaptic potentials generated in dendrites may be standing potentials which are not propagated except perhaps by passive electrotonic spread.

Theoretically, the cortical neuron axon may consist of membrane which responds in all-or-none fashion, is electrically excitable, and appears to transmit the impulse it receives from its somatic end unaltered to the distal end. The membrane of the cell body or soma may also share the all-or-none response property and is also electrically excitable. It may be that portions of the cell body covered by synaptic boutons contain "graded response" postsynaptic membrane. The dendrite at the other end of the neuron is largely made up of graded response membrane and is electrically unexcitable; its membrane responds to chemical transmitter substances liberated by the synaptic boutons which cover essentially all the dendritic surface. It may be that the very terminal axonal segment leading up to the synaptic bouton of the presynaptic axon also consists of graded response membrane. Thus, following chemical stimulation at its synaptic end, the dendritic membrane produces standing postsynaptic potentials which can in turn affect the electrically excitable membrane of the cell body by electrotonic spread from the dendrite. Dendrites, therefore, may integrate incoming information and control the firing of the cell body and its axon. Larger, slower dendrites may help adjust the central excitatory state; whereas the smaller number of somatic synaptic knobs may rapidly trigger reflex discharge.

Dermatomes.

The skin areas supplied by the dorsal (posterior) roots of a single segment have been studied by many technics. Foerster severed 3 roots above and below the dermatome studied (in man) (see p. 201). Other technics, such as pilomotor response and vasodilatation, generally indicate smaller though similarly located dermatomes. Kellgren made diagrams of the segmental innervation of the deep tissues based on the area of induced pain following injection of 6% saline into a muscle (see p. 203). Inman and Saunders attempted to show the nerve supply of superficial and deep muscles and the skeleton ("sclerotome") based upon injections of irritant solutions into various deep somatic structures of volunteers (see pp. 200 and 201).

Motor Unit.

The motor unit is made up of the anterior horn cell of the spinal cord and the muscle group it innervates. The **anterior horn cell** has a cell body, dendrites, axon, and end plates. The **cell body** contains, in addition to its nucleus and nucleolus, specialized cytoplasmic elements such as Nissl bodies, neurofibrils, and pigment. The **dendrites** receive impulses from many posterior roots and many levels of the spinal cord and brain. The **axon** begins at the axon hillock and extends via the anterior (ventral) nerve root to the peripheral nerve and muscle.

Innervation Ratio.

The proportion of nerve fiber to muscle fibers in motor units is designated as the innervation ratio.

In some diseases, such as poliomyelitis, disorders and degeneration occur which affect motor units rather than individual muscle fibers.

The **segmental spinal reflex** involves the afferent neuron and a motor unit at the same level. Motor units of many spinal segments, however, may be excited by one afferent neuron. Patterns of movement rather than specific muscle contractions are concerned in the simplest reflex reactions. The junction between 2 neurons is known as a **synapse**. The bouton, or terminal knob, is intimately concerned in the synapses in the CNS; upon injury or severing of the axon, early degeneration is found in the enlarged terminals, and within a week these may fragment and disappear without altering the structure of the cell upon which they terminate. A time interval (usually between 0.001 and 0.0005 seconds) is required for an impulse to pass across a synapse in mammalian spinal cord. The delay or latency in reflexes is caused principally by a number of synaptic delays. Motor nerve fiber axons terminate at a specialized portion of the muscle fiber called the end-plate, which represents localized specialization of the sarcolemma. Transmission of the nerve impulse to the muscle occurs across the neuromuscular synapse, and it is at this junction that the muscle action current which stimulates contraction originates. The end-plate potential is the prolonged negative potential at the end-plate, which is not propagated but localized to the neuromyal junction and produced by the passage of the nerve impulse. The end-plate potential generates a muscle spike potential by depolarizing to a critical level the muscle membrane around the junction. The end-plate potential itself can be as large as the muscle action potential.

Spatial summation, in which a recipient neuron receives almost simultaneous impulses from many afferent neurons, is believed to play an important role in synaptic transmission of impulses. **Temporal summation**, which refers to the repeated stimuli occurring within a short excitable period of the synapse, is not believed to play a significant role in synaptic transmission.

CNS neurons may exhibit spike action potentials as well as negative and positive afterpotentials. Negative potentials of large amplitude following the spike potential are usually associated with increased excitability. A large positive potential is usually associated with depressed excitability. The action potentials of nerves are believed to be intimately related to the release of acetylcholine, especially in the transmission of nerve impulses across synapses. Cholinesterase, an enzyme which splits acetylcholine, is concentrated at synaptic terminals and at the surface of nerve fibers. Anticholinesterases, such as DFP (diisopropylfluorophosphate), hinder conduction in proportion to their concentration in the axon.

Inhibition, which refers to the prevention or diminution of a reflex muscle contraction, is believed to be produced in or near anterior horn cells. Humoral mechanisms, inhibitory fibers, and specialized electric behavior have been invoked to explain the phenomenon of inhibition. Two types of central inhibition have been recognized: indirect inhibition refers to inhibition consequent to subnormal period of recovery in nerve; direct inhibition is said to be due to polarization of adjacent neurons essential to the transmission of the reflex which is inhibited.

The **flexion reflex** represents a withdrawal mechanism by means of which an extremity may be removed from a harmful stimulus. "Spinal" animals exhibit prominent flexion responses. Several segments are involved. A single afferent nerve may stimulate many motor units; in general, the smaller nerve branches to the skin are more effective than the deep sensory nerves in exciting flexor motor units. **Occlusion** is the phenomenon which occurs when 2 sensory nerves are stimulated together, in which case the response of a given flexor muscle is little greater than that produced by stimulation of each nerve singly. It is felt that under these circumstances the 2 sensory nerves activate a certain number of the same motor neurons.

Continued discharge of motor neurons after cessation of the afferent stimulus in the simple spinal reflex is designated as **after-discharge** and is presumably due to continued discharge among internuncial reflex circuits.

The responses seen in some forms of prolonged irritation are believed to be caused by **flexor reflexes.** Retraction of the neck and flexor hip responses (Kernig's sign) occur in meningitis; the patient with peritonitis assumes a doubled-up, frozen attitude; chronic semi-flexed postures, with atrophy of the relaxed, reciprocally innervated extensors, may be observed in arthritis of the knee joint.

Extensor reflexes are concerned with resisting the action of gravity upon body posture. The stretch or myotatic reflex, whose receptors are in muscle, is the basis for the extensor reflex. During intervals of constant stretch, stretch reflexes may produce continued prolonged muscle tension without alteration or fatigue. Upon increased stretch, more motor units are brought into action. Posterior or anterior root section destroys the stretch reflex reaction. In stretch reflexes, slowly contracting red muscle motor units are activated. When extensor muscles contract, antagonistic flexor muscles relax.

Three types of receptors have been noted in muscle. Sherrington stated that at least 40% of nerve fibers innervating a given muscle subserve sensory rather than motor end organs: (1) The muscle spindle, a stretch receptor, is highly differentiated and contains intrafusal fibers which receive ventral root innervation from small myelinated fibers known as gamma fibers, originating in spinal cord. (2) Golgi tendon organs, which lie in series with muscle fibers and may theoretically serve to inhibit contractile responses evoked by muscle spindles. (3) Fine nerve endings, which for the most part are associated with blood vessels and probably convey muscle pain.

Two routes of muscle innervation from motor cortex have been proposed, designated as the alpha route and the gamma route. The alpha route is direct or through relays to the alpha anterior horn cells and so to muscles. The gamma route is composed of impulses conducted over both rapid and slow pathways to small gamma cells of the anterior horn of the cord. Excitation of gamma elements results in contraction of muscle spindles, which in turn triggers off a barrage of afferent impulses coming back to the spinal cord and ending monosynaptically on the alpha motor neuron.

By integration of elementary reflexes, the spinal cord can produce movement patterns with apparent purpose. The **final common pathway** refers to motor units upon which there is convergence from many afferent sources. Thus, sensory impulses from many segments, involving many types of receptors, may influence the anterior horn cells for a time.

When reflexes produce the same pattern of movement, they may be classed as **allied reflexes.** Such reflexes may be active simultaneously or successively. The stretch reflex and the positive supporting reaction, both of which produce sustained extensor muscle contraction, are allied reflexes. **Antagonistic reflexes** are those which produce opposite effects. When stimuli act which would produce different or opposing reflexes, the resultant response depends upon which stimulus is the more powerful. In general, **nociceptive reflexes** are dominant.

Some patterns of intersegmental reflexes are relatively fixed. Lower extremity stimulation produces extension of the ipsilateral upper extremity and flexion of the contralateral upper extremity in the spinal animal.

Spinal shock refers to the depression of reflexes that follows soon after spinal cord transection and is believed to be due to loss of stimulation from higher levels. In primates and man, interruption of the corticospinal tracts is believed to be related to the onset of spinal shock. Spinal shock is usually transient and is followed by a period of increased reflex response.

Spinal shock occurs irrespective of the level of injury. All body segments below the level of transection become paralyzed and anesthetic, so that voluntary motion and sensation are abolished. There is suppression of all reflexes below the transection, the suppression usually being complete during the first 2 weeks after injury. Autonomic reflexes are even more completely suppressed than somatic reactions.

Beevor's sign is seen with spinal cord lesions at the level of the tenth thoracic segment. When the patient tenses his abdominal muscles, as in trying to rise from a recumbent position, the umbilicus moves upward because of the paralysis of the lower abdominal segments. Normally the umbilicus does not move.

The **mass reflex** refers to a spread of reaction to include many reflexes and may give the appearance of a stereotyped pattern of response inappropriate to the stimulus in spinal animals and man. Upon pressing the thigh, there occur flexion of the limbs, defecation, emptying of the bladder, sweating, and elevation of blood pressure.

By the third and fourth weeks after spinal transection, withdrawal responses become more vigorous and the toes, especially the great toe, tend to extend during the response (Babinski's sign). Several months after spinal transection, withdrawal reflexes tend to become quite exaggerated and spread to include visceral and autonomic outflow (mass reflex). Mass reflexes may be evoked unintentionally, and at times appear spontaneously without obvious stimulation.

Section II: Peripheral Nerves and Autonomic System

3...

Introduction

The peripheral nerves constitute an intricate conduction system which serves as the mediator of neural impulses travelling in both directions between the CNS and other tissues of the body and through which many important bodily functions are regulated. For descriptive purposes the peripheral nerves may be classified according to their function and site of origin in the CNS: **cranial nerves** emerge from the base of the brain; **spinal nerves** originate in the spinal cord; the **autonomic system** is intricately associated with the cranial and spinal nerves but differs in function and in the details of structure and distribution.

Structure of a Nerve Fiber.

Each fiber represents the greatly elongated process of a nerve cell, whose cell body lies within the CNS or one of the outlying ganglia. The nerve cell, or neuron, consisting of a cell body and all of its processes, constitutes the structural and functional unit of the nervous system (the neuron doctrine). The cell body, which contains the nucleus, is the vital center controlling metabolic activity of the cell; any injury which severs a nerve fiber will result in degeneration of the distal segment.

Components of a Peripheral Nerve Trunk.

A peripheral nerve trunk is composed of many nerve fibers bound together by supporting connective tissue. Functionally, 3 main groups of fibers occur in peripheral nerves: (1) Motor (efferent) fibers deliver impulses from the CNS to skeletal muscles for the control of voluntary muscular activity. Their cell bodies are located in the gray matter of the spinal cord and brain stem. (2) Sensory (afferent) fibers carry impulses arising from various receptors in the skin, muscles, special sense organs, etc. to the CNS, where they are interpreted as sensations. The cell bodies lie in special ganglia located along the roots of origin of the sensory nerves. (3) Autonomic fibers (efferent in function) are concerned with the control of smooth muscle, glandular activities, and probably certain trophic functions of the body. Anatomic details are described in the section on the autonomic system (see p. 138).

Lesions of the Peripheral Nerves.

Lesions of the peripheral nerves include the various types of pathologic disturbances which affect other tissues of the body: congenital defects, neoplasms; inflammatory, traumatic, vascular, toxic, and degenerative lesions; and functional disorders.

Symptoms and signs: The abolition of conductivity in a nerve results in an impairment of neurologic function in the motor, sensory, and trophic spheres. **Motor** loss is manifested by paralysis or weakness of muscles. **Sensory** involvement may be subjective or objective. Subjective sensory findings include pain and paresthesias (numbness, tingling, crawling sensations, etc.). These usually indicate partial or irritative lesions. The pain of peripheral nerve lesions is frequently worse at night. Objective findings include the loss of various sensibilities (analgesia, anesthesia, etc.). **Trophic** disturbances are related to impaired nutritional and metabolic activities in tissues which are partially under neurogenic control. Signs are most marked in the cutaneous tissues, e.g., dryness, cyanosis, loss of hair, brittleness of the nails, ulcerations, and slow healing of wounds.

4 . . .

The Cranial Nerves

The cranial nerves are customarily described as comprising 12 pairs, which are referred to by numbers. Nerves I (olfactory) and II (optic) are not true nerves but fiber tracts of the brain. Except for a part of nerve XI (accessory), which is derived from the upper cervical segments of the spinal cord, the caudal 10 pairs emerge from the brain stem, in which lie their nuclei of origin.

The superficial origin of a cranial nerve is that area of the brain where the nerve appears or attaches. Those cranial nerves which have motor function take their origin from collections of cells deep within the brain stem (motor nuclei) which are analogous to the anterior horn cells of the spinal cord. The sensory cranial nerves originate from collections of cells outside the brain stem, usually in ganglia which may be considered analogous to the dorsal root ganglia of the spinal nerves.

Anatomic Relations.

Cranial nerve I (olfactory): This term commonly refers to the olfactory tract on the ventral portion of the frontal lobe, which arises from the olfactory bulb and continues posteriorly to end just lateral to the optic chiasm, where it penetrates the cerebrum.

Cranial nerve II (optic): The optic nerve contains nerve fibers arising from the inner layer of the retina which proceed posteriorly to enter the cranial cavity via the optic foramen, some crossing to the opposite side via the optic chiasm.

Cranial nerve III (oculomotor): The oculomotor nerve leaves the brain on the medial side of the cerebral peduncle, where it lies posterior to the posterior cerebral artery, anterior to the superior cerebellar artery, and lateral to the basilar artery. It then passes anteriorly, lateral to the internal carotid artery, in the cavernous sinus, to leave the skull by way of the superior orbital fissure.

Cranial nerve IV (trochlear): The trochlear nerve takes its superficial origin on the dorsal surface of the brain stem, then curves ventrally between the posterior cerebral and superior cerebellar arteries (lateral to the oculomotor nerve). It continues anteriorly in the lateral wall of the cavernous sinus, between the oculomotor nerve and the ophthalmic branch of the trigeminal nerve, to enter the orbit via the superior orbital fissure.

Cranial nerve V (trigeminal): The trigeminal nerve contains a large sensory root and a smaller motor root. The sensory or main portion arises from cells in the large semilunar (gasserian) ganglion in the lateral portion of the cavernous sinus, passes posteriorly between the superior petrosal sinus and the tentorium, and penetrates the middle cerebellar peduncle to enter the pons. Fibers of the **ophthalmic division** enter the skull via the superior orbital fissure. Fibers of the **maxillary branch** penetrate the foramen rotundum. Sensory fibers of the **mandibular division** of the nerve, joined by the motor or masticator portion (which leaves the pons ventromedial to the sensory rootlets), leave the cranial cavity through the foramen ovale.

Cranial nerve VI (abducens): The abducens nerve emerges from the ventral surface of the brain stem in the groove between the pyramid of the medulla and the caudal end of the pons, then passes through the cavernous sinus to exit from the cranial cavity via the superior orbital fissure.

Cranial nerve VII (facial): The motor root of the facial nerve emerges from the posterior border of the pons just lateral to the inferior olive through the medial side of the cerebellopontine angle to leave the cranium by way of the internal acoustic meatus. The sensory root takes its origin in cells of the geniculate ganglion, and passes through the internal acoustic meatus via the dorsally situated portion (nerve of Wrisberg) to penetrate the medulla.

Cranial nerve VIII (acoustic): The acoustic nerve enters the cranial cavity via the internal acoustic meatus and enters the brain stem behind the posterior edge of the middle cerebellar peduncle. The vestibular portion arises from cells of the vestibular ganglion (ganglion of Scarpa) located in the dorsal portion of the internal auditory meatus. The cochlear portion arises from the spiral ganglion.

Cranial nerve IX (glossopharyngeal): The glossopharyngeal nerve contains sensory fibers

Components of Human Cranial Nerves*

No.	Nerve	Components†	Primary Cell Body	Course	Peripheral Termination
I	Olfactory		Olfactory epithelium.	Through roof of nasal cavity.	Olfactory epithelium.
II	Optic	SSS	Ganglionic layer of retina.	Orbit ⟶ optic chiasm ⟶ optic tracts.	Bipolar cells of retina ⟶ rods and cones.
III	Oculomotor	SM	Oculomotor nucleus.	Orbit.	Rectus superior, inferior, medial; obliquus inferior, levator palpebrae muscles.
		VM	Edinger-Westphal nucleus.	Ciliary ganglion ⟶ ciliary nerves.	Constrictor pupillae and ciliary muscles of eyeball.
IV	Trochlear	SM	Trochlear nucleus.	Orbit.	Obliquus superior muscle.
V	Trigeminal	BM	Masticator nucleus.	With mandibular.	Muscles of mastication.
		GSS	Semilunar ganglion.	Ophthalmic, maxillary, mandibular branches.	Face, nose, mouth.
		GSS	Mesencephalic nucleus.	With mandibular and maxillary branches.	Proprioceptive to jaw muscles and tooth sockets.
VI	Abducens	SM	Abducens nucleus.	Under pons, into orbit.	Rectus lateralis.
VII	Facial	BM	Facial nucleus.	Temporal bone, side of face.	Muscles of expression, hyoid elevators.
		VM	Superior salivatory nucleus.	a. Greater superficial petrosal to sphenopalatine ganglion.	a. Glands of nose, palate, lacrimal gland.
				b. Chorda tympani to submaxillary ganglion.	b. Submaxillary and sublingual glands.
		VS	Geniculate ganglion.	Chorda tympani.	Anterior taste buds.
VIII	Vestibular	SSS	Vestibular ganglion.	Internal acoustic meatus.	Cristae of semicircular canals, maculae of utricle and saccule.
	Cochlear	SSS	Spiral ganglion.	Internal acoustic meatus.	Organ of Corti.
IX	Glossopharyngeal	BM	Ambiguus nucleus.	Jugular foramen ⟶ side of pharynx.	Superior constrictor, stylopharyngeus muscles.
		VM	Inferior salivatory nucleus.	Lesser superficial petrosal ⟶ otic ganglion ⟶ auriculotemporal nerve.	Parotid gland.
		VS	Petrous ganglion.	Side of pharynx.	Taste buds of vallate papillae.
		GSS	Superior ganglion.	Side of pharynx.	Auditory tube.
X	Vagus	BM	Ambiguus nucleus.	Recurrent and external branch of superior laryngeal nerve.	Pharyngeal and laryngeal muscles.
		VM	Dorsal motor nucleus.	Along carotid artery, esophagus, stomach.	Viscera of thorax and abdomen.
		VS	Nodose ganglion.	With motor.	Viscera of thorax and abdomen.
		GSS	Jugular ganglion.	Auricular branch.	Pinna of ear.
XI	Accessory	BM	Accessory nucleus.	Side of neck.	Sternomastoid.
XII	Hypoglossal	SM	Hypoglossal nucleus.	Side of tongue.	Muscles of tongue.

*Reproduced, with permission, from Krieg: Brain Mechanisms in Diachrome, 2nd Ed. (Brain Books, 1957.) (Box 9, Evanston, Ill.)

†BM = branchial motor   GSS = general somatic sensory   SM = somatic motor
  SSS = special somatic sensory   VM = visceral motor   VS = visceral sensory

which originate in cells in the superior and petrous ganglia, pass through the jugular foramen, and enter the medulla on the lateral side of the inferior olive just behind the facial nerve. The motor part arises in the nucleus ambiguus and leaves the lateral medulla to join the sensory part of the nerve.

Cranial nerve X (vagus): The vagus nerve contains afferent fibers which originate in cells in the jugular and nodose ganglia just below the jugular foramen and pass through the jugular foramen to enter the medulla just behind the glossopharyngeal nerve. Motor fibers leave the medulla to join the sensory part of the nerve.

Cranial nerve XI (accessory): The accessory nerve arises superficially from a series of filaments located behind the root filaments

of the vagus nerve, from the lateral surface of the medulla and upper cervical spinal cord, and leaves the cranial cavity by way of the jugular foramen.

Cranial nerve XII (hypoglossal): The hypoglossal nerve takes its superficial origin by way of several filaments in the ventrolateral sulcus of the medulla between the inferior olive and pyramid; these filaments then fuse and leave the posterior fossa of the skull by way of the hypoglossal canal.

Cranial Nerve Nuclei.

The nuclei of the cranial nerves lie chiefly in the brain stem. The sensory nuclei develop within the dorsal or alar plate of the neural tube, the motor nuclei within the basal plate. In the hindbrain, the alar plate lies lateral to

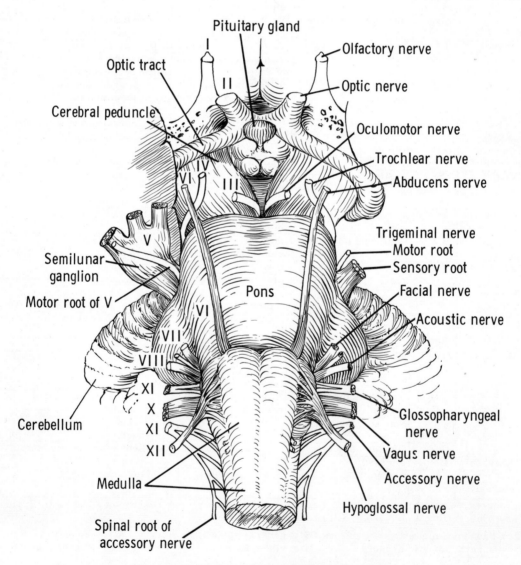

Emergence of Cranial Nerves From the Brain

FORAMENS	STRUCTURES
Cribriform plate of ethmoid	Olfactory nerves
Optic foramen	Optic nerve / Ophthalmic artery
Superior orbital fissure	Oculomotor, trochlear, abducent + ophthalmic div. of trigeminal nerve
Foramen rotundum	Maxillary division of trigeminal nerve
Foramen ovale	Mandibular division of trigeminal nerve
Foramen lacerum	Internal carotid art. / Sympathetic nerve
Foramen spinosum	Middle meningeal artery and vein
Innominate canal	Lesser superficial petrosal nerve
Internal acoustic meatus	Facial and auditory nerves / Int. auditory artery
Jugular foramen	Glossopharyngeal, vagus and spinal accessory nerves / Transverse sinus
Hypoglossal canal	Hypoglossal nerve
Foramen magnum	Medulla and meninges / Spinal accessory n. / Vertebral arteries / Ant. and post. spinal arteries

Diagram of Base of Skull Showing the Principal Foramens (Superior View)

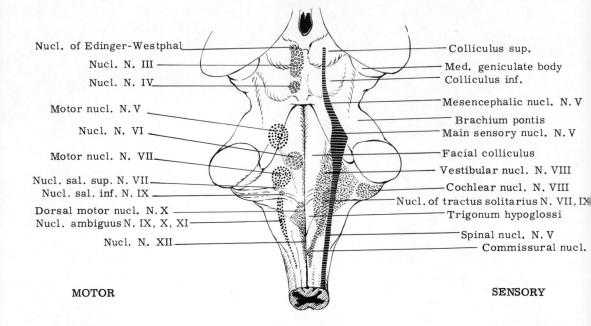

Nucl. of Edinger-Westphal ———— Colliculus sup.
Nucl. N. III ———— Med. geniculate body
Nucl. N. IV ———— Colliculus inf.
Motor nucl. N. V ———— Mesencephalic nucl. N. V
———— Brachium pontis
Nucl. N. VI ———— Main sensory nucl. N. V
Motor nucl. N. VII ———— Facial colliculus
———— Vestibular nucl. N. VIII
Nucl. sal. sup. N. VII ———— Cochlear nucl. N. VIII
Nucl. sal. inf. N. IX ———— Nucl. of tractus solitarius N. VII, IX
Dorsal motor nucl. N. X ———— Trigonum hypoglossi
Nucl. ambiguus N. IX, X, XI ————
———— Spinal nucl. N. V
Nucl. N. XII ———— Commissural nucl.

MOTOR   SENSORY

Cranial Nerve Nuclei. Dorsal view of the human brain stem with the positions of the cranial nerve nuclei projected upon the surface. Sensory nuclei on the right side, motor nuclei on the left. (After Herrick. Redrawn and reproduced, with permission, from Ranson and Clark: The Anatomy of the Nervous System, 9th Ed. Saunders, 1953.)

the basal plate in the floor of the fourth ventricle.

A. Motor Nuclei:
1. Edinger-Westphal nucleus and nucleus of oculomotor nerve in midbrain at level of superior colliculus.
2. Nucleus of trochlear nerve in midbrain at level of inferior colliculus.
3. Motor nucleus of trigeminal nerve at level of mid pons.
4. Nucleus of abducens nerve in dorsal pons.
5. Motor nucleus of facial nerve near caudal border of pons.
6. Nucleus salivatorius superior (facial nerve) and nucleus salivatorius inferior (glossopharyngeal nerve) at border of pons and medulla.

7. Dorsal motor nucleus of vagus nerve in dorsal medulla.
8. Nucleus ambiguus (glossopharyngeal, vagus, and accessory nerves) in dorsal medulla.
9. Nucleus of hypoglossal nerve in medulla beneath fourth ventricle.

B. Sensory Nuclei:
1. Mesencephalic nucleus of trigeminal nerve in midbrain.
2. Main sensory nucleus of trigeminal nerve in pons.
3. Vestibular and cochlear nuclei of acoustic nerve in pons and medulla.
4. Nucleus of tractus solitarius (facial and glossopharyngeal nerves) in dorsal medulla.
5. Nucleus of spinal tract of trigeminal nerve in dorsolateral medulla.

CRANIAL NERVE I: OLFACTORY NERVE AND TRACT
(Sensory Nerve)

Structurally, cranial nerve I is not a true nerve but a fiber tract of the brain. Its **peripheral and intermediate connections** consist of primary, secondary, and tertiary neurons.

(1) Primary neurons: Unmyelinated processes of the ciliated receptors in the upper part of the nasal mucosa are gathered into about 20 branches which pass through the cribriform plate of the ethmoid bone to the olfactory bulb.

(2) Secondary neurons: Myelinated processes of the bipolar cells of the bulb form the olfactory tract and terminate in the subcallosal and hippocampal gyri.

(3) Tertiary neurons: In the subcallosal and hippocampal gyri tertiary neurons pass via the lateral olfactory stria to the pyriform area and hippocampus.

The **central connections** of the olfactory nerve are complex. Association fibers to the tegmentum and pons pass directly as third-order neurons from the anterior perforated substance, and indirectly from the hippocampus via the fornix and olfactory projection tracts through the mammillary bodies and anterior nuclei of the thalamus. Reflex connections thus established with nuclei of the other cranial and spinal nerves may be functionally significant in swallowing and digestion.

The olfactory nerve may serve as a portal of entry for cryptogenic infections of the brain and meninges, e.g., poliomyelitis, epidemic meningitis, and encephalitis.

Disorders of the sense of smell may be caused by inflammatory and other lesions of the nasal cavity, fracture of the anterior fossa of the skull, tumors of the frontal lobe and pituitary region, meningitis, hydrocephalus, post-traumatic cerebral syndrome, arteriosclerosis, cerebrovascular accidents, certain drug intoxications, psychoses, neuroses, and congenital defects.

Special **syndromes** involving the olfactory nerve include the Foster Kennedy syndrome (see p. 84) and the aura of epilepsy (see p. 346).

Symptoms of First Nerve Involvement.

A. Anosmia (loss of sense of smell) may be of great significance. Bilateral anosmia commonly occurs with colds, rhinitis, etc. Unilateral anosmia may be of diagnostic significance in locating brain lesions, such as tumors at the base of the frontal lobe. Hyperosmia (acute sense of smell) is present in some hysterias and is sometimes noted in cocaine addicts. Parosmia (perverted sense of smell)

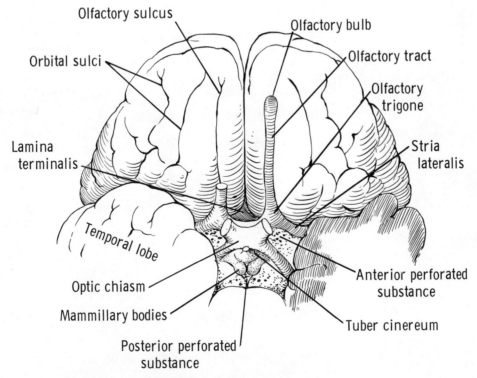

Olfactory sulcus

Olfactory bulb

Orbital sulci

Olfactory tract

Olfactory trigone

Lamina terminalis

Stria lateralis

Temporal lobe

Optic chiasm

Anterior perforated substance

Mammillary bodies

Tuber cinereum

Posterior perforated substance

The Olfactory Nerve (Inferior View)

is a subjective disorder seen in some cases of schizophrenia, uncinate gyrus lesions, and hysterias. Cacosmia (unpleasant odors) is usually due to decomposition of tissues and is noticed by the patient on expiration.

B. Hallucinations of smell are present in some psychoses and in uncinate gyrus fits, caused by lesions of the uncus and hippocampus.

Tests.

A. Each nostril must be tested separately by occluding one nostril and holding the mouth of a small bottle containing the test substance under the other nostril.

B. Familiar nonirritating odors are best (volatile oils). Oil of cloves, turpentine, citron, camphor, or oil of wintergreen may be used. Avoid the use of irritant substances such as ammonia or vinegar.

C. The odors correctly or incorrectly identified should be noted for each nostril. A record should also be made of whether the nasal airway is clear and whether nasal catarrh is present. Although the patient may be unable to name the test substance, awareness of an odor excludes anosmia.

CRANIAL NERVE II: OPTIC NERVE AND TRACT
(Sensory Nerve)

Structurally, cranial nerve II is not a true nerve but a fiber tract of the brain. Its **peripheral and intermediate connections** are as follows:

(1) Rods and cones of the retina are the first-order neurons which connect with bipolar cells.

(2) Bipolar cells of the retina in turn synapse with the ganglion cells.

(3) Ganglion cells are third-order neurons whose myelinated axons form the optic nerve fibers. At the optic chiasm the nerve fibers from the nasal half of each retina cross; the nerve fibers from the temporal half of each retina are uncrossed. Thus fibers from the ipsilateral halves of the retinas form the optic tract, passing to the lateral geniculate bodies, superior colliculi, and pretectal region.

(4) The geniculocalcarine tract contains the fourth-order neurons from the lateral geniculate bodies, passing to the occipital (calcarine) cortex. **Meyer's loop** is the fanlike radiating portion which curves around the inferior horn of the lateral ventricle.

The Olfactory Nerve (Lateral View)

The **central connections** of the optic nerve include the following: (1) from the pretectal region to the Edinger-Westphal nucleus via the posterior commissure; (2) from the superior colliculi via the tectobulbar and tectospinal tracts to other cranial and spinal nuclei; and (3) from the occipital cortex to other cortical and subcortical areas. Fibers from the pretectal region are responsible for the simple and consensual light reflexes; those from the superior colliculi for involuntary oculoskeletal reflexes. Association and reflex fibers pass from the occipital cortex to other cortical centers (related to higher function, e.g., reading, speech) and to the superior colliculi and thus through the tectobulbar and tectospinal tracts to (1) cranial and spinal nuclei for voluntary reflexes (e.g., accommodation); and to (2) the pontile nuclei, via the corticopontile tract, for postural reflexes.

The portion of the spectrum which stimulates the retina to produce sight ranges from 4000-8000 Ångstrom units. Stimulation of the normal eye by this entire range of wavelengths simultaneously or by mixtures from certain different parts of this range produces the sensation of white light. Monochromatic radiation from one part of the spectrum is perceived as having a specific color or hue. The Young-Helmholtz theory postulates that the retina contains 3 receptor groups, each with its own absorption property. However, recent studies suggest that conversion of light to an impression of color may involve 3 or more identical photochemical receptors.

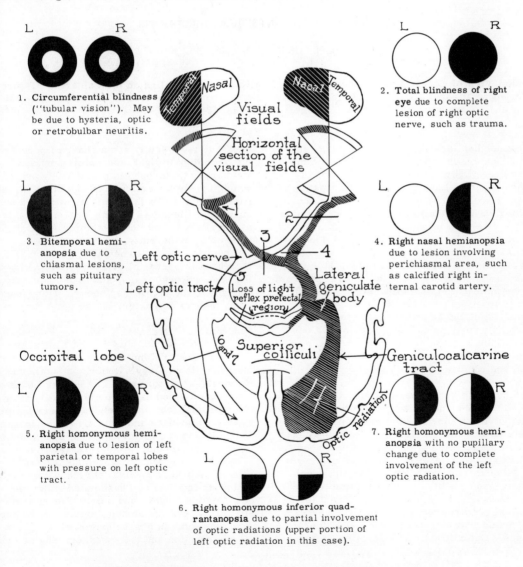

1. **Circumferential blindness** ("tubular vision"). May be due to hysteria, optic or retrobulbar neuritis.

2. **Total blindness of right eye** due to complete lesion of right optic nerve, such as trauma.

3. **Bitemporal hemianopsia** due to chiasmal lesions, such as pituitary tumors.

4. **Right nasal hemianopsia** due to lesion involving perichiasmal area, such as calcified right internal carotid artery.

5. **Right homonymous hemianopsia** due to lesion of left parietal or temporal lobes with pressure on left optic tract.

7. **Right homonymous hemianopsia** with no pupillary change due to complete involvement of the left optic radiation.

6. **Right homonymous inferior quadrantanopsia** due to partial involvement of optic radiations (upper portion of left optic radiation in this case).

Labels within figure: Visual fields — Temporal — Nasal — Nasal — Temporal — Horizontal section of the visual fields — Left optic nerve — Left optic tract — Loss of light reflex pretectal region — Lateral geniculate body — Occipital lobe — Superior colliculi — Geniculocalcarine tract — Optic radiation

Visual Field Defects Associated With Lesions of Visual System

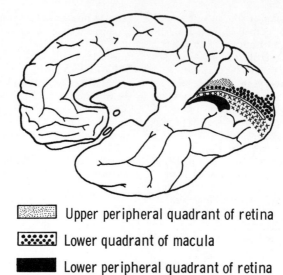

[dotted] Upper peripheral quadrant of retina

[dotted] Lower quadrant of macula

[solid black] Lower peripheral quadrant of retina

[xx pattern] Upper quadrant of macula

Medial View of Cerebral Hemisphere Showing Projection of the Retina on the Calcarine Fissure in Man. (Redrawn and reproduced, with permission, from Brouwer: Projection of the retina on the cortex in man. Res. Publ. A. Nerv. & Ment. Dis. **13**:529, 1934.)

Binocular fusion of color can occur, so that if one eye is exposed to red light and the other green light, a subjective sensation of yellow occurs. Land believes that sensation of color is produced by interplay of longer and shorter wavelengths rather than by stimulation of the eye by any particular wavelength.

In normal color (trichromatic) vision the eye can perceive 3 light primaries (red, blue, and green), and can mix these in suitable portions so that white or any color of the spectrum can be matched. Color blindness can result from a lessened capacity to match 3 primary colors, or it can be dichromatic vision, in which only one pair of primary colors is perceived, the 2 colors being complementary to each other. Most dichromats are red-green blind and confuse red, yellow, and green.

Lesions of the Visual Apparatus.

Retrobulbar neuritis involves the optic nerve or tract. Involvement may be axial, peripheral, or diffuse. The most common cause is multiple sclerosis. **Optic or bulbar neuritis** includes various forms of retinitis, e. g., simple, albuminuric, syphilitic, diabetic, hemorrhagic, and hereditary. **Papilledema** (choked disk) is usually a symptom of increased intracranial pressure from brain tumors, abscesses, hemorrhage, hypertension, and other causes. **Optic atrophy** is associated with de-

creased visual acuity and a change in color of the optic disk to light pink, white, or gray. Primary optic atrophy is produced by processes which involve the optic nerve and do not produce papilledema; secondary optic atrophy is a sequel of papilledema. Primary (simple) optic atrophy may be due to tabes dorsalis, multiple sclerosis, or heredity. Secondary optic atrophy may be due to neuritis, glaucoma, or increased intracranial pressure. Opacities of the lens, corneal scars, and arteriosclerotic changes in the retina may occur. Tumors and other lesions may interrupt the optic pathways.

Syndromes.

Syndromes involving the optic apparatus include the Foster Kennedy syndrome, amaurotic familial idiocy, Argyll Robertson pupil, and Holmes-Adie syndrome. The **Foster Kennedy syndrome** may be caused by tumors at the base of the frontal lobe and is characterized by ipsilateral blindness and anosmia (with atrophy of the optic and olfactory nerves) and contralateral papilledema. **Amaurotic familial idiocy** (Tay-Sachs disease, cerebromacular degeneration) is a severe mental deficiency occurring in Jewish families and associated with blindness, optic atrophy, and a dark cherry-red spot in place of the macula lutea. The **Holmes-Adie syndrome** is characterized by a tonic pupillary reaction and the absence of one or more tendon reflexes. The pupil is said to be "myotonic," with a very slow, almost imperceptible contraction to light and upon near vision, followed by a slower dilatation upon removal of the stimulus. Abnormal sensitivity to weak solutions (2.5%) of methacholine (Mecholyl®) instilled into the conjunctival sac is demonstrable in affected eyes: tonic pupils constrict while pupils of normal eyes remain unaffected (Adler-Scheie test).

Visual Defects.

A. Scotomas: (Abnormal blind spots in the visual fields.) Positive scotomas are apparent to the patient as dark spots; negative scotomas may exist without the patient's knowledge. Motile scotomas result from opacities floating in the vitreous. In absolute scotoma, perception of light is entirely lost over the defective area; in relative scotoma it is not.

1. Central scotomas (loss of macular vision) are due to axial neuritis. The point of fixation is involved and central visual acuity correspondingly impaired.

2. Other scotomas are due to patchy lesions, as in hemorrhage and glaucoma. Paracentral scotomas are adjacent to the point of fixation. Cecocentral scotomas involve the point of fixation and extend to the normal blind spot. Ring or annular scotomas encircle the point of fixation. Scintillating scotomas are subjective experiences of bright colorless or colored lights in the line of vision.

B. Amblyopia (dim vision) is a defect of visual acuity.

C. Amaurosis (complete blindness) may be hereditary or acquired. The term is sometimes restricted to blindness occurring without apparent ocular lesions, e.g., due to disease of the brain, retina, or optic nerve.

D. Field defects are diagrammed on p. 83. Contraction of field of vision is a common defect due to psychogenic causes. In severe cases it may result in tubular or gun-barrel vision. The tendency for the fields to remain small rather than to enlarge appropriately when the patient is moved away from the screen is characteristic of psychogenic etiology.

Visual acuity is not affected in papilledema or choked disk unless secondary atrophy occurs, after which the visual fields become contracted. Most lesions of the retina or optic nerve characteristically produce a central scotoma, although contractions of visual field, or even blindness, may occur.

E. Other Disorders:

1. Hemeralopia (day blindness) is a fatigue syndrome; vision is best in dim light.

2. Nyctalopia (night blindness) is sometimes associated with vitamin A deficiency.

3. Color blindness may be hereditary or acquired. Hereditary types are transmitted as recessive characteristics, sometimes sex-linked. These include total color blindness (achromatopsia) and partial color blindness (monochromatism, ability to recognize one of the 3 basic colors; and dichromatism, ability to recognize 2 of the 3 basic colors).

Tests.

A. Visual Acuity: Snellen card test for persons with fairly normal vision; finger counting and finger movement tests for subnormal cases; light perception and light projection for markedly subnormal cases. (Cataracts are not removed if light perception is gone.) Near vision is tested with standard reading cards.

B. Perimetry: Plotting fields of vision for determining presence of scotomas and field defects. For equal-sized targets, the visual field for white is most extensive; visual fields for blue, red, yellow, and green follow in that order.

C. Color blindness tests, using colored wools or special cards.

D. Fundus examination with the ophthalmoscope.

CRANIAL NERVES III, IV, VI:
OCULOMOTOR, TROCHLEAR, ABDUCENS
(Motor to Muscles of the Eye,
Including Levator Palpebrae)

Peripheral and Intermediate Connections.

(1) Oculomotor (III): **Motor fibers** arise from a group of nuclei in the central gray matter ventral to the cerebral aqueduct at the level of the superior colliculus. Crossed and mainly uncrossed fibers course through the red nucleus and the inner side of the substantia nigra to emerge on the sella turcica in the outer wall of the cavernous sinus and through the superior orbital fissure to supply the internal, superior, and inferior recti muscles and the inferior ob-

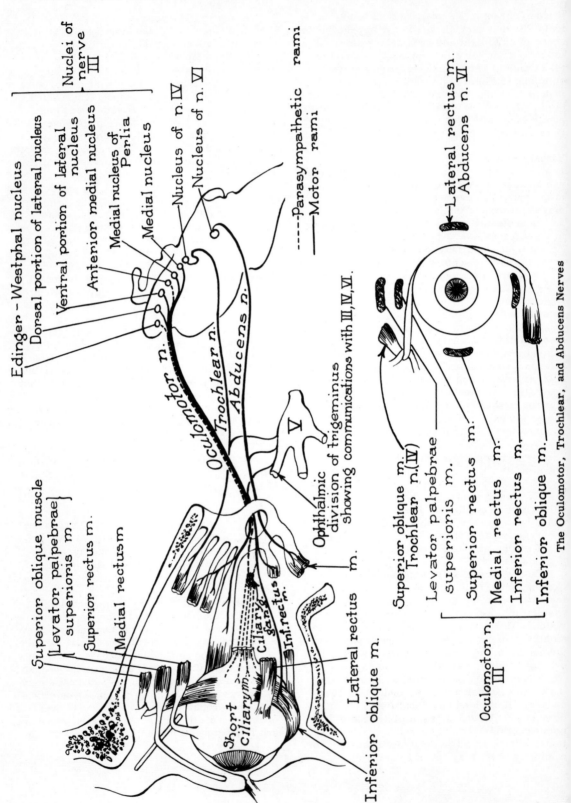

The Oculomotor, Trochlear, and Abducens Nerves

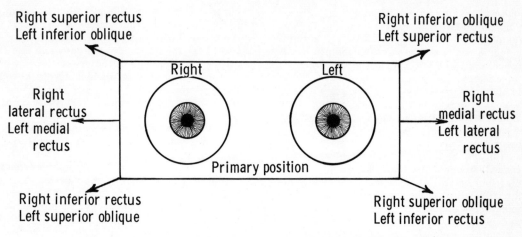

**Diagram Showing Muscles Used in Conjugate Ocular Movements
in the Six Cardinal Directions of Gaze**

Chart of Paralyses of Individual Eye Muscles*

Muscle	Nerve	Deviation of Eyeball	Diplopia Present When Looking*	Direction of Image
Internal rectus	III	Outward (external squint)	Toward nose	Vertical
Superior rectus	III	Downward and inward	Upward and outward	Oblique
Inferior rectus	III	Upward and inward	Downward and outward	Oblique
Inferior oblique	III	Downward and outward	Upward and inward	Oblique
Superior oblique	IV	Upward and outward	Downward and inward	Oblique
External rectus	VI	Inward (internal squint)	Toward temple	Vertical

*Diplopia is noted only when the affected eye attempts these movements.

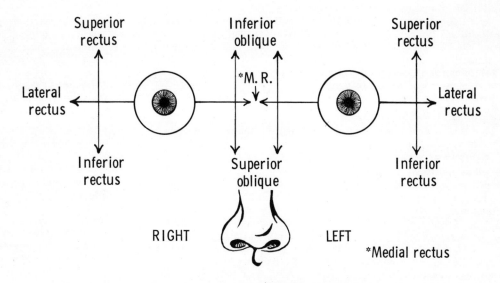

Diagram of Eye Muscle Action

lique and levator palpebrae muscles. **Parasympathetic fibers** arise (1) from the Edinger-Westphal nucleus, just rostral to the motor nucleus of III, passing via the nasociliary branch of III to the ciliary ganglion, from where short ciliary nerves are distributed to the sphincter muscle of the iris; and (2) from the upper portion of the medial nucleus of III, passing via the ciliary ganglion and short ciliary nerves to the ciliary muscle, which on contraction thickens the lens.

(2) Trochlear (IV): **Motor (entirely crossed) fibers** arise from the trochlear nucleus just caudad to III at the level of the inferior colliculus, run posteriorly, decussate in the anterior medullary velum, and wind around the cerebral peduncles. The nerve then follows III along the cavernous sinus to the orbit, where it supplies the superior oblique muscle, which moves the axis of vision downward and in.

(3) Abducens (VI): **Motor (entirely uncrossed) fibers** arise from the nucleus in the floor of the fourth ventricle in the lower portion of the pons near the internal genu of the facial nerve. The fibers pierce the pons and emerge anteriorly, the nerve running a long course over the tip of the petrous portion of the temporal bone to the outer wall of the cavernous sinus. The nerve then enters the orbit with III and IV to supply the external rectus muscle, which rotates the eyeball outward.

The **central reflex connections** from these nerves include the following: (1) from the pretectal region via the posterior commissure to the Edinger-Westphal nucleus, for mediation of ipsilateral and consensual light reflexes (interruption of this pathway is believed to cause the Argyll Robertson pupil); (2) from the superior colliculi via the tectobulbar tract to the nuclei of III, IV, and VI for the mediation of accommodation and other reflexes; (3) from the inferior colliculi via the tectobulbar tract to the eye muscle nuclei for reflexes correlated with hearing, and from the vestibular nuclei via the medial longitudinal fasciculus for reflex correlation with balance; and (4) from the cortex through the corticobulbar tract, for mediation of voluntary and conditioned movements of the eyes.

A few sensory (proprioceptive) fibers from the muscles of the eye are present for each of these nerves. The central terminations of these fibers are not known.

Among the **disorders** which may involve these nerves are the following: Syphilis, meningitis, encephalitis, diphtheria, botulism, cavernous sinus thrombosis, polioencephalitis hemorrhagica superior, suppuration of the accessory nasal sinuses, tumors of the orbit and brain, cerebral hemorrhage, aneurysm of the internal carotid artery or the circle of Willis, multiple sclerosis, skull fracture, hysterias, and certain drug intoxications.

Symptoms and Signs.

A. Squint or Strabismus: Deviation of either eye or both. In internal strabismus the visual axes cross each other. In external strabismus the visual axes diverge from each other

B. Diplopia (Double Vision): A subjective phenomenon present usually when looking with both eyes. (Monocular diplopia is generally hysterical in nature.)

C. Tilting of head to compensate for diplopia.

D. Conjugate Deviation: Both eyes turned to same side; may be spasmodic or paralytic. Usually caused by central lesions.

E. Nystagmus: Rhythmic or undulating movements of the eyes may be physiologic or due to central or labyrinthine lesions.

F. Ptosis (Lid Drop): Due to weakness or paralysis of the superior levator muscle.

Local Effects of Drugs on the Eye

PARASYMPATHOMIMETIC Used as miotics (constrict pupil) for control of intraocular pressure in glaucoma.	PARASYMPATHOLYTIC Used as mydriatics (dilate pupil) to aid in eye examination or as cycloplegics (relax ciliary muscles).	SYMPATHOMIMETIC Used for mydriasis; do not cause cycloplegia.
A. Act on Myoneural Junction: 　1. Pilocarpine 　2. Carbachol (Doryl®) 　3. Methacholine (Mecholyl®) B. Cholinesterase Inhibitors: 　1. Physostigmine (eserine) 　2. Isoflurophate (Floropryl®, DFP)	A. Mydriatic: Eucatropine (Euphthalmine®) B. Cycloplegic and Mydriatic: 　1. Homatropine 　2. Scopolamine (hyoscine) 　3. Atropine 　4. Cyclopentolate (Cyclogyl®)	1. Phenylephrine (Neo-Synephrine®) 2. Hydroxyamphetamine (Paredrine®) 3. Epinephrine (adrenalin) 4. Cocaine

G. Dizziness: Often associated with diplopia.

H. Limitations of movement, loss of reflexes, etc. (see Tests, p. 90).

I. Hippus: Alternate dilatation and contraction of the pupil under uniform illumination can be observed in normal persons only under high magnification. These movements are exaggerated in hysteria.

Classification of Disorders of These Nerves.
A. Ophthalmoplegias (Paralyses): Lesions causing these may be acute, chronic, or progressive, and central or peripheral.
1. Oculomotor paralysis (III) -
a. External ophthalmoplegia - Divergent strabismus, diplopia, and ptosis of lid.
b. Internal ophthalmoplegia - Dilated pupil, loss of light and accommodation reflexes.
c. Paralysis of individual muscles - See chart above.
d. Paralysis of levator palpebrae - Ptosis (common in myasthenia gravis).
e. Argyll Robertson pupil - Miosis with loss of light and ciliospinal reflexes. Accommodation is retained.
f. Paralysis of convergence (central lesion). Internal recti are normal except that they cannot converge the eyes. Double vision for near but not for distant objects may be present. Associated pupil contraction is lost also.
2. Trochlear paralysis (IV) - (Rare.) Slight convergent strabismus and diplopia on looking downward. The patient cannot look down and in, hence has difficulty in descending stairs. The head is tilted as a compensatory adjustment and may be the first indication of a trochlear lesion.
3. Abducens paralysis (VI) - (Most common of eye palsies; due to long course of nerve.) Convergent strabismus and diplopia;

especially common in late syphilis, basilar diseases and trauma.
4. Chronic progressive ophthalmoplegia (Graefe's disease) - (Rare.) Usually involves all 3 nerves together; caused by nuclear lesion, e. g., bulbar paralysis, late tabes, or progressive muscular atrophy.
5. Ophthalmoplegia internuclearis - A dissociation of eye movements which results from injury to the medial longitudinal fasciculus in the pons. Efforts to move the eyes to the side of the lesion result in partial outward movement plus nystagmoid movements of the ipsilateral eye; the contralateral eye fails to move beyond the position of central fixation.

B. Myasthenic States: An effort is required to keep the visual axis parallel. Functional, congenital, and neurasthenic weaknesses are also present. Muscular weakness causes visual disturbances, vertigo, migraine, paresthesia, and pains in the head, especially in the occipital and cervical regions.

C. Supranuclear Lesions: Lesions of the frontal or occipital lobes may produce paralysis of the conjugate gaze to the opposite side with deviation of the eyes to the side of the lesion. Spontaneous recovery usually occurs in a few days. Irritative lesions usually produce conjugate deviation of the eyes to the opposite side.

D. Nystagmus: Nystagmus is an involuntary back-and-forth, up-and-down, or rotating movement of the eyeballs. It usually results from lesions affecting the neural mechanism which tends to keep the eyes in a constant relation to their environment and which is concerned with equilibrium. Physiologic nystagmus may be elicited by turning the eyes far to one side and is characterized by rapid jerks with a quick component in the direction of gaze. Peripheral vestibular nystagmus results from stimulation of the peripheral vestibular apparatus and is always accompanied by vertigo. CNS nystagmus seldom is associated with vertigo and occurs with lesions in the region of the fourth ventricle. Optokinetic nystagmus (railway nystagmus) occurs when there is continuous movement of the visual field past the eyes. Pendular nystagmus has no quick and slow component and is either of ocular origin, due to poor vision, or hereditary, associated with good vision. Toxic nystagmus may follow treatment with certain drugs, e. g., diphenylhydantoin (Dilantin®), bromides, barbiturates, and alcohol.

Syndromes Involving These Nerves.
Benedikt's syndrome, bulbar palsy, Gradenigo's syndrome, Graefe's disease (see p.

Right Abducens Paralysis. Right eye fails to abduct on right lateral gaze.

89), Foville's syndrome, Korsakoff's syndrome, Nothnagel's syndrome, Weber's syndrome, Argyll Robertson pupil (see p. 89), Millard-Gubler syndrome, syndrome of the superior colliculus, and Wernicke's syndrome. Duane's retraction syndrome may follow paralysis of the lateral rectus muscle, and is characterized by retraction of the eyeball on adduction of the eye, with oblique upward movement of the eyeball and narrowing of the palpebral fissure. Gradenigo's syndrome may be produced by meningitis at the tip of the petrous bone and characterized by pain in the face (from irritation of the semilunar ganglion) and external rectus palsy, from paralysis of the sixth cranial nerve, resulting in an internal strabismus and diplopia. It is usually a complication of purulent otitis media.

Tests.

A. Finger following tests for ocular movements.

B. Accommodation: By noting convergence and pupillary change when patient follows objects brought from a distance up close to the eyes.

C. Light Reflex: By shining light into eye from side (also depends on optic nerves).

D. Consensual Light Reflex: By shining light into one eye and noting change in opposite pupil.

E. Prism Tests: For ability of internal and external recti to coalesce images. Normally the external rectus muscles should over-

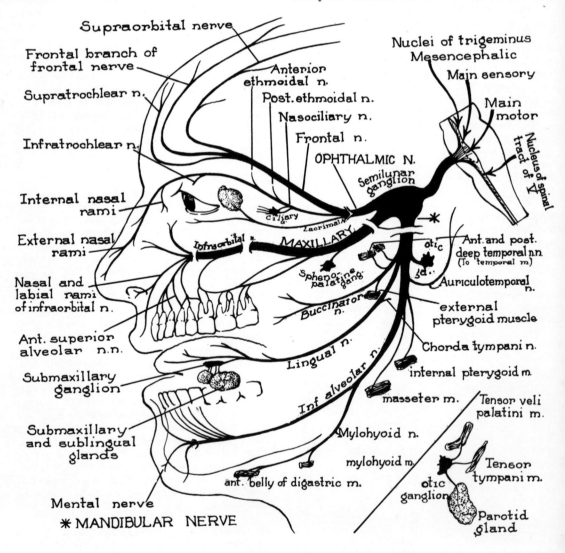

The Trigeminal Nerve

come a prism of 8° or more; the internal rectus muscles should overcome a prism of 23° to 25° or more.

F. Diplopia Testing: May be performed with the aid of red glass or a Maddox rod and the relative positions of false and true images determined for various portions of the visual fields. The false image commonly appears in the direction in which the paralyzed muscle usually should pull the eye.

CRANIAL NERVE V: TRIGEMINAL
(Mixed Nerve)

Peripheral and Intermediate Connections.
A. Sensory fibers arise from unipolar cells in the semilunar (gasserian) ganglion. Peripherally they supply sensation (1) via the **ophthalmic division**, from the forehead, eyes, nose, temples, meninges, paranasal sinuses, and part of the nasal mucosa; (2) via the **maxillary division**, from the upper jaw, teeth, lip, cheeks, hard palate, maxillary sinuses, and nasal mucosa; and (3) via the **mandibular division**, from the lower jaw, teeth, lip, buccal mucosa, tongue, and part of the external ear, auditory meatus, and meninges. Centrally the fibers pass as the portio major and split into (1) short ascending rami ending in the main sensory nucleus of V (just lateral to the motor nucleus) and subserving mainly touch; and (2) long descending rami, giving off collaterals to the spinal nucleus of V, which extends through the medulla to overlap with Lissauer's tract, subserving touch, pain, and temperature.

B. Sensory proprioceptive fibers arise from unipolar cells within the mesencephalic nucleus of V; the peripheral processes pass via the motor root to nerve spindles in the muscles of mastication, and possibly also to the extraocular muscles.

C. Motor fibers from the motor nucleus of V (at the mid-level of the pons) pass (1) as the motor root (portio minor) from the ventral surface of the pons through the foramen ovale to supply the muscles of mastication (the masseter, temporal, internal and external pterygoids); (2) via the otic ganglion to supply the tensor tympani and tensor veli palatini; and (3) via the mylohyoid nerve to the mylohyoid muscle and the anterior belly of the digastric muscle.

Central Connections.
The motor nucleus receives bilateral (mainly crossed) cerebral connections from the corticobulbar tracts, reflex connections from the spinal tract of V and extrapyramidal tracts. From the main sensory nucleus of V, touch pathways pass to the thalamus and higher centers via the dorsal secondary tract of V. From the spinal nucleus of V, touch, pain, and temperature pathways pass to the thalamus via the ventral secondary tract of V and reflex connections pass to the motor nuclei of cranial nerves V, VII, and IX. Pain and temperature fibers whose cell bodies lie within the semilunar ganglion run caudally to form the spinal root of the trigeminal nerve with terminal branches to the spinal root of the trigeminal nerve descending through the pons and medulla. New fibers arise from cells of the spinal root and cross to opposite side of brain stem in diffuse pattern and then ascend via the trigeminal lemniscus to the posterior ventral nucleus of thalamus. Central connections of the mesencephalic nucleus are obscure.

Disorders.
Disorders which may affect the trigeminal nerve include neuralgias and neuritis, syphilis, tuberculosis, syringobulbia, tumors of the brain, basilar meningitis, pontine diseases, skull fracture, aneurysm of the carotid artery or circle of Willis, psychoneuroses, and cavernous sinus thrombosis.

Syndromes Involving the Trigeminal Nerve.
Tic douloureux (trifacial neuralgia, prosopalgia, Fothergill's neuralgia, chronic paroxysmal trigeminal neuralgia) is characterized by severe pains in the distribution of one or more branches of the trigeminal nerve. Individual pains are abrupt in onset and brief in duration, usually lasting a fraction of a second to several seconds. The pain has a lightning-like or electric shock-like quality. Between paroxysms the patient may be quite comfortable. Excruciating, paroxysmal pain of short duration may follow irritation of the "trigger zone," a point on the lip, face, gum, or tongue which is frequently sensitive to cold, pressure, or a blast of air. Flushing of the face, watering of the eyes, and running of the nose are also present. Involvement is usually unilateral and confined to one division of the nerve. The disorder occurs in adults over 40. Although the cause is unknown and little or no pathologic change has been noted, trigeminal neuralgia is sometimes associated with dental or sinus pathology. Treatments used include analgesics, anticonvulsants, neurotomy, alcohol injection, trichloroethylene inhalations, intramedullary and mesencephalic tractotomy, and decompression of the posterior root.

The **paratrigeminal syndrome** (Raeder's syndrome) is a rare disorder produced by tumors arising in the semilunar ganglion and characterized by trigeminal neuralgia at the onset followed by facial anesthesias on the affected side. The muscles of mastication are weakened or paralyzed, and the adjacent third nerve may be paralyzed. Ipsilateral Horner's syndrome may occur from involvement of the carotid sympathetic plexus.

The **auriculotemporal nerve syndrome** (Frey's syndrome) consists of flushing and sweating of the ipsilateral face in the distribution of the auriculotemporal nerve upon eating or tasting. It occasionally follows injury or infection of the parotid gland area. Bonnier's syndrome is discussed on p. 105.

Symptoms of Fifth Nerve Involvement.

A. Pain: Marked if gasserian ganglion or peripheral branches are involved.

B. Loss of sensation over sensory distribution; corneal anesthesia early.

C. Dissociate Anesthesia: Loss of pain but not touch may be noted when the spinal tract of the fifth nerve is involved (e.g., in syringobulbia).

D. Paresthesia: Occasionally seen in anemia and in nervous and hysterical patients.

E. Paralysis of muscles of mastication, with deviation of jaw to affected side.

F. Loss of jaw jerk, sneeze, lid, conjunctival, and corneal reflexes.

G. Impaired hearing from paralysis of tensor tympani.

H. Trismus (Lockjaw): Tonic spasm of muscles of mastication, in rabies, tetany, tetanus, epilepsy, and hysteria.

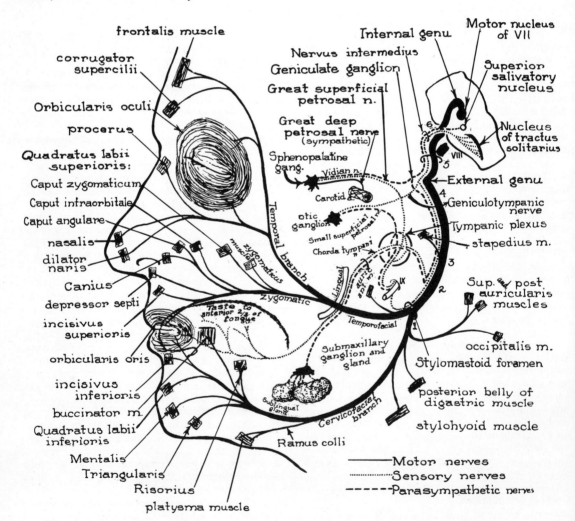

The Facial Nerve

I. Trophic and Secretory Disturbances: Herpes, neurokeratitis, dryness of nose (causes anosmia, as moisture is necessary to smell), ulcerations of face, and loss of teeth.

Tests.
    A. Sensation: With wisps of cotton, pin pricks, and warm or cold objects.

    B. Reflexes: Corneal (wink), conjunctival, jaw jerk, sneeze.

    C. Motor Status: Ability to chew; palpation of masseter and temporal muscles when the jaws are clamped tightly together. Wasting of the masseter muscles and deviation of the mandible to one side on attempting to lower the jaw against resistance are noted when present.

CRANIAL NERVE VII: FACIAL
(Mixed Nerve - Mainly Motor)

Peripheral and Intermediate Connections.
    A. Motor fibers from the motor nucleus of VII in the caudal portion of the pons loop around the nucleus of VI (internal genu) and leave the skull by a long course through the petrous portion of the temporal bone. These fibers supply the stapedius muscle of the middle ear, the superficial musculature of the face and scalp, the platysma, the posterior belly of the digastric muscle, and the stylohyoid muscle.

    B. Parasympathetic fibers from the superior salivatory nucleus pass via the nervus intermedius (glossopalatinus, or nerve of Wrisberg) to the glands and mucous membranes of the pharynx, palate, nasal cavity, and paranasal sinuses via the great superficial petrosal and the sphenopalatine ganglion; and to the submaxillary and sublingual glands via the chorda tympani and lingual nerves and the submaxillary ganglion.

    C. Sensory fibers arise from unipolar cells in the geniculate ganglion. Peripheral branches carry taste from the anterior two-thirds of the tongue via the lingual and chorda tympani nerves, and sensation from the parotid gland via the otic ganglion and the geniculotympanic nerve. Central branches pass via the nervus intermedius to the nucleus of the tractus solitarius. (There are also some proprioceptive fibers carrying deep pressure and position sense from the facial muscles via the facial nerve.)

Central Connections.
    A. The motor nucleus receives crossed and uncrossed fibers from the corticobulbar tract, extrapyramidal tracts, and tectospinal tract, and reflex connections from the nucleus of the tractus solitarius and the nucleus of the spinal tract of the trigeminus. The facial muscles below the forehead receive contralateral cortical innervation (crossed corticobulbar fibers); however, the frontalis muscle receives bilateral cortical innervation and is, therefore, not paralyzed by lesions involving one motor cortex or its pathways.

    B. The superior salivatory nucleus receives cortical impulses via the dorsal longitudinal tract and reflex connections from the nucleus of the tractus solitarius.

    C. The sensory fibers are connected with the cortex via the medial lemnisci and thalamus, and with the salivatory nuclei and motor nuclei of VII by reflex neurons.

    D. The cortical taste area is located in the inferior central (face) region and is believed to extend onto the opercular surface of the parietal lobe.

Lesions of the Facial Nerve.
    A. Bell's Palsy (Peripheral Facial Paralysis, Prosopoplegia): May be caused by chilling of the face, middle ear infections, tumors, fractures, meningitis, hemorrhage, infectious diseases, and other less commonly encountered disorders. Seventy-five per cent of all facial nerve lesions fall into this group. Bell's palsy may occur at any age, but is slightly more common in the age group from 20-50. On attempting to close the eyelids the eyeball on the affected side may be seen to turn upward (Bell's phenomenon). Symptoms and signs depend upon the location of the lesions, as follows: (Numbers in the text refer to numbers in the diagram on p. 92.)
    1. Lesion outside the stylomastoid foramen (signs are on affected side) - The mouth droops and may draw to the other side, food collects between cheeks and gums, and deep facial sensation is lost. The patient cannot whistle, wink or close his eye, or wrinkle his forehead. Tearing occurs if the eye is unprotected. Paralysis is of the flaccid lower motor neuron (LMN) type. The reaction of degeneration (see p. 238) appears in 10-14 days, depending upon the extent of damage.
    2. Lesion in facial canal and involving the chorda tympani nerve - All the above signs are present, as well as loss of taste in the anterior two-thirds of the tongue and reduced salivation on the affected side.
    3. Lesion higher in the facial canal and involving the stapedius muscle - Signs of (1) and (2) plus hyperacusis.
    4. Higher lesion involving the geniculate ganglion - Onset is often acute, with pain be-

hind and within the ear. Herpes of the tympanum and concha may precede the palsy. The Ramsay Hunt syndrome is Bell's palsy associated with herpes zoster of the geniculate ganglion, herpetic lesions being visible on tympanic membrane, external auditory canal, and on the pinna.

5. Lesion in the internal auditory meatus - Signs of Bell's palsy and deafness from eighth nerve involvement.

6. Lesions at the emergence of the facial nerve from the pons (e. g., meningitis) - Bell's palsy with involvement of other nerves as well, e. g., V and VIII and, at times, VI, XI, and XII. In the Marcus Gunn (jaw-winking) phenomenon, seen in congenital ptosis, elevation of a ptotic eyelid occurs on movement of the jaw to the contralateral side. The Marin-Amat syndrome is usually observed after peripheral facial paralysis and is referred to as an inverted Marcus Gunn phenomenon. Closing of the eyes occurs when the patient opens his mouth forcefully and maximally.

Treatment and prognosis: Reassure the patient that recovery may occur in 2-8 weeks (or up to 1-2 years in older patients). Keep the face warm and avoid further exposure, especially to wind and dust. Protect the eye with a patch if necessary. Support the face with tape or wire anchored at the angle of the mouth and looped about the ear. Electric stimulation (every other day after the 14th day) may be used to help prevent muscle atrophy. Gentle upward massage of the involved muscles for 5-10 minutes 2-3 times daily may help to maintain muscle tone. Heat from an infra-red lamp may hasten recovery. In the vast majority of cases partial or complete recovery occurs. When recovery is partial, contractures may develop on the paralyzed side. Recurrence on the same or the opposite side is occasionally reported.

B. Nuclear Type of Facial Palsy: Signs of Bell's palsy plus contralateral hemiplegia (from pyramidal involvement) with paralysis of the sixth and sometimes the eighth nerve. The Millard-Gubler syndrome is a form of crossed paralysis (facial hemiplegia alternans) produced by a pontile lesion and characterized by contralateral hemiplegia and ipsilateral facial palsy. In many cases the sixth nerve is also involved, producing an internal strabismus. Foville's syndrome is a form of crossed hemiplegia from a pontile lesion. It consists of contralateral hemiplegia with ipsilateral palsies of the sixth and seventh cranial nerves, internal strabismus with diplopia, and paralysis of the muscles of facial expression.

C. Supranuclear Type of Facial Palsy: Often associated with ipsilateral hemiplegia or monoplegia. The facial paralysis is of the spastic type. Taste and salivation are not affected, and the frontalis muscle is spared (due to bilateral cortical innervation). Reflexes and emotional responses are retained, and there is no reaction of degeneration.

D. Geniculate Neuralgia (Rare): Pain behind and within the ear and loss of the taste sense. It is usually a transient accompaniment of Bell's palsy, type (4) (see above), but may appear with herpes of the tympanum and concha with or without facial palsy (Hunt's syndrome).

E. Crocodile Tears Syndrome: Paroxysmal lacrimation during eating, occurring usually as a result of injury to the facial nerve proximal to the geniculate ganglion.

F. Facial spasm (paroxysmal hyperkinesia of the facial muscles) begins with twitching, is usually unilateral, and cannot be inhibited at will. During an attack voluntary movements are impossible. Facial spasm commonly occurs after suture of a divided seventh nerve.

G. Bilateral facial palsy (facial diplegia; rare) causes a flat, expressionless, drooling facies. It occurs with bulbar lesions, polyneuritis, and myasthenia gravis.

H. Striatum lesions cause grimaces, choreiform movements, etc.

I. Moebius' Syndrome: (Congenital oculofacial paralysis, congenital facial diplegia, infantile nuclear aplasia.) A congenital disorder characterized by paresis or paralysis of both external rectus muscles and face muscles and sometimes associated with other musculoskeletal anomalies.

Tests.

A. Motor Status: Ability to smile, whistle, etc. Electric testing of the facial nerve and facial muscles and electromyography may provide valuable prognostic information.

B. Reflexes: Corneal (wink), conjunctival, and lid reflexes should be examined.

C. Sensory Status: Taste is tested as follows: sweet with sugar, sour with citric acid, bitter with quinine, and salty with salt.

D. Facial Symmetry: Asymmetry of the face at rest or during voluntary facial movement should be noted.

CRANIAL NERVE VIII: ACOUSTIC
(Composite Sensory Nerve)

The acoustic nerve consists of 2 separate parts known as the cochlear and vestibular nerves.

Peripheral and Intermediate Connections.

A. Cochlear Nerve (for Hearing): Fibers from bipolar cells in the spiral ganglion consist of peripheral branches which end in the spiral organ of Corti, and central branches which terminate in the ventral and dorsal cochlear nuclei.

B. Vestibular Nerve: Fibers from bipolar cells in the vestibular ganglion (ganglion of Scarpa) consist of peripheral branches which pass to the neuroepithelium in the ampullae of the semicircular canals and in the maculas of the utricle and saccule, and central branches which enter the brain stem median to the restiform body and end in the vestibular nuclei. Some central branches pass without interruption to the cerebellum.

Central Connections.

A. From the cochlear nuclei fibers pass by second-order neurons through the trapezoid body and lateral lemnisci to the medial geniculate bodies. From this area the auditory radiations are projected to the auditory cortex and reflex connections pass to the eye muscle nuclei and other motor nuclei of the cranial and spinal nerves via the tectobulbar and tectospinal tracts.

B. Vestibular connections are from the superior and lateral vestibular nuclei to the cerebellum; from the lateral nuclei to ipsilateral spinal centers via the direct vestibulospinal tracts; and from the superior, medial, and spinal nuclei to eye muscle nuclei and other motor nuclei of the cranial and spinal nerves via the medial longitudinal fasciculi of the same and opposite sides.

Diseases and Lesions Which May Involve the Eighth Nerve.

Peripheral lesions usually involve both the cochlear and vestibular nerves. Examples include otitis media, meningitis, skull fractures, otosclerosis, basal tumors, infectious diseases, degenerative diseases, and Ménière's syndrome. Central lesions may involve either of the nerves independently and include syphilis, multiple sclerosis, congenital defects, brain tumors, hysterias and other psychogenic disorders, and degenerative diseases of the brain and blood vessels. Certain drugs, e.g., quinine, cinchophen, and salicylates, may affect the cochlear nerve. Streptomycin sometimes causes vestibular nuclear degeneration. Seasickness (due to continuous movement of the endolymph in susceptible individuals) is characterized by vertigo and disturbances in equilibrium, nausea and vomiting (not related to diet); and occasionally pallor, sweating, tachycardia, dyspnea, tremor, and faintness. It is treated with hypnotics; by lying down and varying the position of the head; and with antihistamines and tranquilizing drugs.

Other syndromes and diseases affecting the eighth nerve are Ménière's syndrome (paroxysmal vertigo), syndrome of pontocerebellar angle tumors, Bonnier's syndrome (from a lesion of Deiters' nucleus), Lermoyez's syndrome (paroxysmal deafness), and Costen's syndrome. Lermoyez's syndrome consists of

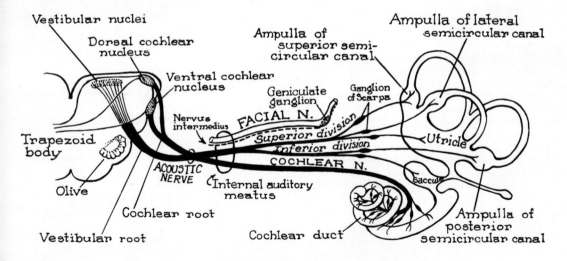

The Acoustic Nerve

attacks of decreased auditory acuity followed by vertigo, at which time the hearing returns to normal. The etiology and mechanism are not known. Costen's syndrome is said to result from pressure or distortion changes of the temporomandibular joints and characterized by pains in the head, neck, ear, tongue, nose, and eyes as well as tinnitus, impaired hearing, and dizziness. Cogan's syndrome consists of keratitis and deafness in nonsyphilitic patients, predominantly young adults, of sudden onset and unknown etiology.

Symptoms of Eighth Nerve Involvement.
A. Cochlear:

1. Tinnitus - Ringing, buzzing, hissing, singing, or roaring noises in the ear are a frequent sign of early peripheral cochlear disease. Central tinnitus is rare and more complex, taking the form of music, etc. Noises from sclerotic cerebral vessels and aneurysms are transmitted to the eighth nerve. In organic cochlear lesions, tinnitus is usually followed by deafness.

2. Deafness - Nerve deafness is due to interruption of the nerve pathway; conduction deafness is due to middle or external ear pathology. Cortical lesions do not cause deafness unless bilateral.

3. Hearing scotomas (deafness to certain pitches and noises) are not infrequent in hysterias, multiple sclerosis, paresis, and schizophrenia.

4. Supranuclear disorders - Sensory aphasia (word deafness; ability to hear but not comprehend words) is associated with lesions of the posterior portion of the superior temporal gyrus of the dominant cerebral hemisphere. Auditory hallucinations may occur in psychoses or drug intoxications. Epileptic auras occur in the auditory sphere.

B. Vestibular:

1. Vertigo - A feeling of giddiness with disorientation in space, usually resulting in a disturbance of equilibrium, is often a sign of labyrinthine disease of middle or internal ear origin. It may also result from lesions of the eighth nerve (e. g., tumors), or from reflex phenomena (e. g., seasickness). It is often relieved or induced by placing the head in certain positions.

2. Nystagmus - A rhythmic to-and-fro ocular movement with a slow pull and a rapid return jerk usually accompanies vertigo in vestibular disease. It represents a disturbance in the reflex control of the ocular muscles which is mainly a function of the semicircular canals. Nystagmus is named from the quick component, which is a compensatory adjustment to the slow reflex movement. There are various types: vertical, horizontal, rotatory, etc. Other forms of nystagmus occur in central, cerebellar, and cerebral lesions.

3. General symptoms which may be associated with labyrinthine disease include diaphoresis, tachycardia, nausea, vomiting, and lowered blood pressure.

Tests.
A. Cochlear:

1. Hearing acuity - Cover the other ear and test with a watch, whisper, or acumeter.

2. Weber's test (for nerve deafness) - Place a tuning fork (C = 256 vibrations/second) on the vertex and cover one ear. Normally, the closed ear hears sound best by bone conduction. If no sound is heard in the closed ear, nerve deafness is suspected.

3. Rinne's test - A tuning fork is placed on the mastoid bone and, when sound is no longer heard, placed in front of the ear. If sound is not heard in front of the ear, suspect middle ear disease. (Normally, air conduction is greater than bone conduction.) As a rule, no sound is heard in either case in severe nerve deafness.

4. Objective examination of the ear with an otoscope for foreign bodies, congenital malformations, etc.

B. Vestibular:

1. Caloric test - Following irrigation of the right ear with cold water (up to 10°C.), with the subject seated and his head tilted back 60°, there normally occur nausea, horizontal nystagmus with slow component to the right, past-pointing to the left, and falling to the right. (With warm water, the quick component is to the right.) Complete interruption of vestibular nerve function is characterized by absence of reaction to irrigation; partial interruption of vestibular nerve function produces diminished responses.

2. Electric test - The amount of galvanic current (in milliamperes) necessary to produce nystagmus, past-pointing, and inclination of the head when the current is passed between 2 saline-soaked pads placed over each ear is noted. The comparative effect of placing the cathode (the stimulating electrode) on the right and left ear is determined.

CRANIAL NERVE IX: GLOSSOPHARYNGEAL
(Mixed Nerve)

Cranial nerve IX leaves the skull via the jugular foramen with X and XI and lies antero-lateral to X.

Peripheral and Intermediate Connections.
A. Motor fibers from the nucleus ambiguus pass to the stylopharyngeus muscle.

B. Parasympathetic fibers from the inferior salivatory nucleus pass via the nerve of Jacobson, tympanic plexus, and small superficial petrosal nerve to the otic ganglion, from which the postganglionic fibers pass to the parotid gland.

C. Sensory fibers arise from unipolar cells in the petrous and jugular ganglia. Centrally they terminate in the tractus solitarius and its nucleus. Peripherally they supply general sensation to the pharynx, soft palate, posterior third of the tongue, fauces, tonsils, eustachian tube, and tympanic cavity. Through the sinus nerve they supply special receptors in the carotid body and carotid sinus concerned with reflex control of the posterior third of the tongue. A few fibers join the auricular branch of the vagus nerve and pass to the external auditory meatus.

Central Connections.
A. The nucleus ambiguus receives cortical connections via the corticobulbar tract and reflex connections from the extrapyramidal tracts, tectobulbar tracts, and from the nucleus of the tractus solitarius.

B. The inferior salivatory nucleus receives cortical impulses via the dorsal longitudinal tract and reflexes from the nucleus of the tractus solitarius.

C. The sensory fibers are connected with the cortex via the medial lemnisci and thalamus and reflexly with the salivatory nuclei, nucleus ambiguus, and the motor nucleus of VII.
The glossopharyngeal nerve is rarely involved alone (e.g., by neuralgia), but generally together with the vagus and accessory nerves by compression, inflammation, or trauma. Lesions which may involve the ninth nerve include bulbar diseases, syphilis, tuberculosis, basal tumors, jugular thrombosis, trauma in the retroparotid space, aneurysm of the circle of Willis, and diphtheritic neuritis.

Syndromes.
Syndromes involving the ninth nerve include the following: (1) Bonnier's syndrome (see p.

105); (2) Vernet's syndrome (see p. 105); (3) **glossopharyngeal neuralgia**, characterized by paroxysmal pain, similar in type to trigeminal neuralgia, which starts in the throat, radiates to the eustachian tube and behind the ear, and is often initiated by coughing, swallowing, or clearing the throat; and (4) neuralgia of the tympanic branch (Jacobson's nerve), characterized by pain limited to the ear and eustachian tube. The pain of glossopharyngeal neuralgia usually starts in the tonsillar fossa and extends to the ipsilateral ear. Paroxysms of pain of increasing intensity last 20-30 seconds and are often followed by burning sensation for 2-3 minutes. Reichert's syndrome is an "incomplete" neuralgia affecting the tympanic branch of the glossopharyngeal nerve, which may be relieved by intracranial section of the glossopharyngeal nerve.

Tests.
A. The pharyngeal (gag) reflex depends on the ninth nerve for its sensory component; stroking of the affected side does not produce gagging if the nerve is injured.

B. Vernet's rideau phenomenon (constriction of the posterior pharyngeal wall in saying, "ah") is absent when the ninth nerve is involved.

C. The carotid sinus reflex depends on the ninth nerve for its sensory component. Pressure over the sinus normally produces slowing of the heart and a fall in blood pressure.

D. Taste tests on posterior third of tongue are discussed on p. 94.

Symptoms of Ninth Nerve Involvement.
1. Loss of gag (pharyngeal) reflex.
2. Slight dysphagia.
3. Loss of taste in posterior third of tongue.

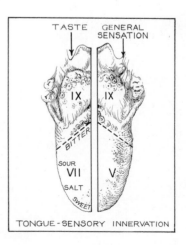

TONGUE-SENSORY INNERVATION

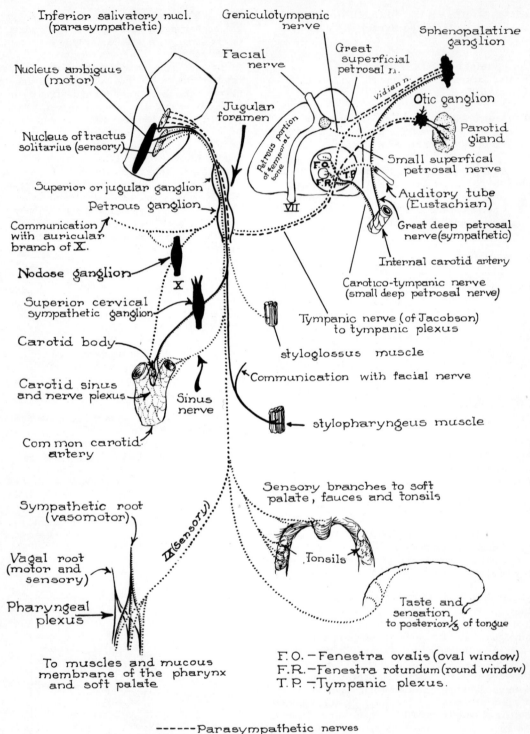

Inferior salivatory nucl. (parasympathetic)

Nucleus ambiguus (motor)

Nucleus of tractus solitarius (sensory)

Superior or jugular ganglion

Petrous ganglion

Communication with auricular branch of X.

Nodose ganglion

Superior cervical sympathetic ganglion

Carotid body

Carotid sinus and nerve plexus

Common carotid artery

Sympathetic root (vasomotor)

Vagal root (motor and sensory)

Pharyngeal plexus

To muscles and mucous membrane of the pharynx and soft palate

Geniculotympanic nerve

Facial nerve

Great superficial petrosal n.

Jugular foramen

Petrous portion of temporal bone

VII

Sphenopalatine ganglion

Vidian n.

Otic ganglion

Parotid gland

Small superfical petrosal nerve

Auditory tube (Eustachian)

Great deep petrosal nerve (sympathetic)

Internal carotid artery

Carotico-tympanic nerve (small deep petrosal nerve)

Tympanic nerve (of Jacobson) to tympanic plexus

styloglossus muscle

Communication with facial nerve

stylopharyngeus muscle

Sinus nerve

IX (sensory)

Sensory branches to soft palate, fauces and tonsils

Tonsils

Taste and sensation, to posterior ⅓ of tongue

F.O. — Fenestra ovalis (oval window)
F.R. — Fenestra rotundum (round window)
T.P. — Tympanic plexus.

- - - - - - Parasympathetic nerves
. . . . Sensory nerves
———— Motor nerves
▬▬▬▬ Sympathetic nerves

The Glossopharyngeal Nerve

4. Deviation of the uvula to the well side.

5. Loss of sensation in pharynx, tonsils, fauces, and back of tongue.

6. Loss of constriction of the posterior pharyngeal wall when saying, "ah."

7. Increased salivation from involvement of the tympanic plexus in middle ear lesions.

8. Rarely, "nystagmus" of the uvula in central inflammatory and vascular lesions.

9. Tachycardia in some ninth nerve lesions, probably from disturbance of carotid sinus reflex.

CRANIAL NERVE X: VAGUS
(Mixed Nerve)

Peripheral and Intermediate Connections.

A. Motor fibers from the nucleus ambiguus contribute to the rootlets of the glossopharyngeal nerve, vagus, and the internal ramus of the accessory nerve (XI). Those of the vagus nerve pass to the muscles of the soft palate and pharynx. Those to the accessory nerve join the vagus outside the skull and pass via the recurrent laryngeal nerve to the intrinsic muscles of the larynx.

B. Parasympathetic fibers from the dorsal motor nucleus of the vagus are distributed to the thoracic and abdominal viscera. Their postganglionic fibers arise in the terminal ganglia of the viscera. They inhibit heart rate and suprarenal secretion and stimulate gastrointestinal peristalsis and gastric, hepatic, and pancreatic glandular activity.

C. Somatic sensory fibers of unipolar cells in the jugular ganglion send peripheral branches via the auricular branch to the external auditory meatus and part of the ear and, via the recurrent meningeal branch, to the dura of the posterior fossa; and central branches to the spinal tract of the trigeminus and its nucleus.

D. Visceral sensory fibers of unipolar cells in the ganglion nodosum send peripheral branches to the pharynx, larynx, trachea, esophagus, and the thoracic and abdominal viscera; and a few special afferents to taste buds in the epiglottic region. Central branches run to the tractus solitarius and terminate in its nucleus. The visceral afferents of the vagus nerve carry the sensation of abdominal distention and nausea and impulses concerned with regulation of the depth of respiration and the control of blood pressure.

Central Connections.

For central connections of the nucleus of the tractus solitarius and nucleus ambiguus,

see p. 97. For central connections of the nucleus of the spinal tract of the trigeminus, see p. 91. The central connections of the **dorsal motor nucleus** of the vagus include reflex neurons from the nucleus of the tractus solitarius and the nucleus of the spinal tract of the trigeminal nerve.

Lesions of the Vagus Nerve.

Intramedullary lesions include hemorrhage, thrombosis, tumors, multiple sclerosis, syphilis, syringobulbia, and amyotrophic lateral sclerosis. Basilar disease is caused by spirochetal and other types of meningitis, hemorrhage, tumors, and aneurysms. **Peripheral lesions** include primary neuritis (alcoholic, diphtheritic, lead, arsenic), tumors (e. g., goiter), adenopathies of the retroparotid space, trauma of retroparotid space, and aortic aneurysms. Vagus nerve lesions often involve the glossopharyngeal, accessory, and hypoglossal nerves also.

Syndromes.

Special syndromes of the last 4 cranial nerves are discussed on p. 104.

Diseases and Syndromes Involving the Tenth Nerve.

A. Complete Bilateral Vagal Paralysis: (Rapidly fatal.) Complete laryngeal paralysis, aphonia and vomiting, dyspnea or pseudoasthma, dilatation and pain in the stomach, cardiac arrhythmia and death.

B. Unilateral Vagal Paralysis From Peripheral Lesions: Unilateral paralysis of soft palate, unilateral paralysis and anesthesia of pharynx and larynx, hoarseness and nasal speech, dyspnea and dysphagia, paralysis of one vocal cord.

C. Unilateral Vagal Paralysis From Nuclear Lesions: Symptoms of (B), plus contralateral loss of pain and temperature senses from interruption of the spinothalamic tract (see Avellis's syndrome).

D. Unilateral Paralysis of Recurrent Laryngeal Nerve: The voice is weakened. Aortic aneurysms are a frequent cause of left-sided palsies.

E. Unilateral Paralysis of Superior Laryngeal Nerve: (Rare; usually traumatic.) Anesthesia of larynx, hoarseness, voice tires easily.

F. Superior Laryngeal Neuralgia: Pain radiating from the side of the thyroid to the ear.

G. Hysterical Aphonia: From laryngospasm.

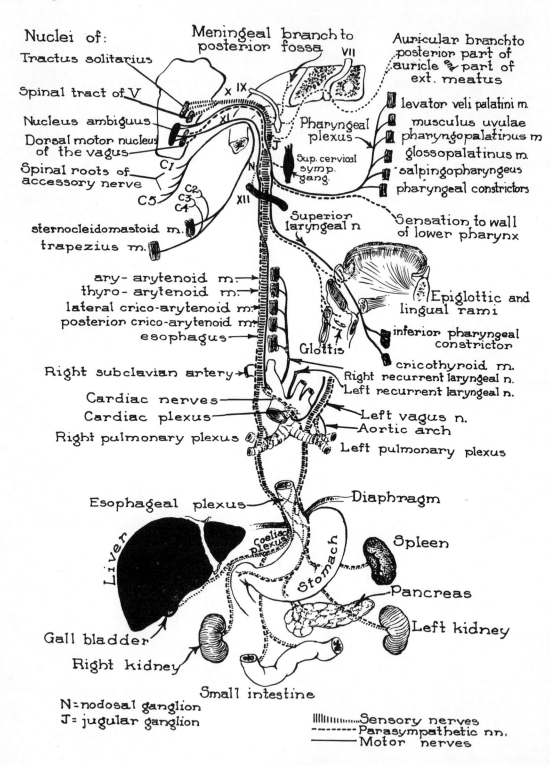

The Vagus Nerve

Symptoms and Signs Suggestive of Tenth Nerve Involvement.

A. Motor Disturbances:

1. Aphonia - Loss of voice (from paralysis of vocal cords or hysteria).

2. Dysphonia - Impairment of voice; may occur with unilateral lesions.

3. Objective changes in position of the vocal cords.

4. Dysphagia - Difficulty in swallowing; may be associated with regurgitation of fluids through the nose, as in pharyngeal and laryngeal spasms (occurs in some hysterias and in rabies).

5. Esophageal, cardiac, or pyloric spasm not due to local causes may be of vagal origin.

6. Paralysis of soft palate, with loss of the gag reflex.

B. Sensory Disturbances: Pain or paresthesias in the pharynx, larynx, and external auditory meatus occur with irritative lesions. Anesthesia of the lower pharynx and larynx occurs in complete lesions. Cough is a constant symptom of vagal irritation. Dyspnea and pseudoasthma are due to interruption of the reflex vagal control of respiration. Temporary salivary hypersecretion occurs with irritative lesions, and hyposecretion with palsies.

C. Vegetative (Parasympathetic) Disturbances: Bradycardia with irritative lesions, tachycardia with palsies of the vagus, and dilatation of the stomach.

Tests.

A. Laryngoscopic examination.

B. Sensory status of pharynx and larynx.

C. Pharyngeal (gag) reflex.

D. Oculocardiac Reflex: Press over orbit.

E. Carotid Sinus Reflex: Press on carotid sinus to produce cardiac slowing.

CRANIAL NERVE XI: ACCESSORY
(Motor Nerve)

Two separate branches of cranial nerve XI leave the skull together through the jugular foramen.

Peripheral and Intermediate Connections.

A. Internal or Medullary Branch: Motor fibers from the nucleus ambiguus to the intrinsic muscles of the larynx (and possibly a few parasympathetic fibers) join the vagus outside the skull. These have been described with the vagus nerve on p. 99.

B. External or Spinal Branch: Motor fibers from the lateral part of the anterior horns of the first 5 or 6 cervical cord segments ascend as the spinal root of the accessory nerve through the foramen magnum to leave the skull via the jugular foramen and supply part of the trapezius and sternocleidomastoid muscles.

Central Connections.

For the central connections of the internal branch, see p. 99. The central connections of the spinal or external branch are those of the typical lower motor neuron: voluntary impulses via the corticospinal tracts, postural impulses via the extrapyramidal tracts, reflexes through the vestibulospinal and tectospinal tracts, and intersegmental and intrasegmental arcs.

Lesions Which May Affect the Accessory Nerve.

Cerebral disorders (certain epilepsies, multiple sclerosis, CNS syphilis, tumors, etc.) cause irregular and spasmodic contractions. Nuclear affections are rare and involve other cranial nerve nuclei as well (see p. 105). Peripheral palsies may be due to diseases of the base of the skull (meningitis, syphilis, osteitis, etc.) or to trauma (bullets, stab wounds, operations on tuberculous nodes, etc.). Torticollis (wryneck) is discussed on p. 331.

Syndromes Involving the Accessory Nerve.

(See p. 104.)

Avellis's (X and internal ramus of XI) (nuclear lesion), Schmidt's (X and XI) and Jackson's (X, XI, and XII) (nuclear or radicular lesions), Vernet's (IX, X, and XI) (peripheral lesion), and Villaret's and Collet's (IX, X, XI, and XII) (peripheral lesion).

Signs of Eleventh Nerve Paralysis.

A. Unilateral, From Peripheral Lesions: Cannot rotate head to healthy side; atrophy of sternocleidomastoid and reaction of degeneration; cannot shrug affected shoulder; drooping of affected shoulder; scapula displaced downward; depression of shoulder contour from atrophy of trapezius.

B. Bilateral, From Nuclear or Peripheral Lesion: Difficulty in rotating head or raising chin (sternocleidomastoid muscle). Head drops forward; atrophy of trapezius causes squareness of shoulders.

C. Central Paralysis: Produces similar limitations of movement, but no muscle atrophy or reaction of degeneration. The muscles are spastic and, if the lesion is unilateral, torticollis results.

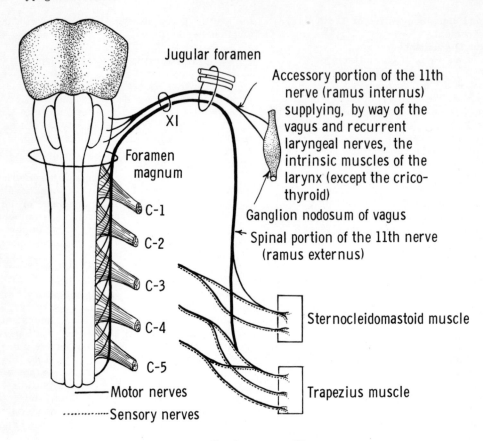

Jugular foramen

Accessory portion of the 11th nerve (ramus internus) supplying, by way of the vagus and recurrent laryngeal nerves, the intrinsic muscles of the larynx (except the crico-thyroid)

XI

Foramen magnum

Ganglion nodosum of vagus

Spinal portion of the 11th nerve (ramus externus)

C-1

C-2

C-3

Sternocleidomastoid muscle

C-4

C-5

Trapezius muscle

——— Motor nerves

············· Sensory nerves

The Accessory Nerve

Tests.

A. Ability to shrug shoulders and rotate head against resistance.

B. Deviation on bending chin downward against resistance indicates paralyzed side.

C. Objective examination for muscle atrophy, shoulder drop, etc.

D. Electric examination of affected nerves and muscles; electromyography, etc.

CRANIAL NERVE XII: HYPOGLOSSAL
(Motor Nerve)

Peripheral and Intermediate Connections.

A. Motor fibers from the hypoglossal nucleus in the ventromedian portion of the gray matter of the medulla emerge from the antero-lateral sulcus between the pyramid and the olive to form the hypoglossal nerve. The nerve leaves the skull through the hypoglossal canal and passes to the muscles of the tongue.

B. A few proprioceptive fibers from the tongue probably course in the hypoglossal nerve. With fibers derived from communications with the first cervical nerve, the hypoglossal distributes motor branches to the geniohyoid and infrahyoid muscles and a sensory recurrent meningeal branch to the posterior fossa of the skull.

Central Connections.

Central connections of the hypoglossal nucleus include the corticobulbar (crossed), extrapyramidal, and tectobulbar tracts, and reflex neurons from the sensory nuclei of the trigeminal nerve and the nucleus of the tractus solitarius.

Lesions Which May Affect the Hypoglossal Nerve.

A. Peripheral (Usually From Mechanical Causes): Basal skull fractures, dislocations of upper cervical vertebrae, tuberculosis, aneurysm of the circle of Willis, cerebral syphilis, and lead, alcohol, arsenic, and carbon monoxide poisonings.

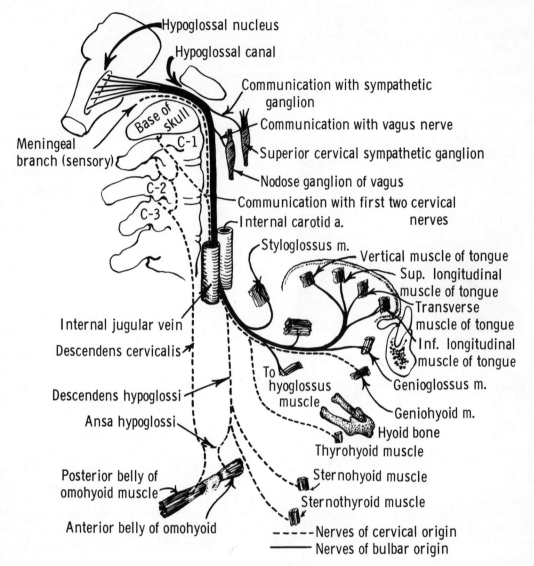

Hypoglossal nucleus

Hypoglossal canal

Communication with sympathetic ganglion

Communication with vagus nerve

Superior cervical sympathetic ganglion

Nodose ganglion of vagus

Communication with first two cervical nerves

Internal carotid a.

Base of skull

C-1

C-2

C-3

Meningeal branch (sensory)

Styloglossus m.

Vertical muscle of tongue

Sup. longitudinal muscle of tongue

Transverse muscle of tongue

Inf. longitudinal muscle of tongue

Internal jugular vein

Descendens cervicalis

Descendens hypoglossi

Ansa hypoglossi

To hyoglossus muscle

Genioglossus m.

Geniohyoid m.

Hyoid bone

Thyrohyoid muscle

Sternohyoid muscle

Sternothyroid muscle

Posterior belly of omohyoid muscle

Anterior belly of omohyoid

- - - - - Nerves of cervical origin
———— Nerves of bulbar origin

The Hypoglossal Nerve

B. Nuclear and Supranuclear Lesions: Medullary hemorrhage, poliomyelitis, bulbar paralysis and pseudobulbar palsy, syphilis, tumors, brain abscess, arteriosclerosis, multiple sclerosis, syringobulbia, and amyotrophic lateral sclerosis (bulbar form). Psychogenic disturbances, e.g., hysterical paralysis, stammering, and tics, must be differentiated.

Syndromes.

Syndromes involving the hypoglossal nerve include (see pp. 104 and 105) Jackson's (X, XI, and XII) (nuclear or radicular lesions), Tapia's (X and XII) (nuclear or radicular lesions), and Villaret's and Collet's (IX, X, XI, and XII)

(peripheral lesion); and hypoglossal hemiplegia alternans, a bulbar lesion involving the pyramid near the decussation and hypoglossal roots near their point of emergence, causing contralateral hemiplegia and ipsilateral paralysis of the tongue.

Symptoms and Signs of Twelfth Nerve Involvement.

A. Supranuclear (Spastic Paralysis): Contralateral hemiplegia and paralysis of tongue; no atrophy or fibrillation of tongue. On protrusion the tongue deviates to the side opposite the lesion.

B. Peripheral (Flaccid Paralysis): Reaction of degeneration, ipsilateral paralysis of the tongue, atrophy on the side of the lesion. On protrusion the tongue deviates to the side of the lesion. Fasciculations of the tongue may be present.

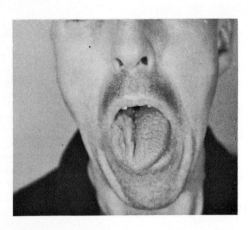

Right Hypoglossal Paralysis. Atrophy of the right side of the tongue and deviation of tongue to right following surgical section of the right hypoglossal nerve.

C. Nuclear or Medullary Lesion (Flaccid Paralysis): Signs of peripheral involvement are present in addition to the following:
  1. Fasciculation accompanies or precedes atrophy and other nerves and structures are affected also.
  2. Sensory disturbances are apparent, e. g., loss of deep sensation and/or loss of pain and temperature sense of one-half the face or body, or bilaterally in midline lesions.
  3. If lesion is bilateral, the tongue is completely paralyzed and there is dysphagia, dysarthria, and difficulty in chewing food.

D. Cortical lesions may cause dysarthria and ataxia of the tongue.

E. Striatum lesions (e. g., chorea) cause irregular arrhythmic movements of the tongue.

F. Psychogenic disturbances include tongue tics, stammering, stuttering, and lisping. Hysterical paralysis shows resistance to passive movement and no reaction of degeneration or atrophy.

Tests.
  A. Strength of the tongue is tested by having the patient push the tip of his tongue against the cheek of each side against the resistance of the examiner's finger.

B. Note the deviation of the tongue on protrusion.

C. Note atrophy or tremors of the tongue.

D. Electric examination of the tongue muscles may be performed.

SYNDROMES DUE TO LESIONS OF THE LAST FOUR CRANIAL NERVES

Bulbar and Radicular Syndromes.
Lesions of the medulla oblongata (bulb) produce characteristic symptoms which are referable to involvement of the motor and sensory pathways passing through the bulb and particularly to the involvement of the nuclei of the last 4 cranial nerves which lie within it. Lesions of the posterior fossa (tumors, syphilis, inflammations) may involve roots of the last 4 cranial nerves between their emergence from the medulla and their exit from the skull.

A. Avellis's Syndrome (X and Bulbar XI): Caused by a lesion of the nucleus ambiguus, tractus solitarius and the adjacent spinothalamic tract, thus affecting the vagus, the internal branch of the accessory nerve, and the ascending sensory tracts:
  1. Ipsilateral paralysis of the soft palate, pharynx, and larynx, with dysarthria, dysphagia, and anesthesia of the pharynx and larynx (X and bulbar portion of XI).
  2. Contralateral dissociate hemianesthesia, with loss of pain and temperature sense but not of the touch and pressure senses (spinothalamic tract).

B. Schmidt's Syndrome (X and all of XI): From a lesion of the vagal nuclei and both bulbar and spinal nuclei of the accessory or their radicular fibers:
  1. Ipsilateral paralysis of the soft palate, pharynx, and larynx, with anesthesia of the pharynx and larynx (X and bulbar portion of XI).
  2. Ipsilateral sternocleidomastoid muscle paralysis and, at times, paralysis of part of the trapezius muscle, resulting in inability to rotate the head to the side opposite the lesion and inability to shrug the shoulder (spinal portion of XI).

C. Jackson's Syndrome (X, XI, and XII): Produced by a nuclear or radicular lesion of the vagus, accessory, and hypoglossal nerves:
  1. Ipsilateral paralysis of the soft palate, pharynx, and larynx (X).
  2. Ipsilateral paralysis of the sternocleidomastoid and trapezius muscles (XI).

3. Ipsilateral paralysis and atrophy of the tongue (XII).

D. Tapia's Syndrome (X and XII): Produced by a lesion affecting the motor nuclei or rootlets of the vagus and hypoglossal nerves:
1. Ipsilateral paralysis of the pharynx and larynx (X).
2. Ipsilateral paralysis and atrophy of the tongue (XII).

E. Babinski-Nageotte Bulbar Syndrome (IX, X, Bulbar Portion of XI, and Part of V): Produced by scattered lesions of the nucleus ambiguus, tractus solitarius, spinal tract of V, hypoglossal nucleus, restiform body, and reticular formation:
1. Ipsilateral paralysis of the tongue, pharynx, and larynx.
2. Ipsilateral loss of taste on the posterior third of the tongue.
3. Ipsilateral Horner's syndrome (miosis, ptosis, and enophthalmos).
4. Ipsilateral loss of pain and temperature sense on the face.
5. Ipsilateral asynergia and ataxia and a tendency to fall to the side of the lesion.
6. Contralateral hemiplegia (of arm and leg) with contralateral dissociate hemianesthesia (loss of pain and temperature sense).

F. Syndrome of Thrombosis of the Posterior Inferior Cerebellar Artery (Wallenberg's Syndrome): Resembles that of Babinski-Nageotte but without the hemiplegia.

G. Cestan-Chenais Syndrome: (Of thrombosis of the vertebral artery before it gives off the posterior inferior cerebellar and anterior spinal branches.) Structures involved include the restiform body, spinothalamic tract, sympathetics, nuclei of X and XI, descending tract of V, and sometimes the pyramid; the corresponding symptoms are extensive and variable.

H. Bonnier's Syndrome (VIII, IX, and X): From a lesion of the lateral vestibular (Deiters') nucleus and adjacent pathways:
1. Symptoms of Ménière's disease (paroxysmal vertigo).
2. Symptoms of involvement of IX, X, and sometimes III and V.
3. Contralateral hemiplegia.
4. Somnolence at times.
5. Apprehension, tachycardia, and weakness.

I. Hypoglossal Hemiplegia Alternans (XII): From a lesion of the pyramid near the decussation involving the emerging hypoglossal roots:
1. Contralateral hemiplegia.
2. Ipsilateral paralysis of the tongue.

Syndromes from Peripheral Lesions.
During World Wars I and II many cases were reported of lesions of the last 4 cranial nerves. Because of the proximity of the last 4 cranial nerves to each other, many combined lesions were found:

A. Vernet's Syndrome (of the Jugular Foramen), Involving IX, X, and XI: Usually the result of a basilar skull fracture involving the jugular foramen:
1. Ipsilateral glossopharyngeal paralysis.
2. Ipsilateral vagus paralysis.
3. Ipsilateral accessory paralysis.

B. Villaret's, Collet's, or Sicard's Syndrome (of Retroparotid Space Injury): Ipsilateral paralysis of the last 4 cranial nerves. (Villaret's case also involved the sympathetics, thus adding Horner's syndrome.)

. . .

5...

The Spinal Nerves

The spinal nerves consist of 31 symmetrically arranged pairs, each derived from the spinal cord by 2 roots: a sensory (dorsal) root and a motor (ventral) root. They are divided topographically into 8 cervical pairs, 12 thoracic, 5 lumbar, 5 sacral, and one coccygeal.

Each nerve contains several kinds of fibers. **Motor fibers** originate in large cells in the anterior gray column of the spinal cord. These form the ventral root and pass to the skeletal muscles. **Sensory fibers** originate in unipolar cells in the spinal ganglia which are interposed in the course of the dorsal roots. Peripheral branches of these ganglion cells are distributed to both visceral and somatic structures as mediators of sensory impulses to the CNS. The central branches convey these impulses through dorsal roots into the dorsal gray column and the ascending tracts of the spinal cord. **Sympathetic fibers** from the thoracic and lumbar cord segments are distributed throughout the body to the viscera,

blood vessels, glands, and smooth muscle. **Parasympathetic fibers**, which are present in the middle 3 sacral nerves, pass to the pelvic and lower abdominal viscera. (For details on sympathetic and parasympathetic distribution, see pp. 139, 140, and 143.)

Spinal Nerve Roots.

The Bell-Magendie law states that the posterior (sensory) roots convey impulses to the CNS. (The anterior roots are motor roots.) The medial portion of the posterior roots consists of thick myelinated fibers; the lateral part consists mostly of unmyelinated and small myelinated fibers. Cathode ray oscillographic studies have made possible a classification into 3 groups of fibers, as follows: **A group** (myelinated) fibers are largest and convey impulses most rapidly. **B group** fibers are next largest and consist of the smaller myelinated fibers. **C group** fibers are smallest and convey impulses most slowly (see table on p. 69). These fibers are mostly

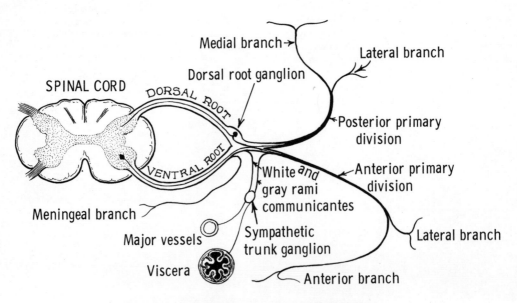

Schematic Illustration of a Typical Spinal Nerve

unmyelinated fibers carrying pain.

The **central connections** of motor and sensory roots of spinal nerves are diagrammed in Chapters 8 and 10.

Branches of Typical Spinal Nerves.

The **posterior primary** divisions usually consist of a medial branch, which is in most instances largely sensory; and a lateral branch, which is mainly motor. **Anterior primary** divisions are usually larger than the posterior primary divisions. They form the cervical, brachial, and lumbosacral plexuses. In the thoracic region they remain segmental, as intercostal nerves, dividing into the lateral cutaneous branch (sensory) and a mixed anterior branch. **Rami communicantes** join the spinal nerves to the sympathetic trunk. The white ramus is present only in the thoracic and upper lumbar nerves. The gray ramus is present in all spinal nerves. **Meningeal or recurrent** branches are quite small, carrying sensory and vasomotor innervation to the spinal meninges.

The distribution and clinical aspects of the various spinal nerves are presented in detail on the following pages. Segmental and peripheral cutaneous distribution is diagrammed on pp. 197, 198, and 199.

Lesions of the Spinal Nerves.

The spinal nerves are subject to the various types of disorders outlined for peripheral nerves in general on p. 75. Traumatic lesions, however, constitute the majority of peripheral nerve lesions. Most of the cases in the literature are from war records. The 1020 cases of peripheral nerve injuries compiled by Pollock and Davis included 165 radial, 160 sciatic, 136 ulnar, 120 peroneal, 93 median, 71 brachial plexus, and 58 combined median and ulnar nerve lesions.

Diagnosis.

The diagnosis of peripheral nerve lesions depends upon a careful history and physical examination. The examination should be performed with the patient's clothes removed, taking particular note of the site of the injury, obvious deformities, gait, etc.

A. Motion is studied to determine muscle weakness or paralysis. Active (voluntary) movements are observed, taking care to rule out modifying factors such as pain, swelling, fractures, dislocations, adhesions, ankylosis, and contractures. Passive movements may be reserved for further study of the range of motion where active motion seems to be abnormally limited. Posture of the limb is important, e. g., wrist-drop, foot-drop, claw hand, or ape hand. Supplementary or trick movements should be sought since they may mask a true paralysis. Joint changes and contractures must be noted as possible factors in limitations of motion. Careful dynamometric examination will demonstrate the distribution and degree of weakness in involvement of the muscles of the fingers.

B. Muscle atrophy and loss of tone of the affected muscles occur after the nerve has been interrupted and is often an obvious sign of the distribution of the disorder.

C. Subjective sensory changes (e. g., pain, hyperesthesia, and paresthesias) are uncommon after nerve injuries except in partial lesions. **Causalgia**, however, may occur with incomplete median, sciatic, or tibial nerve injuries, although it may not appear until several weeks after the injury. It is characterized by severe pain in the affected part, brought on by the slightest exposure or jarring, and may be partially relieved by wet compresses. Trophic skin and nail changes are usually associated with it.

D. Objective Sensory Disturbances: The degree and distribution of pain, temperature sense, deep touch and pressure, vibration, and joint sense can be evaluated with the aid of an esthesiometer or algesiometer. The patient's cooperation must be obtained. Nerve overlap must be kept in mind in evaluating sensory loss.

E. Vasomotor, trophic, and secretory disturbances, e. g., cyanosis, swelling, edema, discoloration, hypertrichosis or hypotrichosis, nail changes, and trophic ulcers, should be noted.

F. Electric Examination: Stimulation of the affected muscles at their respective motor points with electric currents may serve as an aid in diagnosis and prognosis of nerve injury. The electric resistance of denervated skin is usually higher than that of the surrounding normal skin because of the absence of the normal skin fluids and electrolytes. With needle electrodes placed directly in nerves or branches of nerves, an accurate assay of functional status may be made by stimulation studies. Electromyographic studies of affected muscles may assist in evaluation of their functional status (see pp. 232-40).

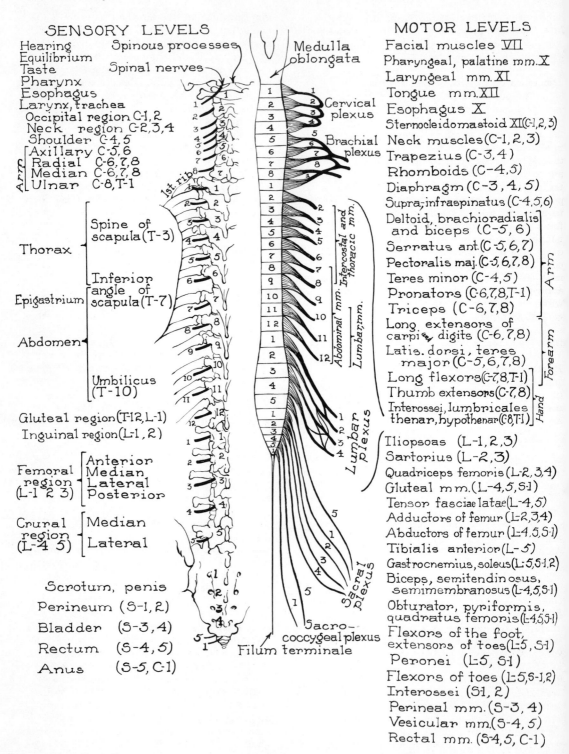

SENSORY LEVELS

Hearing
Equilibrium
Taste
Pharynx
Esophagus
Larynx, trachea
 Occipital region C-1,2
 Neck region C-2,3,4
 Shoulder C-4,5
Arm [Axillary C-5,6
     Radial C-6,7,8
     Median C-6,7,8
     Ulnar C-8,T-1

Spinous processes
Spinal nerves

Medulla
oblongata

Cervical
plexus

Brachial
plexus

Thorax { Spine of
scapula (T-3)

Epigastrium { Inferior
angle of
scapula (T-7)

Abdomen

Umbilicus
(T-10)

Gluteal region (T-12, L-1)
Inguinal region (L-1, 2)

Femoral
region
(L-1 2 3) { Anterior
Median
Lateral
Posterior

Crural
region
(L-4 5) { Median
Lateral

Scrotum, penis
Perineum (S-1, 2)
Bladder (S-3, 4)
Rectum (S-4, 5)
Anus (S-5, C-1)

1st rib

Abdominal mm. Intercostal and thoracic mm.
Lumbar mm.

Lumbar Plexus

Sacral Plexus

Sacro-
coccygeal plexus
Filum terminale

MOTOR LEVELS

Facial muscles VII
Pharyngeal, palatine mm. X
Laryngeal mm. XI
Tongue mm. XII
Esophagus X
Sternocleidomastoid XI (C-1,2,3)
Neck muscles (C-1, 2, 3)
Trapezius (C-3, 4)
Rhomboids (C-4,5)
Diaphragm (C-3, 4, 5)
Supra, infraspinatus (C-4,5,6)
Deltoid, brachioradialis
 and biceps (C-5, 6)
Serratus ant. (C-5,6,7)
Pectoralis maj. (C-5,6,7,8)
Teres minor (C-4,5)
Pronators (C-6,7,8,T-1)
Triceps (C-6,7,8)
Long extensors of
 carpi, digits (C-6,7,8)
Latis. dorsi, teres
 major (C-5,6,7,8)
Long flexors (C-7,8,T-1)
Thumb extensors (C-7,8)
Interossei, lumbricales
 thenar, hypothenar (C-8,T-1)

Arm
Forearm
Hand

Iliopsoas (L-1, 2, 3)
Sartorius (L-2, 3)
Quadriceps femoris (L-2, 3, 4)
Gluteal mm. (L-4, 5, S-1)
Tensor fasciae latae (L-4, 5)
Adductors of femur (L-2,3,4)
Abductors of femur (L-4,5,S-1)
Tibialis anterior (L-5)
Gastrocnemius, soleus (L-5,S-1,2)
Biceps, semitendinosus,
 semimembranosus (L-4,5,S-1)
Obturator, pyriformis,
 quadratus femoris (L-4,5,S-1)
Flexors of the foot,
 extensors of toes (L-5, S-1)
Peronei (L-5, S-1)
Flexors of toes (L-5,S-1,2)
Interossei (S-1, 2)
Perineal mm. (S-3, 4)
Vesicular mm. (S-4, 5)
Rectal mm. (S-4,5, C-1)

Motor and Sensory Levels of the Spinal Cord

G. Reflex changes are specifically re-lated to the nerve injured.

THE CERVICAL PLEXUS
(C1, 2, 3, 4)
(See drawings on p. 110.)

THE CERVICAL NERVES

The 8 pairs of cervical nerves are de-rived from cord segments between the level of the foramen magnum and the middle of the seventh cervical vertebra. These emerge from the spinal column through laterally placed intervertebral foramens. Each nerve is joined with a gray communicating ramus from the sympathetic trunk, through which it receives vasomotor fibers; sends a small re-current meningeal branch back into the spinal canal to supply the dura with sensory and vaso-motor innervation; and branches into anterior and posterior primary divisions, mixed nerves which pass to their respective peripheral dis-tributions. The motor branches carry a few sensory fibers which convey proprioceptive impulses from the neck muscles.

Posterior Primary Divisions.
C1 (suboccipital nerve) is the only branch of the first posterior primary division; it is motor to the muscles of the suboccipital tri-angle, with a few sensory fibers.

Sensory Branches.
The **small occipital nerve** (C2, 3) supplies the skin of the lateral occipital portion of the scalp, the upper median part of the auricle, and the area over the mastoid process. The **great auricular nerve** (C2, 3) supplies the skin of the back of the ear and the area over the mastoid process and parotid gland. The cer-vical cutaneous nerve (cutaneous colli) (C2, 3) supplies the skin over the anterior portion of the neck. Supraclavicular branches (C3, 4) supply the skin over the clavicle and the upper deltoid and pectoral regions as low as the third rib.

Communicating Branches.
Communication with the hypoglossal nerve from C1, 2 carries motor fibers to the genio-hyoid and thyrohyoid muscles and to the sternohyoid and sternothyroid muscles by way of the descendens hypoglossi; and sensory fibers to the dura of the posterior fossa of the skull via the recurrent meningeal branch of the hypoglossal nerve. The communication with the vagus nerve from C1 is of undeter-mined function, although the vagus occasionally

Course of the Posterior Primary Divisions of C2 to C8

Medial Branches	Lateral Branches
C2: Great occipital nerve. Sensory to the occipital portions of the scalp and neck.	C2: Motor twigs to the obliquus capitis inferior, splenius, and longissimus capitis mm.
C3: Third occipital nerve. Sensory to a small portion of the scalp and neck.	C3: Motor twig to the semispinalis capitis muscle.
C4, 5: Sensory to skin of back of neck.	C4-8: Motor to the longissimus capitis and cervicis, semispinalis capitis and cervicis, and iliocostalis cervicis muscles.
C6-8: Motor to the multifides and adja-cent muscles.	

Anterior Primary Divisions.
The anterior primary divisions of the first 4 cervical nerves collectively form the cervical plexus. Those of the second 4 to-gether with the first thoracic nerve form the brachial plexus.

distributes fibers to the infrahyoid muscles which are usually distributed by the descendens hypoglossi. Communications from the supe-rior cervical sympathetic ganglion to the first 4 cervical nerves are probably the source of vasomotor fibers. (These are branches to the spinal nerves rather than to the anterior pri-mary divisions alone.)

Muscular Branches.
The descendens cervicalis (C2, 3) supplies the 2 bellies of the omohyoid and joins with the descendens hypoglossi to form the ansa hypo-glossi. There is a branch to the sternocleido-

mastoid muscle from C2, and branches to the trapezius muscles (C3, 4) via the subtrapezial plexus. Twigs to the adjacent vertebral musculature supply the rectus capitis lateralis and rectus capitis anterior (C1), the longus capitis (C2, 4) and longus colli (C1-4), the scalenus medius (C3, 4) and scalenus anterior (C4), and the levator scapulae (from C3-5). The phrenic nerve (C3-5) passes obliquely over the scalenus anterior muscle and between the subclavian artery and vein to enter the thorax behind the sternoclavicular joint, where it descends vertically through the superior and middle mediastinum to the diaphragm. Motor branches supply the diaphragm and constitute the principal respiratory nerve. Sensory branches supply the pericardium, the diaphragm, and part of the costal and mediastinal pleurae.

Lesions of the First Four Cervical Nerves.

Meningitis or high cord tumors may cause cervico-occipital neuralgia. Peripheral lesions are rare in the cervical region because of the protection afforded by surrounding muscles. They occasionally occur in deep wounds,

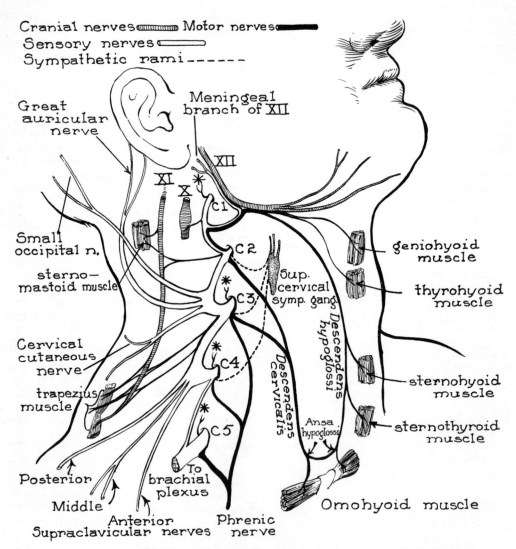

Cranial nerves▭ Motor nerves▬
Sensory nerves▭
Sympathetic rami------

Great auricular nerve

Meningeal branch of XII

XII

XI
X
C1

Small occipital n.

C2

Sup. cervical symp. gang.

geniohyoid muscle

sterno-mastoid muscle

C3

thyrohyoid muscle

Cervical cutaneous nerve

C4

Descendens Cervicalis

Descendens hypoglossi

sternohyoid muscle

trapezius muscle

C5

Ansa hypoglossi

sternothyroid muscle

Posterior

To brachial plexus

Middle

Anterior
Supraclavicular nerves

Phrenic nerve

Omohyoid muscle

* To adjacent vertebral musculature

The Cervical Plexus

operative trauma, fractures, dislocations, infections, multiple neuritis, and other diseases of the cervical vertebrae.

Clinical Features of Upper Cervical Lesions.

A. Phrenic Involvement: The most important of cervical lesions.

1. Unilateral paralysis causes few or no symptoms. Litten's sign may be absent on the affected side. The liver or spleen may appear higher than normal. Fluoroscopy shows relative immobility of the diaphragm on one side.

2. Bilateral paralysis is characterized by dyspnea upon the slightest exertion, a scaphoid abdomen not protruded on expiration; overactivity of accessory respiratory muscles, the chest and shoulders heaving deeply during respiration; and difficulty in coughing and sneezing. X-ray shows the diaphragm drawn high into the chest. Hypostatic congestion and pneumonia often complicate the picture. (Diaphragmatic and pleural disease must be ruled out.)

3. Phrenic neuralgia (diaphragmatic neuralgia; rare) may result from neck tumors, aortic aneurysm, pericardial and other mediastinal affections. Pain is present near the free border of the ribs, beneath the clavicle, and deep in the neck; and may extend as high as the chin and occasionally down the arm. Respiration is short and rapid, as if the patient is afraid to breathe for fear of pain. In most cases the pain is on the left side.

4. Singultus (hiccup) results from brief spasm of the diaphragm associated with vocal cord adduction.

B. Cervico-occipital Neuralgia (Rare): May result from traumatic, psychogenic, infectious, neoplastic, or aneurysmal disease of the upper neck region. Pain and tenderness occur in the distribution of the sensory branches of the cervical plexus, most commonly in the neck and occipital regions.

C. Rigidity of the Neck: Occurs with neuralgia, other neck lesions, posterior fossa masses, and also with irritative lesions of the meninges, e.g., meningitis or blood in the spinal fluid. It is a protective reflex mechanism.

THE BRACHIAL PLEXUS
(See drawings on pp. 112 and 113.)

The brachial plexus is formed by the anterior primary divisions of the last 4 cervical and the first thoracic nerves. The roots of the plexus consist of C5 and C6, which unite to form the upper trunk; C7, which becomes the middle trunk; and C8 and T1, which unite to form the lower trunk. Each of the 3 trunks divides into anterior and posterior divisions. The anterior divisions of the upper and middle trunk form the lateral cord; the anterior division of the lower trunk forms the medial cord; and all 3 posterior divisions unite to form the posterior cord. The 3 cords (named from their relationship to the axillary artery) split to form the main branches of the plexus: Branches from the medial and lateral cords form the **median nerve**; the remainder of the lateral cord becomes the **musculocutaneous nerve**; the remainder of the medial cord becomes the **ulnar nerve**; and the posterior cord splits to become the **radial and axillary nerves.**

Numerous smaller nerves arise from various parts of the plexus. **(1) Branches from the roots of the plexus**: A twig passes to the phrenic nerve from C5. The posterior thoracic nerves consist of the dorsal scapular nerve (C5), motor to the rhomboid muscles; and the long thoracic nerve (of Bell) (C5-7), which descends by a deep course to supply the serratus anterior muscle. Twigs extend to the scaleni and longus colli muscles from C6-8. The first intercostal nerve extends from T1 (see under thoracic nerves). **(2) Branches from the trunks**: A nerve extends to the subclavius muscle (C4-6) from the upper trunk or fifth root. The suprascapular nerve (C4-6) arises from the upper trunk or its anterior division and supplies the supraspinatus and infraspinatus muscles. **(3) Branches from the cords**: The medial and lateral anterior thoracic nerves extend from the medial (C8, T1) and lateral (C5-7) cords, respectively, and are usually united by a loop. They supply the pectoralis major and pectoralis minor muscles. The 3 subscapular nerves from the posterior cord consist of (1) the upper (or short) subscapular nerve (C5, 6) to the subscapularis muscle; (2) the middle (long) subscapular or thoracodorsal nerve (C7, 8), which innervates the latissimus dorsi muscle; and (3) the lower subscapular nerve (C5, 6) to the teres major and part of the subscapularis muscle. Sensory branches of the medial cord (C8, T1) comprise the medial antebrachial cutaneous nerve to the medial surface of the forearm and the medial

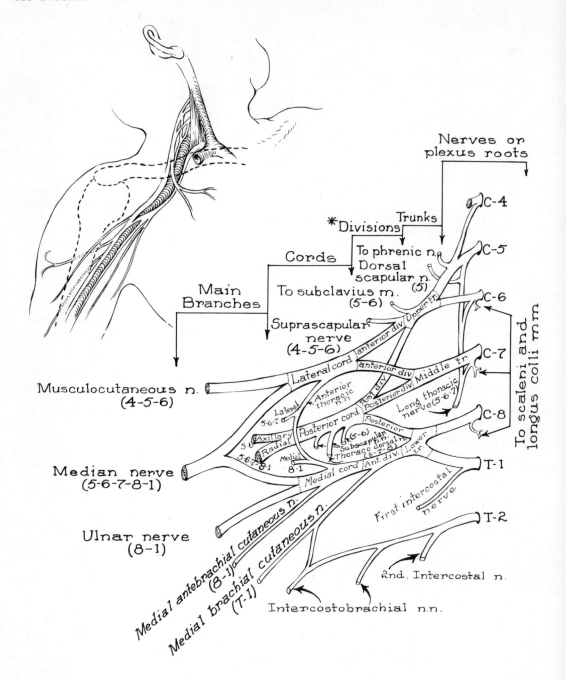

The Brachial Plexus
(Formed from the Anterior Primary Divisions of C5 to T2)

---

*Splitting of the plexus into anterior and posterior divisions is one of the most significant features in the redistribution of nerve fibers, since it is here fibers supplying the flexor and extensor groups of muscles of the upper extremity are separated. Similar splitting is noted in the lumbar and sacral plexuses for the supply of muscles of the lower extremity.

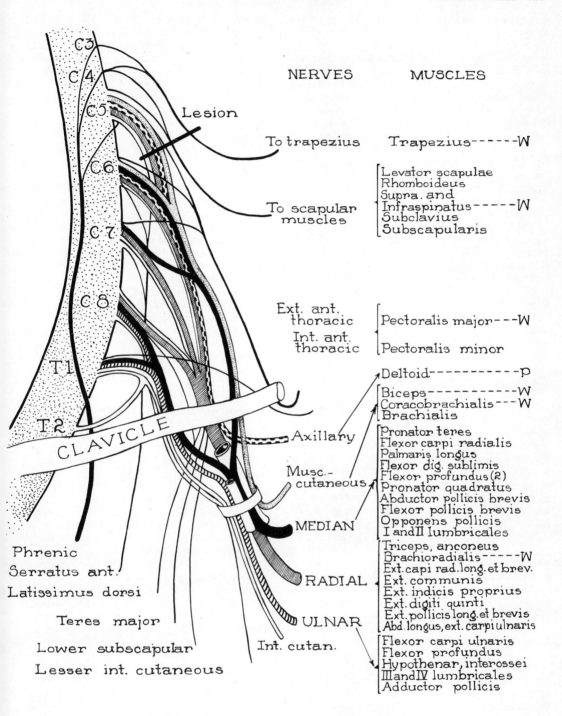

The Brachial Plexus (after Meige), showing an example of a lesion which produced a paralysis of the deltoid and weakness in the supraspinatus and infraspinatus, trapezius, pectoral, biceps, coracobrachialis, and brachioradialis muscles.

brachial cutaneous nerve to the medial surface of the arm.

Lesions of the Brachial Plexus and Its Nerves.

Spinal cord lesions may involve these nerves also, as in traumatic lesions of the lower cervical spine area. Peripheral lesions are more common in wartime but are not infrequently seen in civil practice. Peripheral nerve injury may follow violent pulling or wrenching of the arms, blows to or weight upon the neck, operative trauma in the neck or axilla, childbirth injuries (from pulling on or compressing nerves); gunshot wounds, stab wounds, automobile accidents, etc.; fractures and dislocations of the neck, shoulder, or neck of the humerus; tumors of the neck and aneurysms of the subclavian artery; infectious, toxic, and multiple neuritis; the scalenus anticus syndrome, cervical rib (a congenital anomaly), and certain sleeping postures ("neurovascular syndrome" or "hyperabduction syndrome"). Bikeles' sign (of brachial plexus neuritis or meningitis) may be present, i.e., resistance to extension at the elbow when the arm is upwards and backwards due to stretch put on the brachial plexus.

Classification of Brachial Plexus Injuries.

Attempts have been made to classify the numerous possible types of brachial plexus injuries as radicular, trunk, and cord lesions; upper, middle, and lower types; incomplete and complete types; supraclavicular and infraclavicular lesions, etc. Meige's diagram (see p. 113) illustrates some of the difficulties of these attempts at classification. Meige's technic is to systematically test the muscles by electric stimulation and record the results opposite their names on the chart, placing a "W" for weak and a "P" for paralyzed muscles. By tracing into the plexus to the point where the fibers to the affected muscles are most concentrated, the lesion can be localized. The distribution of sensory and trophic disturbances is also considered in locating the lesion.

Symptoms and Signs of Brachial Plexus Injuries.

Brachial plexus injuries are most commonly seen in children and are usually caused by birth injuries. There are 2 classic types: the upper plexus type (Erb-Duchenne paralysis) and the less common lower plexus type (Klumpke's paralysis).

A. Upper Plexus Type (Erb-Duchenne): This is the most common type. It is caused by compression or tearing of the fifth and sixth plexus roots or upper trunk. There is paralysis and atrophy of the deltoid, biceps, brachialis, and brachioradialis muscles with loss of abduction and external rotation of the arm, and weak forearm flexion and supination. The arm and hand assume the "waiter's tip" position. The supraspinatus and infraspinatus, subscapularis, serratus, and rhomboid muscles are occasionally affected (see below). Sensation is lost over the deltoid and radial surfaces of the forearm and hand.

B. Lower Plexus Type (Klumpke): May result from injury to the eighth cervical and first thoracic plexus roots or lower trunk. Compression of the lower plexus roots or trunk by a cervical rib may be responsible for a lower plexus type of palsy. Prognosis of this type is more favorable. Klumpke's paralysis is characterized by paralysis and atrophy of the small hand muscles and flexors of the wrist, "claw hand" and an ulnar type of sensory loss (see p. 121), edema of the skin, cyanosis, and perhaps trophic nail changes. It may also cause **Horner's syndrome** (when the sympathetic rami of T1 are involved): Ipsilateral miosis, narrowed palpebral fissure, enophthalmos, and absence of sweating and increased temperature over the face and neck.

C. Middle Plexus Type: Involvement of the middle trunk (C7), although rarely seen by itself, is occasionally associated with one of the above types. Symptoms are triceps paralysis and weakening of the extensors of the wrist and fingers.

Signs According to Nerves Involved.

A. Long Thoracic Nerve (C5, 6, 7): Although rarely injured alone, it may be involved in supraclavicular and axillary wounds, neck blows, or carrying weights on shoulders. Paralysis of the serratus anterior (magnus) causes "winging" of the scapula when the arm is extended and pressed against a fixed object in front of the patient (see p. 115). There is difficulty in raising the arm above the horizontal.

B. Suprascapular Nerve (C5, 6): Isolated paralysis is rare; may be involved as the result of carrying heavy weights on the shoulder, severe blows, etc. Symptoms are paralysis of the supraspinatus and infraspinatus muscles, with loss of fixation at the head of the humerus (subluxation) causing difficulty in lifting heavy weights. Atrophy occurs above and below the spine of the scapula.

C. Dorsal Scapular Nerve (C5, 6): Injury results in paralysis of the rhomboids; the

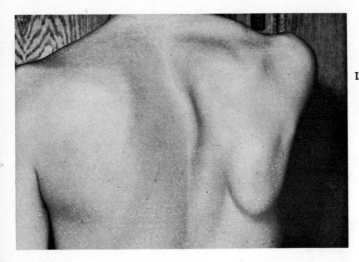

Long Thoracic Nerve Paralysis.
Winging of right scapula after trauma to right long thoracic nerve.

scapula becomes slightly winged and cannot be drawn close to the vertebral column.

D. Thoracodorsal Nerve (C7, 8): Injury results in paralysis and atrophy of the latissimus dorsi. Adduction and internal rotation of the arm are weakened.

E. Anterior Thoracic Nerves (C5, 6, 7, 8, T1): Rarely involved alone; lesions result in atrophy of the pectoralis muscles, apparent below the clavicle and in the anterior axillary fold. Adduction power of the upper arm is lost, and the patient is unable to touch his opposite shoulder.

F. Medial Brachial and Antebrachial Cutaneous Nerves (C8, T1): Although injury of these nerves is unimportant, pain in their distribution and in that of the ulnar nerve, particularly on the left side, is often indicative of cardiac disease.

Tests.

A. Motor Status: Limitations of movement, electromyography, electric stimulation of muscles at their motor points, reflexes, and reaction of degeneration for prognosis.

B. Sensory Status: Pain, tenderness, hyperesthesias; loss of pain, touch, heat and cold, vibration, and temperature senses.

C. Trophic Changes: Muscle atrophy, nail changes, etc.

THE MUSCULOCUTANEOUS NERVE
(C5, 6) (See p. 116.)

The musculocutaneous nerve arises from the lateral cord of the brachial plexus and is composed of fibers from the fifth and sixth cervical segments. At first lying lateral to the axillary artery, it pierces the coracobrachialis muscle and descends obliquely and laterally between the biceps and brachialis muscles. It terminates as the lateral antebrachial cutaneous nerve, which divides into anterior and posterior branches.

Motor branches supply the coracobrachialis, biceps, and brachialis muscles. The **sensory** terminal branch supplies the anterolateral surface of the forearm.

The musculocutaneous nerve is rarely affected alone, but it may be involved in spinal cord or brachial plexus lesions, fractures of the humerus, aneurysms of the axillary artery, bullet wounds, stab wounds, etc. It may be injured by pressure on the arm while asleep. Musculocutaneous neuritis (toxic, diabetic, infectious, etc.) is rare.

The **clinical features** of musculocutaneous involvement include paralysis of the coracobrachialis, biceps, and brachialis muscles, causing inability to flex the forearm when it is supinated, weakened supination, loss of biceps jerk, muscle atrophy, reaction of degeneration (in complete peripheral lesions), and loss of sensation to the anterolateral surface of the forearm.

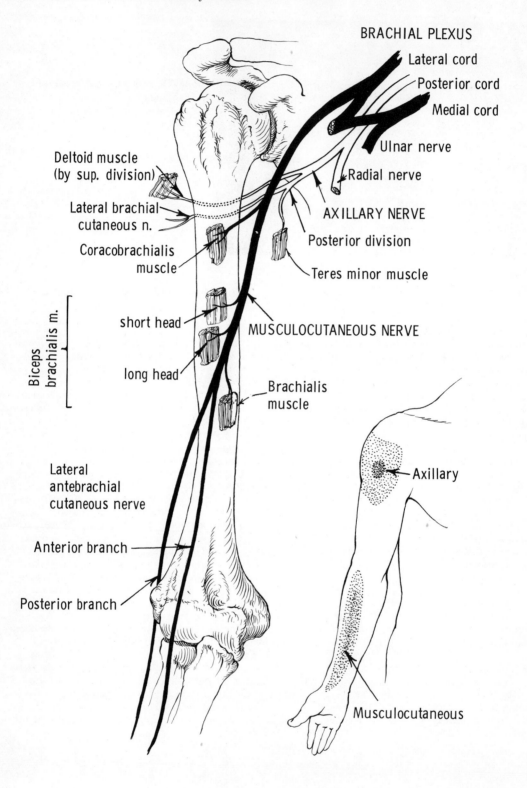

BRACHIAL PLEXUS
Lateral cord
Posterior cord
Medial cord
Ulnar nerve
Radial nerve
AXILLARY NERVE
Posterior division
Teres minor muscle

Deltoid muscle
(by sup. division)
Lateral brachial cutaneous n.
Coracobrachialis muscle
short head
long head
Biceps brachialis m.
Brachialis muscle
MUSCULOCUTANEOUS NERVE
Lateral antebrachial cutaneous nerve
Anterior branch
Posterior branch

Axillary
Musculocutaneous

Musculocutaneous and Axillary Nerves
(C5, 6)   (C5, 6)

THE AXILLARY (CIRCUMFLEX) NERVE
(C5, 6) (See p. 116.)

The axillary nerve is derived from the posterior cord of the brachial plexus and is composed of fibers from the fifth and sixth cervical segments. Passing dorsally it accompanies the posterior circumflex artery around the neck of the humerus and through the quadrilateral space, dividing into a small superior and a larger inferior division. **Motor** branches supply the deltoid (from the superior division) and teres minor (from the inferior division) muscles. **Sensory** branches, mainly from the inferior division, supply the skin over the lower portion of the deltoid muscle.

The axillary nerve is rarely affected alone, but may be involved by spinal cord and brachial plexus lesions, fractures and dislocations of the head of the humerus, violent blows on the shoulder, bullet, stab, and other wounds, pressure or stretching of the shoulder during sleep or anesthesia, and, rarely, tumors. Axillary neuritis (toxic, diabetic, infectious, etc.) is rare. Isolated paralysis occasionally occurs with carbon monoxide poisoning, malaria, and infections.

Deltoid paralysis causes inability to protract or retract the arm or raise it to the horizontal position. After some time supplementary movements may partially take over these functions. Teres minor paralysis causes weakness of external rotation. Atrophy of affected muscles occurs in severe or complete peripheral lesions. Sensation is lost over the deltoid prominence. Pain is present in neuritis.

THE RADIAL (MUSCULOSPIRAL) NERVE
(C6, 7, 8, T1) (See p. 118.)

The radial nerve is the largest branch of the brachial plexus. It begins at the lower border of the pectoralis minor as the direct continuation of the posterior cord, and derives fibers from the last 3 cervical and first thoracic segments of the spinal cord. During its descent in the arm it accompanies the profunda artery behind and around the humerus and in the musculospiral groove. It pierces the lateral intermuscular septum and reaches the lower anterior side of the forearm, where its terminal branches arise.

Motor branches in the arm supply the triceps, anconeus, and the upper portion of the extensor-supinator group of forearm muscles.

Motor branches in the forearm supplied by the deep radial nerve pass to the rest of the extensor-supinator group of muscles. **Sensory** branches supplying innervation to skin areas include the posterior brachial cutaneous nerve, to the dorsal aspect of the arm; the posterior antebrachial cutaneous nerve, to the dorsal surface of the forearm; and the superficial radial nerve, to the dorsal aspect of the radial half of the hand. The isolated area of supply is a small patch of skin over the dorsum of the first interosseous space.

Lesions Affecting the Radial Nerve.

The radial nerve is the most commonly injured peripheral nerve. It may be involved in cervical cord and brachial plexus lesions. Peripheral injuries may affect the trunk or some of the branches of the nerve, as in dislocations of the shoulder, fractures of the humerus, callus formation around a fracture; pressure from a crutch or during sleep, anesthesia, drunkenness ("Saturday night palsy"), violent blows on the arm, tuberculosis of the bone, tumors, syphilis (rare), or fractures of the neck of the radius. Toxic (alcohol, lead, arsenic) or infectious neuritis and polyneuritis involving the radial nerve also occur.

Clinical Features of Peripheral Radial Nerve Lesions.

A. Motor Signs of Complete Radial Nerve Palsy: Extensor paralysis: inability to extend the thumb, proximal phalanges, wrist, and elbow; pronation of the hand, with the wrist and fingers flexed in a position termed "wrist-drop"; adduction of the thumb, which may interfere with flexion of the index finger; and inability to grasp objects adequately or to make a fist because of the wrist-drop interferes with the action of the flexors. Triceps, radial, and periosteal-radial reflexes absent. (Supplementary movements may partially mask a radial palsy; energetic contraction of finger flexors and occasionally the pronator teres may extend the wrist.)

B. Sensory Disturbances: Sensory loss is slight (due to overlap), being most marked on the dorsal radial surface of the hand. Pain is rare.

C. Vasomotor and secretory disturbances are absent or very slight.

D. Muscle atrophy develops in 2-3 months and may be very marked on the dorsum of the forearm. Palsies due to pressure do not show atrophy.

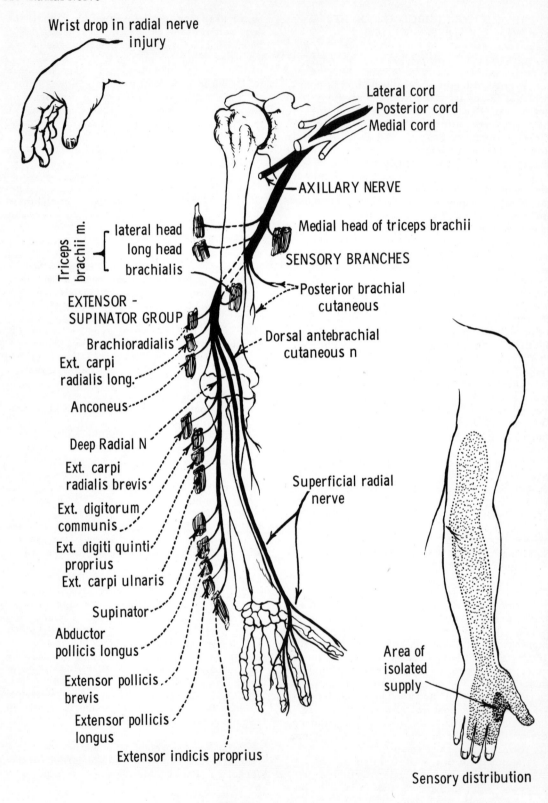

Wrist drop in radial nerve injury

Lateral cord
Posterior cord
Medial cord

AXILLARY NERVE

Medial head of triceps brachii

SENSORY BRANCHES

Posterior brachial cutaneous

Dorsal antebrachial cutaneous n

Triceps brachii m. { lateral head, long head, brachialis

EXTENSOR - SUPINATOR GROUP

Brachioradialis

Ext. carpi radialis long.

Anconeus

Deep Radial N

Ext. carpi radialis brevis

Ext. digitorum communis

Ext. digiti quinti proprius

Ext. carpi ulnaris

Supinator

Abductor pollicis longus

Extensor pollicis brevis

Extensor pollicis longus

Extensor indicis proprius

Superficial radial nerve

Area of isolated supply

Sensory distribution

The Radial (Musculospiral) Nerve (C6, 7, 8, T1)

E. Radial Nerve Lesions Which Occur:

1. Below the triceps innervation - Power to extend elbow retained.

2. Below the brachioradialis branch - Retain some supination ability.

3. In the forearm - May affect branches to small muscle groups: extensors of the thumb, extensors of the index finger, extensors of the fingers and extensor carpi ulnaris.

4. On the dorsum of the wrist - Show only sensory loss on the hand.

F. Partial lesions of the radial nerve in the arm occasionally affect fascicles to small muscle groups like those cited above.

THE MEDIAN NERVE (C6, 7, 8, T1)

The median nerve arises from the brachial plexus by 2 heads: a medial head from the medial cord and a lateral head from the lateral cord. The 2 heads unite at the lower margin of the pectoralis minor muscle. The trunk thus derives its fibers from the lower 3 (sometimes 4) cervical and the first thoracic segments of the spinal cord. In the arm it has no branches; the trunk descends along the course of the brachial artery and passes onto the volar side of the forearm, where it gives off muscular branches, and enters the hand where it terminates with muscular and cutaneous branches. **Motor** branches pass to most of the flexor-pronator muscles of the forearm, supplying all of the superficial volar muscles except the flexor carpi ulnaris, and all of the deep volar muscles except the ulnar half of the flexor digitorum profundus. In the hand they supply the first 2 lumbricales and the thenar muscles which lie superficial to the tendon of the flexor pollicis longus. **Sensory** rami supply the skin of the palmar aspect of the thumb and the lateral 2 and one-half fingers, and the distal ends of the same fingers. Many **vasomotor and trophic** fibers are also distributed by the median nerve.

Lesions. - Cervical cord and brachial plexus lesions may involve the median nerve. Peripheral nerve injuries may occur in lacerations of the arm, forearm, wrist, or hand due to auto accidents, stab wounds, bullets, broken water faucets, suicidal attempts, etc.; due to prolonged compression in sleep, anesthesia, or, rarely, by cervical rib; or due to dislocations of the ulna or fractures of the elbow joint and lower radius. Toxic or infectious neuritis or polyneuritis involving the median nerve also occurs.

Clinical Features of Peripheral Median Nerve Lesions.

A. Motor Signs (of Complete Lesions): Paralysis of the flexor-pronator and thenar muscles. In the forearm, pronation is weak or lost and is supplemented by flexing the forearm and holding the elbow out. At the wrist, weak flexion and abduction; hand inclining to ulnar side. In the hand, "ape hand" deformity (thumb in plane of hand and tenar atrophy): Inability to oppose or flex the thumb or abduct it in its own plane; weakened grip, especially in thumb and index finger, with tendency for these digits to become hyperextended and the thumb adducted; inability to flex the distal phalanx of the thumb and index finger (never supplemented), tested by patient clasping hands as in prayer, or attempting to make a fist. Flexion of middle finger is weakened. (Supplementary Movements: In addition to pronation as above, flexion of the middle and proximal phalanges of the first 2 fingers may be affected by action of the deep flexor through its pull on the inert lumbricales and by the influence of flexion of the ring finger on the second finger.)

B. Sensory Disturbances. Loss of sensation to a variable degree over the cutaneous distribution of the median nerve most constantly over the distal phalanges of the first 2 fingers. Pain is present in many median nerve lesions, particularly partial injuries, and may be extreme. These cases, together with similar sciatic nerve injuries, are described under the name of causalgia.

C. Atrophy of the thenar eminence is seen early; atrophy of the flexor-pronator group of muscles in the forearm is seen after a few months

D. Vasomotor and Trophic Signs The skin of the palm is frequently dry cold discolored, chapped, and at times keratotic. Nails are often ridged and brittle. Once injured, the skin in these areas heals slowly.

E. Partial lesions of the median nerve are not uncommon, and may produce weakness in all or part of the motor distribution and/or paralysis of small groups of muscles. Sensory loss is usually less. Pain is more frequently present.

F. Carpal Tunnel Constriction: Progressive partial paralysis and atrophy of the thenar muscles, and sensory disturbances involving the radial half of the palm and the palmar aspect of the first 3 fingers, may follow compres-

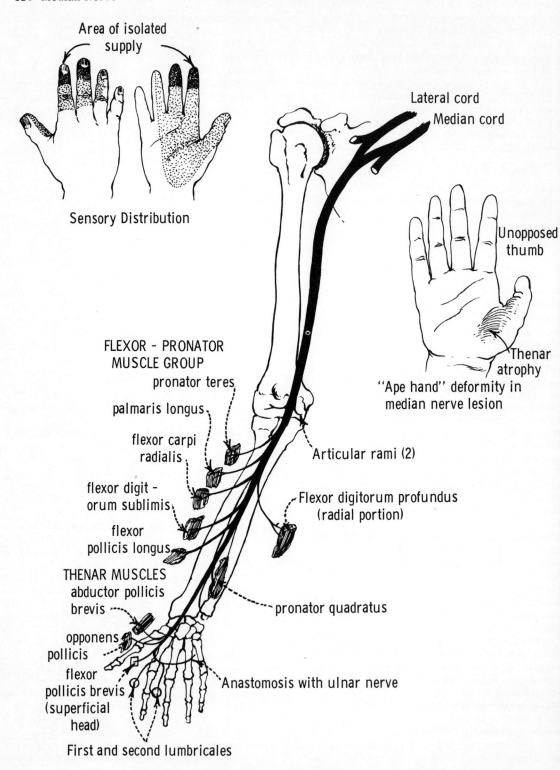

Area of isolated supply

Sensory Distribution

Lateral cord
Median cord

Unopposed thumb

Thenar atrophy

"Ape hand" deformity in median nerve lesion

FLEXOR - PRONATOR MUSCLE GROUP

pronator teres

palmaris longus

flexor carpi radialis

flexor digit - orum sublimis

flexor pollicis longus

THENAR MUSCLES
abductor pollicis brevis

opponens pollicis

flexor pollicis brevis (superficial head)

First and second lumbricales

Articular rami (2)

Flexor digitorum profundus (radial portion)

pronator quadratus

Anastomosis with ulnar nerve

The Median Nerve (C6, 7, 8, T1)

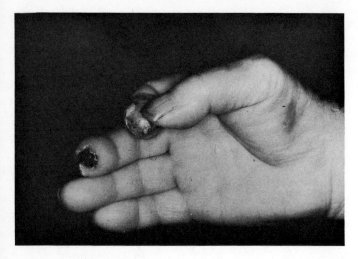

Carpal Tunnel Syndrome With Median Nerve Paralysis. Thenar atrophy and paralysis, trophic changes of fingertips, and sensory disturbance of first 3 fingers relieved subsequently by section of transverse carpal ligament at the wrist.

sion of the median nerve in the carpal tunnel at the wrist. Decompression of the nerve by section of the transverse carpal ligament may be required for relief.

THE ULNAR NERVE (C8, T1)

The ulnar nerve is the largest branch of the medial cord of the brachial plexus, and is composed of fibers from the eighth cervical and first thoracic segments. It originates at the lower border of the pectoralis minor, descends on the medial side of the arm, and pierces the medial intermuscular septum to continue its descent in a groove on the medial head of the triceps. From there it passes behind the medial epicondyle of the humerus and down the ulnar side of the forearm into the hand. **Motor** branches in the forearm supply the flexor carpi ulnaris and the ulnar head of the flexor digitorum profundus. Motor branches in the hand supply all of the small muscles deep and medial to the long flexor tendon of the thumb except the first 2 lumbricales. **Sensory** branches supply the skin of the little finger and the medial half of the hand and the ring finger.

Cervical cord and brachial plexus lesions may involve the fibers of the ulnar nerve. Peripheral injuries include fractures and dislocations of the head of the humerus and at the elbow; direct trauma in lacerating wounds, e.g., knife stabs or auto accidents; pressure on the nerve during sleep, drunkenness, or general anesthesia; and, less commonly, cervical rib, callus formation, and neurinoma.

Mononeuritis may occur with lead poisoning or as a complication of typhus fever, malaria, or influenza.

Clinical Features of Peripheral Ulnar Nerve Lesions.
A. Motor Signs (Complete Lesions):

1. Claw hand - From unopposed action of the extensor digitorum communis in the fourth and fifth digits (associated with interosseous atrophy): The patient is unable to flex the proximal or distal phalanges of the fourth and fifth digits. The first phalanges of these fingers remain hyperextended, the distal 2 flexed. The fifth finger is abducted.

2. Inability to extend the second and distal phalanges of any of the fingers.

3. Inability to adduct or abduct the fingers or to oppose all the finger tips as in making a cone with the fingers and thumb.

4. Inability to adduct the thumb. In holding a paper between the thumb and index finger, the patient substitutes flexion of the thumb to compensate for paralysis of the adductor pollicis (Froment's sign).

5. At the wrist - Flexion weak, ulnar abduction lost. Ulnar reflex lost.

B. Atrophy of the interosseous spaces (especially the first) and of the hypothenar eminence.

C. Supplementary Movements: Slight flexion of the ring finger and sometimes of the fifth finger may occur with violent contraction of the flexor digitorum sublimis. Adduction of the thumb is supplemented by the extensor pollicis longus. Abduction of the first 2 fingers is produced by forced extension and in

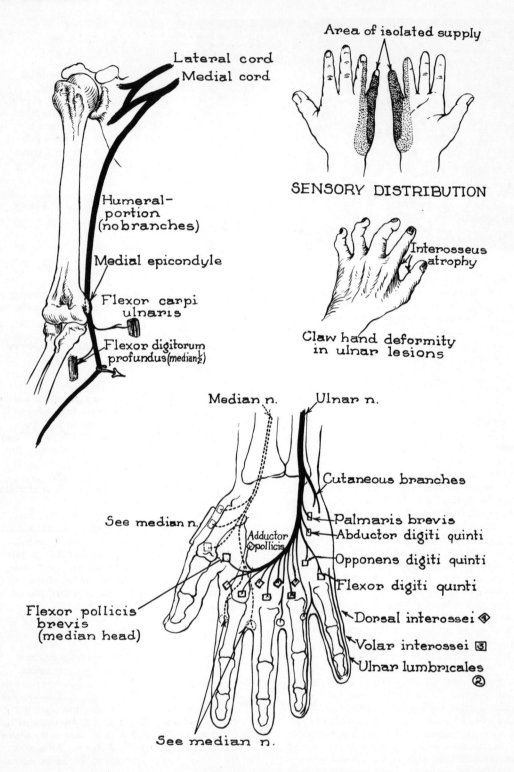

Lateral cord
Medial cord

Area of isolated supply

SENSORY DISTRIBUTION

Humeral-
portion
(no branches)

Medial epicondyle

Flexor carpi
ulnaris

Flexor digitorum
profundus (median ½)

Interosseus
atrophy

Claw hand deformity
in ulnar lesions

Median n.   Ulnar n.

Cutaneous branches

See median n.

Adductor
pollicis

Palmaris brevis
Abductor digiti quinti

Opponens digiti quinti

Flexor digiti quinti

Flexor pollicis
brevis
(median head)

Dorsal interossei ④

Volar interossei ③

Ulnar lumbricales
②

See median n.

The Ulnar Nerve (C8, T1)

some cases possibly by their interossei receiving dual innervation. Slight extension of the distal phalanges may occur with contraction of the common extensor by its pull on tendons of the inert interossei.

D. Sensory Disturbances: Loss of sensation on the ulnar side of the hand and ring finger and most markedly over the entire little finger. Subjective pain is uncommon except with neuritis and partial lesions. Referred pain in the ulnar distribution may occur in coronary disease.

E. Vasomotor and Trophic Changes: The skin of the hypothenar eminence and little finger is cold and dry and at times discolored. The nail of the little finger may be deformed. Ulcerations may occur on the little finger from cigarette burns, etc. (healing poor).

F. Partial lesions may produce only motor weakness or paralysis of a few of the muscles supplied by the ulnar nerve. Lesions low in the forearm or at the wrist spare the deep flexor and the flexor carpi ulnaris.

COMBINED MEDIAN AND ULNAR NERVE LESIONS

The median and ulnar nerves are frequently injured together. If the lesion is complete, the functional disturbances are constant, but if one or both nerves are only partially involved, the symptoms differ widely and are classified according to the varied appearance and functions of the hand.

Clinical Features.
A. Motor Symptoms (in Total Paralysis of Both Nerves): The wrist is slightly hyperextended and inclined to the radial side. "Ape hand" deformity is present, with the thumb in the plane of the hand and slightly abducted. The first phalanges are moderately extended, the last 2 slightly flexed. Flexor movements are not possible except with supplementary movements. The patient cannot abduct or adduct the fingers.

B. Atrophy is marked in the dorsal interosseous spaces and in the thenar and hypothenar eminences; the flexor tendons ridge the palm.

C. Supplementary Movements: Slight passive flexion of the wrist or fingers is produced by sudden relaxation following hyperextension of the hand or fingers. Slight abduction of the fingers by energetic contraction of the extensors.

D. Sensory Symptoms: Touch is lost over the combined distribution of both nerves. Pain and temperature senses are lost to a lesser degree, corresponding to the overlap of the radial and musculocutaneous nerves.

E. Vasomotor and Trophic Changes: These are common in the sensory distribution and include deformities of the nails; dryness, coldness, and discoloration of the skin; and, when associated with a vascular lesion, which is common, marked vasomotor changes with cyanosis, glossy skin, or edema.

F. Partial lesions may produce many types of dissociated paralysis, e.g., paralysis of the small hand muscles and flexors of the fingers; or, paralysis of the small hand muscles and weakness of the deep flexors, resulting in a marked clawing of the proximal phalanges.

Tests.
Careful dynamometric studies of the motor power of the various phalanges is useful in determining the exact distribution of muscle weakness and paralysis.

THE THORACIC NERVES

The thoracic nerves consist of 12 pairs of spinal nerves derived from cord segments located between the seventh cervical and ninth thoracic vertebrae. In general, they retain their segmental relationship throughout their distribution, each one branching into posterior primary and anterior primary divisions, a small recurrent meningeal branch to the spinal dura, and gray and white communicating branches to the sympathetic trunk. The **posterior primary division** divides into a medial branch, distributed to short, medially placed back muscles and the skin of the back as far as the midscapular line; and a lateral branch, supplying twigs to the sacrospinalis muscles. The lower 6 thoracic nerves also send sensory branches to the skin of the lower lateral part of the back. The **anterior primary division** becomes an intercostal nerve, having a lateral branch, sensory to the skin of the lateral aspect of the trunk and an anterior branch, supplying the intercostal muscles, parietal pleura, and the skin over the anterior aspect of the thorax and abdomen. The lower 6 nerves also innervate the muscles of the abdominal wall.

Exceptions.
The major portion of the first thoracic nerve enters the brachial plexus. T2 and T3 contribute sensory branches to the axilla and the medial side of the arm. T12 contributes to the lumbar plexus, and the rest of its anterior division becomes a subcostal rather than an intercostal nerve. The lower 3 or 4 thoracic nerves supply a variable number of twigs to the periphery of the diaphragm and to the serratus posterior inferior muscle.

Clinical Aspects.
The thoracic nerves may be involved by the same types of lesions which affect other peripheral nerves. However, loss of function of one or even several thoracic nerves is not in itself of great importance, although this information may be of diagnostic aid in localizing spinal cord lesions.

Involvement of the first thoracic segments may produce **Horner's syndrome**, char-acterized by enophthalmos, miosis, and ptosis, due to interruption of sympathetic nerves to the face and eye. Paralysis of the intercostal muscles is often difficult to diagnose; but if 2 or more thoracic nerves are involved, the segmental sensory loss is characteristic.

Lesions of the lower thoracic nerves may produce partial or complete paralysis of the abdominal muscles. The abdominal reflexes are lost in the affected quadrants, and in unilateral lesions the umbilicus is usually drawn toward the well side. If the umbilicus moves upward when the patient tenses his abdomen (as in trying to sit up from a reclining position), it is known as **Beevor's sign** and indicates paralysis of the lower abdominal muscles due to a lesion at the level of the tenth thoracic segment.

Girdle-like root pains occurring with injuries to the mid-thoracic vertebrae demonstrate the segmental distribution of the thoracic nerves. The segmental arrangement of these nerves is again illustrated by the distribution of vesicles in herpes zoster (shingles), a disease of the posterior root ganglia caused by a virus

Thoracic cord levels which should be kept in mind include the anterior aspect of the chest (T1-6), the nipple line (T4), the upper abdomen (T7-9), the umbilicus (T10), and the lower abdomen (T11, 12, and L1).

THE LUMBAR NERVES

The lumbar nerves are 5 pairs of spinal nerves derived from cord segments located between the ninth and the lower portion of the eleventh thoracic vertebrae. Each follows the division of a typical spinal nerve. **Posterior primary divisions** split into (1) medial branches, which supply the multifidus spinae muscles (the lower 3 also send small sensory rami to the skin of the sacral region); and (2) lateral branches, the upper 3 of which give twigs to the adjacent sacrospinal muscles and become cutaneous as the **superior clunical nerves.** The lower 2 lateral branches are small and end in the sacrospinal muscles. **Anterior primary divisions** of the lumbar nerves together with those of the sacral and coccygeal nerves form the lumbosacral plexus from which the major nerves of the pelvic girdle and lower extremity are derived. A variable number of **communicating rami** join the lumbar nerves to the sympathetic trunk. Small **recurrent branches** supply the spinal dura.

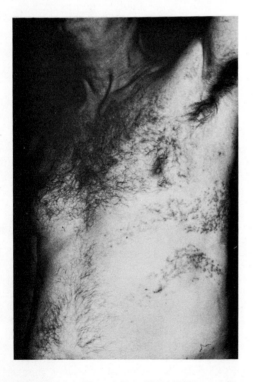

Herpes Zoster, Thoracic. Vesicular eruption of herpes zoster in left thoracic area (Th6, 8).

THE LUMBAR PLEXUS

The lumbar plexus, located in the substance of the psoas muscle, is the upper portion of the lumbosacral plexus. It is ordinarily formed by the anterior primary divisions of the first 3 lumbar nerves and part of the fourth, and in 50% of cases it receives a contribution from the last thoracic nerve.

(1) L1, L2, and L4 each divide into upper and lower branches. The upper branch of L1 forms the **iliohypogastric** and **ilioinguinal** **nerves**. The lower branch of L1 joins the upper branch of L2 to form the **genitofemoral** **nerve**. The lower branch of L4 joins L5 to form the lumbosacral trunk. (2) The lower branch of L2, all of L3, and the upper branch of L4 each split into a smaller anterior and a large posterior division. The 3 anterior divisions unite to form the **obturator** nerve. The

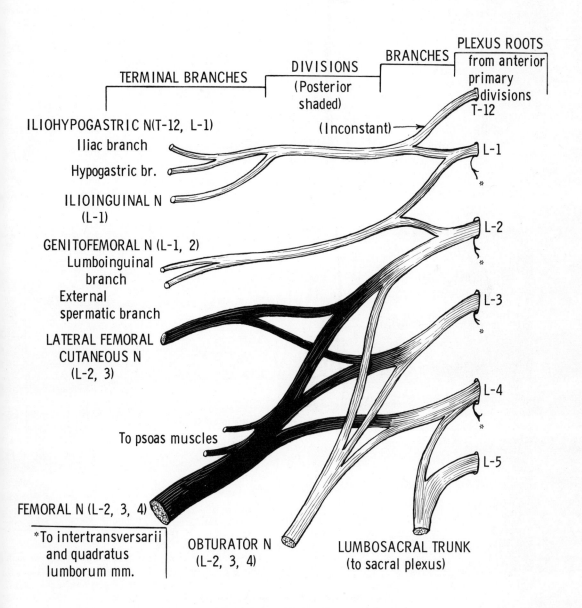

The Lumbar Plexus

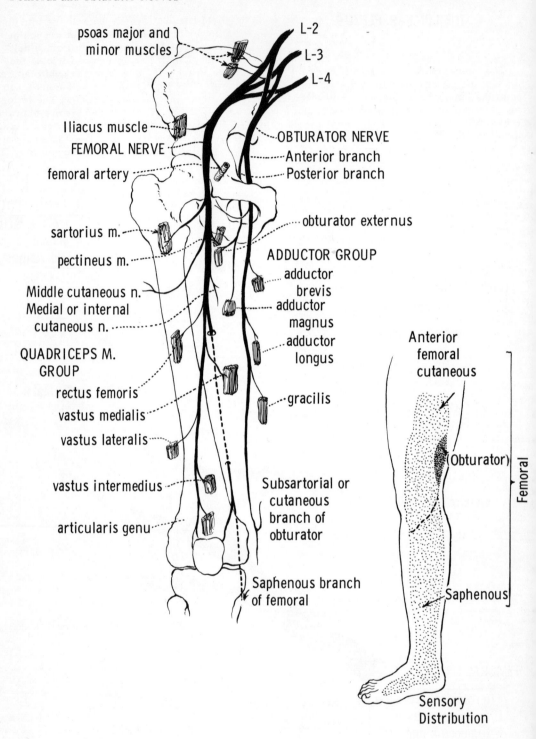

psoas major and
minor muscles

L-2
L-3
L-4

Iliacus muscle
FEMORAL NERVE
femoral artery

OBTURATOR NERVE
Anterior branch
Posterior branch

obturator externus

sartorius m.
pectineus m.

ADDUCTOR GROUP
adductor
brevis
adductor
magnus
adductor
longus

Middle cutaneous n.
Medial or internal
cutaneous n.

QUADRICEPS M.
GROUP

rectus femoris
vastus medialis
vastus lateralis

gracilis

vastus intermedius

articularis genu

Subsartorial or
cutaneous
branch of
obturator

Saphenous branch
of femoral

Anterior
femoral
cutaneous

(Obturator)

Femoral

Saphenous

Sensory
Distribution

The Femoral and Obturator Nerves
(L2, 3, 4)   (L2, 3, 4)

3 posterior divisions unite to form the **femoral nerve**, and the upper 2 give off twigs which form the **lateral femoral cutaneous nerve.** (3) Collateral muscular branches supply the quadratus lumborum and intertransversarii, from L1 and L4; and the psoas muscle, from L2 and L3.

Distribution of Terminal Branches.

The **iliohypogastric nerve** (T12, L1) passes laterally around the iliac crest between the transversus and internal oblique muscles and divides into an iliac (lateral) branch, to the skin of the upper lateral part of the thigh; and a hypogastric (anterior) branch, descending anteriorly to the skin over the symphsis. The **ilioinguinal nerve** (L1) follows a course slightly inferior to the iliohypogastric, with which it may anastomose, and is distributed to the skin of the upper medial part of the thigh and the root of the penis and scrotum or mons pubis and labium majus. The **genitofemoral nerve** (L1, 2) emerges from the anterior surface of the psoas, runs obliquely downward on the surface of this muscle, and divides into the **external spermatic nerve** to the cremasteric muscle and the skin of the scrotum or labia, and the **lumboinguinal nerve** to the skin of the middle upper part of the thigh. The **lateral femoral cutaneous nerve** (L2, 3) passes obliquely across the iliacus muscle and under Poupart's ligament to divide into several rami distributed to the skin of the anterolateral side of the thigh. The **lumbosacral trunk** (L4, 5) descends into the pelvis, where it enters into the formation of the sacral plexus. The **femoral and obturator nerves** are described opposite and on p. 128.

Lesions of the Lumbar Plexus.

Spinal cord and cauda equina lesions may involve fibers of these nerves. Nonfatal injuries to the lumbar plexus are rare because of its deep location, but the following may occur: fractures, dislocations, bullet wounds, and tuberculosis of the vertebrae; psoas abscess and pressure from pelvic tumors (including the gravid uterus).

Clinical Features According to Nerves Involved. (Femoral and obturator nerves, see opposite and p. 128.)

A. Ilioinguinal, Iliohypogastric, and Genitofemoral Nerves: Injury to these nerves in itself is of little importance; however, sensory loss or pain in their distribution may be of value in locating spinal cord and root lesions. Referred pain in their distribution occurs with diseases of the renal pelvis and ureter.

B. Lateral Femoral Cutaneous Nerve: Of clinical significance because it is frequently the seat of paresthesias and occasionally pain. "Meralgia paresthetica of Roth" is the term applied to such disorder. Symptoms include numbness, tingling, and pain over the outer aspect and front of the thigh, most marked on walking and standing. The cause is unknown. Various pathologic entities have been incriminated, e.g., neuritis, angulation of the nerve as it leaves the pelvis, fascial pressure, flat feet, obesity, spondylitis, and pressure from tight clothing. It is commonest in middle-aged men, and may occur as the first sign of a lumbar cord tumor.

THE FEMORAL (ANTERIOR CRURAL) NERVE (L2, 3, 4)

The femoral nerve is the largest branch of the lumbar plexus. It arises from the 3 posterior divisions of the plexus, which are derived from the second, third, and fourth lumbar nerves; emerges from the lateral border of the psoas just above Poupart's ligament; and descends beneath this ligament to enter the femoral trigone on the lateral side of the femoral artery, where it divides into terminal branches. **Motor** branches above the inguinal ligament supply the iliopsoas muscle. Motor branches in the thigh supply the sartorius, pectineus, and quadriceps femoris muscles. **Sensory** branches include the anterior femoral cutaneous branches to the anterior and medial surfaces of the thigh, and the saphenous nerve to the medial side of the leg and foot.

Lesions of the femoral nerve frequently involve the obturator nerve also. Spinal cord, cauda equina, and lumbar plexus lesions must be considered. Peripheral injuries may result from pelvic tumors, psoas abscess, and fractures of the pelvis and upper femur; forceps injury during labor, and injury during reduction of congenital dislocation of the hips; pressure during prolong operations when the thighs are strongly abducted; bullet and stab wounds; aneurysms of the femoral artery (especially in wartime); and neuritis, particularly in diabetes mellitus.

Clinical Features. (Depend upon the level of the involvement.)

A. Motor Symptoms: Paralysis of the iliopsoas causes inability to flex the thigh on the trunk. If the iliacus alone is paralyzed, flexion of the thigh is weakened. In paralysis of the quadriceps, extension of the leg is lost as well as the knee jerk. Walking forward is difficult (impossible in bilateral involvement), and the patient uses a pseudosteppage gait, often steadying his thigh with his hand. Walking backward is often easier.

B. Atrophy develops over the anterior aspect of the thigh.

C. Sensory Disturbances: Sensation is lost in the cutaneous distribution of the femoral. Pain occurs with irritative lesions and is often most marked in the knee.

D. Injuries in the thigh may involve only single branches of the femoral nerve, e.g., the saphenous nerve alone or the branches to the quadriceps.

THE OBTURATOR NERVE (L2, 3, 4)

The obturator nerve arises from the lumbar plexus by a fusion of the 3 anterior divisions of the plexus, which are derived from the second, third, and fourth lumbar nerves. Emerging from the medial border of the psoas near the brim of the pelvis, it passes on the lateral side of the hypogastric vessels and ureter; and descends through the obturator canal in the upper part of the obturator foramen to the medial side of the thigh. In the canal it splits into anterior and posterior branches. **Motor rami** from the posterior branch supply the obturator externus and adductor magnus muscles. Motor rami from the anterior branch supply the adductors longus and brevis and the gracilis muscles. **Sensory rami** from the anterior branch supply the hip joint and a small area of skin on the middle internal part of the thigh.

Lesions.

The obturator nerve may be involved by the same processes which affect the femoral nerve; isolated paralysis is rare. Pressure from a gravid uterus and damage in severe labor are not uncommon. External rotation and adduction of the thigh are impaired, and crossing of the legs is difficult. Sensory loss is usually not significant. Howship-Romberg syndrome is caused by pressure on the obturator nerve by obturator hernia (rare). The chief symptom is pain, which radiates down the inner side of the thigh and is usually most marked at the knee.

THE SACRAL NERVES

The sacral nerves are 5 pairs of spinal nerves derived from cord segments located opposite the bodies of the twelfth thoracic and first lumbar vertebrae. The upper 4 **posterior primary divisions** pass through the posterior sacral foramens, the fifth emerging between the sacrum and the coccyx. The upper 3 divide into medial branches, distributed to the multifidi muscles; and lateral branches which become the medial clunical nerves, supplying the skin over the medial part of the gluteus maximus. The lower 2 posterior primary divisions, with the posterior division of the coccygeal nerve, supply the skin over the coccyx.

The anterior primary divisions appear at the anterior sacral foramens and contribute to part of the lumbosacral plexus. This is described below.

White rami (parasympathetic in this instance) pass from the second, third, and fourth sacral nerves to the pelvic and lower abdominal viscera via the hypogastric plexus. **Gray rami** (sympathetic) join each sacral nerve from the sympathetic trunk.

Small **recurrent meningeal branches** pass back to the spinal dura.

THE SACRAL PLEXUS

The sacral portion of the lumbosacral plexus lies against the piriformis muscle on the posterior wall of the pelvis. In front of it are the pelvic colon, the hypogastric vessels, and the ureter. It ordinarily arises by 5 plexus roots formed by the anterior primary divisions of the fifth and part of the fourth lumbar nerves (lumbosacral trunk) and the first and parts of the second and third sacral nerves. One main terminal branch, the sciatic nerve, and several collateral branches are formed by the plexus.

Each of the 5 plexus roots splits into an anterior and a posterior division. The upper 4 posterior divisions (L4, 5 and S1, 2) join to form the common peroneal nerve. All 5 of the

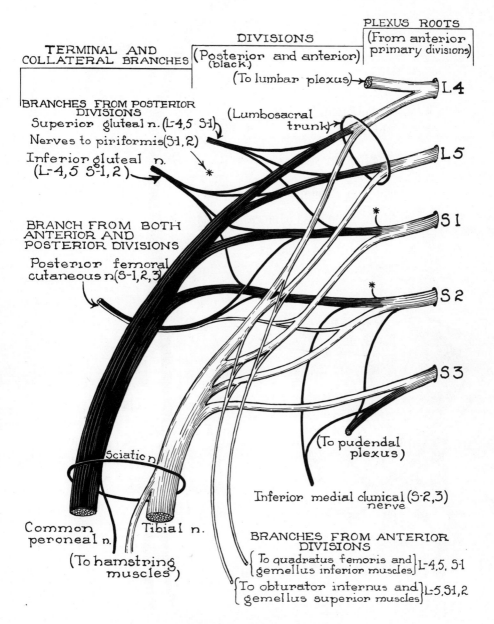

PLEXUS ROOTS
(From anterior primary divisions)

DIVISIONS
(Posterior and anterior)
(black.)

TERMINAL AND COLLATERAL BRANCHES

(To lumbar plexus)→ L4

BRANCHES FROM POSTERIOR DIVISIONS
Superior gluteal n.(L-4,5 S-1)
Nerves to piriformis(S-1,2)
Inferior gluteal n. (L-4,5 S-1,2)

(Lumbosacral trunk)

L5

S1

BRANCH FROM BOTH ANTERIOR AND POSTERIOR DIVISIONS
Posterior femoral cutaneous n.(S-1,2,3)

S2

S3

Sciatic n.

(To pudendal plexus)

Inferior medial clunical (S-2,3) nerve

Common peroneal n.   Tibial n.

(To hamstring muscles)

BRANCHES FROM ANTERIOR DIVISIONS
{ To quadratus femoris and gemellus inferior muscles } L-4,5, S-1
{ To obturator internus and gemellus superior muscles } L-5, S-1,2

The Sacral Plexus

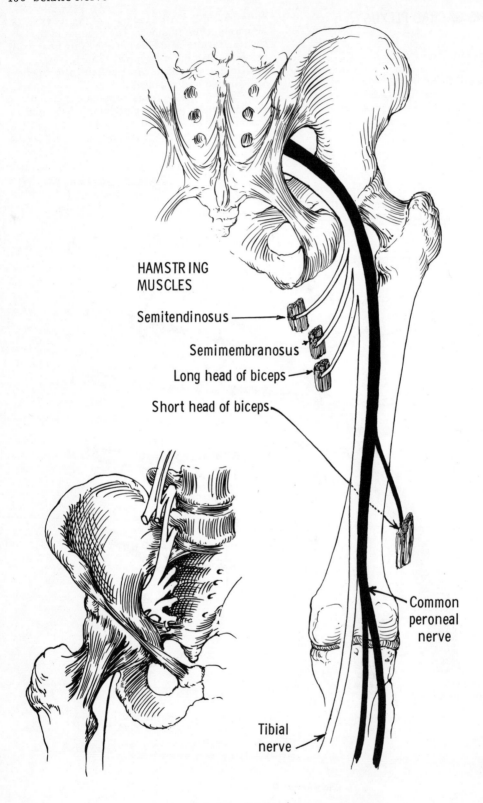

HAMSTRING
MUSCLES

Semitendinosus

Semimembranosus

Long head of biceps

Short head of biceps

Common
peroneal
nerve

Tibial
nerve

The Sciatic Nerve (L4, 5, S1, 2, 3)

anterior divisions (L4, 5 and S1, 2) join to form the **tibial nerve.** (In the thigh the peroneal and tibial nerves are fused as the **sciatic nerve.**) The posterior division of S3, together with twigs from the anterior divisions of S2, 3, contribute to the pudendal plexus (see p. 135).

Collateral Branches From the Posterior Divisions.

The **superior gluteal nerve** (L4, 5 and S1, 2) passes above the piriformis muscle through the greater sciatic foramen into the buttock, where it supplies the gluteus medius and minimus and the tensor fasciae latae muscles. The **inferior gluteal nerve** (L5 and S1, 2) passes below the piriformis muscle through the greater sciatic foramen to the gluteus maximus muscle. Nerves to the piriformis consist of short twigs from S1 and S2. The **inferior medial clunical** (perforating cutaneous) nerve (S2, 3) perforates the sacrotuberous ligament and is distributed to the lower medial gluteal region.

The **posterior femoral cutaneous** (small sciatic) nerve constitutes a collateral branch with roots from both anterior and posterior divisions of S1, 2 and the anterior divisions of S2, 3. Perineal branches pass to the skin of the upper medial aspect of the thigh and the skin of the scrotum or labium majus. **Inferior clunical nerves** extend to the lower lateral gluteal region, and femoral cutaneous branches to the back of the thigh toward the medial side. **Collateral branches** from the anterior divisions extend to the quadratus femoris and gemellus inferior muscles (from L4, 5 and S1) and to the obturator internus and gemellus superior muscles (from L5 and S1, 2).

Lesions.

Spinal cord and cauda equina lesions may involve these nerves. Injury to the plexus itself is infrequent but may result from pelvic fractures, dislocations, stab and gunshot wounds, tuberculosis and malignant tumors of the pelvis, pressure from the fetal head or trauma from forceps during childbirth, or toxic or infectious neuritis.

Clinical Features According to the Nerves Involved. (The sciatic nerve is discussed separately.)

A. Superior Gluteal Nerve (L4, 5, S1, 2): Rarely injured alone. Paralysis of the gluteus medius and minimus weakens abduction of the leg, which interferes with walking and causes inclination of the pelvis to the opposite side when standing on the affected limb. One can test abductor power against passive adduction.

B. Inferior Gluteal Nerve (L5, S1, 2): Injured more frequently than the superior gluteal, though rarely alone. Paralysis of the gluteus maximus renders it difficult for the patient to rise from a seated position, or to run and jump or climb stairs due to the weakened extensor power at the hip. In unilateral lesions the contracted buttocks are asymmetric.

C. Posterior Femoral Cutaneous (Small Sciatic) Nerve (S1, 2, 3): Pain in its distribution may occur in partial and irritative plexus or root lesions. Complete interruption is followed by sensory loss in its distribution.

THE SCIATIC NERVE (L4, 5, S1, 2, 3)

The sciatic nerve is the largest nerve in the body. It consists of 2 separate nerves in one sheath: the **common peroneal nerve,** formed by the upper 4 posterior divisions of the sacral plexus; and the **tibial nerve,** from all 5 anterior divisions. The nerve leaves the pelvis through the greater sciatic foramen, usually below the piriformis muscle, and descends between the greater trochanter of the femur and the ischial tuberosity along the posterior surface of the thigh to the popliteal space, where it terminates by dividing into the tibial and common peroneal nerves. Branches in the thigh supply the hamstring muscles. Rami from the tibial trunk pass to the semitendinosus and semimembranosus muscles, the long head of the biceps, and the adductor magnus muscle. A ramus from the common peroneal trunk supplies the short head of the biceps. (The peroneal and tibial nerves are described on pp. 133 and 135.)

Lesions.

Injury to the sciatic nerve may result from herniated intervertebral disk (protruded nucleus pulposus), dislocations of the hip or attempts at reducing them; childbirth injury to the infant by traction on the legs, or injury to the mother from compression by the fetus or from forceps; pelvis fractures, tumors, or stab or gunshot wounds; or injections of arsphenamine, ether, alcohol, mercury, emetine, penicillin, or thiamine into or near the nerve. Alcoholic, lead, arsenic, or infectious polyneuritis may occur, as well as mononeuritis due to osteoarthritis of the spine or sacroiliac joint.

Clinical Features.

A. Motor Signs:

1. Hamstring paralysis - Flexion of the leg is lost (or weakened in partial lesions, which often spare the semitendinosus and semimembranosus).

2. Paralysis of all the muscles of the leg and foot, causing a steppage gait and inability to stand on the heels or toes. Running is impossible.

3. Loss of Achilles jerk and plantar reflex.

B. Supplementary movements do not occur in complete sciatic lesions.

C. Sensory Disturbances: Sensibility is lost on the outer side of the leg and the entire foot except for the instep and internal malleolus. Causalgic pain is often present with irritative or partial lesions, particularly of the tibial trunk.

D. Atrophy of the involved muscles occurs, but it may be masked by edema.

E. Vasomotor and Trophic Changes: Edema of the leg and foot is common, the skin being dry or discolored. Plantar hyperkeratosis is often seen. Slight injuries to the sole may cause ulcerations which heal slowly.

F. Partial lesions produce dissociated paralysis from greater damage to either the tibial or common peroneal trunks, or from partial injury of both. Experience shows the common peroneal usually suffers the greater damage.

G. Patrick's "F-ab-er-e" Sign (of Hip Joint Disease): With the heel of the painful extremity placed on the opposite knee, the affected knee remains elevated and cannot be depressed toward the bed without pain. In short, there is pain upon attempting flexion, abduction, and external rotation and extension simultaneously (f-ab-er-e). In sciatica the knee of the affected side is only slightly elevated and can be depressed to the bed without pain or rotation of the pelvis.

H. Lasègue's Sign (of Sciatic Nerve Disease): Pain is present along the course of the sciatic nerve when it is put on the stretch by flexing the thigh on the abdomen and extending the leg at the knee. When sitting in a chair, the patient may be unable to fully extend the knee because of pain.

THE COMMON PERONEAL (EXTERNAL POPLITEAL) NERVE (L4, 5, S1, 2)

The common peroneal nerve is formed by a fusion of the upper 4 posterior divisions of the sacral plexus, and thus derives its fibers from the lower 2 lumbar and the upper 2 sacral cord segments. In the thigh it is a component of the sciatic nerve as far as the upper part of the popliteal space. Here it begins its independent course, descending along the posterior border of the biceps femoris, diagonally across the dorsum of the knee joint to the upper external portion of the leg near the head of the fibula, where it turns forward between the peroneus longus and the bone and divides into 3 terminal rami.

Branches given off in the popliteal space are **sensory** and include the superior and inferior articular branches to the knee joint, and the **lateral sural cutaneous nerve**, which joins the medial sural cutaneous nerve (from the tibial nerve) to form the sural nerve, supplying the skin of the lower dorsal aspect of the leg, the external malleolus, and the lateral side of the foot and fifth toe.

The 3 terminal branches are the recurrent articular and the superficial and deep peroneal nerves. The **recurrent articular nerve** accompanies the anterior tibial recurrent artery, supplying the tibiofibular and knee joints and a twig to the tibialis anterior muscle. The **superficial peroneal nerve** descends along the intermuscular septum to supply muscular branches to the peroneus longus and brevis muscles, cutaneous branches to the lower front of the leg, and terminal cutaneous branches to the dorsum of the foot, part of the big toe, and adjacent sides of the second to fifth toes up to the second phalanges. The **deep peroneal** (anterior tibial) nerve descends in the anterior compartment of the leg. Muscular branches extend to the tibialis anterior, extensor digitorum longus, extensor hallucis longus, and peroneus tertius muscles. Articu-lar filaments supply the inferior tibiofibular and ankle joints. Terminal branches extend to the skin of the adjacent sides of the first 2 toes and to the extensor digitorum brevis muscle and adjacent joints.

Lesions.

Sacral plexus and sciatic nerve lesions may involve fibers of the common peroneal nerve. Peripheral injury may result from direct trauma, especially in the region of the neck of the fibula; and fractures of the leg or compression from prolonged kneeling, prolonged sitting with crossed knees, and compression of the legs in a lying position. Primary neuritis has a special predilection for this nerve.

Clinical Features.

A. Motor Disturbances: Paralysis of the extensor-abductor muscles of the foot causes inability to extend (dorsiflex) the foot or proximal phalanges of the toes, resulting in a "foot-drop" deformity; inability to abduct and evert the foot, or to stand on the affected heel; and steppage gait (patient raises the knee high, and the foot hangs flexed and adducted).

B. Supplementary Movements: Slight extension of the foot may accompany vigorous flexion of the toes. Slight extension of the toes may occur upon sudden relaxation of the flexors.

C. Sensory Disturbances: Sensibility is lost over the dorsum of the foot and outer side of the leg. Pain is rarely present and, if so, is usually mild.

D. Vasomotor and trophic changes are not marked; the involved muscles atrophy.

E. Partial lesions are infrequent; they produce dissociated paralysis, e.g., loss of activity of the tibialis anterior alone, or of only the extensors of the toes.

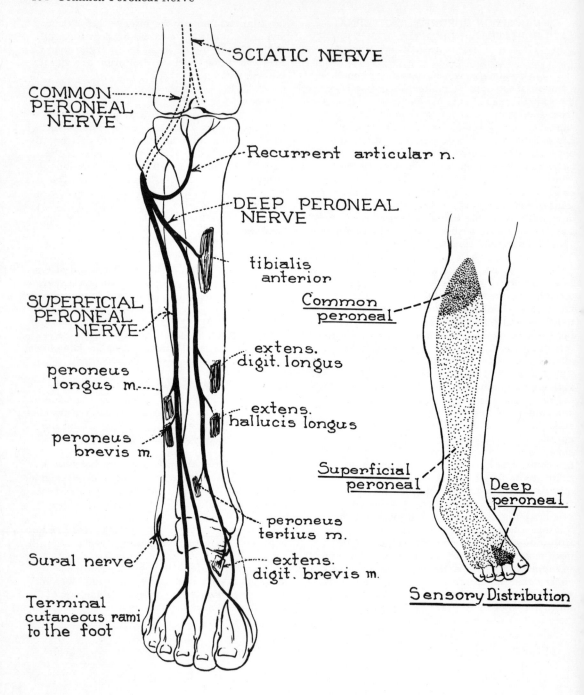

SCIATIC NERVE

COMMON PERONEAL NERVE

Recurrent articular n.

DEEP PERONEAL NERVE

tibialis anterior

Common peroneal

SUPERFICIAL PERONEAL NERVE

extens. digit. longus

peroneus longus m.

extens. hallucis longus

peroneus brevis m.

Superficial peroneal

Deep peroneal

peroneus tertius m.

Sural nerve

extens. digit. brevis m.

Terminal cutaneous rami to the foot

Sensory Distribution

The Common Peroneal Nerve (L4, 5, S1, 2)

THE TIBIAL (INTERNAL POPLITEAL) NERVE (L4, 5, S1, 2, 3)

The tibial nerve is formed by all 5 of the anterior divisions of the sacral plexus, thus receiving fibers from the lower 2 lumbar and the upper 3 sacral cord segments. The tibial nerve forms the largest component of the sciatic nerve in the thigh. It begins its own course in the upper part of the popliteal space and descends vertically through this space and the dorsum of the leg to the dorsomedial aspect of the ankle, from which point its terminal branches, the medial and lateral plantar nerves, continue into the foot. The portion of the tibial trunk below the popliteal space was formerly called the posterior tibial nerve; that portion within the space, the internal popliteal nerve.

Branches from the Tibial Proper.
Motor branches extend to the gastrocnemius, plantaris, soleus, popliteus, tibialis posterior, flexor digitorum longus pedis, and flexor hallucis longus muscles. A **sensory branch**, the medial sural cutaneous nerve, joins the lateral sural cutaneous nerve from the common peroneal to form the sural nerve (external saphenous), which supplies the skin of the dorsolateral part of the leg and the lateral side of the foot. Articular branches pass to the knee and ankle joints.

There are 2 **terminal branches** (as well as numerous small articular rami not listed). The **medial plantar nerve** (comparable to the median nerve in the hand) sends motor branches to the flexor digitorum brevis, abductor hallucis, flexor hallucis brevis, and first lumbrical muscles; and sensory branches to the medial side of the sole, the plantar surfaces of the medial 3 and one-half toes, and the ungual phalanges of the same toes. The **lateral plantar nerve** (comparable to the ulnar nerve in the arm and hand) sends motor branches to all of the small muscles of the foot except those innervated by the medial plantar nerve (see diagram); and sensory branches to the lateral portions of the sole, the plantar surface of the lateral one and one-half toes, and the ungual phalanges of these toes.

Lesions.
Sacral plexus and sciatic nerve injuries usually involve fibers of the tibial nerve. Isolated tibial paralysis is usually due to an injury in or below the popliteal space, e.g., by gunshot or stab wounds, auto accidents, or fractures of the leg. The frequency of injuries to the tibial nerve is much less than for the peroneal nerve because of its deeper location and more protected course.

Clinical Features.
A. Motor Signs: Inability to plantar-flex, adduct, or invert the foot; elevation of the foot often results from contracture of the tibialis anterior; inability to flex, abduct (separate), or adduct the toes; and inability to stand on the tip toes. Walking is difficult, fatiguing, and often painful. The foot may become deformed from fibrosis of the tibiotarsal articulation, and unopposed action of the dorsal flexors may produce a "claw-foot." The ankle jerk is absent.

B. Supplementary Movement: Feeble plantar flexion by the peroneus longus.

C. Sensory Disturbances: Sensibility is lost over the sole (except inner border), the lateral surfaces of the heel, and the plantar surface of the toes and ungual phalanges. Pain, of severe causalgic nature, is common with incomplete and irritative lesions.

D. Atrophy of the calf and foot muscles occurs; may be masked by edema.

E. Vasomotor and trophic changes are common. The foot becomes edematous, discolored, and cold. Nail changes and hypotrichosis are often seen. Trophic ulcers may occur on the malleoli, heel, and toes.

F. In partial lesions dissociated paralysis may occur. Injuries in the calf spare the innervation of the calf muscles, so that the motor loss is limited to the muscles of the foot. Pain is usually present.

THE PUDENDAL AND COCCYGEAL PLEXUSES

The pudendal and coccygeal plexuses are the most caudal portions of the lumbosacral plexus and supply nerves to the perineal structures. The plexus roots are from the anterior primary divisions of the lower 4 sacral and coccygeal nerves. The fourth sacral nerve is the chief component, as most of S2, 3 passes to the sacral plexus and the last 2 spinal nerves are quite small.

Branches of the Pudendal Plexus.
Muscular rami extend from the fourth sacral nerve to the coccygeus, levator ani,

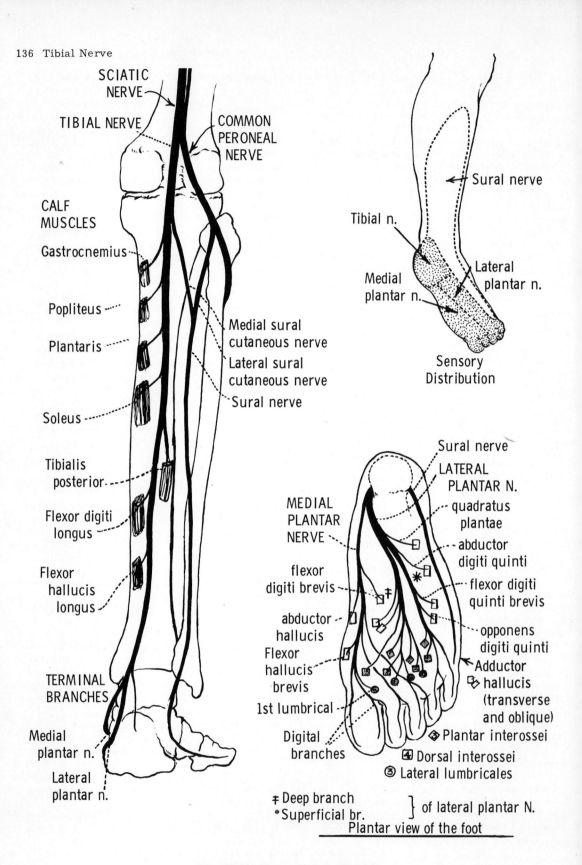

SCIATIC NERVE

TIBIAL NERVE

COMMON PERONEAL NERVE

CALF MUSCLES

Gastrocnemius

Popliteus

Plantaris

Medial sural cutaneous nerve

Lateral sural cutaneous nerve

Sural nerve

Soleus

Tibialis posterior

Flexor digiti longus

Flexor hallucis longus

TERMINAL BRANCHES

Medial plantar n.

Lateral plantar n.

Sural nerve

Tibial n.

Medial plantar n.

Lateral plantar n.

Sensory Distribution

Sural nerve

LATERAL PLANTAR N.

quadratus plantae

abductor digiti quinti

flexor digiti quinti brevis

opponens digiti quinti

Adductor hallucis (transverse and oblique)

MEDIAL PLANTAR NERVE

flexor digiti brevis

abductor hallucis

Flexor hallucis brevis

1st lumbrical

Digital branches

Plantar interossei

Dorsal interossei

Lateral lumbricales

‡ Deep branch
*Superficial br. } of lateral plantar N.

Plantar view of the foot

The Tibial Nerve (L4, 5, S1, 2, 3)

and sphincter ani externus muscles. The **pudendal** (pudic) nerve from S2, 3, 4 accompanies the internal pudic artery through the greater sciatic foramen below the piriformis muscle and across the ischial spine, where it re-enters the lower portion of the pelvis via the small sciatic foramen and Alcock's canal in the lateral wall of the ischiorectal fossa. At this point it divides into (1) the **inferior hemorrhoidal nerves** to the external anal sphincter and adjacent skin; (2) the **perineal nerve**; and (3) the **dorsal nerve of the penis**. The perineal nerve has a deep branch, which pierces the urogenital diaphragm (after giving twigs to the levator and sphincter ani) to supply the muscles of the perineal compartments and a few sensory twigs to the urethra; and a superficial branch, which divides into the posterior scrotal or labial nerves. The dorsal nerve of the penis runs obliquely through the urogenital diaphragm, gives a branch to the corpus cavernosum penis, and passed forward to supply the skin of the dorsum of the penis and the glans. In the female this nerve is small and supplies the clitoris.

Branches of the Coccygeal Plexus.

These are the small sensory anococcygeal nerves derived from the last 3 segments (S4, 5, C). They pierce the sacro-tuberous ligament and supply the skin in the region of the coccyx.

Visceral Rami.

Visceral rami from S2-4 are parasympathetic (see p. 140). They are primary branches of these spinal nerves rather than plexus branches.

Lesions.

Lesions of the pudendal and coccygeal plexuses are usually part of a sacral plexus involvement.

Clinical Features.

A. The motor signs of rare pudendal nerve involvement include partial incontinence of urine and feces, tenesmus, and difficulty on urination.

B. Subjective sensory disturbances seen with partial or irritative lesions are usually spoken of as neuralgia of the pudendal plexus, which is characterized by pain in the anus, perineum, scrotum, penis, or vagina; difficulty and burning on urination and defecation, and occasionally priapism or even ejaculation.

C. Coccygeal Neuralgia: Practically limited to women. There is severe pain and tenderness limited to the tip of the coccyx.

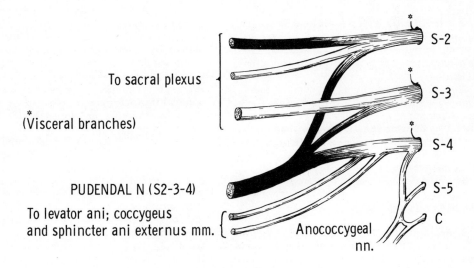

To sacral plexus

*(Visceral branches)

PUDENDAL N (S2-3-4)

To levator ani; coccygeus and sphincter ani externus mm.

Anococcygeal nn.

S-2

S-3

S-4

S-5

C

The Pudendal and Coccygeal Plexuses

6 . . .

The Autonomic Nervous System

The autonomic nervous system is a division of the peripheral nervous system which is distributed to the smooth muscle and glands throughout the body. By definition it is entirely a motor (efferent) system, and it is "automatic" in the sense that most of its functions are carried out below the conscious level. It is, however, highly integrated in structure and function with the rest of the nervous system. Anatomically, the autonomic system is divided, according to the location of the preganglionic cell bodies, into 2 divisions: the sympathetic and parasympathetic nervous systems.

Structure of Autonomic Nerves.

A two-neuron chain characterizes the structure of the autonomic nerves. The cell body of the primary (presynaptic or preganglionic) neuron, located within the CNS, sends its axon out to synapse with the secondary (postsynaptic or postganglionic) neuron located in one of the outlying autonomic ganglia, whence the postganglionic axon passes to its terminal distribution.

Since the postganglionic outnumber the preganglionic neurons by a ratio of about 32:1, a single primary neuron may serve to discharge a number of ganglion cells; thus the autonomic functions of a rather extensive terminal area may be controlled by relatively few central connections.

The autonomic nervous system helps maintain the constancy of the internal environment of the body (homeostasis).

The Sympathetic (or Thoracolumbar) Division.

The sympathetic division of the autonomic nervous system arises from preganglionic cell bodies located in the intermediolateral cell column of the 12 thoracic and upper 3 or 4 lumbar segments of the spinal cord. The axons of these cells (preganglionic fibers) are mostly myelinated fibers. After traversing the ventral roots, they form the white communicating rami of the thoracic and lumbar nerves, through which they reach the trunk ganglia of the sympathetic chain. These lie on the lateral sides of the bodies of the thoracic and lumbar vertebrae. Upon entering the trunk ganglia these fibers may synapse with a nest of ganglion cells, pass up or down the sympathetic trunk to synapse with ganglion cells at a higher or lower level, or pass through the trunk ganglia and out to one of the collateral or intermediary sympathetic ganglia (e.g., the celiac ganglion).

Branches from the sympathetic trunk may be classified as follows: (1) Those composed of postsynaptic fibers* (mainly unmyelinated). The **gray communicating rami** join all of the spinal nerves. Through these rami vasomotor, pilomotor, and sweat gland innervation is distributed throughout the somatic areas. Branches of the **superior cervical sympathetic ganglion** enter into the formation of the sympathetic plexuses about the internal and external carotid arteries for distribution of sympathetics to the head. The **superior cardiac nerves** from the 3 pairs of cervical sympathetic ganglia pass to the cardiac plexus at the base of the heart and distribute accelerator fibers to the myocardium. Branches from the **upper 5 thoracic ganglia** pass to the thoracic aorta (vasomotor) and the posterior pulmonary plexus, through which dilator fibers reach the bronchi. (2) Those composed of presynaptic fibers* (mainly myelinated). The **splanchnic nerves** arising from the lower 7 thoracic ganglia pass to the celiac and superior mesenteric ganglia, where synaptic connections occur with ganglion cells whose axons then pass to the abdominal viscera via the celiac plexus. The **lumbar splanchnic nerves** arising from trunk ganglia in the lumbar region convey fibers to synaptic stations in the inferior mesenteric ganglia and small ganglia associated with the hypogastric plexus, through which postsynaptic fibers are distributed to the lower abdominal and pelvic viscera.

---

*These nerves also carry some visceral afferent fibers, which convey sensory impulses. By definition, however, these do not belong to the autonomic system.

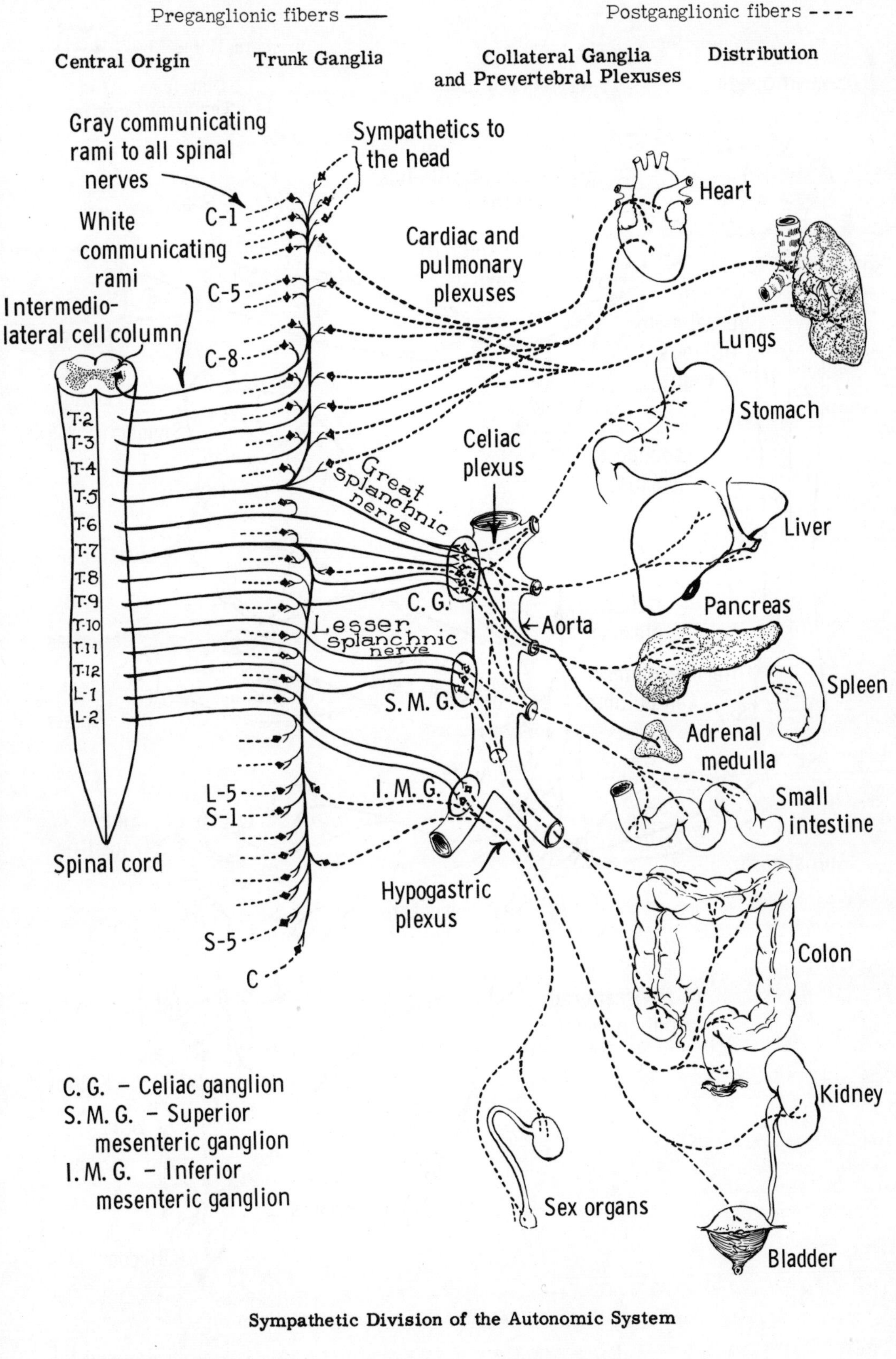

Preganglionic fibers ——   Postganglionic fibers - - - -

Central Origin   Trunk Ganglia   Collateral Ganglia   Distribution
                                           and Prevertebral Plexuses

Gray communicating rami to all spinal nerves

Sympathetics to the head

Heart

White communicating rami

Cardiac and pulmonary plexuses

Intermedio-lateral cell column

C-1

C-5

C-8

Lungs

Stomach

T-2
T-3
T-4
T-5
T-6
T-7
T-8
T-9
T-10
T-11
T-12
L-1
L-2

Great splanchnic nerve

Celiac plexus

Liver

C. G.

Pancreas

Lesser splanchnic nerve

← Aorta

Spleen

S. M. G.

Adrenal medulla

Spinal cord

L-5
S-1

I. M. G.

Small intestine

Hypogastric plexus

S-5

C

Colon

Kidney

C. G. – Celiac ganglion
S. M. G. – Superior
    mesenteric ganglion
I. M. G. – Inferior
    mesenteric ganglion

Sex organs

Bladder

Sympathetic Division of the Autonomic System

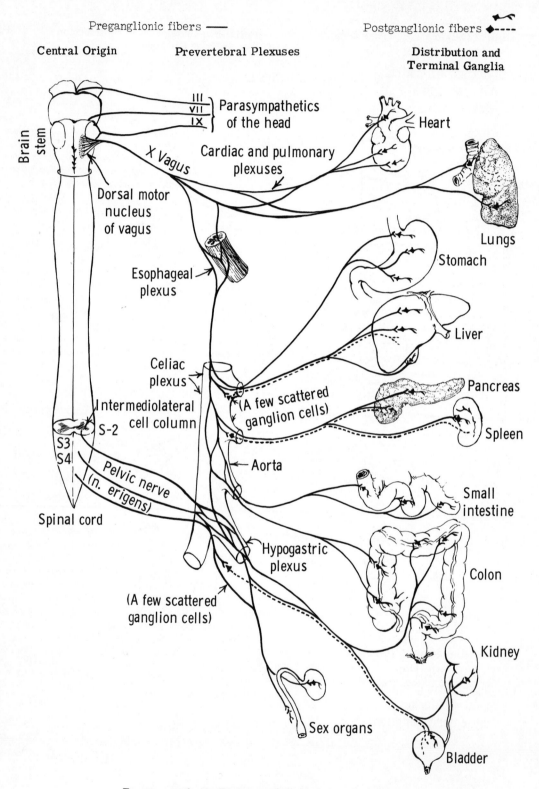

Preganglionic fibers ———   Postganglionic fibers ◆----

Central Origin   Prevertebral Plexuses   Distribution and
                                                        Terminal Ganglia

Brain stem

III
VII   } Parasympathetics
IX   of the head

X Vagus

Cardiac and pulmonary plexuses

Heart

Dorsal motor nucleus of vagus

Lungs

Esophageal plexus

Stomach

Liver

Celiac plexus

Pancreas

(A few scattered ganglion cells)

Intermediolateral cell column

S-2

Spleen

S3
S4

Aorta

Pelvic nerve (n. erigens)

Spinal cord

Small intestine

Hypogastric plexus

Colon

(A few scattered ganglion cells)

Kidney

Sex organs

Bladder

Parasympathetic Division of the Autonomic System

The Parasympathetic (or Craniosacral) Division.

The parasympathetic division of the autonomic nervous system arises from preganglionic cell bodies in the gray matter of the brain stem and the middle 3 segments of the sacral cord. The parasympathetic distribution, in contrast to that of the sympathetics, is confined entirely to visceral structures. Most of its preganglionic neurons run without interruption from their central origin to the wall of the viscus they supply, or where they synapse with terminal ganglion cells associated with the plexuses of Meissner and Auerbach in the intestinal tract. (The parasympathetic supply in the head follows a unique pattern which is outlined below.)

Nerves conveying parasympathetic fibers (preganglionic) consist of the **vagus nerve** (cranial nerve X), which distributes its autonomic fibers to the thoracic and abdominal viscera via the prevertebral plexuses; the **pelvic nerve** (nervus erigens), which distributes parasympathetics to most of the large intestine and to the pelvic viscera and genitalia via the hypogastric plexus; and **cranial nerves III, VII, and IX,** which distribute parasympathetics to the head.

The Great Prevertebral Plexuses of the Autonomic System.

These are large networks of nerves which serve as areas of redistribution for the sympathetic and parasympathetic (and sensory) fibers which enter into their formation. The cardiac plexus is located about the bifurcation of the trachea and roots of the great vessels at the base of the heart. It is divided into superficial and deep parts. It is formed from the cardiac sympathetic nerves and cardiac branches of the vagus nerve, which it distributes to the myocardium and walls of the vessels leaving the heart. The **right and left pulmonary plexuses** are intimately joined with the cardiac plexus and are located about the primary bronchi and pulmonary arteries at the roots of the lungs. They are formed from both the vagus and the upper thoracic sympathetic nerves and are distributed mainly to the vessels and bronchi of the lung.

The **celiac (or solar) plexus** is located in the epigastric region of the abdomen over the abdominal aorta near the origin of the celiac and superior mesenteric arteries. It is formed from vagal fibers reaching it via the esophageal plexus and sympathetic fibers arising from the associated celiac ganglia which are located on the sides of the celiac axis, together with some sympathetic fibers continued down from the thoracic aortic plexus. Its distribution includes most of the abdominal viscera, which it reaches by numerous subplexuses continued out along the various visceral branches of the aorta. These plexuses include the phrenic plexuses, the hepatic plexus, the splenic plexus, the superior gastric plexus, the suprarenal plexuses, the renal plexuses, the spermatic or ovarian plexuses, the superior and inferior mesenteric plexuses, and the abdominal aortic plexus.

The **hypogastric plexus** is located in front of the fifth lumbar vertebra and the promontory of the sacrum. It receives sympathetic fibers from the aortic plexus and lumbar trunk ganglia and parasympathetic fibers from the pelvic nerve. Its 2 lateral portions, the pelvic plexuses, lie on either side of the rectum. Distribution to the pelvic viscera and genitalia is effected by subplexuses extending out along the visceral branches of the hypogastric artery. These include the middle hemorrhoidal plexus, to the rectum; the vesical plexus, to the bladder, seminal vesicles, and ductus deferens; the prostatic plexus to the prostate, seminal vesicles, and penis; the vaginal plexus, to the vagina and clitoris; and the uterine plexus, to the uterus and uterine tubes.

AUTONOMIC NERVES TO THE HEAD

The autonomic supply to the head deserves special consideration. The skin of the face and scalp receives sympathetic innervation from the superior cervical ganglion via plexuses extending along the branches of the external carotid artery. The intrinsic muscles of the eye, salivary glands, and mucous membranes of the nose and pharynx, however, receive a dual autonomic supply. This is mediated via 4 pairs of cranial autonomic ganglia, each of which receives a sympathetic, a parasympathetic, and a sensory root. Only the parasympathetic fibers effect synaptic connections within these ganglia, which contain the cell bodies of the postganglionic parasympathetic fibers. The sympathetic and sensory fibers pass through these ganglia without interruption.

The **ciliary ganglion** is located between the optic nerve and the lateral rectus muscle in the posterior part of the orbit. It is composed of a **parasympathetic root**, which originates from cells of the Edinger-Westphal nucleus and the upper medial oculomotor nucleus, fibers of which reach the ganglion via

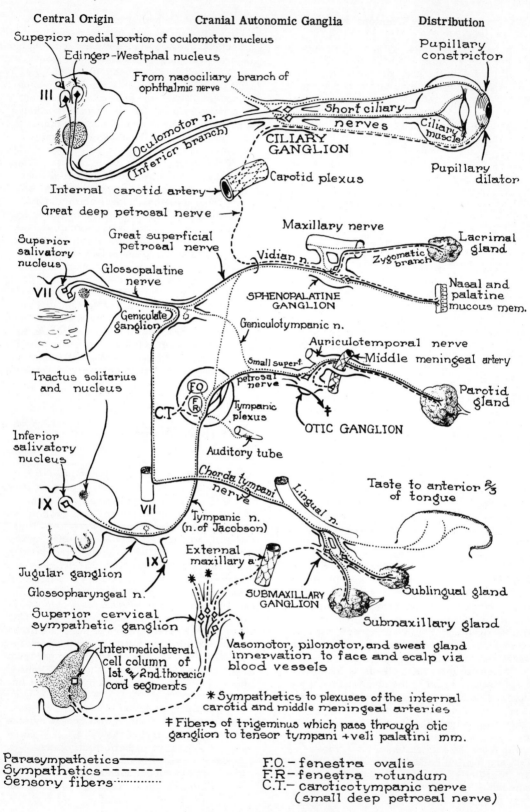

Autonomic Nerves to the Head

the inferior division of the oculomotor nerve; a **sympathetic root**, consisting of postsynaptic fibers from the superior cervical sympathetic ganglion via the carotid plexus about the internal carotid artery; and a **sensory root** from the nasociliary branch of the ophthalmic nerve. Distribution is via 12-15 short ciliary nerves, which supply the ciliary muscle of the lens and the muscles of the iris.

The **sphenopalatine ganglion** is located deep in the pterygopalatine fossa and associated with the maxillary nerve. It is composed of a **parasympathetic root** from cells of the superior salivatory nucleus via the glosso-palatine nerve, great superficial petrosal nerve, and vidian nerve through the pterygoid (vidian) canal (see diagram, p. 140); a **sympathetic root** from the internal carotid plexus via the great deep petrosal nerve, which joins the great superficial petrosal nerve to form the vidian nerve; and **sensory fibers**, most of which originate in the maxillary nerve but a few of which arise in cranial nerves VII and IX via the tympanic plexus and vidian nerve. Distribution is via pharyngeal rami to the mucous membranes of the roof of the pharynx; via nasal and palatine rami to the mucous membranes of the nasal cavity, uvula, palatine tonsil, and hard and soft palates; and via orbital rami to the periosteum of the orbit and the lacrimal glands. **Vail's syndrome** consists of severe attacks of unilateral, often nocturnal neuralgic pains of nose, face, eye, neck, and shoulder, attributed to neuralgia of the vidian nerve.

The **otic ganglion** is located medial to the mandibular nerve just below the foramen ovale in the infratemporal fossa. It is composed of **parasympathetic root** fibers arising in the inferior salivatory nucleus in the medulla, which course via the ninth cranial nerve, the tympanic plexus, and the lesser superficial petrosal nerve (see p. 140); a **sympathetic root** from the superior cervical sympathetic ganglion via the plexus on the middle meningeal artery; and a **sensory root**, which probably includes fibers from the ninth cranial nerve and from the geniculate ganglion of the seventh cranial nerve via the tympanic plexus and the lesser superficial petrosal nerve. The otic ganglion supplies secretory and sensory fibers to the parotid gland. A few somatic motor fibers from the trigeminal nerve pass through the otic ganglion and supply the tensor tympani and tensor veli palatini muscles.

The **submaxillary ganglion** is located on the medial side of the mandible between the lingual nerve and the submaxillary duct. It is composed of **parasympathetic root** fibers from the superior salivatory nucleus via the glosso-palatine, chorda tympani, and lingual nerves; a **sympathetic root** from the plexus of the external maxillary artery; and a **sensory root** from the geniculate ganglion via the glosso-palatine, chorda tympani, and lingual nerves. It is distributed to the submaxillary and sublingual glands.

AUTONOMIC NERVES TO THE UROGENITAL ORGANS AND RECTUM

URINARY BLADDER

The urinary bladder and sphincters are under the control of the autonomic nervous system. Major integrating centers are in the spinal cord, and these may be considered to be both sympathetic and parasympathetic in type.

Sympathetic Innervation.

A. Afferent fibers are believed to pass from their origin in the body of the bladder (detrusor muscle) through the hypogastric plexus to the upper lumbar sympathetic ganglia, then through the posterior upper lumbar nerve roots to terminate in the intermediolateral cells of the second and third lumbar segments of the spinal cord. Pain and proprioceptive sensation from the bladder may be conveyed along this route.

B. Efferent fibers are said to then proceed via the anterior second and third lumbar nerve roots as white rami through the sympathetic ganglia to the hypogastric plexus, whence gray rami then innervate the detrusor muscle and internal sphincter. This system is felt to be concerned with bladder filling, the efferent fibers being inhibitory to the bladder detrusor and motor to the internal sphincter.

Parasympathetic Innervation.

A. Afferent fibers are believed to pass via the pudendal nerve to the first to third sacral posterior nerve roots, entering and terminating in the anterolateral gray matter of the sacral spinal cord at this level. These fibers are assumed to convey pain, touch, temperature, and muscle stretch sensation from the bladder and internal sphincter.

B. Efferent fibers pass from the first to third sacral segments of the spinal cord as preganglionic fibers to the hypogastric plexus, whence postganglionic fibers emerge to innervate the detrusor of the bladder and the internal sphincter. These fibers are believed to be motor to the detrusor and inhibitory to the internal sphincter. Their role in emptying the bladder is comparatively more potent in effect upon the detrusor than the bladder sympathetic fibers; on the other hand, they are less important in inhibitory action upon the internal sphincter.

The **external sphincter** is innervated by pudendal nerve branches which arise in the anterior horns of S2, 3, 4 segments of the spinal cord and which leave via the corresponding anterior roots (pudendal plexus). These fibers are felt to be motor for the external sphincter (and perineal musculature), which are under predominantly voluntary control. Afferent fibers within the pudendal nerve convey sensation from the external sphincter and the posterior urethra.

Suprasegmental Innervation.

Cortical representation of the bladder is present in the paracentral lobule, whose stim-

ulation may evoke bladder contractions. This system may play a part in initiating voluntary micturition and in stopping micturition by initiating contraction of the external sphincter. Other higher level representation is believed to occur also, but the specific participating structures remain obscure.

Physiology of Bladder Function.

The ability to voluntarily relax the perineal muscles is essential to initiate urination, and normal tone of the pelvic diaphragm is necessary for urinary continence. Cinefluorographic studies indicate that the voluntary muscles of micturition are the levator and the sphincter urethrae and the bulbocavernosus (in the male). As voiding is initiated, a progressive descent of the pelvic diaphragm occurs and the posterior urethra fills. As the diaphragm reaches its most inferior level there occurs a wave-like detrusor contraction which continues uninterrupted until the bladder is emptied. If the urinary stream is voluntarily interrupted, the contraction of the external sphincter interrupts the urethral

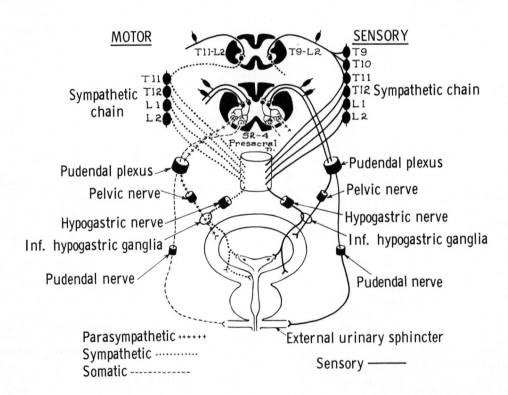

Segmental and Peripheral Innervation of the Urinary Bladder. (Reproduced, with permission, from Bors, J.Nerv. & Mental Dis. **116**:572-8, 1952.)

stream; simultaneously, the pelvic diaphragm rapidly elevates the bladder. The distal urethra in the female then empties immediately; in the male, contraction of the bulbourethral muscle occurs to empty the distal urethra.

The bladder wall musculature, through variation in muscle tone, tends to maintain a relatively constant intravesical pressure despite varying volumes of urine. The desire to urinate usually occurs when intravesical pressure reaches about 5 mm. Hg.

Voluntary micturition may be initiated even when the bladder contains only a small amount of urine. Suprasegmental stimulation, presumably arising from the paracentral lobe of the cerebral hemisphere, activates contraction of the detrusor, with relaxation of the internal and external sphincters. Associated voluntary contraction of the abdominal wall muscles plus contraction of the diaphragm with closure of the glottis, thus raising the intra-abdominal pressure, may also occur.

Following urination, voluntary contraction of the ischiocavernosus and bulbocavernosus muscles and the external sphincter (compressor urethrae) closes off the bladder. Strong voluntary contractions of these muscles are required to interrupt the act of urination.

Suprasegmental, higher level inhibition may be overcome involuntarily when intravesical pressure reaches a very high level, the detrusor muscle contracting and the external sphincter relaxing. Involuntary urination in response to smaller quantities of urine may occur in a pathologically affected bladder or under emotional stress.

Disorders of Bladder Function.

After acute transection of the spinal cord, control of micturition by higher centers is abolished. Complete retention occurs as a result of paralysis of the detrusor muscle and the tonic status of the internal sphincter. Overflow incontinence results from the rise of intravesical pressure, overcoming the tone of the internal sphincter. Days or weeks later a **reflex bladder** occurs, with automatic evacuation of the bladder taking place (sometimes aided by increased intra-abdominal extravesical pressure). A mass reflex may precipitate or assist emptying of bladder by increased extravesical pressure resulting from abdominal muscle spasm. **Automatic bladder** may also occur when innervation from segmental spinal connection is interrupted, as in the cauda equina syndromes.

In diseases involving the afferent pathways to the CNS (such as tabes dorsalis), distention of the bladder with accumulation of urine may result, presumably because of interruption of the sensory path leading from the bladder. Involuntary automatic urinary expulsion and subsequent dribbling of urine may then occur as a result of the reaction of the bladder wall musculature and a rise in intravesical pressure above that of the internal sphincter. Disorders involving the sympathetic pathway may give rise to dilatation of ureteral orifices, relaxation of internal sphincters, and frequency of urination.

Impaired sacral parasympathetic action at the spinal cord level may cause **flaccid paralysis** of the bladder wall. If this is incomplete, difficult and inadequate evacuation may result and residual urine will collect in the bladder. Automatic periodic expulsion of urine may occur later. Hypesthesia or anesthesia, with partial retention and overflow incontinence, may occur in congenital spinal cord disorders associated with lumbosacral spina bifida.

In children urinary control is self-taught. Enuresis can be stopped when the bladder can hold 300-350 ml. The ability to initiate or stop micturition develops when the child learns how to control abdominal pressure by coordination of the levator ani, the abdominal muscles, and the diaphragm. The bladder enlarges in children and, by the age of $4\frac{1}{2}$ years, is usually sufficient to hold the nightly output of urine. The ability to initiate micturition comes between $3\frac{1}{2}$-6 years. Contraction of the diaphragm and abdominal musculature and relaxation of the pubococcygeus muscle depress the vesicle neck and initiate detrusor contraction, which expels urine. Treatment of enuresis by increasing bladder capacity by means of forcing fluids and instructing the child to hold his urine as long as possible may be effective. Drugs such as atropine sulfate given during the daytime and at night may help relax the bladder detrusor and promote bladder distention.

DEFECATION

The mechanisms involved in defecation are believed to be more or less similar to those of micturition. The afferent fibers enter the S3, 4, 5 segments of the spinal cord. The external anal sphincter is under voluntary control; its action is less important than that of the internal anal sphincter. Distention of the walls of the rectum is felt to be an adequate stimulus for defecation, producing contraction of the rectal muscles and relaxation of the internal anal sphincter. Stimulation of lower sacral dermatomes and bladder activity facilitate more complete response.

Abdominal wall muscular action (sixth to twelfth thoracic spinal cord segments) is under voluntary control and may act as a detrusor mechanism. Transverse lesions of the spinal cord may not affect internal anal sphincter tone, but the resultant impaired contraction of the rectal wall may lead to fecal retention. Intermittent rectal incontinence may also be encountered with lesions of the spinal cord above the lower sacral level. With lesions of the third, fourth, and fifth sacral spinal cord segments, fecal incontinence is apt to occur, especially if the stool is soft or fluid. Anesthesia of the anal area may occur with lesions of the conus medullaris or tabes dorsalis, resulting in loss of internal sphincter tone and reflex activity, with incontinence. Automatic rectal activity, like automatic bladder activity, may occur independently of CNS connections of the terminal bowel.

SEXUAL FUNCTION

The male sexual organs are innervated by 2 sets of fibers. **Parasympathetic** fibers, originating in intermediolateral cells of the second, third, and fourth sacral spinal segments, pass via the pelvic nerves to form perivesicular, prostatic, and cavernous plexuses. Vasodilator fibers pass to the corpora cavernosa. The compressor urethrae and the ischiocavernosus and bulbocavernosus muscles, which are concerned in erection and ejaculation, are innervated by the perineal branch of the pudendal nerve (S2, 3, 4). **Sympathetic** nerves to the sexual organs come from the lumbar spinal cord via the hypogastric plexus. Fibers from the hypogastric plexus and fibers from the pelvic nerves form the perivesicular plexuses. The dorsal nerves of the penis are believed to carry sympathetic fibers causing vasoconstriction in the corpora cavernosa and resultant relaxation of penis.

Erection results from parasympathetic stimulation and is effected by engorgement of the corpora cavernosa. A purely spinal reflex erection may follow stimulation of the glans penis. Erections presumably upon a purely hormonal basis without spinal cord or higher level participation may occur. Relaxation of the penis following ejaculation is believed to be due to decreased stimulation via the pelvic nerves and contraction of the smooth muscle of the corpora cavernosa, innervated by sympathetic fibers. Emotional changes such as anger or fear, or the application of cold to the skin of the trunk, may lead to relaxation of the erect penis.

Ejaculation involves reflex patterns originating in the genital corpuscles of the glans. By way of the dorsal nerve of the penis and the common pudendal nerves, impulses enter the posterior roots of the S2, 3, 4 spinal cord segments, also travelling in part to the upper lumbar spinal cord. From the upper lumbar spinal cord the rami communicantes pass via the hypogastric nerves to the perivesicular and prostatic plexuses, from which the unstriated musculature of the ductus deferens, the seminal vesicles, and the prostate are innervated. It is felt that soon after activation of the upper lumbar reflex mechanisms, sacral spinal cord stimulation of muscle fibers of the compressor urethrae and the bulbocavernosus and ischiocavernosus muscles leads to their clonic contraction. **Nocturnal** ejaculations presumably do not require the same stimuli as do ejaculations in the waking state. Sleep probably depresses the inhibitory effects of higher centers on spinal cord reflex mechanisms.

Orgasm is made up of the associated reactions and sensations occurring with ejaculation of semen in men and probably with expulsion of secretions from Bartholin's glands and mucous from the cavity of the uterus in women. Autonomic effects, such as increase in heart rate and blood pressure and altered respiratory patterns, may occur. Tonic contractions of the thigh muscles may accompany orgasm.

PHYSIOLOGY OF THE AUTONOMIC SYSTEM

The Sympathetic Division.

The sympathetic division of the autonomic nervous system is thrown into activity in preparation of the organism for "flight or fight." It gives rise to mass responses as a possible consequence of the existence of sympathetic ganglion chains or plexuses where the preganglionic synapse occurs. In action it tends to produce vasoconstriction of the skin and viscera, shifting more blood to the brain, skeletal muscles, and heart. Removal of the sympathetic chain in animals and man may lower blood pressure and body temperature.

The Parasympathetic Division.

The parasympathetic division, on the other hand, tends to give more localized reactions, and this may be related to the anatomic fact that the preganglionic synapse is usually embedded in the organ to be affected.

Functional Antagonism of the Two Systems.

The viscera receive a dual autonomic supply. In most cases the 2 sets of nerves function antagonistically to one another. However, some autonomic effectors appear to have a sympathetic nerve supply only. In some cases, where there is a dual nerve supply, the action of the 2 divisions (sympathetic and parasympathetic) may not be antagonistic. Classification of autonomic postganglionic neurons as adrenergic or cholinergic may be more useful clinically and functionally than their classification as sympathetic and parasympathetic. Most (but not all) sympathetic postganglionic elements are adrenergic. Most (but probably not all) parasympathetic postganglionic elements are cholinergic.

Autonomic Representation of the Cerebral Cortex.

Autonomic representation also takes place within the cerebral cortex and indicates that higher integration may occur. Autonomic and motor cortical overlapping often occurs, as demonstrated by lacrimation and pupillary changes on stimulation of the eye field area of the cortex (Brodmann area 8) and the production of conjugate ocular movements. Blood pressure changes, inhibition of respiration, vasoconstriction and vasodilatation, gastrointestinal hypermotility, salivation, and abnormalities of sweating have been produced by cortical stimulation. Cardiovascular reactions may occur after stimulation of Brodmann areas 4 and 6; elevation or depression of blood pressure, alteration of heart rate, and vasoconstriction and vasodilatation of the blood vessels of the extremities have been described. Respiration may be inhibited by stimulation of the orbital surface (area 47), cingulate gyrus (area 24), the anterior portion of the insula, and the tip of the temporal lobe (area 38). Sweat secretion is altered by area 6 stimulation. Gastrointestinal function may be affected by cortical stimulation. Increased peristaltic movement and gastric secretion may follow stimulation of area 8, and inhibition of the gastric musculature may follow stimulation of area 47. Evidence of marked hunger is evident in animals with premotor ablation. Salivation may occur following stimulation of the motor area of the tongue and face (area 4). Urinary incontinence may follow bilateral lesions of the portions of areas 4 and 6 lying on the medial surface of the cerebral hemispheres.

Integration of autonomic activity at other suprasegmental levels can occur. The medulla oblongata integrates sweating reflexes and blood pressure alterations. The hypothalamus affects heat regulation (peripheral vasoconstriction, vasodilatation, and sweating).

PHARMACOLOGY OF THE AUTONOMIC SYSTEM

Studies of the effects of drugs on the autonomic system have added greatly to our knowledge of these nerves. The diagram below (adapted from Myerson) serves to illustrate the site of action of the principal autonomic drugs.

Sympathin, an epinephrine-like substance, may be liberated at most sympathetic postganglionic neuro-effector junctions. Similarly, **acetylcholine** is liberated at parasympathetic postganglionic neuro-effector junctions. Acetylcholine may be rapidly broken down by the enzyme cholinesterase. Acetylcholine is also liberated at ganglionic synapses, sympathetic or parasympathetic (see p. 71).

When autonomic effectors (smooth muscle, cardiac muscle, or glands) are partially or completely separated from their normal nerve connections, they become more sensitive to the action of chemical substances. This effect is more pronounced after postganglionic as opposed to preganglionic interruption. This sensitization was formulated by Cannon as a "law of denervation."

DISORDERS OF THE AUTONOMIC SYSTEM

Disturbances Clearly Related to Autonomic Involvement.

Horner's syndrome is a unilateral enophthalmos, ptosis, miosis, and flushing of the face often caused by an ipsilateral involvement of the sympathetic fibers in the cervical sympathetic chain or upper thoracic cord.

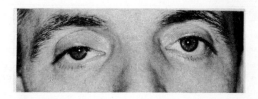

Horner's Syndrome. Right Horner's syndrome associated with right superior sulcus lung tumor.

Responses of Effector Organs to Autonomic Nerve Impulses in Man*

	Adrenergic Impulses	Cholinergic Impulses
Eye		
Iris	Mydriasis	Miosis
Ciliary muscle	Relaxed for far vision (slight effect)	Accommodated for near vision
Heart		
Rate	Accelerated	Slowed
Output	Increased	Decreased
Rhythm	Ventricular extrasystoles, tachycardia, fibrillation	Bradycardia, atrioventricular block, vagal arrest
Blood vessels		
Coronary	Dilated	?
Skin and mucosa	Constricted	--
Skeletal muscle	Constricted†	Dilated‡
Cerebral	Constricted (slight)	--
Pulmonary	Constricted	--
Abdominal viscera	Constricted†	--
Lung		
Bronchial muscle	Relaxed	Constricted
Bronchial glands	?	Stimulated
Stomach		
Motility and tone	Decreased	Increased
Sphincters	Contracted as a rule	Relaxed as a rule
Secretion	Inhibited	Increased, particularly enzymes
Intestine		
Motility and tone	Decreased	Increased
Sphincters	Contracted as a rule	Relaxed as a rule
Secretion	?	Increased
Gallbladder	Relaxed	Contracted
Urinary bladder		
Detrusor	--	Contracted
Trigone and internal sphincter	--	Relaxed
Ureter		
Tone and motility	Decreased	--
Uterus	Variable§	Variable§
Skin		
Pilomotor muscles	Contracted	--
Sweat glands	Slight, localized secretion**	Generalized secretion
Spleen capsule	Contracted	--
Adrenal medulla	--	Secretion of epinephrine and norepinephrine
Salivary glands		
Parotid gland	No secretion	Profuse, watery secretion
Submaxillary gland	Thick, viscous secretion	Profuse, watery secretion
Pancreatic islets	--	Insulin secretion
Lacrimal glands	--	Secretion
Nasopharyngeal glands	--	Secretion
Autonomic ganglion cells	--	Stimulated

The somatic nerve supply to skeletal muscle is cholinergic.

*Modified from Goodman & Gilman: The Pharmacological Basis of Therapeutics, 2nd ed. Macmillan, 1955.

†Epinephrine from the adrenal medulla dilates the blood vessels of liver and muscle, constricts other vessels.

‡Cholinergic sympathetic vasodilator system causes vasodilatation in skeletal muscle.

§Depends on stage of menstrual cycle, amount of circulating estrogen and progesterone, and other factors. Responses of pregnant uterus different from those of nonpregnant.

**On palms of hands and in some other locations ("adrenergic sweating").

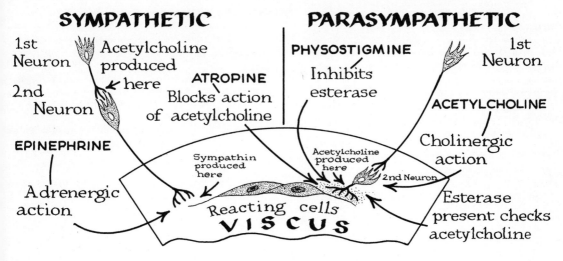

Sites of Action of Drugs on a Viscus

Hirschsprung's disease (megacolon) consists of a tremendous dilatation of the colon with chronic constipation. It is associated with congenital lack of parasympathetic ganglia and the existence of abnormal nerve fibrils in an apparently normal segment of large bowel wall. **Spinal shock** or **diaschisis** is a type of vascular failure possibly due to sudden release of sympathetic vasomotor tone resulting from transection of or severe injury to the spinal cord, or from an overdose of spinal anesthesia.

Vasomotor, Trophic, and Secretory Disturbances.

Disturbances occurring in the affected tissues in various central and peripheral nerve injuries may be partly the result of interruption of the sympathetic fibers, but the importance of concomitant circulatory disturbances and disuse must not be overlooked. Included in this group are muscle atrophy, skin and nail changes, etc., which are described under Trophic Changes on p. 215.

Trophoneuroses.

These are probably related to autonomic dysfunction. **Acroparesthesia** is a slowly progressive disorder most commonly found in women of middle age and characterized by crawling and tingling sensations, usually of the hands, and often associated with pain, hyperesthesia, hyperalgesia, and coldness of the hands. Some claim it is a mild form of Raynaud's disease (see below). **Erythromelalgia** (Weir Mitchell's disease) is a rare condition of middle life characterized by periodic reddening of the skin and severe pain in one or more extremities. Attacks seldom last more than a few hours, and are associated with

marked hyperalgesia and sweating of the affected parts. Trophic changes usually develop in the skin and nails.

Raynaud's disease is a disease of young women which affects the toes, fingers, the borders of the ears, and the tip of the nose and spreads to involve large areas. Beginning with local changes, when the parts are pale and cold, it may progress to local asphyxia characterized by a blue-gray cyanosis and, finally symmetrical dry gangrene. It is a disorder of the peripheral vascular innervation. **Scleroderma** is a diffuse or circumscribed thickening of the skin which may be accompanied by or follow Raynaud's disease or other vasomotor-trophic disturbances. **Angioneurotic edema** (Quincke's disease) consists of attacks of acute circumscribed nonpitting edema occurring on the arms or face and preceded by general malaise, chills, and slight fever. It may be precipitated by emotional stresses, but lasts only a few hours. In rare cases death has resulted from involvement of the respiratory passages. **Hereditary trophedema** (Milroy's disease) is a rare chronic, familial nonpitting edema of one or more extremities, producing local elephantiasis.

Lipodystrophy is a rare affection, more common in women, characterized by wasting of the fatty tissues of the upper part of the body and excessive obesity of the hips and lower extremities. **Progressive facial hemiatrophy** (Romberg's disease) is a rare disorder of early life characterized by marked wasting of one side of the face. Total hemiatrophy, an allied condition, is even less common.

Morvan's disease is a term applied to the atrophic changes of the bones, skin, and muscles of the hand in syringomyelia. **Adiposis dolorosa** (Dercum's disease) is characterized by large painful lumps or layers of fat over the shoulders, arms, and legs, usually in women. The cause is not known. **Hemiedema** is a unilateral edema associated with hemiplegia.

Causalgia is a painful condition of the hands or feet caused by irritation of the median or sciatic nerve by injury and characterized by severe burning pain, glossy skin, swelling, redness, sweating, and trophic nail changes. Causalgia may frequently be relieved by sympathetic blocks or sympathectomy of the involved areas.

The **Riley-Day syndrome** (familial dysautonomia) is characterized by defective lacrimation, absence of tears on crying, excessive sweating, sialorrhea, emotional lability, symmetric blotchy erythema upon emotional stress or eating, relative indifference to pain, poor motor coordination, hyporeflexia, postural hypotension, and behavioral difficulties. This congenital condition is seen most often in children of Jewish extraction. Response to intradermal histamine (1:1000) may serve as a diagnostic test since the usual zone of erythema ("flare") is absent in affected subjects.

•   •   •

7...

Muscle

COMPOSITION OF MUSCLE

The chemical composition of muscle has been most completely studied in striated muscle, where it consists of 75% water, 20% protein, and 5% inorganic material, organic "extractives," and carbohydrates (glycogen and its derivatives).

Muscle Proteins.

The muscle fibrils are mainly protein, and these fibrillar proteins are characterized by their elasticity, or contractile power.

A. Myosin: Myosin is the most abundant protein in muscle, and probably the only protein in the fibril. Other muscle proteins are extracellular in origin. Myosin is a globulin, soluble in dilute salt solution and insoluble in water. In the presence of ATP (adenosinetriphosphate), a complex of actin and myosin (actomyosin) dissociates into actin and myosin A, accompanied by muscular contraction. The energy for the contraction is supplied by the breakdown of ATP to ADP (adenosinediphosphate), a reaction catalyzed by adenosinetriphosphatase (ATPase).

B. Actin: Also has been isolated from muscle.

C. Globulin X: After myosin has been removed from a saline extract of muscle, globulin X remains. It is believed to be a protein of the sarcoplasm. It coagulates at 50°C. and has a molecular weight of about 160,000.

D. Myogen: This is another protein of sarcoplasm and probably an albumin. One myogen fraction is said to have enzymatic properties.

E. Myoglobin: This conjugated protein, often called muscle hemoglobin, is similar to hemoglobin and may function as an oxygen carrier. The molecular weight of myoglobin is one-fourth that of hemoglobin. In crush injuries and some muscle disorders, myoglobin appears in the urine. It may precipitate in the renal tubules, causing obstruction of the tubules and anuria.

Muscle Extractives.

A variety of compounds can be easily extracted from muscle with water, alcohol, or ether. Those containing nitrogen include creatine and phosphocreatine; the purines, adenine, guanine, xanthine, hypoxanthine, uric acid, and adenylic acid (from ATP); carnosine, anserine, and the betaine, carnitine.

Other extractives of muscle (nonnitrogenous) are mainly glycogen and its derivatives formed in glycolysis.

Inorganic Constituents of Muscle.

The cations of muscle include potassium, sodium, magnesium, and calcium, with potassium characteristically high. The anions include phosphate, chloride, and small amounts of sulfate.

Intracellular potassium is important in muscle metabolism. A considerable amount of potassium is incorporated into tissue when glycogen is deposited in muscle and when protein is being synthesized. Muscle weakness is associated often with potassium deficiency. Calcium and magnesium of muscle appear to function as activators or inhibitors of intramuscular enzyme systems.

STRUCTURE OF MUSCLE

Muscles usually are classified as striated or smooth depending upon their appearance under an ordinary light microscope. **Striated muscle** is made up of muscle fibers which may run the whole length of the muscle and join with tendons at its ends. Around each fiber is an electrically polarized membrane, the inside of which is about 100 millivolts negative with respect to the outside. If this membrane is temporarily depolarized, the muscle fiber contracts. The nerve impulse traveling down the motor nerve is transmitted at the motor endplate and then a wave of depolarization ("action potential") sweeps down the muscle fiber and in some way causes a single twitch.

The great mass of somatic musculature is striated. It has well developed cross-striations; usually does not contract in the absence of nervous stimulation; lacks anatomic and functional connections between individual muscle fibers; and is generally under voluntary control. Cardiac muscle also has cross-striations but appears functionally to be syncytial and contracts rhythmically even when denervated. Smooth muscle, present in walls of blood vessels and most hollow viscera, is sometimes syncytial and has inherent rhythmic contractile activity.

Striated muscle in man may also be classified grossly as red or white. The red or "slow" muscles contain more myoglobin, have less evident striations, respond more slowly, and have a longer latency than the white. They are adapted for long, slow posture-maintaining contractures. (The long muscles of the back are typical examples.) White muscles are "fast," have fewer muscle fibers per motor unit and short twitch durations, and are specialized for fine skilled movements. Extraocular muscles and hand muscles belong to the white muscle group. Eccles has found that in kittens the muscle changes from slow to fast when single nerve fibers are crossed from fast to slow muscles, suggesting that a nerve cell affects the properties of the muscle it innervates.

In mammalian skeletal muscle at least 2 different histologic and morphologic types of striated muscle fibers occur. These are known as type I and type II fibers, and histochemical differences between the 2 types of fibers are being established. Differences between the 2 fiber types have been noted in their glycogen, phosphorylase, cytochrome oxidase, several dehydrogenases, etc. by histochemical methods.

The chemical reactions, which are the source of energy for muscle contraction, must be controlled not only by the changes in length of the muscle but also by the tension placed on the muscle during the change. The contractile structure of muscle consists mostly of protein (myosin, actin, and tropomyosin). Myosin is especially abundant and can catalyze the removal of a phosphate group from ATP, a reaction closely associated with the events of contraction. Myosin and actin in solution can combine to form a complex known as actomyosin, and threads of actomyosin contract in the presence of ATP.

The striated appearance of skeletal muscle arises from a repeating variation in the density,

Electron Micrograph of Skeletal Muscle of Rabbit (X24,000), Showing Z-Lines (Narrow Dark Bands) and A-Bands (Broad Dark Bands) (Reproduced, with permission, from Huxley: The contraction of muscle. Scientific American 199:66 [Nov.], 1958.)

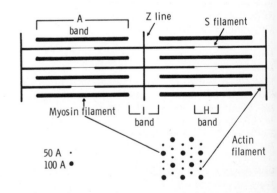

Probable Arrangement of Filaments Within Muscle Fibril. Longitudinal section at the top, cross section through A-band at the bottom. (Redrawn and reproduced, with permission, from Huxley: Muscle structure and theories of contraction. Progress in Biophysics 7:255, 1957.)

i. e., the concentration of protein along the myofibril. There is a regular alternation of dense bands (A-bands) and light bands (I-bands). The central region of the A-band, known as the H-zone, is often less dense than the rest of this band. The Z-membrane, or Z-line, is a dense narrow line that bisects the I-band. The area between 2 adjacent Z-lines is called a sarcomere.

Electron microscopy indicates that myofibrils contain 2 types of filament, one twice as thick as the other. The thick filaments are believed to be myosin (mol. wt. about 800,000) and the thin filaments actin (mol. wt. about 70,000). Overlapping of filaments is believed to give rise to the striations or cross-bands of the myofibril. Changes in pattern occur during contraction, when it is believed that the 2 sets of filaments (thick and thin) slide past each other.

FUNCTION OF MUSCLE

Upon effective stimulation several almost instantaneous transformations occur in muscle. The muscle shortens or attempts to shorten; and electrical, structural, chemical, and thermal changes occur which are reversible and can repeat themselves after very brief intervals, resulting in cycles of contraction and relaxation. Contraction of muscle under a constant load is called isotonic. Contraction at a constant length of muscle is called isometric contraction.

One of the factors determining muscle tension is the number of fibers or motor units activated by a given stimulus. A twitch is the response of skeletal muscle to a single nerve impulse. With a maximal single stimulus, all motor units are activated and maximal twitch tension or shortening is developed. If 2 maximal stimuli are delivered in quick enough succession so that the second stimulus arrives before the contraction cycle is over, the response is greater than that elicited by a single maximal stimulus to the single muscle fiber, motor unit, or whole muscle. There is thus a mechanical fusion or summation of contractions. The degree of fusion is greater when the stimulus interval is shortest; the degree of summation decreases as the interval between the stimuli approaches the duration of the single mechanical response.

When a series of repetitive stimuli are applied at a rate high enough to cause summation of contraction, it may be possible to cause complete mechanical fusion and a sustained smooth response, known as **tetanus**. The critical fusion rate (the frequency of stimulus necessary to produce a complete tetanus) is higher for "fast" muscle, with relatively brief contraction time, and lower for "slow" muscle with longer contraction.

Gradation of muscular activity may be affected also by such factors as the number of motor units activated, variations in stimulus frequency, and the arrival of impulses at various motor units nonsimultaneously.

Neuromuscular transmission refers to the process by which nerve impulse is converted into a muscle action current. Each nerve fiber terminates at a specialized region of the muscle fiber, a delicate and intricate arborization called the **end-plate**. The end-plate represents a localized specialization of the sarcolemma. Transmission of the nerve impulse to the muscle is across the neuromuscular or neuromyal junction, and it is at this junction that the muscle action current which stimulates contraction originates.

A nerve impulse produces a prolonged negative potential at the end-plate which is not propagated but is localized at the myoneural junction. This end-plate potential generates the muscle spike potential by depolarizing, to a critical level, the muscle membrane around the junction. The end-plate potential itself can be as large as the muscle spike potential. Neuromuscular delay refers to the time interval between the arrival of the nerve impulse at the terminals and the beginning of the end-plate potential.

Muscle action potentials resemble those of nerve (spike potentials and after-potentials). The muscle action potential is a conducted process, normally all-or-none in skeletal muscle, with a propagation rate of about 3 meters/second. The refractory period is related to the time necessary for repolarization of membrane. The muscle action potential serves as the trigger to an additional response of muscle, the mechanical response. The energy of the isotonic twitch may be 1000 times the energy of the muscle spike potential.

METABOLISM OF MUSCLE

The nerve impulse to the muscle initiates muscle contraction, and breakdown of ATP to ADP supplies the energy for this contraction. The resynthesis of ATP from ADP and phosphate (as well as that of phosphocreatine) is accomplished with the aid of energy from glycolytic mechanisms. The hydrolysis of phos-

phocreatine can also be used for prompt resynthesis of ATP. The maintenance of the activity
of the muscle is dependent upon a steady supply
of high-energy phosphate as ATP or phosphocreatine.

Resting muscle does not require breakdown of glycogen to secure energy. Sixty per
cent of the energy required for maintenance of
resting muscle can be obtained by direct use
of carbohydrates diffusing into tissues from the
blood. Other metabolites from the blood supply the remainder. Preformed stores of ATP
and phosphocreatine in the muscle may also be
called upon.

MUSCLE RECEPTORS

A large number of the nerve fibers of muscles are sensory in function. Sherrington estimated that at least 40% of nerve fibers innervating a given muscle subserve sensory rather
than motor end organs. Three major groups
or types of receptors in muscle have been recognized.

Muscle Spindles (Intrafusal Fibers).
The regular contractile units of muscle
are known as **extrafusal fibers.** In contrast,
the term **intrafusal fibers** refers to muscle
spindles, which are more embryonal in character and have less striations than the remaining muscle fibers. The intrafusal fibers (muscle spindles) are in parallel with the rest of
the muscle fibers, with the ends of their capsules attached to tendons at either end of the
muscle or to the sides of adjacent extrafusal
fibers.

The 2 ends of each intrafusal fiber (muscle spindle) are contractile, but the middle
portion (nuclear bag region) is considered to
be noncontractile. In this region are located
the annulospiral endings, continuous with
rapidly conducting afferent nerves ($8-12\,\mu$ in
diameter). These are wrapped around the
intrafusal fibers (muscle spindles) in a complex manner and serve as receptors for the
stretch reflex.

On either side of the annulospiral endings
are **flower-spray endings**, which are receptors
of smaller myelinated fibers and are also responsive to stretch, producing increased flexor
and decreased extensor motor neuron activity.

The gamma efferents or the small motor
nerve system are the motor supply to the
muscle spindle, distributed to the motor end-
plate on the contractile ends of the intrafusal
fibers.

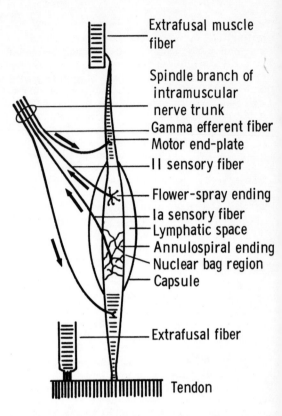

Extrafusal muscle
fiber

Spindle branch of
intramuscular
nerve trunk
Gamma efferent fiber
Motor end-plate
II sensory fiber

Flower-spray ending
Ia sensory fiber
Lymphatic space
Annulospiral ending
Nuclear bag region
Capsule

Extrafusal fiber

Tendon

Muscle Spindle (Highly Diagrammatic). Reproduced, with permission, from Ganong: Review
of Medical Physiology. Lange, 1963.)

Golgi Tendon Organs.
These lie in series with muscle fibers and
may serve to inhibit contractile responses
evoked by the muscle spindle (intrafusal fiber).
When the tension developed at a tendon becomes
of dangerous magnitude, active muscle contraction is automatically inhibited so that the
interaction of these 2 groups (Golgi tendon
organs and muscle spindles) assures smooth-
ness of muscle performance. The threshold
of Golgi tendon organs is considerably higher
than that of muscle spindles. The Golgi tendon organs are net-like collections of knobby
nerve endings among fascicles of a tendon.
These nerve fibers are myelinated and rapidly
conducting and are believed to end in the spinal
cord on inhibitory interneurons (Renshaw cells
which, in turn, terminate directly on motor
neurons to the same muscle.

Free Nerve Endings.

These have long been recognized in muscles, for the most part associated with blood vessels. Muscle pain can be evoked by deep palpation of the muscle mass or by squeezing the tendon.

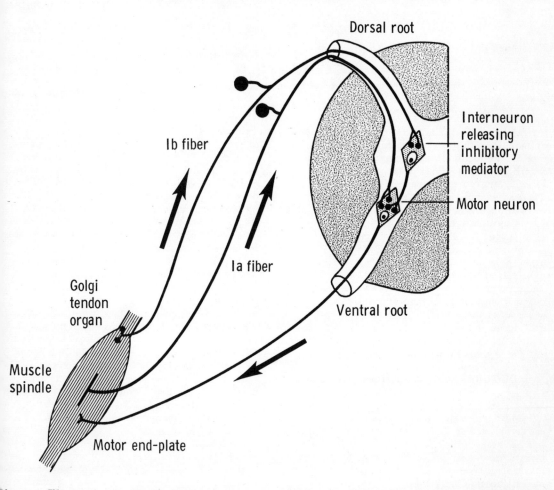

Diagram Illustrating the Pathways Responsible for the Stretch Reflex and the Inverse Stretch Reflex. Moderate stretch stimulates the spindle and impulses pass up the Ia fiber to excite the motor neuron. Strong stretch also stimulates the Golgi tendon organ, and impulses passing up the Ib fiber activate the interneuron to release inhibitory mediator and hyperpolarize the motor neuron. (Reproduced, with permission, from Ganong: Review of Medical Physiology. Lange, 1963.)

Section III: Principles of Neurodiagnosis

8...

Motion

Motion is a fundamental property of most animal life. In the simple unicellular animals motion and locomotion depend upon the contractility of protoplasm and the action of accessory organs such as cilia, flagella, etc. The lowest multicellular animals possess rudimentary neuromuscular mechanisms; in higher forms motion is based upon the transmission of impulses from a receptor through an afferent neuron and ganglion cell to muscle. This same principle is found in the reflex arc of higher animals, including man, in whom the anterior spinal cord has developed into a central regulating mechanism, the brain, which is concerned with initiating and integrating movements.

DISTURBANCES IN MOTOR POWER

Motor disturbances include weakness and paralysis, which may result from lesions of the voluntary motor pathways or of the muscles themselves. Impaired motor functioning may result from involvement of muscle, myoneural junction, peripheral nerve, or CNS.

The **lower motor neuron** (final common pathway) consists of a cell body located in the anterior gray column of the spinal cord or brain stem and an axon passing by way of the peripheral nerves to the motor end-plates of the muscles. It is the essential motor cell concerned with skeletal activity. It is called the "final common pathway" because it is acted upon by the corticospinal, rubrospinal, olivospinal, vestibulospinal, reticulospinal, and tectospinal tracts as well as by intersegmental and intrasegmental reflex neurons, and is the ultimate pathway through which neural impulses reach the muscle. **Lesions** of the lower motor neurons may be located in the cells of the ventral gray column of the spinal cord or brain stem or in their axons, which constitute the ventral roots and spinal nerves or the cranial nerves. Lesions may result

from trauma, toxins, infections, vascular disorders, degenerative processes, neoplasms, or congenital malformations. Signs of lower motor neuron lesions include flaccid paralysis of the involved muscles, muscle atrophy (with degeneration of muscle fibers), and reaction of degeneration (10-14 days after injury). Reflexes of the involved muscle are diminished or absent, and no pathologic reflexes are obtainable.

The **upper motor neuron** conveys impulses from the motor area of the cerebrum and is essential to voluntary muscular activity. It is the nerve cell of the motor cortex with its process which passes through the internal capsule, brain stem, and spinal cord by way of the corticobulbar or corticospinal tract to the lower motor neuron. **Lesions** of the upper motor neuron may be located in the cerebral cortex, the internal capsule, the cerebral peduncles, the brain stem, or the spinal cord. These may be due to birth injuries, neoplasms, inflammation, hemorrhage, thrombosis, degenerative processes, or trauma. Signs of upper motor neuron lesions include spastic paralysis or paresis of the involved muscles, little or no muscle atrophy (probably atrophy of disuse), and hyperactive deep reflexes, diminished or absent superficial reflexes, and pathologic reflexes and signs.

Muscle may be unable to react normally to stimuli conveyed to it by the lower motor neuron, manifesting weakness, paralysis, or tetanic contraction due to disturbances in the muscle itself or at the myoneural junction. Myasthenia gravis, myotonia congenita, and progressive muscular dystrophy are typical disorders characterized by muscular dysfunction in the presence of apparently normal nerve tissue.

According to Yakovlev, the vertebrate neuraxis may be considered to contain 3 longitudinal effector systems of neuronal assemblies arranged from within outward (see p. 157). The **innermost** system is diffuse and reticulate in its neuronal pattern. This arrangement is suited to slow propagation of

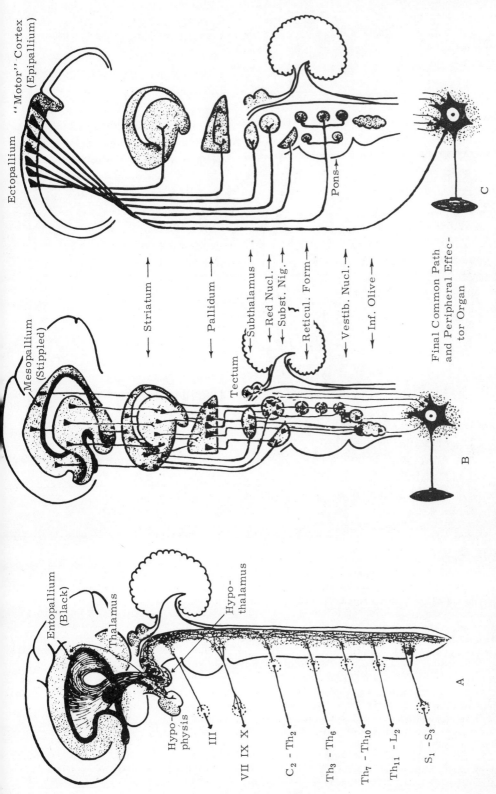

Effector Systems in the Neuraxis. A. Innermost system of visceration (reticulate system); B. Intermediate system of outward expression of internal states (nucleate system in series); C. Outermost system of effective transaction with the world about (stratilaminate system in parallel). (Reproduced, with permission, from Yakovlev: Motility behavior and the brain. J. Nerv. & Ment. Dis. **107**:313, 1948.)

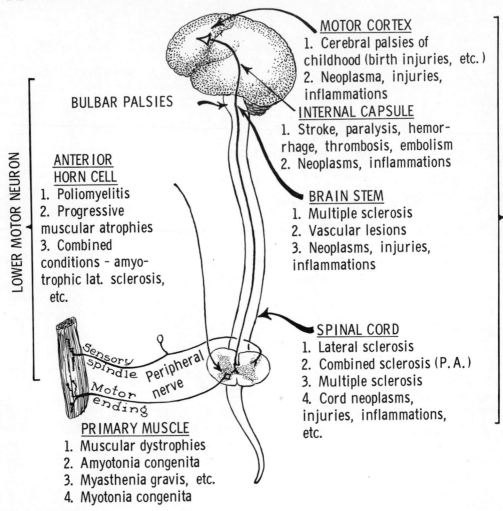

MOTOR CORTEX
1. Cerebral palsies of childhood (birth injuries, etc.)
2. Neoplasma, injuries, inflammations

INTERNAL CAPSULE
1. Stroke, paralysis, hemorrhage, thrombosis, embolism
2. Neoplasms, inflammations

BULBAR PALSIES

BRAIN STEM
1. Multiple sclerosis
2. Vascular lesions
3. Neoplasms, injuries, inflammations

LOWER MOTOR NEURON

UPPER MOTOR NEURON

ANTERIOR HORN CELL
1. Poliomyelitis
2. Progressive muscular atrophies
3. Combined conditions - amyotrophic lat. sclerosis, etc.

SPINAL CORD
1. Lateral sclerosis
2. Combined sclerosis (P.A.)
3. Multiple sclerosis
4. Cord neoplasms, injuries, inflammations, etc.

Sensory
spindle
Peripheral
nerve
Motor
ending

PRIMARY MUSCLE
1. Muscular dystrophies
2. Amyotonia congenita
3. Myasthenia gravis, etc.
4. Myotonia congenita

Motor Pathways. (Reproduced, with permission, from Chor: Some problems in muscle disorde: Physiotherapy Rev. **16**:2, 1936.)

neuronal activity in all directions and for long-term maintenance of excitatory and inhibitory states in the neuraxis. It is related to physiologic activities in the sphere of "visceration." The **intermediate** system, which is nucleate in its pattern of neuronal collections, contains units arranged in series. Such a type of arrangement is suited to the instantaneous activation or modification of the activities of diverse neuronal fields in distant areas of the neuraxis. It is concerned with external expression of internal (visceral) states through the activities of the body wall (skeletal musculature). The **outermost** system is stratilaminate in its pattern of neuronal assembly, containing cell collections arranged in parallel.

This variety is especially well suited to patterns of organismal behavior whose ends are constantly changing, requiring the widest possible opportunities for recombination of available patterns of behavior to meet the unpredictable needs of adaptation. The cerebral cortex is representative of this type.

Types of Paralysis or Paresis Based on Location.

Hemiplegia is a spastic or flaccid paralysis of one side of the body and extremities limited by the median line in front and in back **Monoplegia** is a paralysis of one extremity only. **Diplegia** is a paralysis of any 2 corresponding extremities, usually both lower exremities (but may be both upper). **Paraplegia** is a symmetric paralysis of both lower extremities. **Quadriplegia** or **tetraplegia** is a paralysis of all 4 extremities. **Hemiplegia alternans** (crossed paralysis) is a paralysis of one or more ipsilateral cranial nerves and contralateral paralysis of the arm and leg.

INCREASED MOVEMENTS AND DISTURBANCES IN TONUS

Hyperkinesias and hypertonic states (rigidity) are with a few exceptions due to involvement of the **extrapyramidal system.** In general, the extrapyramidal system includes all descending pathways exclusive of the pyramidal tract which act directly or through internuncial neurons on primary motor neurons.

Muscle **tonus** is a state of continuous mild contraction of muscle dependent upon the integrity of nerves and their central connections and the complex properties of muscles such as contractility, elasticity, ductility, and extensibility. Atonic muscles are soft and flabby; hypertonic muscles are rigid and spastic. Normal muscle at rest has a certain resilience rather than absolute flabbiness; when muscle is passively stretched by a joint movement, a certain amount of involuntary resistance is encountered. These features are considered clinical manifestations of muscle tonus. Tonus is usually greatly diminished or abolished by section of the motor nerve fibers to the muscle or of the sensory fibers from the muscle.

The stretch reflex is considered essential in maintaining muscle tonus and can produce increased tension of certain muscle groups so as to provide a background of postural muscle tonus against which voluntary movements can occur. Although most reflex arcs include at least one internuncial neuron between the afferent and efferent fibers, the stretch reflex has no such internuncial or intermediary neuron and the afferent neuron makes direct contact with the efferent neuron across a single synapse in the spinal cord.

Stretching a muscle stimulates its muscle spindles, specialized receptors which lie parallel with and interspersed among muscle fibers. Afferent nerve fibers from muscle spindles enter the spinal cord through dorsal root nerves and go anteriorly through the gray matter of the spinal cord to reach the anterior horn, where synapses with motor cells are

made. Higher supraspinal motor centers are believed to send impulses to skeletal muscle by 2 routes - one involving large alpha motoneuron cells and the other small gamma motoneurons.

The gamma neuron may be stimulated by afferent dorsal root fibers coming from the muscle and tendon spindles so as to cause contraction of intrafusal muscle fibers via a stretch reflex. Although this is a relatively minor change, it appears adequate to activate the main muscle mass so that gamma innervation may serve as a "starter" for activation of alpha motoneurons and the main muscle mass.

The gamma efferent fibers appear to make up almost one-third of the efferent ventral root fibers and go to the muscular portion of the muscle spindles via slow small motor fibers. The large alpha motor fibers from the anterior horn cells innervate the main muscle mass. The parallel arrangement of intrafusal muscle spindles and the main muscle mass provide activation of spindle discharge by passive muscle stretch and interruption of spindle discharge by active muscle contraction.

The "gamma loop" refers to the circuits to and from the spinal cord involving the muscle spindle with its gamma efferent fibers. The muscle spindle may be considered the sensing element of a reflex system which registers differences in length between itself and the main muscle mass and acts to reduce this difference. Steady voluntary or postural contraction may be considered a result of tonic innervation and facilitation of alpha motoneurons via this loop.

The role of supraspinal controls on the gamma system is not clear. Gamma facilitation or inhibition has been obtained by electric stimulation of certain areas of the cerebral cortex, some subcortical nuclei, and the cerebellum. Stimulation of the ventrolateral nucleus of the thalamus inhibits muscle spindle afferent discharge provided the motor cortex remains intact. Dysfunction of various components of the alpha and gamma systems at various peripheral and central levels have been implicated in theories to explain rigidity, akinesia, and tremor. "Blockade" of gamma motoneurons by intrathecal procaine or phenol has been reported to improve patients with parkinsonism. Paralysis of the gamma efferent system to the muscle spindles as well as hyperactivity of the same system have been proposed as the pathophysiologic basis of parkinsonism by different investigators.

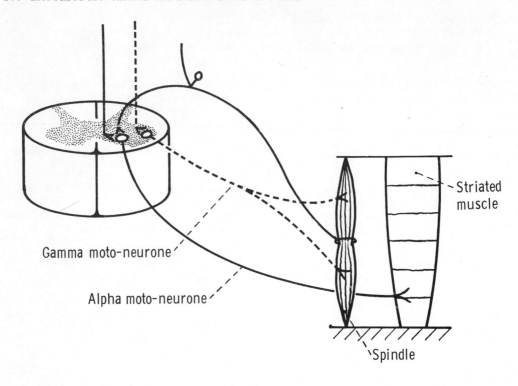

Gamma moto-neurone

Alpha moto-neurone

Striated muscle

Spindle

Gamma Loop Showing Parallel Alignment of Muscle Spindle and Striated Fiber. Gamma efferent fiber (broken line) to contractile portion of muscle spindle; sensory afferent fiber from spindle (solid line). (Reproduced, with permission, from Stern and Ward, Arch. Neurol. **3**:193-204, 1960.)

Neurologic Basis of Muscle Tone.

The maintenance and control of muscle tone is dependent upon normal function at 6 levels: (1) The precentral motor cortex (Brodmann areas 4 and 6), (2) the basal ganglia, (3) the midbrain, (4) the vestibulum, (5) the spine, and (6) the neuromuscular system.

The reticular formation of the brain stem contains an "inhibitory" area caudad and inferior to a "facilitatory" area. Appropriate stimulation of the inhibitory area decreases muscle tonus; similar excitation of the facilitatory area increases muscle tonus. Conversely, destruction of the inhibitory area or inhibitory afferents gives rise to increased tone (such as decerebrate rigidity), and destruction of the facilitatory area or facilitatory efferents gives rise to decreased tone. Experimental studies indicate that the so-called suppressor strips of the cerebral cortex, the basal ganglia, and the anterior lobe of the cerebellum connect with the bulbar inhibitory areas.

Normal muscle tone may be increased (hypertonic) or decreased (hypotonia). Hypertonic muscles are noted in spasticity, rigidity, and flexor spasms. In **spasticity**, there is increased resistance to sudden passive movements, and after the initial resistance there may be muscle relaxation (clasp-knife phenomenon). In **rigidity**, there is increased resistance on passive motion in any direction, usually unrelated to speed or direction of movement, dut to steady contraction of flexors and extensors. Marked mass flexor spasms leading to permanent contracture of flexor muscles may occur in complete lesions of the spinal cord.

Hypotonic muscles feel soft and flabby and may offer less than normal resistance to passive movement; in marked hypotonia, the joints may be hyperextended when the extremity is shaken. Hypotonia may occur with impaired muscle proprioceptive or motor innervation, cerebellar disease, or muscular disease.

The **spinal cord** is the seat of the stretch (myotatic) reflex which functions in the maintenance of tone or "static activity." The impulses pass through the simple reflex arc, which includes the neuromuscular spindles, afferent nerves, and spinal cord connections, to the anterior horn cells, and the efferent nerves. **Neuromuscular or idiomuscular activity** depends upon the contractility, elasticity, irritability, ductility, and extensibility of the muscle itself.

Lesions Affecting Tonus and Causing Increased Movements.

A. Extrapyramidal involvement, especially in the region of the basal ganglia, produces spasms and excessive movements by a mechanism known as the "release phenomenon." Since normally these centers may inhibit spontaneous rhythmic movements initiated by the cortex, disease results in the "release" of such movements, which manifest themselves as tremors, choreiform or athetoid movements, etc. Degenerative diseases, encephalitis, and tumors are the most common lesions affecting the extrapyramidal system.

B. Involvement of the Spinal Level and Reflex Arc: Fascicular movements result from progressive lesions of the anterior horn cells or motor nuclei of the cranial nerves. Reflex rigidity is due to sensory irritation, e.g., stiff neck with meningitis, board-like abdomen with peritonitis. Tone is lost or diminished when the reflex arc is interrupted.

C. Neuromuscular or idiomuscular activity is frequently manifest in the late stages of chronic wasting diseases as a local hyperirritability of the muscles known as myoedema: pinching or tapping a muscle produces a local contraction lasting several seconds.

D. Psychogenic causes are the basis of many tics; bizarre forms of increased movement are seen in certain hysterias.

Signs of Disturbed Tonus and Increased Movements.

A. Rigidity: Generalized hypertonicity of the muscles occurs with extrapyramidal lesions, as in parkinsonism caused by encephalitis, which has an affinity for the basal ganglia. Local reflex rigidity occurs with peripheral irritative lesions as cited above.

B. Increased Movements and Release Phenomena:

1. Tremors - In examining tremors, the distribution, rate, and rhythm and the effects of movement and rest should be noted. Tremors are involuntary movements resulting from the contraction of opposing muscle groups, which produces rhythmic or alternating movements of a joint or group of joints. Slow tremors range from 3-6/second, and rapid tremors may range from 10-20/second. Resting tremors may disappear or diminish with action; intention tremors may appear only on voluntary movement of a limb. The amplitude of a tremor may be coarse or fine.

In parkinsonism, a coarse tremor may be noted at rest with a rate of 3-6/second. The tremor is "pill-rolling," i.e., the affected fingers show less tremor on movement. There is usually greater shaking of the distal than the proximal portions of the extremities. Associated increased muscle tone is noted, together with other signs of parkinsonism.

Senile tremor may resemble the tremors of parkinsonism in degree, amplitude, rate, and occurrence at rest. It most commonly affects the head, jaws, and lips, and the head may nod to and fro or from side to side. Increased muscle tone and other evidences of parkinsonism are not present.

Cerebellar tremor, sometimes referred to as intention tremor, occurs during movement and is intensified at the termination of the movement. It may be noted in multiple sclerosis.

Familial or essential tremor is absent at rest and appears when muscles act to move or support an extremity. This tremor is not intensified toward the end of movement and is not associated with other evidence of neurologic disease. It may be lessened by alcohol or sedatives but is not affected by drugs of the belladonna group.

Toxic tremors are associated with endogenous disorders (thyrotoxicosis, uremia) or exogenous toxic disorders (alcohol, tobacco). Usually these are fine and rapid.

Physiologic tremors are usually transient and may occur in normal people under emotional stress, extreme fright, and exposure to cold.

In Wilson's disease, a resting tremor similar to that of parkinsonism may be noted; however, it becomes aggravated by motion of the extremity. Violent up-and-down movements of the upper extremities, resembling wing-beating movements in birds, may occur.

In advanced hepatic disease, coarse flapping movements resulting from alternate flexion and extension of the wrists of the outstretched arms have been noted and are referred to as "wrist-flapping." Tremors of the fingers may also occur.

2. Spasms (involuntary contraction of large groups of muscles) may involve the arm,

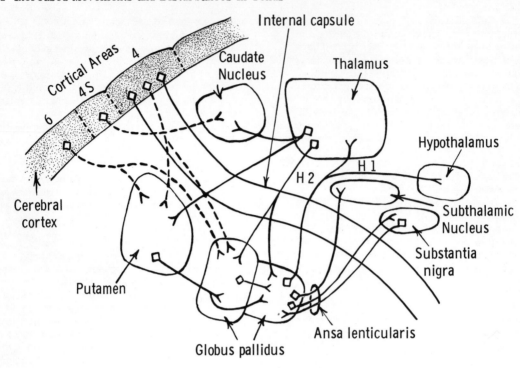

Connections Between Basal Ganglia and Cortex. (Reproduced, with permission, from Kennard: Experimental analysis of the functions of the basal ganglia in monkeys and chimpanzees. J. Neurophysiol. **7**:142, 1944.)

leg, or neck muscles (spastic torticollis). Causes include extrapyramidal involvement and hypoparathyroid tetany. Oculogyric spasm (or crisis), characterized by a fixed upward gaze, is usually a sequel of encephalitis, and attacks may last from several minutes to several hours. These tonic spasms of the extraocular muscles may sometimes result in forced conjugate movements in other directions, rarely in fixation of gaze in the eyes-centered position

3. Choreiform movements are extremely variable, purposeless, coarse, quick, and jerky; they begin suddenly and show no rhythmicity. When the movement is over, the part remains at rest and is atonic until the next one begins. Choreiform movements are usually due to an involvement of the basal ganglia. These movements are of variable distribution and may occur in sleep.

4. Athetoid movements are continuous, arrhythmic, slow, and worm-like; they are always the same in the same patient and cease only during sleep. The muscles are always hypertonic and may show transient stages of spasm.

5. Dystonia is characterized by bizarre twisting movements of the body and trunk, some of the muscles being hypertonic. Dystonia usually refers to mobile spasms of the axial and proximal muscles of the extremities. Torsion spasm, with resulting twisting or turning movements, is included, and spasmodic torticollis is the most commonly encountered torsion spasm. Dystonic movements tend to involve large portions of the body and have an undulant sinuous character which may produce grotesque posturing and bizarre writhing movements.

6. Tics or habit spasms are brief, recurrent, inappropriate, stereotyped, irresistible, compulsive movements involving a relatively small segment of the body, frequently on a psychogenic basis.

7. Myoclonus refers to abrupt, sudden isolated muscle contractions which occur irregularly, especially in the limbs, and frequently produce no associated movement. A sudden jerk or series of jerks may occur with rates as fast as 50-60/minute or as slow as 5-10/minute. They are apt to occur in the muscles of the limbs, face, and oral cavity,

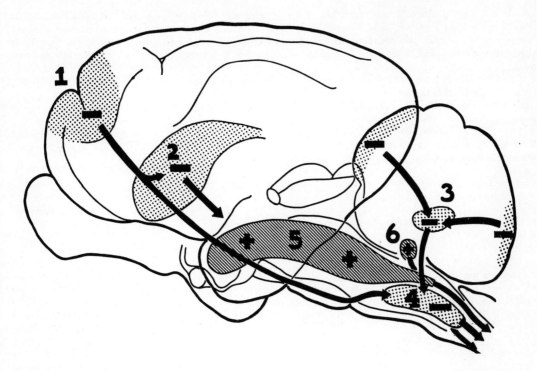

Spasticity. Suppressor pathways are as follows: (1) corticobulboreticular; (2) caudatospinal; (3) cerebelloreticular; and (4) reticulospinal. Facilitatory pathways are: (5) reticulospinal; and (6) vestibulospinal. (Reproduced, with permission, from Lindsley, Schreiner, and Magoun: An electromyographic study of spasticity. J. Neurophysiol. **12**:188, 1949.)

and disappear during sleep. If large groups of muscles are affected they may produce joint movements which may be of sufficient violence to jar the patient or throw him to the ground. Palatal myoclonus usually results from lesions in the pathways connecting the red nucleus, the olivary bodies of the medulla, and the dentate nucleus of the cerebellum.

8. Hemiballism is a rare symptom characterized by continuous coordinated activity of the axial and proximal extremity musculature, sometimes to such a degree that the limbs fly about. It is usually confined to one side of the body and sometimes resembles hemichorea. In most cases, lesions of the opposite subthalamic nucleus are noted, particularly vascular lesions (hemorrhagic softening). Onset is usually sudden, with involvement principally of the leg and relative sparing of the face. Mental symptoms (confusion, disorientation, or dementia) are often associated. Medical therapy usually is ineffective.

DISTURBANCES IN SYNERGY

Lesions of the cerebellum or its pathways are characterized by dyssynergia, a failure in the integrated, coordinated action between muscle groups. The mechanism of synergy (the regulation of reciprocal innervation) is as follows: The unpaired vermis of the cerebellum regulates bilaterally innervated muscles of the head, neck, and trunk. The right and left cerebellar hemispheres regulate antagonistic muscular activity on their ipsilateral sides as extension and flexion. The spinal cord is important in controlling bilaterally innervated muscular activity of the extremities as in walking.

Anatomy of the Cerebellum. (See p. 37.)

The cerebellum is the highest proprioceptive ganglion. **Afferent** tracts enter the cerebellum from the cortex, brain stem, and cord. Impulses from the cerebral cortex pass via the corticopontocerebellar tracts entering through the brachium pontis (middle cerebellar peduncle). Impulses from the spinal cord pass via the dorsal spinocerebellar tract, spino-olivocerebellar tract, and external arcuate fibers to enter the cerebellum through the restiform body (inferior cerebellar peduncle); and via the ventral spinocerebellar tract and brachium conjunctivum (superior cerebellar peduncle) to the cerebellum. Impulses from the vestibular labyrinth and vestibular nuclei enter via the vestibulocerebellar tract located medial to the restiform body. **Efferent** tracts from the cerebellum pass to the lower motor neurons via the brachium conjunctivum, red nucleus, and rubrospinal tract. Impulses from the cerebellar hemisphere pass via the dentate nucleus or the globose and emboliform nuclei to the opposite red nucleus and thalamus. Impulses from the vermis pass via the fastigial (roof) nuclei to vestibular nuclei.

Diseases of the Cerebellum.

The cerebellum, like other organs, may be involved in hereditary or congenital anomalies or inflammatory, traumatic, neoplastic, vascular, degenerative, functional, toxic, or metabolic disorders. Symptoms and signs are essentially the same regardless of the cause.

Cerebellar Symptoms and Signs.

The following clinical findings suggest cerebellar disorders: **Ataxia**, a reeling, drunken, unsteady gait with a wide base and a tendency to fall toward the side of the lesion. **Adiadokokinesia**, inability to perform rapidly alternating movements such as supination and pronation. **Dysmetria** (past-pointing phenomenon), inability to estimate the range of voluntary movement. In the finger-to-nose test, the finger shoots past the nose onto the cheek. In **decomposition of movement** ("by-the-numbers" phenomenon), voluntary movements are jerky and broken up; a coarse **tremor** precipitated by movement and disappearing at rest may be associated. In the **rebound phenomenon of Holmes** (lack of check reflex), when the patient flexes his arm against resistance of the examiner and the arm is suddenly released, it will strike the patient's body or face. **Nystagmus** is often present in cerebellar lesions but occurs usually when the eyes move away from a central fixation or rest point. It is most marked when looking to the side of the lesion. **Vertigo** may accompany the ataxia. **Dysarthria**, explosive, slurred speech. **Plurosthotonus**, a tendency to lean and fall to the side of the lesion. **Hypotonia**, noted by "floppiness" of the limbs and decreased resistance to passive move-

ment. **Skew deviation of the eyes**, a condition in which one eyeball is deviated up and out, the other down and in, occurring particularly with lesions of the middle cerebellar peduncle (brachium pontis). **Cerebellar fit** is a rigid convulsion sometimes seen in cerebellar disease.

GAITS

Tabetic or Ataxic Gait.

Tabetic or ataxic gait is characteristic of posterior column disease, and results from the loss of proprioceptive sense in the extremities. The patient walks on a wide base, slapping his feet, and usually watches his legs so he will know where they are. With his eyes closed or in the dark his ataxia is much worse. Clumsiness and uncertainty are characteristic. The feet are placed too widely apart, and in taking a step the subject lifts the advancing leg abruptly and too high and then stamps or slaps the foot solidly to the ground. Uneven spacing of steps, tottering, and swaying occur, usually with deviation to one side or the other.

Hemiplegic Gait.

The affected leg is rigid and is swung from the hip in a semicircle by movements of the trunk; the patient leans to the affected side, and the arm on that side is held in a rigid, semiflexed position. A somewhat similar gait occurs with any disorder producing an immobile hip or knee. The affected spastic limb is moved forward with difficulty because of impaired joint mobility. The toes of hemiplegic lower limbs tend to be forced down, so that abduction and circumduction of the limb is necessary to move it forward.

Scissors Gait.

Scissors gait is characteristic of spastic paraplegia. The legs are adducted, crossing alternately in front of one another with the knees scraping together. The resulting steps are short and progression slow. Both lower limbs are spastic. The lower extremities are moved forward in a stiff, jerky manner, often accompanied by pronounced compensatory motions of the trunk and upper extremities.

Drunken or Staggering Gait.

Drunken or staggering gait as seen in acute alcoholism may also result from drug poisoning, multiple neuritis, brain tumors, multiple sclerosis, or general paresis.

Waddling or Clumsy Gait.

Waddling or clumsy gait results from dislocated hips or muscular dystrophies with weakness of the hips. In either case, the trunk muscles are drawn into play so that the patient rolls from side to side. Weakness of trunk and pelvic girdle muscles produces pelvic tilt. The waddle results from difficulty in maintaining the pelvis at a proper angle to the weight-bearing extremity, with slump of the pelvis toward the nonweight-bearing side, which in turn produces exaggerated compensatory sway of the trunk toward the weight-bearing side. Muscular dystrophy is characterized by weakness of trunk and pelvic girdle muscles, producing a sway-backed, pot-bellied posture and waddling gait.

Steppage Gait.

Steppage gait (or foot-drop gait) is characterized by high knee action and flopping of the feet (or foot). Even when the leg is raised, the toes tend to drag along the floor. It occurs with paralysis of the anterior tibial group of muscles, as in alcoholic neuritis, peroneal nerve injuries, poliomyelitis, and progressive muscular atrophy. With bilateral foot drop, the gait may resemble that of a high-stepping horse.

Cerebellar Gait or Ataxia.

Cerebellar gait or ataxia is characterized by marked irregularity and unsteadiness associated with vertigo and a tendency to reel to one side. The lower extremities appear loose; movement of the advancing limb starts slowly, but is unexpectedly, erratically, and vigorously flung forward and lands with a stamp on the floor. The gait is wide-based, irregular, reeling or deviated, and staggering on turning in quality.

Propulsion or Festination Gait.

Propulsion or festination gait of paralysis agitans is characterized by a forward-leaning posture and short shuffling steps, beginning slowly at first and becoming more rapid ("marche à petits pas"). The patient with the classical features of parkinsonism has a stooped posture, takes short steps, and frequently accelerates rapidly so that he appears to be chasing his center of gravity.

Hysterical Gaits.

Hysterical gaits simulate various paralyses (e. g., monoplegias, hemiplegias, or paraplegias) but differ from the organic forms in being more pronounced and complete, with the ability to use the limb in emergencies. The gait is apt to be bizarre or fantastic, characterized by inconsistency with ability to move limbs and exaggerated balancing motions. There may be lurching, wildly weaving, irregular bobbing movements or exaggerated, very slow, hesitant, slow motion action.

Astasia-Abasia.

Astasia-abasia is a hysterical ataxia with such bizarre incoordination that the patient is unable to stand or walk; yet all leg movements can be performed normally while sitting or while in bed.

Limping Gait.

When pain is produced by weight-bearing on a lower extremity, the patient puts the affected extremity down carefully and takes a short step to get the weight off the painful limb as soon as possible. The good limb is brought forward rapidly and lands vigorously on the floor. Limping may be associated with a variety of conditions including shortening of the lower extremity and deformity of the foot.

DEFORMITIES AND POSTURES

Deformities of the **spine** (lordosis, scoliosis, or kyphosis) are often seen with muscular dystrophies, syringomyelia, and Friedreich's ataxia. **Clubfoot** is usually present in cases of Friedreich's ataxia. Dangling and swinging of the **hands** suggests lower motor neuron paralysis, e. g., poliomyelitis or polyneuritis. **Accoucheur's hand** or "waiter's tip" position occurs with Erb's upper arm type of brachial plexus (birth) palsy. **Opisthotonos** (stiff extended neck and spine) suggests meningeal irritation. **Sardonic smile** is associated with facial muscle spasms of tetanus. **Pot-belly** in children may be due to a muscular dystrophy. **Hemiplegic arm** is adducted, flexed at the elbow and fingers, and is maintained in this position by muscle rigidity. Inability of the patient to **lower his arm** is a characteristic of a lesion at the level of the seventh cervical cord segment. The patient may raise his arm as the examiner places it at his side. When the patient sleeps, the affected arm lies on the pillow beside his head (Jolly's position).

Various peripheral nerve injuries produce characteristic postural changes (e. g., wrist-drop, foot-drop, claw-hand, ape-hand, winged scapula, shoulder-drop). These are described elsewhere.

Posture in paralysis agitans is stooped, with the head forward and elbows flexed.

9...

Muscle Innervation and Testing

SEGMENTAL MOTOR INNERVATION - UPPER EXTREMITY

	C4	C5	C6	C7	C8	T1
Shoulder	-------- Supraspinatus ---	-------				
	------- Teres minor ------					
		-------- Deltoid --------				
	------	-- Infraspinatus --------				
	-------- Subscapularis --	-------			
Arm	------	- Teres major	-------			
	-------- Biceps --------				
	------ Brachialis -------				
	-------- Coracobrachialis ----------				
		---------- Triceps brachialis ---------			
		-------- Anconeus --------			
	---- Supinator longus ----					
	------- Supinator brevis--	------			
Forearm	-----Extensor carpi radialis -----				
	-----Pronator teres-----				
	--Flexor carpi radialis--					
		-----Flexor pollicis longus -----			
		-Abductor pollicis longus-			
		-Ext. pollicis brevis-			
	-----Extensor pollicis longus----				
	---Extensor digitorum longus----				
	----Extensor indicis proprius----				
	-----Extensor carpi ulnaris-----				
	------Extensor digiti quinti------				
		-----Flexor digitorum sublimis-------			
		-----Flexor digitorum profundus------			
		--------Pronator quadratus----------			
		-------Flexor carpi ulnaris---------			
		-----Palmaris longus------			
		------Abductor pollicis brevis-------			
		-----Flexor pollicis brevis-----			
		---- Opponens pollicis ----			
		----Flexor digiti quinti----			
		---Opponens digiti quinti---			
Hand		---Adductor pollicis----			
		---Palmaris brevis-----			
		-Abductor digiti quinti---			
		----Lumbricales-------			
		------Interossei--------			

SEGMENTAL MOTOR INNERVATION - LOWER EXTREMITY

	L1	L2	L3	L4	L5	S1	S2
Hip	----------Iliopsoas------------						
				--Tensor fasciae latae-			
				--------Gluteus medius---------			
				-------Gluteus minimus--------			
				------Quadratus femoris--------			
				-------Gemellus inferior--------			
				------Gemellus superior------			
				--------Gluteus maximus---------			
				--Obturator internus--			
				-----Piriformis------			
Thigh		------Sartorius-------					
		------Pectineus------					
		--Adductor longus----					
		-----Quadriceps femoris-----					
		-----------Gracilis-----------					
		---------Adductor brevis--------					
		--Obturator externus--					
		---Adductor magnus---					
		--Adductor minimus--					
				--------Semitendinosus---------			
				-------Semimembranosus-------			
				------------Biceps femoris------------			
Leg				---Tibialis anticus-			
				--Extensor hallucis longus---			
				----------Popliteus-----------			
				-----------Plantaris-----------			
				----Extensor digitorum longus----			
				---------- Soleus ----------			
				--------Gastrocnemius--------			
				---Peroneus longus----			
				---Peroneus brevis----			
				---Tibialis posterior---			
				-----Flexor digitorum longus----			
				------Flexor hallucis longus-----			
Foot				---Extensor hallucis brevis--			
				---Extensor digitorum brevis----			
				Flexor digitorum brevis			
				---Abductor hallucis---			
				------Flexor hallucis brevis-----			
				---------Lumbricales----------			
				--Adductor hallucis--			
				-Abductor digiti quinti--			
				-Flexor digiti quinti--			
				-Opponens digiti quinti-			
				-Quadratus plantaris-			
				------Interossei-----			

Muscle Innervation Listed by Individual Nerves

UPPER EXTREMITY

Suprascapular Nerve
Shoulder girdle
Supraspinatus
Infraspinatus
Long Thoracic Nerve
Shoulder girdle
Serratus anterior
Axillary Nerve
Shoulder girdle
Teres minor
Deltoid
Musculocutaneous Nerve
Arm
Biceps brachii
Coracobrachialis
Brachialis
Median Nerve
Forearm
Pronator teres
Flexor carpi radialis
Palmaris longus
Flexor digitorum sublimis
Flexor digitorum profundus
Flexor pollicis longus
Pronator quadratus
Hand
Abductor pollicis brevis
Opponens pollicis
Flexor pollicis brevis
Lumbricales I and II
Radial Nerve
Arm
Triceps (long head, lateral head, medial head)
Anconeus
Brachioradialis
Extensor carpi radialis
Forearm
Extensor carpi radialis brevis
Supinator longus
Extensor digitorum communis
Extensor digiti quinti
Extensor carpi ulnaris
Abductor pollicis longus
Extensor pollicis longus
Extensor pollicis brevis
Extensor indicis proprius
Ulnar Nerve
Forearm
Flexor carpi ulnaris
Flexor digitorum profundus (medial half)
Hand
Flexor digiti quinti brevis
Abductor digiti quinti
Opponens digiti quinti
Interossei
Lumbricales III and IV
Adductor pollicis
Flexor pollicis brevis (deep part)

LOWER EXTREMITY

Superior Gluteal Nerve
Buttock
Gluteus medius
Gluteus minimus
Tensor fasciae latae
Inferior Gluteal Nerve
Buttock
Gluteus maximus
Femoral Nerve
Thigh
Pectineus
Sartorius
Quadriceps femoris (rectus femoris, vastus lateralis, vastus intermedius, vastus medialis)
Obturator Nerve
Thigh
Adductor longus
Gracilis
Adductor brevis
Obturator externus
Adductor magnus
Sciatic Nerve, Tibial Division
Thigh
Semitendinosus
Biceps (long head)
Semimembranosus
Popliteal space (tibial nerve)
Gastrocnemius
Plantaris
Popliteus
Soleus
Leg
Tibialis posterior
Flexor digitorum longus
Flexor hallucis longus
Foot
Abductor hallucis
Abductor digiti minimi
Dorsal interossei
Sciatic Nerve, Peroneal Division
Thigh
Biceps (short head)
Leg (deep peroneal nerve)
Tibialis anterior
Extensor hallucis longus
Extensor digitorum longus
Peroneus tertius
Foot
Extensor digitorum brevis
Leg (superficial peroneal nerve)
Peroneus longus
Peroneus brevis

Motor Function Chart*

SHOULDER GIRDLE AND UPPER EXTREMITY

Action to be Tested	Muscles	Cord Segment	Nerves	Plexus	
Flexion of neck	Deep neck muscles (Sternomastoid and trapezius also participate)	C1, 2, 3, 4	Cervical	Cervical	
Extension of neck					
Rotation of neck					
Lateral bending of neck					
Elevation of upper thorax	Scaleni	C3, 4, 5	Phrenic		
Inspiration	Diaphragm				
Adduction of arm from behind to front	Pectoralis major and minor	C5, 6, 7, 8, T1	Thoracic anterior (from med. and lat. cords of plexus)		
Forward thrust of shoulder	Serratus anterior	C5, 6, 7	Long thoracic		Brachial
Elevation of scapula	Levator scapulae	C5(3, 4)	Dorsal scapular		
Medial adduction and elevation of scapula	Rhomboids	C4, 5			
Abduction of arm	Supraspinatus	C4, 5, 6	Suprascapular		
Lateral rotation of arm	Infraspinatus	C4, 5, 6,			
Medial rotation of arm	Latissimus dorsi, teres major and subscapularis	C5, 6, 7, 8	Subscapular (from posterior cord of plexus)		
Adduction of arm from front to back					
Abduction of arm	Deltoid	C5, 6	Axillary (from posterior cord of plexus)		
Lateral rotation of arm	Teres minor	C4, 5			
Flexion of forearm	Biceps brachii	C5, 6	Musculocutaneous (from lateral cord of plexus)		
Supination of forearm					
Adduction of arm	Coracobrachialis	C5, 6, 7			
Flexion of forearm					
Flexion of forearm	Brachialis	C5, 6			
Ulnar flexion of hand	Flexor carpi ulnaris	C7, 8, T1	Ulnar (from medial cord of plexus)		
Flexion of terminal phalanx of ring finger / little finger	Flexor digitorum profundus (ulnar portion)	C7, 8, T1			
Flexion of hand					
Adduction of metacarpal of thumb	Adductor pollicis	C8, T1			
Abduction of little finger	Abductor digiti quinti	C8, T1			
Opposition of little finger	Opponens digiti quinti	C7, 8, T1			
Flexion of little finger	Flexor digiti quinti brevis	C7, 8, T1			
Flexion of proximal phalanx, extension of 2 distal phalanges, adduction and abduction of fingers	Interossei	C8, T1			

*Modified from J. C. McKinley. Reproduced with permission.

SHOULDER GIRDLE AND UPPER EXTREMITY (Cont'd.)

Action to be Tested	Muscles	Cord Segment	Nerves	Plexus
Pronation of forearm	Pronator teres	C6, 7		
Radial flexion of hand	Flexor carpi radialis	C6, 7		
Flexion of hand	Palmaris longus	C7, 8, T1		
Flexion of middle phalanx of { index finger, middle finger, ring finger, little finger	Flexor digitorum sublimis	C7, 8, T1	Median (C6, 7 from lateral cord of plexus; C8, T1 from medial cord of plexus)	
Flexion of hand				
Flexion of terminal phalanx of thumb	Flexor pollicis longus	C7, 8, T1		
Flexion of terminal phalanx of { index finger, middle finger	Flexor digitorum profundus (radial portion)	C7, 8, T1		
Flexion of hand				
Abduction of metacarpal of thumb	Abductor pollicis brevis	C7, 8, T1		
Flexion of proximal phalanx of thumb	Flexor pollicis brevis	C7, 8, T1		
Opposition of metacarpal of thumb	Opponens pollicis	C8, T1		
Flexion of proximal phalanx and extension of the 2 distal phalanges of { index finger, middle finger	Lumbricals (the two lateral)	C8, T1		
{ ring finger, little finger	Lumbricals (the two medial)	C8, T1	Ulnar	Brachial
Extension of forearm	Triceps brachii and anconeus	C6, 7, 8		
Flexion of forearm	Brachioradialis	C5, 6		
Radial extension of hand	Extensor carpi radialis	C6, 7, 8		
Extension of phalanges of { index finger, middle finger, ring finger, little finger	Extensor digitorum communis	C6, 7, 8		
Extension of hand			Radial (from posterior cord of plexus)	
Extension of phalanges of little finger	Extensor digiti quinti proprius	C6, 7, 8		
Extension of hand				
Ulnar extension of hand	Extensor carpi ulnaris	C6, 7, 8		
Supination of forearm	Supinator	C5, 6, 7		
Abduction of metacarpal of thumb	Abductor pollicis longus	C7, 8		
Radial extension of hand				
Extension of thumb	Extensor pollicis brevis and longus	C7, 8		
Radial extension of hand		C6, 7, 8		
Extension of index finger	Extensor indicis proprius	C6, 7, 8		
Extension of hand				

TRUNK AND THORAX

Action to be Tested	Muscles	Cord Segment	Nerves
Elevation of ribs	Thoracic, abdominal and back		Thoracic and posterior lumbosacral branches
Depression of ribs			
Contraction of abdomen			
Anteroflexion of trunk			
Lateral flexion of trunk			

HIP GIRDLE AND LOWER EXTREMITY

Action to be Tested	Muscles	Cord Segment	Nerves	Plexus
Flexion of hip	Iliopsoas	L1, 2, 3	Femoral	Lumbar
Flexion of hip (and eversion of thigh)	Sartorius	L2, 3		
Extension of leg	Quadriceps femoris	L2, 3, 4		
Adduction of thigh	Pectineus	L2, 3	Obturator	
	Adductor longus	L2, 3		
	Adductor brevis	L2, 3, 4		
	Adductor magnus	L3, 4		
	Gracilis	L2, 3, 4		
Adduction of thigh / Lateral rotation of thigh	Obturator externus	L3, 4		
Abduction of thigh	Gluteus medius and minimus	L4, 5 S1	Superior gluteal	
Medial rotation of thigh				
Flexion of thigh	Tensor fasciae latae	L4, 5		
Lateral rotation of thigh	Piriformis	L5, S1		
Abduction of thigh	Gluteus maximus	L4, 5, S1, 2	Inferior gluteal	
Lateral rotation of thigh	Obturator internus	L5, S1	Muscular branches from sacral plexus	Sacral
	Gemelli	L4, 5, S1		
	Quadratus femoris	L4, 5, S1		
Flexion of leg (assist in extension of thigh)	Biceps femoris	L4, 5, S1, 2	Sciatic (trunk)	
	Semitendinosus	L4, 5, S1		
	Semimembranosus	L4, 5, S1		
Dorsal flexion of foot / Supination of foot	Tibialis anterior	L4, 5	Deep peroneal	
Extension of toes II-V / Dorsal flexion of foot	Extensor digitorum longus	L4, 5, S1		
Extension of great toe / Dorsal flexion of foot	Extensor hallucis longus	L4, 5, S1		
Extension of great toe and the 3 medial toes	Extensor digitorum brevis	L4, 5, S1		
Plantar flexion of foot in pronation	Peronei	L5, S1	Superficial peroneal	
Plantar flexion of foot in supination	Tibialis posterior and triceps surae	L5, S1, 2	Tibial	
Plantar flexion of foot in supination / Flexion of terminal phalanx of toes II-V	Flexor digitorum longus	L5, S1, 2		
Plantar flexion of foot in supination / Flexion of terminal phalanx of great toe	Flexor hallucis longus	L5, S1, 2		
Flexion of middle phalanx of toes II-V	Flexor digitorum brevis	L5, S1		
Flexion of proximal phalanx of great toe	Flexor hallucis brevis	L5, S1, 2		
Spreading and closing of toes / Flexion of proximal phalanx of toes	Small muscles of foot	S1, 2		
Voluntary control of pelvic floor	Perineal and sphincters	S2, 3, 4	Pudendal	

FUNCTIONAL TESTS FOR THE PRINCIPAL MUSCLES

Muscle testing depends upon a thorough understanding of which muscles are used in performing certain movements. Testing is best performed when the subject is warm, rested, comfortable, attentive, and alone with the examiner. Since several muscles may function similarly, it is not always easy for the patient to contract a single muscle upon request. By positioning or fixation of parts, the contraction of a particular muscle can be emphasized while other muscles of similar function are inhibited. The effect of gravity must be considered since it may enhance or reduce certain movements.

Two technics of testing may be used: active motion against the examiner's resist-ance, and resistance against a movement performed by the examiner. The degree of impairment of muscle function may be difficult to estimate by inspection. It is helpful to palpate the body or tendon of a muscle for evidence of contraction or movement. The normal or least affected muscles should be tested first to gain the cooperation and confidence of the subject. The strength of the muscle tested should always be compared with that of its contra-lateral analogue.

Grading of Strength of Muscle.

The strength of various muscles should be graded and charted periodically (see p. 184). Grading scales of various types are used, e.g., minus to 4+, 0 to 100%, and letter codes such as "N" for normal, "G" for good, "F" for fair, "P" for poor, "T" for trace, and "O" for zero.

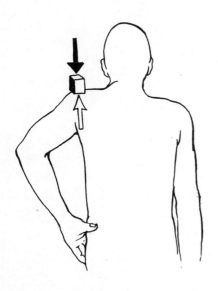

Trapezius, upper portion (C3, 4; spinal accessory nerve). The shoulder is elevated against resistance.

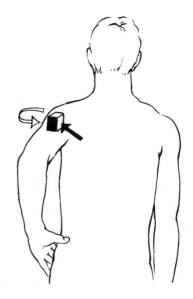

Trapezius, lower portion (C3, 4; spinal accessory nerve). The shoulder is thrust backward against resistance.

White arrows indicate the direction of movement in testing a given muscle. Black arrows show the direction of resistance. The blocks show the site of application of resistance.

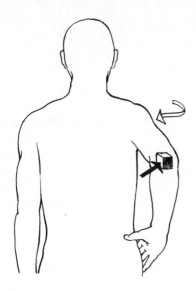

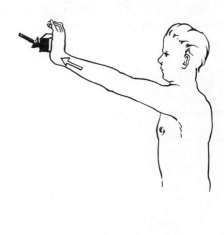

Serratus Anterior (C5, 6, 7; long thoracic nerve). The subject pushes hard with outstretched arms; the inner edge of the scapula remains against the thoracic wall. (If the trapezius is weak, the inner edge may move from chest wall.)

Rhomboids (C4, 5; dorsal scapular nerve). The shoulder is thrust backward against resistance.

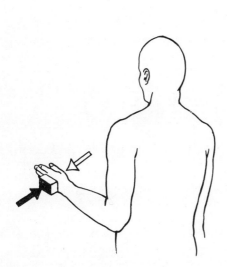

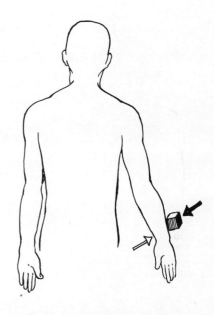

Infraspinatus (C4, 5, 6; suprascapular nerve). With the elbow flexed at the side, the arm is externally rotated against resistance on the forearm.

Supraspinatus (C4, 5, 6; suprascapular nerve). The arm is abducted from the side of the body against resistance.

White arrows indicate the direction of movement in testing a given muscle. Black arrows show the direction of resistance. The blocks show the site of application of resistance.

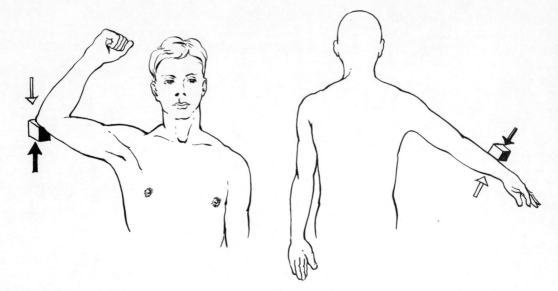

Latissimus Dorsi (C6, 7, 8; subscapular nerve).
The arm is adducted from a horizontal and
lateral position against resistance.

Deltoid (C5, 6; axillary nerve). Abduction
of laterally raised arm (30-75° from
body) against resistance.

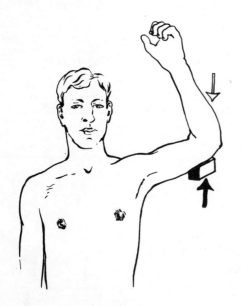

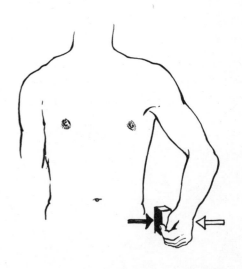

Pectoralis Major, upper portion (C5, 6, 7, 8;
lateral and medial pectoral nerves). The
arm is adducted from an elevated or horizontal and forward position against resistance.

Pectoralis Major, lower portion (C5, 6, 7, 8,
T1; lateral and medial pectoral nerves).
The arm is adducted from forward position
below horizontal against resistance.

White arrows indicate the direction of movement in testing a given muscle. Black arrows show
the direction of resistance. The blocks show the site of application of resistance.

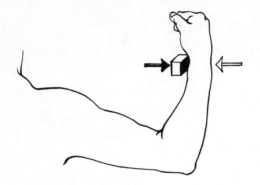

Biceps (C5, 6; musculocutaneous nerve). The supinated forearm is flexed against resistance.

Triceps (C6, 7, 8; radial nerve). The forearm, flexed at the elbow, is extended against resistance.

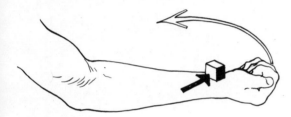

Brachioradialis (C5, 6; radial nerve). The forearm is flexed against resistance, while it is in "neutral" position (neither pronated nor supinated).

Extensor Digitorum (C7, 8; radial nerve). The fingers are extended at the metacarpophalangeal joints against resistance.

Supinator (C5, 6; radial nerve). The hand is supinated against resistance, with arms extended at the side. Resistance is applied by the grip of the examiner's hand on patient's forearm near the wrist.

White arrows indicate the direction of movement in testing a given muscle. Black arrows show the direction of resistance. The blocks show the site of application of resistance.

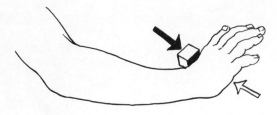

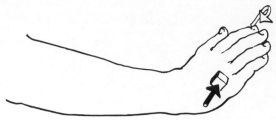

Extensor Carpi Radialis Longus (C6, 7, 8; radial nerve). The wrist is extended to the radial side against resistance; fingers extended.

Extensor Carpi Ulnaris (C6, 7, 8; radial nerve). The wrist joint is extended to the ulnar side against resistance.

Extensor Pollicis Longus (C7, 8; radial nerve). The thumb is extended against resistance.

Extensor Pollicis Brevis (C7, 8; radial nerve). The thumb is extended at the metacarpophalangeal joint against resistance.

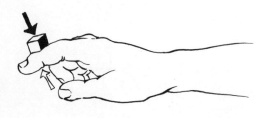

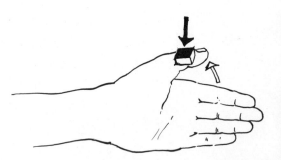

Extensor Indicis Proprius (C6, 7, 8; radial nerve). The index finger is extended against resistance placed on the dorsal aspect of the finger.

Abductor Pollicis Longus (C7, 8, T1; radial nerve). The thumb is abducted against resistance in a plane at right angle to the palmar surface.

White arrows indicate the direction of movement in testing a given muscle. Black arrows show the direction of resistance. The blocks show the site of application of resistance.

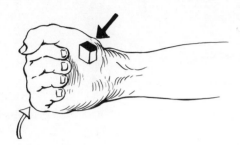

Flexor Carpi Radialis (C6, 7; median nerve). The wrist is flexed to the radial side against resistance.

Flexor Digitorum Sublimis (C7, 8, T1; median nerve). Fingers are flexed at first interphalangeal joint against resistance; proximal phalanges fixed.

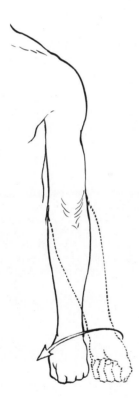

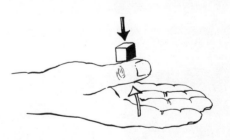

Flexor Digitorum Profundus I and II (C7, 8, T1; median nerve). The terminal phalanges of the index and middle fingers are flexed against resistance; the second phalanges being held in extension.

Pronator Teres (C6, 7; median nerve). The extended arm is pronated against resistance. Resistance is applied by grip of examiner's hand on patient's forearm near the wrist.

Abductor Pollicis Brevis C7, 8, T1; median nerve). The thumb is abducted against resistance in a plane at right angle to the palmar surface.

White arrows indicate the direction of movement in testing a given muscle. Black arrows show the direction of resistance. The blocks show the site of application of resistance.

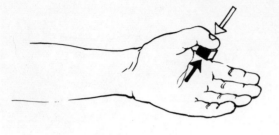

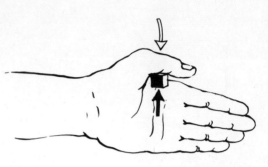

Flexor Pollicis Longus (C7, 8, T1; median nerve). The terminal phalanx of the thumb is flexed against resistance as the proximal phalanx is held in extension.

Flexor Pollicis Brevis (C7, 8, T1; median nerve). The proximal phalanx of the thumb is flexed against resistance placed on its palmar surface.

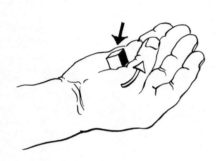

Opponens Pollicis (C8, T1; median nerve). The thumb is crossed over the palm against resistance to touch the tip of the little finger, with the thumbnail held parallel to the palm.

Lumbrical-Interossei (radial half) (C8, T1; median and ulnar nerves). The second and third phalanges are extended against resistance; the first phalanx is in full extension. The ulnar half has the same innervation and can be tested in the same manner.

Flexor Carpi Ulnaris (C7, 8, T1; ulnar nerve). The little finger is abducted strongly against resistance as the supinated hand lies with fingers extended on table.

Flexor Digiti Quinti (C7, 8, T1; ulnar nerve). The proximal phalanx of the little finger is flexed against resistance.

White arrows indicate the direction of movement in testing a given muscle. Black arrows show the direction of resistance. The blocks show the site of application of resistance.

Flexor Digitorum Profundus III and IV (C8, T1; ulnar nerve). The distal phalanges of the little and ring fingers are flexed against resistance; the second phalanges are held in extension.

Abductor Digiti Quinti (C8, T1; ulnar nerve). The little finger is abducted against resistance as the supinated hand with fingers extended lies on the table.

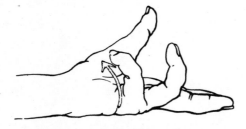

Opponens Digiti Quinti (C7, 8, T1; ulnar nerve). With fingers extended, the fifth finger is moved across the palm to the base of the thumb.

Adductor Pollicis (C8, T1; ulnar nerve). A piece of paper grasped between the palm and the thumb is held against resistance with the thumbnail kept at right angle to the palm.

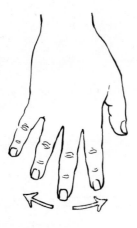

Dorsal Interossei (C8, T1; ulnar nerve). The second and fourth fingers are abducted from midline against resistance as the palm of the hand lies flat on the table.

Palmar Interossei (C8, T1; ulnar nerve). The abducted second, fourth, and fifth fingers are adducted to midline against resistance as the palm of the hand lies flat on the table.

White arrows indicate the direction of movement in testing a given muscle. Black arrows show the direction of resistance. The blocks show the site of application of resistance.

Sartorius (L2, 3; femoral nerve). With
the subject sitting and the knee flexed,
the thigh is rotated outward against
resistance on the leg.

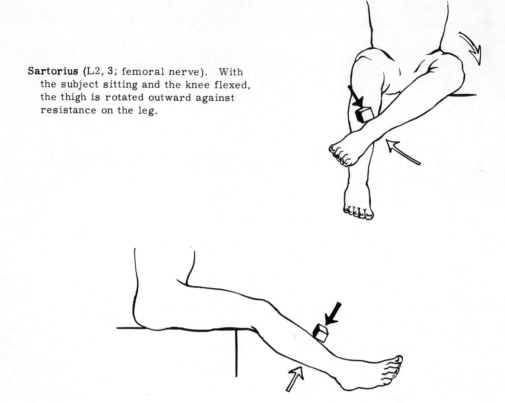

Quadriceps Femoris (L2, 3, 4; femoral nerve). The knee
is extended against resistance on the leg.

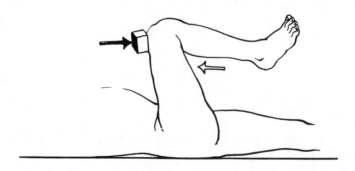

Iliopsoas (L 1, 2, 3; femoral nerve). The subject lies supine with knee flexed. The
flexed thigh (at about 90°) is further flexed against resistance.

White arrows indicate the direction of movement in testing a given muscle. Black arrows show
the direction of resistance. The blocks show the site of application of resistance.

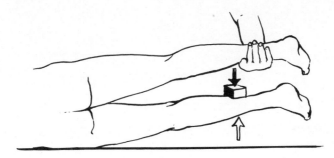

Adductors (L2, 3, 4; obturator nerve). With the subject on his side and knees extended, the lower extremity is adducted against resistance; the upper leg is supported by the examiner.

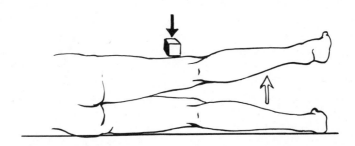

Gluteus Medius and Minimus; Tensor Fasciae Latae (L4, 5, S1; superior gluteal nerve). Testing abduction: With the subject lying on his side and his thigh and leg extended, the uppermost lower extremity is abducted against resistance.

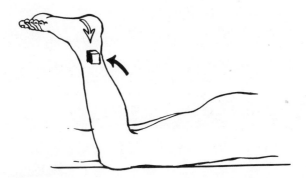

Gluteus Medius and Minimus; Tensor Fasciae Latae (L4, 5, S1; superior gluteal nerve). Testing internal rotation: With the subject prone and his knee flexed, the foot is moved laterally against resistance.

White arrows indicate the direction of movement in testing a given muscle. Black arrows show the direction of resistance. The blocks show the site of application of resistance.

Gluteus Maximus (L4, 5, S1, 2; inferior gluteal nerve). With the subject prone, the knee is lifted off the table against resistance.

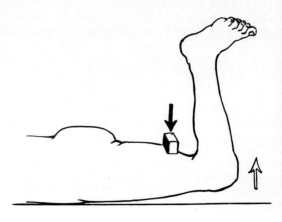

"Hamstring" Group (L4, 5, S1, 2; sciatic nerve). With the subject prone, the knee is flexed against resistance.

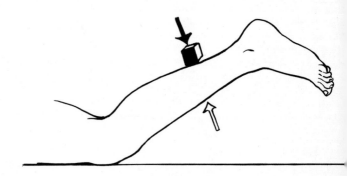

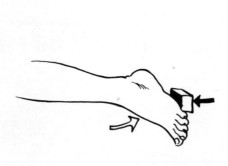

Gastrocnemius (L5, S1, 2; tibial nerve). With the subject prone, the foot is plantar-flexed against resistance.

Flexor Digitorum Longus (S1, 2; tibial nerve). The toe joints are plantar-flexed against resistance.

White arrows indicate the direction of movement in testing a given muscle. Black arrows show the direction of resistance. The blocks show the site of application of resistance.

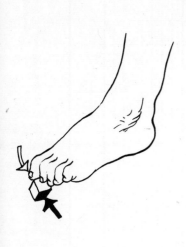

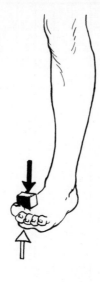

Flexor Hallucis Longus (L5, S1, 2; tibial nerve). The great toe is plantar-flexed against resistance. The second and third toes are also flexed.

Extensor Hallucis Longus (L4, 5, S1; deep peroneal nerve). The large toe is dorsiflexed against resistance.

Extensor Digitorum Longus (L4, 5, S1; deep peroneal nerve). The toes are dorsiflexed against resistance.

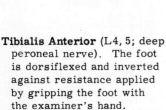

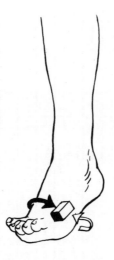

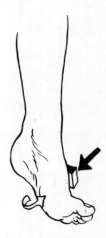

Tibialis Anterior (L4, 5; deep peroneal nerve). The foot is dorsiflexed and inverted against resistance applied by gripping the foot with the examiner's hand.

Peroneus Longus and Brevis (L5, S1; superficial peroneal nerve). The foot is everted against resistance applied by gripping the foot with the examiner's hand.

Tibialis Posterior (L5, S1; tibial nerve). The plantar-flexed foot is inverted against resistance applied by gripping the foot with examiner's hand.

White arrows indicate the direction of movement in testing a given muscle. Black arrows show the direction of resistance. The blocks show the site of application of resistance.

MUSCLE EXAMINATION

Patient's Name_____   Chart No._____

Date of Birth_____   Name of Institution_____

Date of Onset_____   Attending Physician_____ M. D.

Diagnosis:

LEFT   RIGHT

Examiner's Initials

Date

	NECK	Flexors
		Extensor group
		Sternocleidomastoid
	TRUNK	Flexors
		Rectus abdominis
		Rt. ext. obl. } Rotators { Lt. ext. obl.
		Lt. int. obl. } { Rt. int. obl.
		Extensors { Thoracic group / Lumbar group
		Pelvic elev.
		Quadratus lumb.
	HIP	Flexors
		Iliopsoas
		Extensors
		Gluteus maximus
		Abductors
		Gluteus medius
		Adductor group
		External rotator group
		Internal rotator group
		Sartorius
		Tensor fasciae latae
	KNEE	Flexors { Biceps femoris / Inner hamstrings
		Extensors
		Quadriceps
	ANKLE	Plantar flexors
		Gastrocnemius
		Soleus
	FOOT	Invertors { Tibialis anterior / Tibialis posterior
		Evertors { Peroneus brevis / Peroneus longus
	TOES	M. P. flexors
		Lumbricales
		I. P. flexors (1st) Flex. digit. br.
		I. P. flexors (2nd) Flex. digit. l.
		M. P. extensors { Ext. digit. l. / Ext. digit. br.
	HALLUX	M. P. flexor Flex. hall. br.
		I. P. flexor Flex. hall. l.
		M. P. extensor Ext. hall. br.
		I. P. extensor Ext. hall. l.

Measurements:

Cannot walk	Date
Stands	Date
Walks unaired	Date
Walks with apparatus	Date

Speech
Swallowing
Diaphragm
Intercostals

KEY

N Normal Complete range of motion against gravity with full resistance.
G Good*   Complete range of motion against gravity with some resistance.
F Fair*   Complete range of motion against gravity.
P Poor*   Complete range of motion with gravity eliminated.
T Trace   Evidence of slight contractility. No joint motion.
0 Zero   No evidence of contractility.

S or SS Spasm or severe spasm.
C or CC Contracture or severe contracture.
* Muscle spasm or contracture may limit range of motion. A question mark should be placed after the grading of a movement that is incomplete from this cause.

Muscle Examination. (Courtesy of The National Foundation for Infantile Paralysis.)

LEFT   RIGHT

Examiner's Initials

Date

	SCAPULA	Abductor Serratus anterior
		Elevator Upper trapezius
		Depressor Lower trapezius
		Adductors { Middle trapezius / Rhomboids
	SHOULDER	Flexor Anterior deltoid
		Extensors { Latissimus dorsi / Teres major
		Abductor Middle deltoid
		Horiz. abd. Posterior deltoid
		Horiz. add. Pectoralis major
		External rotator group
		Internal rotator group
	ELBOW	Flexors { Biceps brachii / Brachioradialis
		Extensor Triceps
	FOREARM	Supinator group
		Pronator group
	WRIST	Flexors { Flex. carpi rad. / Flex. carpi uln.
		Extensors { Ext. carpi rad. l. & br. / Ext. carpi uln.
	FINGERS	M. P. flexors Lumbricales
		I. P. flexors (1st) Flex. digit. sub.
		I. P. flexors (2nd) Flex. digit. prof.
		M. P. extensor Ext. digit. com.
		Adductors Palmar interossei
		Abductors Dorsal interossei
		Abductor digiti quinti
		Opponens digiti quinti
	THUMB	M. P. flexor Flex. poll. br.
		I. P. flexor Flex. poll. l.
		M. P. extensor Ext. poll. br.
		I. P. extensor Ext. poll. l.
		Abductors { Abd. poll. br. / Abd. poll. l.
		Adductor pollicis
		Opponens pollicis
	FACE:	

Additional data:

Supplied by The National Foundation for Infantile Paralysis, 301 East 42nd Street, N. Y. 17, N. Y., Publication PE 3.

Revised 7-56

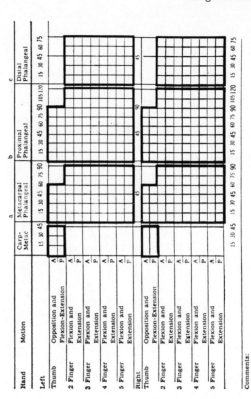

Bellevue Hospital
First Ave. and 26th St.
New York 16, N. Y.

Department of Physical Medicine and Rehabilitation

Name: _____   Ward: _____   Date: _____

Diagnosis: _____   Disability: _____   Joint: _____

Range of Motion Chart

Range is measured with cauda as zero, cranium as 180°. In rotating motions from midsagittal plane as zero to lateral plane as 180°. A = active, P = passive range of motion. Passive motion may be forced up to the threshold of pain.

The scale is divided in units of 15°. Range of motion is recorded by filling in the blocks in black. ▶ means that only the first named, ◀ that only the second named motion is possible. Progress is recorded by filling in the blocks in red, retrogression by marking X across the block, and by noting the dates under Comments.

Joint	Motion and Range		Left 15 30 45 60 75 90 105 120 135 150 165	Right 15 30 45 60 75 90 105 120 135 150 165
Shoulder	Flexion-Extension 0-180	A		
		P		
	Abduct-Adduction 0-180	A		
		P		
	Int-Ext Rotation 0-180	A		
		P		
Elbow	Flexion-Extension 0-150	A		
		P		
	Pronation-Supin 0-180	A		
		P		
Wrist	Dorsal-Palmar Fl 15-165	A		
		P		
	Radial-Ulnar Fl 60-150	A		
		P		
Hip	Flexion-Extension 0-120	A		
		P		
	Abduct-Adduction 0-45	A		
		P		
	Int-Ext Rotation 45-135	A		
		P		
Knee	Flexion-Extension 0-120	A		
		P		
Ankle	Dorsal-Plantar Fl 45-105	A		
		P		
	Invers-Eversion 60-120	A		
		P		
Toes	Flexion-Extension 60-165	A		
		P		

Comments:

Hand	Motion		Carp-Metac 15 30 45	a Metacarpal Phalangeal 15 30 45 60 75 90	b Proximal Phalangeal 15 30 45 60 75 90 105 120	c Distal Phalangeal 15 30 45 60 75
Left						
Thumb	Opposition and Flexion-Extension	A				
		P				
2 Finger	Flexion and Extension	A				
		P				
3 Finger	Flexion and Extension	A				
		P				
4 Finger	Flexion and Extension	A				
		P				
5 Finger	Flexion and Extension	A				
		P				
Right						
Thumb	Opposition and Flexion-Extension	A				
		P				
2 Finger	Flexion and Extension	A				
		P				
3 Finger	Flexion and Extension	A				
		P				
4 Finger	Flexion and Extension	A				
		P				
5 Finger	Flexion and Extension	A				
		P				

Comments:

Examiner _____

Range of Motion Chart. (Courtesy of Institute of Physical Medicine and Rehabilitation, New York University–Bellevue Medical Center.)

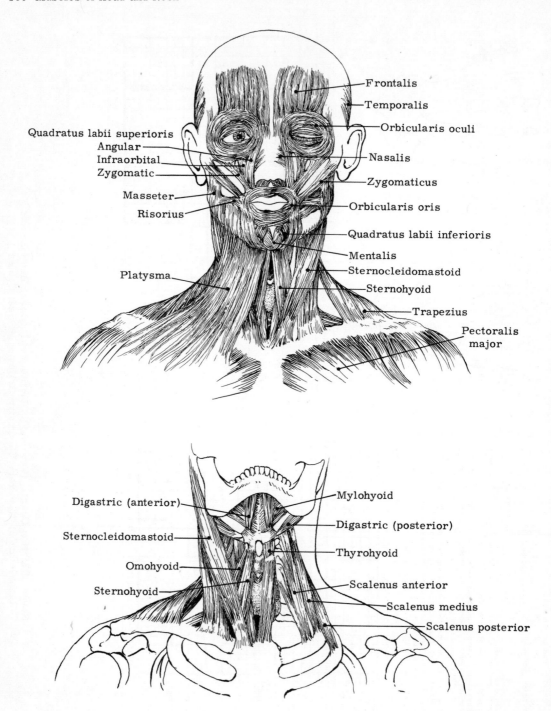

Frontalis

Temporalis

Orbicularis oculi

Quadratus labii superioris

Angular

Infraorbital

Zygomatic

Masseter

Risorius

Nasalis

Zygomaticus

Orbicularis oris

Quadratus labii inferioris

Mentalis

Sternocleidomastoid

Sternohyoid

Platysma

Trapezius

Pectoralis major

Digastric (anterior)

Sternocleidomastoid

Omohyoid

Sternohyoid

Mylohyoid

Digastric (posterior)

Thyrohyoid

Scalenus anterior

Scalenus medius

Scalenus posterior

Superficial Muscles of Head and Neck

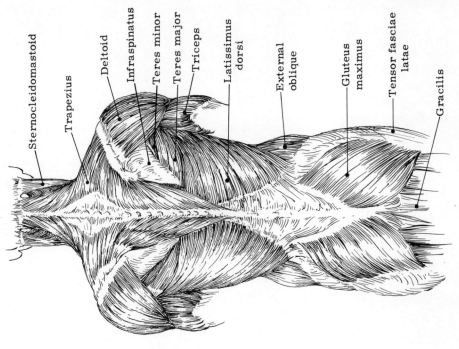

Sternocleidomastoid
Trapezius
Deltoid
Infraspinatus
Teres minor
Teres major
Triceps
Latissimus dorsi
External oblique
Gluteus maximus
Tensor fasciae latae
Gracilis

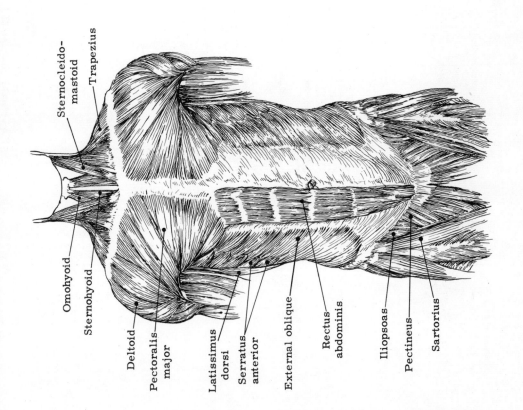

Sternocleido-mastoid
Trapezius
Omohyoid
Sternohyoid
Deltoid
Pectoralis major
Latissimus dorsi
Serratus anterior
External oblique
Rectus abdominis
Iliopsoas
Pectineus
Sartorius

Superficial Muscles of Trunk

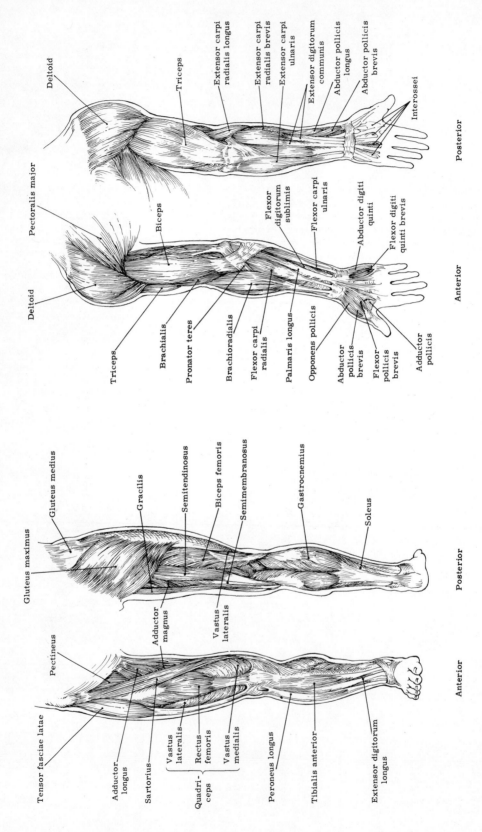

Deltoid

Triceps

Extensor carpi radialis longus

Extensor carpi radialis brevis

Extensor carpi ulnaris

Extensor digitorum communis

Abductor pollicis longus

Abductor pollicis brevis

Interossei

Posterior

Pectoralis major

Biceps

Deltoid

Triceps

Brachialis

Pronator teres

Brachioradialis

Flexor carpi radialis

Palmaris longus

Opponens pollicis

Abductor pollicis brevis

Flexor pollicis brevis

Adductor pollicis

Flexor digitorum sublimis

Flexor carpi ulnaris

Abductor digiti quinti

Flexor digiti quinti brevis

Anterior

Gluteus medius

Gluteus maximus

Gracilis

Semitendinosus

Biceps femoris

Semimembranosus

Adductor magnus

Vastus lateralis

Gastrocnemius

Soleus

Posterior

Pectineus

Tensor fasciae latae

Adductor longus

Sartorius

Vastus lateralis

Rectus femoris } Quadri- ceps

Vastus medialis

Peroneus longus

Tibialis anterior

Extensor digitorum longus

Anterior

Superficial Muscles of Right Extremities

10 . . .

Sensation

Sensation may be divided into 3 groups: superficial, deep, and combined. **Superficial** sensation is concerned with touch, pain, temperature, and two-point discrimination; **deep** sensation with muscle and joint position sense (proprioception), deep muscle pain, and vibration sense (pallesthesia). **Both** superficial and deep sensory mechanisms are involved in stereognosis, the recognition and naming of familiar objects placed in the hand; and topognosis, the ability to localize cutaneous stimuli. Stereognosis depends upon the integrity of the cerebral cortex.

Sensory Modalities and Sense Organs*†

Sensory Modality	Sense Organ	Classification	
		Receptors	Senses
Vision	Eye	Teleceptor	Special senses
Audition	Ear	Teleceptor	Special senses
Smell	Olfactory mucous membrane	Teleceptor	Special senses
Taste	Taste buds	Interoceptor	Special senses
Rotational acceleration	Semicircular canals		Special senses
Linear acceleration	Utricle		Special senses
Touch	Meissner's corpuscles, etc.	Exteroceptors	Cutaneous senses
Warmth	Ruffini's end organs	Exteroceptors	Cutaneous senses
Cold	Krause's end bulbs	Exteroceptors	Cutaneous senses
Pressure	Pacinian corpuscles	Exteroceptors	Cutaneous senses
Muscle stretch	Golgi tendon organs	Proprioceptors	
Muscle stretch	Muscle spindles	Proprioceptors	
Arterial blood pressure	Wall of carotid sinus and aortic arch	Interoceptors	Visceral senses
"Central" venous pressure	Wall of great veins, atria	Interoceptors	Visceral senses
Inflation of lung	Vagal endings in lung parenchyma	Interoceptors	Visceral senses
Temperature of blood in head	Cells in hypothalamus	Interoceptors	Visceral senses
Arterial partial pressure of O_2 (P_{O_2})	Carotid and aortic bodies	Interoceptors	Visceral senses
Arterial partial pressure of CO_2 (P_{CO_2})	Receptors in or near medulla oblongata	Interoceptors	Visceral senses
Osmotic pressure of plasma	Receptors in anterior hypothalamus	Interoceptors	Visceral senses
Blood glucose level	Cells in hypothalamus (?)	Interoceptors	Visceral senses
Some aspect of ECF volume	(?)	Interoceptors	Visceral senses

*Reproduced, with permission, from Ganong: Review of Medical Physiology, Lange, 1963.
†There is considerable dispute about whether the histologic specificity of the cutaneous endings is as definite as the traditional listing given here (see text).

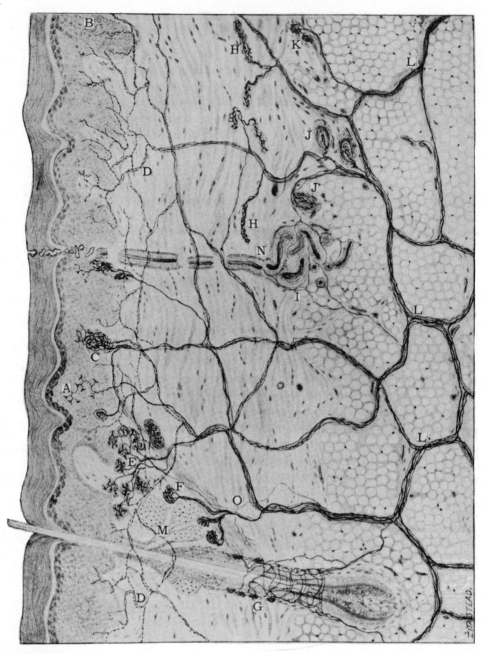

Composite Diagram Showing the Innervation of the Human Skin. (Reproduced, with permission, from Woollard, Weddell, and Harpman, J. Anat. **74**:1939-40.)

A. Merkel's corpuscles, subserving touch.
B. Free nerve endings, subserving pain.
C. Meissner's corpuscles, subserving touch.
D. Nerve fibers, subserving pain.
E. Krause's end bulbs, subserving cold.
F. Nerve endings, subserving warmth (sometimes called Ruffini's endings).
G. Nerve fibers and endings on the hair follicles, subserving touch.
H. Ruffini's endings, subserving pressure.
I. Sympathetic nerve fibers innervating sweat glands.
J. Pacini's corpuscles, subserving pressure.
K. Golgi-Mazzoni endings, subserving pressure.
L. Nerve trunks containing thick and thin fibers.
M. Sebaceous gland.
N. Sweat gland.
O. Sympathetic fibers supplying erector pili muscle.

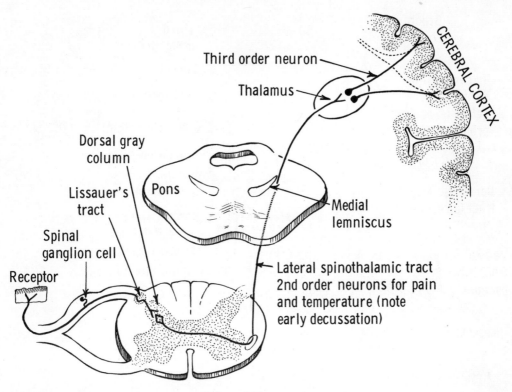

Third order neuron
Thalamus
Dorsal gray column
Lissauer's tract
Pons
Spinal ganglion cell
Receptor
CEREBRAL CORTEX
Medial lemniscus
Lateral spinothalamic tract 2nd order neurons for pain and temperature (note early decussation)

Pain and Temperature

Head's classification divides cutaneous sensibility into 2 groups, epicritic and protopathic, each served by a different type of neuron. His conclusions are based on observations of regenerating nerves following injury. Protopathic senses return rapidly (7-10 weeks), whereas epicritic senses remain impaired for 1-2 years or do not return at all. The **epicritic** senses are concerned with perception of light touch, two-point discrimination, and small differences in temperature; the **protopathic** senses with pain and severe degrees of temperature.

Receptors.

Specialized cells for detecting particular changes in the environment are called receptors. **Exteroceptors** include those receptors affected primarily by the external environment: Meissner's corpuscles, Merkel's corpuscles, and hair cells for touch; Krause's end bulbs for cold, Ruffini's cylinders for warmth, and free nerve endings for pain. **Teleceptors** are sensitive to distant stimuli. **Proprioceptors** receive impulses primarily from muscle spindles and Golgi tendon organs. **Interoceptors** are sensitive to changes within visceral tissues and blood vessels.

Each individual receptor fires completely or not at all when stimulated. The intensity of a stimulus, therefore, is reflected in the stimulation of more end organs at an increased rate of discharge over a longer period of time. **Adaptation** refers to the diminution in rate of discharge of some receptors upon constant stimulation.

Anatomy of Sensation.

The cell bodies of the peripheral sensory neurons are located in the spinal root ranglia and homologous cranial nerve ganglia. These are unipolar cells with a single process (dendraxon), which splits dichotomatously into central and peripheral branches. The peripheral processes form the sensory fibers of the peripheral nerves, which end in special receptors located in the skin, muscles, tendons, etc. The central processes pass via the dorsal roots (or cranial nerve trunks) into the spinal cord and brain stem, where they make synaptic connections with second order neurons.

Central Connections.

Sensory impulses which reach the level of consciousness are transmitted to the postcentral gyrus of the cerebral cortex via the

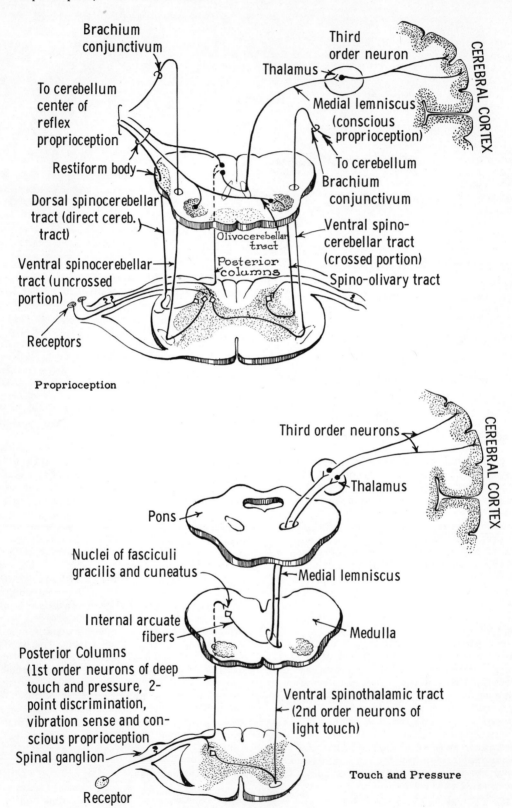

Brachium
conjunctivum

Third
order neuron

Thalamus

CEREBRAL CORTEX

To cerebellum
center of
reflex
proprioception

Medial lemniscus
(conscious
proprioception)

Restiform body

Dorsal spinocerebellar
tract (direct cereb.
tract)

To cerebellum
Brachium
conjunctivum

Olivocerebellar
tract

Ventral spino-
cerebellar tract
(crossed portion)

Ventral spinocerebellar
tract (uncrossed
portion)

Posterior
columns

Spino-olivary tract

Receptors

Proprioception

Third order neurons

CEREBRAL CORTEX

Thalamus

Pons

Nuclei of fasciculi
gracilis and cuneatus

Medial lemniscus

Internal arcuate
fibers

Medulla

Posterior Columns
(1st order neurons of deep
touch and pressure, 2-
point discrimination,
vibration sense and con-
scious proprioception

Ventral spinothalamic tract
(2nd order neurons of
light touch)

Spinal ganglion

Receptor

Touch and Pressure

thalamus and thalamic radiations. Light touch reaches the thalamus through second order neurons of the posterior gray column which, after delayed decussation, form the ventral spinothalamic tract. Light touch fibers ascend via the ipsilateral dorsal columns as well as the opposite ventral spinothalamic tract, and this double representation may account for touch preservation in spinal cord lesions affecting other modalities. Pain and temperature fibers enter Lissauer's tract but soon synapse with second order neurons in the dorsal gray column the axons of which decussate immediately and enter the lateral spinothalamic tract. Pressure sense, two-point discrimination, vibration sense, and conscious proprioception ascend uncrossed in the posterior columns to the gracilis and cuneate nuclei, from where their second order neurons decussate and enter the medial lemniscus, passing to the thalamus. **Proprioceptive** impulses pass to the cerebellum through its superior and inferior peduncles. The brachium conjunctivum or superior cerebellar peduncle includes the ventral spinocerebellar tract. The restiform body or inferior cerebellar peduncle includes fibers of the dorsal spinocerebellar tract, the spino-olivocerebellar tract, and external arcuate fibers from the gracilis and cuneate nuclei.

Symptoms and Signs of Disturbances of Sensation.

A. Symptoms: **Pain** may be local or diffuse, constant or intermittent, burning, shooting, gnawing, sharp, dull, knife-like, etc. **Paresthesia** consists of abnormal sensations, numbness, tingling, formication (crawling sensations). The character of the pain may reflect the underlying site of the disorder. In peripheral nerve lesions, pain is usually limited to the area supplied by the affected nerve or nerves. Pain is often burning or prickling in type, often worse at night and unrelated to position.

The pain of trigeminal and other neuralgias is limited to the tissues supplied by one or more branches of the affected nerve. Pains are usually very severe, although individual pains may be brief in duration and abrupt in onset with lightning-like or electric shock qualities. These are frequently precipitated by peripheral stimuli activating a trigger zone.

Root pains usually are localized to the dermatome supplied by the affected root. These pains are often produced or aggravated by coughing, sneezing, or straining, and they may awaken the patient after several hours of sleep and may be relieved within one-half hour after assuming the upright position.

Maneuvers which stretch the involved roots aggravate or produce the pains.

Thalamic pains affect the contralateral half of the body. Pains are persistent and readily aggravated by emotional stress and fatigue. Usually they are described as burning, drawing, pulling, swelling, tense pains of a highly distressing type.

B. Signs: Hypesthesia, diminished sensation. Anesthesia, complete loss of sensation. Hypalgesia, diminished sensibility to pain. Analgesia, complete loss of pain sensibility. Hyperesthesia, increased tactile sensibility. Hyperalgesia, increased sensibility to pain (tenderness). Dissociate anesthesia, loss of some forms of cutaneous sensibility (usually pain and temperature) and preservation of others (tactile). Astereognosis, inability to recognize familiar objects by the sense of touch, anesthesia not being present, usually indicates a lesion in the parietal cerebral cortex. Atopognosis, inability to localize tactile stimuli. **Extinction.** - With 2 simultaneous stimulations, one sensation is well localized and the other poorly perceived or not at all. **Displacement.** - With 2 simultaneous stimulations, one is well localized and the other is displaced toward it. **Allesthesia (allochiria).** - A single stimulation is perceived displaced across the midline to a homologous region. **Synesthesia (synchiria).** - With a single stimulation 2 sensations are perceived, one well localized and the other appearing in an area in which there is dysesthesia or burning pain, or on the opposite side of the body. Baragnosis is inability to distinguish between different weights.

Overlap.

In peripheral nerve injuries the impairment of touch perception corresponds more nearly to the anatomic distribution of the involved nerve than does the impairment of pain perception, which is less extensive because overlap from adjacent peripheral nerves supplies many pain endings. However, in lesions of the dorsal roots the loss of pain perception closely parallels the anatomic distribution of the root and touch perception is largely retained, due to overlap supplied by adjacent roots.

Methods of Examination. (These require the cooperation of the patient.)

Light touch may be tested with a wisp of cotton; pressure sense with the unsharpened end of a lead pencil; pain with a pin or a simple algesimeter (made by placing a large-headed pin in the barrel of a glass syringe, allowing the point to extend through the tip, and replacing the plunger; the weight of the plunger thus assures uniform stimulation); temperature with test tubes containing hot and cold water; vibration sense with a tuning fork placed over the bone of the part tested; stereognosis with the use of familiar objects, e.g., coins, pen, knife. **Position sense.** - While blindfolded, the patient is asked to describe the various positions of his extremities as the examiner moves them. Other tests of proprioception include the heel-to-knee test, finger-to-finger test, finger-to-nose test, and Romberg's test or sign (see p. 295). **Number writing.** - Test ability of patient to recognize numbers traced lightly on the skin. **Two-point discrimination.** - Using calipers, determine the smallest area in which 2 points can be separately perceived. **Double stimulation.** - Two stimulations may be presented together to both sides of the body in homologous areas (simultaneous homologous), or to nonhomologous areas (simultaneous nonhomologus). Similarly, 2 stimulations of the same side of the body can be carried out.

DISORDERS CHARACTERIZED BY MARKED SENSORY DISTURBANCES

Acroparesthesia.

Acroparesthesia is characterized by numbness and prickly or tingling sensations of the tips of the fingers and toes. This is classed as a vasomotor-trophic disorder in which the nerve endings or end organs are probably involved.

Brown-Sequard Syndrome.

(Due to hemisection of the spinal cord as a result of syringomyelia, cord tumor, hematomyelia, bullet or stab wounds, etc.): (1) Ipsilateral lower motor neuron paralysis in the segment of the lesion. (2) Ipsilateral upper motor neuron paralysis below the level of the lesion. (3) Ipsilateral zone of cutaneous anesthesia in the segment of the lesion. (4) Ipsilateral hyperesthesia below the anesthetic zone. (5) Ipsilateral loss of proprioceptive, vibratory, and two-point discrimination sense below the level of the lesion. (6) Contralateral zone of hyperesthesia in the segment of the lesion. (7) Contralateral loss of pain and temperature sense below the lesion.

Syringomyelia.

Syringomyelia is characterized by loss of pain and temperature sense (see p. 195) but preservation of touch and pressure senses in the affected parts (dissociate anesthesia). It is produced by gliosis around the central canal of the spinal cord.

Causalgia.

Causalgia is characterized by disagreeable, painful, burning sensations, usually along the distribution of the median or tibial nerves, associated with trophic changes in the skin and nails. Moist applications seem to bring relief. Causalgia results from partial injuries of the median and posterior tibial or sciatic nerves. It may frequently be relieved by sympathetic block or sympathectomy.

Multiple Sclerosis.

Numbness and paresthesia are often present in the early stages. Later there are marked sensory and motor disturbances caused by the disseminated patches of gliosis in the cord and brain.

Tabes Dorsalis.

Tabes dorsalis is characterized by marked ataxia due to loss of the proprioceptive pathways (dorsal roots and posterior columns). Subjective sensory disturbances known as tabetic crises consist of severe, cramping pains in the stomach, larynx, or other viscera.

Pernicious Anemia.

Advanced cases are associated with combined degeneration of the posterior and lateral columns of the spinal cord, thus producing marked sensory and motor disturbances. Diminished vibration sense is a prominent feature of the sensory involvement. (See p. 387.)

Thalamic Lesions.

Lesions of the thalamus are characterized by outbursts of severe, poorly localized pain (thalamic pain) associated with weakness, ataxia, hyperkinesia, paresthesia, and loss of ability to discriminate or localize simple crude sensations. Slight stimuli may evoke severe and disagreeable sensations.

Déjerine's Cortical Sensory Syndrome.

Lesions of the sensory parietal cortex may impair the ability to make fine sensory distinctions, although the ability to recognize pain, temperature, and vibration may be unimpaired. Thus there may be contralateral astereognosis, inability to appreciate or identify numbers or figures traced on the skin, inability to perceive passive joint motions, difficulty in distinguishing between different weights, and inability to recognize various textures by touch.

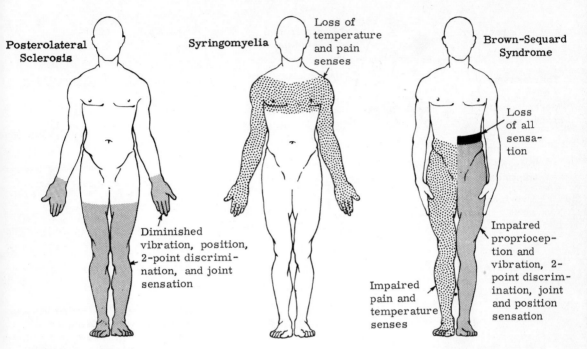

Posterolateral Sclerosis

Syringomyelia

Loss of temperature and pain senses

Brown-Sequard Syndrome

Loss of all sensation

Diminished vibration, position, 2-point discrimination, and joint sensation

Impaired pain and temperature senses

Impaired proprioception and vibration, 2-point discrimination, joint and position sensation

Characteristic Sensory Disturbances. Left: Posterolateral sclerosis (diminished vibration, position, joint, two-point discrimination, more so in lower than upper extremities). Center: Syringomyelia (dissociated sensory loss of pain and temperature). Right: Brown-Sequard syndrome with lesion at left tenth thoracic level.

Herpes Zoster.

Herpes zoster (shingles) is due to a viral inflammation of the posterior root ganglia, producing pain and vesicle formation in the segmental distribution of the involved roots. The disease is self-limited, but sensation is sometimes lost after the inflammation disappears. Motor paralysis, usually transient, may also occur. Painful persistent paresthesias, resistant to treatment, may occur in the later phases (post-herpetic neuralgia).

Restless Legs Syndrome.

Paresthesias of legs, coldness of feet, and tiredness of the lower extremities of intermittent occurrence and unknown etiology. Paresthesias (pins and needles, numbness, vibration, and cramps) cause the patient to seek temporary relief by keeping his legs in motion while in bed.

"Root Pains."

These are segmental in distribution and occur with various lesions of the dorsal roots of the spinal nerves, e.g., cord tumors, fractures, or inflammatory diseases of the vertebrae, and meningitis. The pains are sharp and lightning-like.

Neuritis.

Inflammation or other alteration of a peripheral nerve (toxic, traumatic, or infectious) is characterized by pain and tenderness in the distribution and along the course of the nerve. In advanced cases there is complete loss of both motor and sensory functions of the nerve, with diminution or loss of reflexes.

Neuralgia.

Neuralgia is characterized by bouts of severe pain which are often set off by accidental stimulation of a "trigger zone." Usually there is no demonstrable pathology. Trigeminal neuralgia (tic douloureux, trifacial neuralgia) is a form in which the paroxysms occur in the distribution of one of the main branches of the trigeminal nerve; the bouts of pain last only a few seconds.

Complete Peripheral Nerve Injuries.

These are characterized by loss of all forms of sensibility in the dependent areas. The loss of touch is most marked and corresponds most nearly to the anatomic distribution of the nerve than does the loss of pain, because overlap from adjacent peripheral nerves supplies many pain endings. **Incomplete** peripheral nerve injuries show a lesser degree of sensory loss and often show subjective symptoms such as pain.

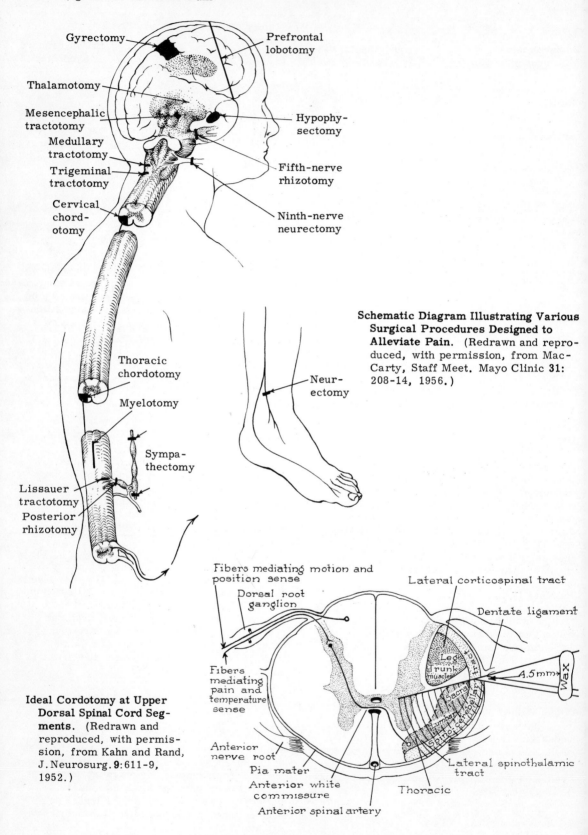

Gyrectomy

Prefrontal lobotomy

Thalamotomy

Mesencephalic tractotomy

Hypophysectomy

Medullary tractotomy

Trigeminal tractotomy

Fifth-nerve rhizotomy

Cervical chordotomy

Ninth-nerve neurectomy

Thoracic chordotomy

Neurectomy

Myelotomy

Sympathectomy

Lissauer tractotomy

Posterior rhizotomy

Schematic Diagram Illustrating Various Surgical Procedures Designed to Alleviate Pain. (Redrawn and reproduced, with permission, from MacCarty, Staff Meet. Mayo Clinic **31**: 208-14, 1956.)

Ideal Cordotomy at Upper Dorsal Spinal Cord Segments. (Redrawn and reproduced, with permission, from Kahn and Rand, J. Neurosurg. **9**:611-9, 1952.)

Fibers mediating motion and position sense

Dorsal root ganglion

Lateral corticospinal tract

Dentate ligament

Leg
Trunk
muscles

Sacral

4.5mm

Wax

Lumbar

Spino-cerebellar tract

Fibers mediating pain and temperature sense

Anterior nerve root

Pia mater

Anterior white commissure

Thoracic

Lateral spinothalamic tract

Anterior spinal artery

11 . . .
Cutaneous Innervation

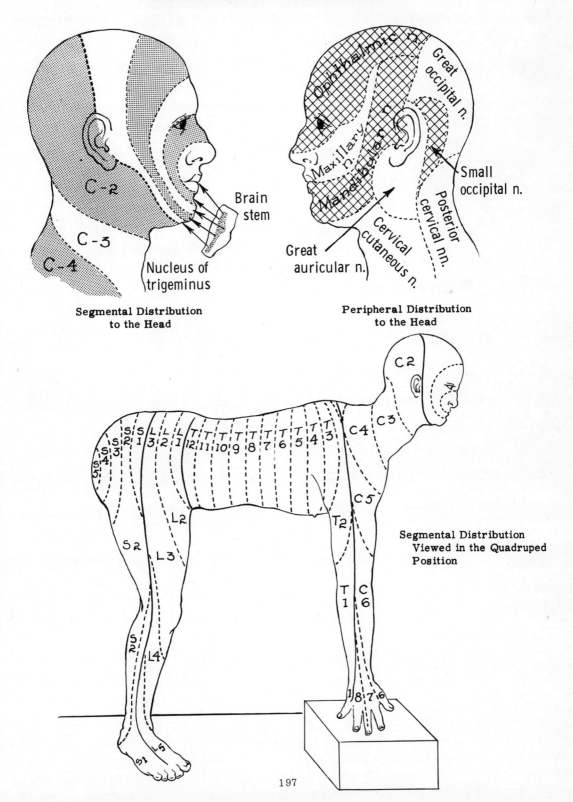

Segmental Distribution
to the Head

Peripheral Distribution
to the Head

Segmental Distribution
Viewed in the Quadruped
Position

198

Peripheral Distribution

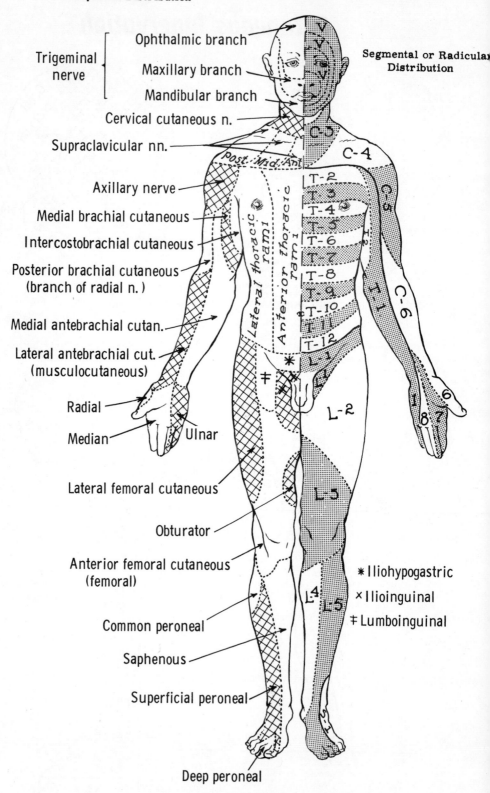

Trigeminal nerve

- Ophthalmic branch
- Maxillary branch
- Mandibular branch

Segmental or Radicular Distribution

Cervical cutaneous n.

Supraclavicular nn.

Axillary nerve

Medial brachial cutaneous

Intercostobrachial cutaneous

Posterior brachial cutaneous (branch of radial n.)

Medial antebrachial cutan.

Lateral antebrachial cut. (musculocutaneous)

Radial

Median

Ulnar

Lateral femoral cutaneous

Obturator

Anterior femoral cutaneous (femoral)

Common peroneal

Saphenous

Superficial peroneal

Deep peroneal

*Iliohypogastric
×Ilioinguinal
‡Lumboinguinal

Cutaneous Innervation

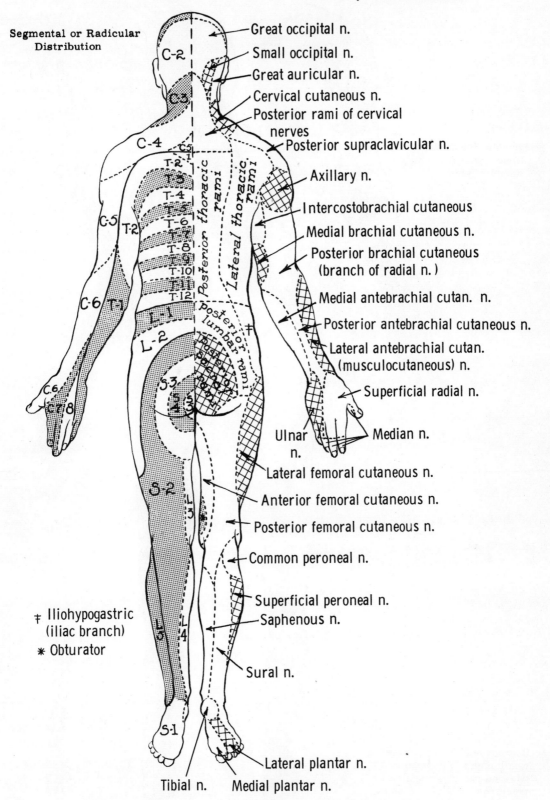

Segmental or Radicular
Distribution

C-2

C-3

C-4   C-5
        T-2
        T-3
        T-4
        T-5
C-5 T-2 T-6
        T-7
        T-8
        T-9
        T-10
        T-11
C-6 T-1 T-12
        L-1
        L-2
        S-3
        S-5
        S-4
C-6
C-7-8

S-2   L-3

‡ Iliohypogastric
   (iliac branch)
✱ Obturator

L-5   L-4

S-1

Tibial n.

Posterior thoracic rami

Lateral thoracic rami

Posterior lumbar rami

Great occipital n.

Small occipital n.

Great auricular n.

Cervical cutaneous n.

Posterior rami of cervical
nerves

Posterior supraclavicular n.

Axillary n.

Intercostobrachial cutaneous

Medial brachial cutaneous n.

Posterior brachial cutaneous
(branch of radial n.)

Medial antebrachial cutan. n.

Posterior antebrachial cutaneous n.

Lateral antebrachial cutan.
(musculocutaneous) n.

Superficial radial n.

Ulnar   Median n.
n.

Lateral femoral cutaneous n.

Anterior femoral cutaneous n.

Posterior femoral cutaneous n.

Common peroneal n.

Superficial peroneal n.
Saphenous n.

Sural n.

Lateral plantar n.

Medial plantar n.

Cutaneous Innervation

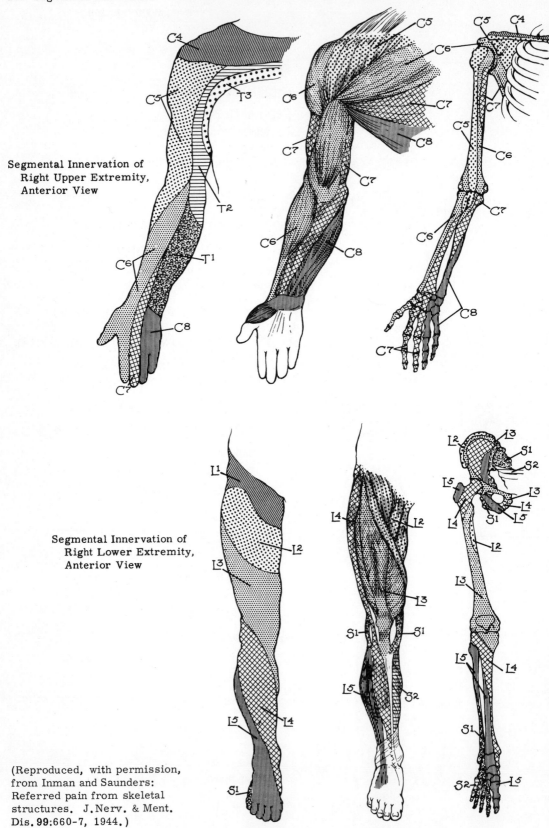

Segmental Innervation of
Right Upper Extremity,
Anterior View

Segmental Innervation of
Right Lower Extremity,
Anterior View

(Reproduced, with permission,
from Inman and Saunders:
Referred pain from skeletal
structures. J.Nerv. & Ment.
Dis.99:660-7, 1944.)

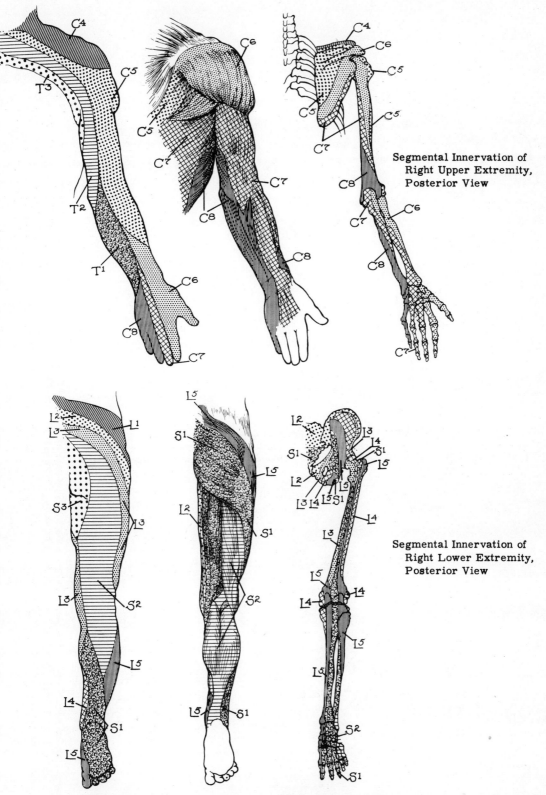

Segmental Innervation of
Right Upper Extremity,
Posterior View

Segmental Innervation of
Right Lower Extremity,
Posterior View

(Reproduced, with permission, from Inman and Saunders: Ibid.)

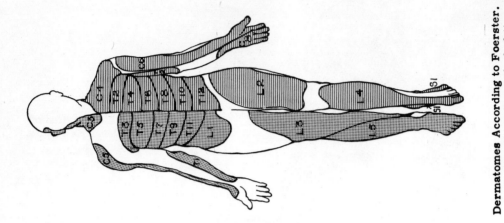

Dermatomes According to Foerster. Determined by the method of "remaining sensibility" on human cases.

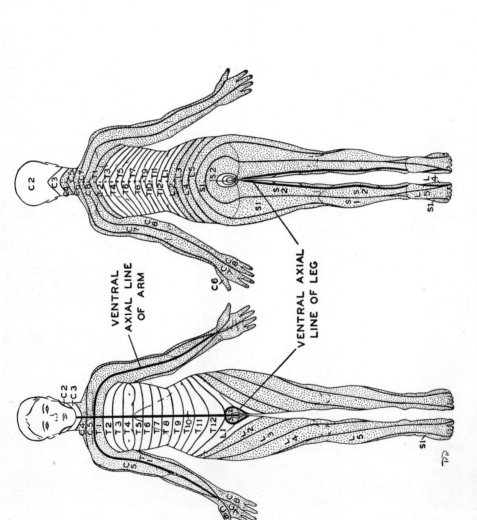

Dermatomes According to Keegan. Based upon hypalgesia from compression of single nerve roots. (Reproduced, with permission, from Keegan and Garrett, Anat. Rec. 102:4, 409-38, 1948.)

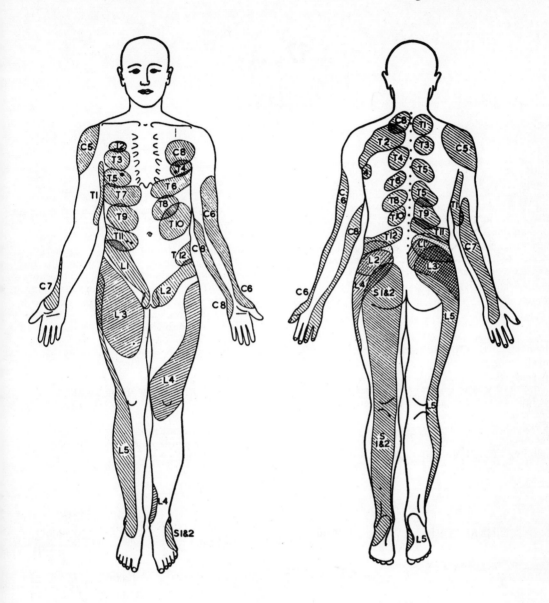

The Segmental Areas of Deep Pain. Developed by injection of 6 per cent saline into corresponding interspinous ligaments; diagrams constructed from Kellgren material. (Reproduced, with
permission, from Lewis: Pain. Macmillan, 1942.)

12 . . .

Reflexes

Reflexes are inborn stimulus-response mechanisms. The instinctive behavior of lower animals is governed largely by reflexes; in man behavior is more a matter of conditioning, and reflexes are subordinated as basic defense mechanisms. The reflexes are, however, extremely important in the diagnosis and localization of neurologic lesions.

ANATOMY OF REFLEXES
(The Reflex Arc)

The essential neural portion of a reflex includes a sensory and a motor neuron. Several structures, however, are involved: (1) A receptor, such as a special sense organ, cutaneous end organ, or a neuromuscular spindle, stimulation of which initiates an im-

pulse. (2) The afferent (or sensory) neuron, which transmits the impulse through a peripheral nerve to the CNS, where synapse occurs with an intercalated neuron. (3) An intercalated neuron, which relays the impulse to the efferent nerve. (4) The efferent (or motor) neuron, which, passing outward in the nerve trunk, delivers the impulse to an effector. (5) An effector, such as a muscle or gland which produces the response.

Interruption of the reflex arc at any point will abolish the response.

TYPES OF REFLEXES

The reflexes which are of importance to the clinical neurologist may be divided into 4 groups: (1) Superficial (or skin and mucous

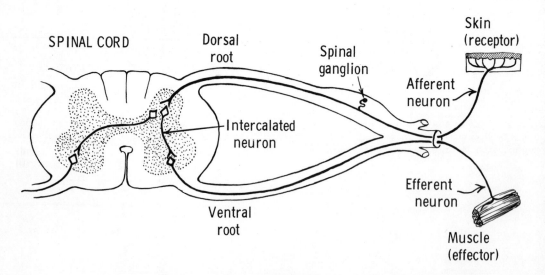

Simple Reflex Arc

membrane) reflexes, (2) deep (or myotatic) reflexes, (3) visceral (or organic) reflexes, and (4) pathologic (or abnormal) reflexes.

Reflexes may also be classified according to the level of their central representation, e.g., as spinal, bulbar (postural and righting reflexes), midbrain, or cerebellar reflexes. Idiomuscular or neuromuscular responses, such as myo-edema, are not true reflexes and so are classified as pseudoreflexes. They are responses of irritable muscle tissue to direct stimulation.

Superficial Reflexes.

A. Mucous Membrane Reflexes:

1. Corneal (or conjunctival) reflex - Blinking of the eye upon gentle irritation of the cornea or conjunctiva with a small piece of absorbent cotton. This reflex is lost in lesions of the fifth or seventh cranial nerves or their central connections in the pons. Corneal ulcers often result when the reflex is abolished; this is due to the absence of the protective mechanism.

2. Nasal (or sneeze) reflex - Sneezing when the nasal membrane is irritated depends upon the afferents of the fifth nerve and the central connections and motor nuclei of the fifth to tenth cranial nerves and the upper cervical nerves.

3. Pharyngeal (or gag) reflex - Retching or gagging when the pharynx is irritated is absent in lesions of the ninth or tenth cranial nerves or their nuclei, and in hysteria.

4. Uvular reflex - Raising of the uvula in phonation or upon irritation of its mucous membrane is also dependent upon the ninth and tenth nerves.

B. Skin Reflexes:

1. Interscapular reflex - Drawing inward of the scapula when the skin of the interscapular space is irritated.

2. Upper and lower abdominal reflexes - (Tested on each side.) Tensing of the muscles beneath the skin area stroked usually causes the umbilicus to move in the direction of the skin area stimulated.

3. Cremasteric reflex - Elevation of the testicle upon stroking the inner aspect of the thigh.

4. Gluteal reflex - Contraction of the buttocks when the skin over them is irritated.

5. Plantar reflex - Plantar flexion of the toes upon stroking the sole of the foot. In children there is usually also a retraction of the foot.

6. Anal reflex - Contraction of the sphincter ani upon stroking the perianal area or upon inserting a gloved finger into the rectum.

C. Significance of Abnormal Reflex Responses: Diminished or absent superficial skin reflexes are of neurologic importance when associated with exaggerated deep reflexes and positive pathologic reflexes. This combination is diagnostic of upper motor neuron involvement. The explanation offered for the absence of skin reflexes in such cases is that the reflex arc, which probably includes the cortex, is interrupted at the higher level.

Deep Reflexes.

A. Important Deep Reflexes:

1. Maxillary (jaw jerk) reflex - Sudden closure of the jaw upon striking the middle of the chin when the mouth is slightly open or upon tapping a pencil laid on the lower teeth or jaw.

2. Biceps reflex - Flexion at the elbow when the biceps tendon is struck.

3. Triceps reflex - Extension at the elbow when the triceps tendon is struck.

4. Periosteoradial reflex - Flexion and supination of the forearm upon striking the styloid process of the radius.

5. Periosteo-ulnar reflex - Extension and ulnar abduction of the wrist when the styloid process of the ulna is struck.

6. Wrist reflexes - Extension or flexion of the wrist when the corresponding tendons are sharply struck.

7. Patellar (knee jerk) reflex - Extension at the knee when the patellar tendon is struck. Absence of this reflex is known as Westphal's sign. If the reflex cannot be obtained in the normal manner, the Jendrassik method of reinforcement should be tried. This is done by having the patient pull on his clenched hands at the moment the test is made.

8. Achilles tendon reflex - Plantar flexion of the foot when the Achilles tendon is struck.

B. Significance of Abnormal Reflex Responses: Diminution or absence of these reflexes may result from any lesion which interrupts the reflex arc, e.g., peripheral nerve disease, involvement of the posterior columns of gray matter of the spinal cord, and cerebellar disease. Since the deep reflexes are normally under partial inhibition by the higher centers, lesions of the motor cortex or pyramidal tracts (upper motor neuron) result in exaggerated deep reflexes and muscular rigidity. Hyperactive reflexes also occur in strychnine poisoning and in some functional disorders.

Visceral Reflexes.

A. Pupillary Reflexes:

1. Light reflex - Constriction of the pupil when light is thrown on the retina. This de-

SUMMARY OF REFLEXES

Reflexes	Afferent Nerve	Center	Efferent Nerve
SUPERFICIAL REFLEXES			
Corneal	Cranial V	Pons	Cranial VII
Nasal (sneeze)	Cranial V	Brain stem and upper cord	Cranials V, VII, IX, X, and spinal nerves of expiration
Pharyngeal and uvular	Cranial IX	Medulla	Cranial X
Upper abdominal	T7, 8, 9, 10	T7, 8, 9, 10	T7, 8, 9, 10
Lower abdominal	T10, 11, 12	T10, 11, 12	T10, 11, 12
Cremasteric	Femoral	L1	Genitofemoral
Plantar	Tibial	S1, 2	Tibial
Anal	Pudendal	S4, 5	Pudendal
DEEP REFLEXES			
Jaw	Cranial V	Pons	Cranial V
Biceps	Musculocutaneous	C5, 6	Musculocutaneous
Triceps	Radial	C6, 7	Radial
Periosteo-radial	Radial	C6, 7, 8	Radial
Wrist (flexion)	Median	C6, 7, 8	Median
Wrist (extension)	Radial	C7, 8	Radial
Patellar	Femoral	L2, 3, 4	Femoral
Achilles	Tibial	S1, 2	Tibial
VISCERAL REFLEXES			
Light	Cranial II	Midbrain	Cranial III
Accommodation	Cranial II	Occipital cortex	Cranial III
Ciliospinal	A sensory nerve	T1, 2	Cervical sympathetics
Oculocardiac	Cranial V	Medulla	Cranial X
Carotid sinus	Cranial IX	Medulla	Cranial X
Bulbocavernosus	Pudendal	S2, 3, 4	Pelvic autonomic
Bladder and rectal	Pudendal	S2, 3, 4	Pudendal and autonomics

pends upon the integrity of cranial nerves II and III and certain of their central connections. (For Argyll Robertson pupil, see p. 294.)

2. Consensual light reflex - Constriction of the pupil when light is thrown into the opposite eye is dependent upon central commissural connections.

3. Accommodation reflex - Constriction of pupils when the patient looks at near objects and the eyes are converged depends upon the occipital cortex and pathways.

4. Ciliospinal reflex - Dilatation of the pupil upon painful stimulation of any sensory area, usually by pinching the neck, is dependent upon the integrity of the cervical sympathetics. This reflex is lost in Horner's syndrome (see p. 147).

B. Oculocardiac Reflex: Slowing of the heart rate produced by pressure over the eyeballs. This reflex is used for testing the integrity of cranial nerves V and X.

C. Carotid Sinus Reflex: Slowing of the heart and fall in blood pressure (vasodilatation) produced by pressure over the carotid sinus in the neck. This reflex is abolished by lesions of cranial nerves IX or X, and hyperactive in certain persons with marked vasomotor instability, in whom slight stimulation of this sort produces fainting (carotid sinus syncope).

D. Bulbocavernosus Reflex: Contraction of the bulbocavernosus muscle (compressor urethrae) upon stroking the dorsum of the glans penis.

E. Bladder and Rectal Reflexes: The normal sphincter control of urine and feces by the pelvic autonomics is dependent upon these reflexes. Interruption of these motor fibers results in incontinence. Interruption in the afferent tract (as in tabes dorsalis) abolishes the urge to urinate or defecate, resulting in distention and dribbling.

F. Mass Reflex (of Riddoch): Sudden emptying of the bladder and bowel, flexion of the lower limbs, and sweating are present in some normal infants, but in adults are under the control of the higher centers and may be released in emotional states such as fear. This reflex is released pathologically by complete severance of the spinal cord, being set off by stimulating the skin below the level of the lesion, as by scratching the sole of the foot.

Pathologic Reflexes.

In this group are found certain primitive defense responses which occur only with lesions of the upper motor neuron. Normally they are suppressed by cerebral inhibition. When the lower motor neuron is separated from the influence of the higher centers, as in pyramidal tract lesions, they are released. Not infrequently they can be elicited in normal infants up to 5-7 months of age. The principal pathologic reflexes are as follows:

A. Lower Extremity:

1. Babinski's sign - Extension of the large toe with fanning of the small toes upon stimulation of the plantar surface of the foot. Szapiro recommends forcibly flexing the second to fifth toes while eliciting Babinski's response in the usual manner.

2. Chaddock's toe sign - Babinski response obtained by stroking the lateral malleolus.

3. Gordon's leg sign - Babinski-like response upon squeezing the calf muscle.

4. Oppenheim's sign - Babinski-like response elicited by firm downward stroking of the tibia and tibialis anterior muscle.

5. Gonda reflex - Upward movement of the big toe upon pressing one of the other toes downward and releasing it with a snap.

6. Schaefer's sign - Babinski-like response upon squeezing the Achilles tendon.

7. Stransky reflex - Dorsiflexion of the great toe accompanying or following the vigorous abduction of the little toe for 1-2 seconds with subsequent sudden release.

8. Rossolimo's sign - Flexion of the toes upon tapping the ball of the foot.

9. Mendel-Bechterew sign - Flexor movement of the 4 outer toes upon striking the dorsum of the foot over the cuboid bone.

10. Hirschberg's sign - Adduction and internal rotation of the foot upon stroking the inner border of the foot.

11. Ankle clonus - A continued rapid flexion and extension of the foot obtained by forcibly and quickly dorsiflexing the foot while the leg is held up by the examiner's other hand placed under the popliteal space. A rapidly exhaustible clonus may be normal.

12. Patellar clonus (trepidation sign) - A rapid up-and-down movement of the patella when it is forcibly depressed with a quick movement while the leg is in extension and relaxed.

13. Grasset and Gaussel sign - When lying on his back, the patient can raise either leg separately but cannot raise both simultaneously. If the paralyzed leg is raised, it will fall back heavily when the examiner raises the unaffected leg.

14. Hoover's sign - With the hemiplegic patient recumbent, the examiner places the

palms of his hands beneath the patient's heels and asks the patient to press down. Pressure will be felt only from the heel of the nonparalyzed leg. The examiner then takes his hand from beneath the nonparalyzed heel, places it on the dorsum of this foot, and instructs the patient to raise the well leg against this resistance. If the patient has a true organic hemiplegia, no added pressure will be felt by the hand remaining beneath the heel of the paralyzed leg. However, if the patient has a hysterical paralysis, the heel of the supposedly paralyzed leg will press down against the examiner's hand as an attempt is made to raise the well leg.

15. Huntington's sign - Flexion at the hip, extension at the knee, and elevation of the affected weak lower extremity upon coughing and straining.

16. Marie and Foix retraction sign - Upon forcing the toes downward, the knee and hip are drawn into flexion.

17. Neri's sign - Upon alternately raising one leg at a time (while recumbent), the knee of the paralyzed side flexes, the other remaining straight.

18. Raimiste's leg sign - With the subject in a recumbent position and the lower extremities moderately abducted, the paretic leg performs a movement similar to that attempted by a normal leg (adduction or abduction).

19. Strümpell's tibialis anterior sign - Flexion of the thigh at the hip joint results in dorsal flexion and adduction of the foot, especially if the leg movement is resisted by the examiner.

B. Upper Extremity:

1. Hoffmann's sign - Clawing movement of the fingers produced by flicking the distal phalanx of the index finger. The thumb is also clawed.

2. Gordon's finger sign - Flexion of the fingers or the thumb and index finger when pressure is exerted over the pisiform bone.

3. Chaddock's wrist sign - Flexion of the wrist with extension and fanning of the fingers upon stroking the ulnar side of the forearm near the wrist.

4. Babinski's pronation sign - The patient places his hands in approximation with the palms upward and the examiner jars them several times with his own hands from below. The affected hand will fall in pronation, the sound hand remaining horizontal.

5. Bechterew's sign - The patient flexes and then relaxes both forearms. The paralyzed forearm falls back more slowly and in a jerky manner, even when contractures are mild.

6. Klippel and Feil thumb sign - When the flexed fingers of the patient are quickly extended by the examiner, flexion and adduction of the patient's thumb ensues.

7. Leri's sign - Absence of normal flexion of the elbow upon forceful passive flexion of the wrist and fingers.

8. Mayer's sign - Absence of adduction and opposition of the thumb upon passive forceful flexion of the proximal phalanges, especially of the third and fourth fingers, of the supinated hand.

9. Souques's sign - In attempting to raise the paralyzed arm, the fingers spread out and remain separated.

10. Sterling's sign - Adduction of a paretic arm upon forceful active adduction, against resistance, of the unaffected normal arm.

11. Strümpell's pronation sign - Upon flexing the forearm, the dorsum of the hand instead of the palm approaches the shoulder.

C. Head:

1. Babinski's platysma sign - If resistance is offered to flexion of the chin against the chest or to the opening of the mouth, the platysma on the sound side will contract whereas that on the affected side will not.

2. McCarthy's sign - Percussion of the supraorbital ridge results in a reflex contraction of the orbicularis oculi muscle.

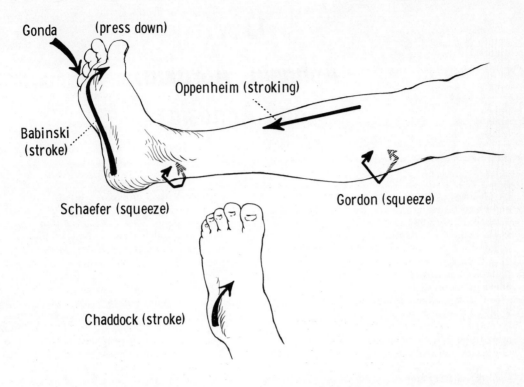

Methods of Testing for Extensor-Plantar Reflexes

•   •   •

13...

Aphasia, Apraxia, and Agnosia

Aphasia, as the term is generally used, refers to those motor and sensory language disturbances caused by brain lesions but not those caused by mental defects, disturbances in the sense organs, or paralysis of the muscles essential for speech.

Lesions of certain areas of the dominant cerebral hemisphere are prone to be associated with aphasia. **Broca** concluded from his study of a pathologic specimen that the third frontal convolution was the seat of "articulated speech"; he described "aphemia" as the clinical condition resulting from a lesion involving this area. **Wernicke** felt that destruction of the first temporal gyrus (superior temporal convolution) could abolish sound images and result in lack of understanding of spoken words through impaired function of the cerebral auditory center. Plentiful, free speech characterized by errors, which Wernicke felt depended on the temporal lobe defect and loss of normal auditory control, associated with defects in writing and reading, became known as **sensory aphasia**, or Wernicke's aphasia.

Pierre Marie disagreed with Broca and demonstrated that widespread cortical and subcortical damage existed in the pathologic specimen which was used as the basis of Broca's report. Marie felt that lesions in a **quadrilateral space** of the cerebral hemisphere would destroy articulate speech. This space, referred to as a "zone of anarthria," included the island of Reil and the underlying claustrum, the internal and external capsule, and the caudate and lenticular nuclei. He felt that "true aphasia" was usually associated with a general intellectual deficiency and a special language defect. He differentiated 3 cerebral zones of disordered function: (1) **temporal zone**, associated with true aphasia in its purest form, with good articulation but great difficulty in understanding, naming, reading, and writing; (2) an **angular zone**, associated with severe alexia and moderate disturbances in other language functions; and (3) a **supramarginal zone**, associated with a "global aphasia" affecting all elements of the function of language.

Hughlings Jackson emphasized that the problem of aphasia had important psychologic aspects. He concluded that "to speak is to propositionize," and that loss of speech in aphasia entailed the loss of the power to propositionize. This power can be lost not only when the subject has lost the power to talk (propositionize aloud) but also when he cannot propositionize "internally." Speech responses which might occur under the influence of emotional excitement or in situations where the speech response was highly automatic were not considered true propositions in an otherwise speechless patient.

Henry Head conceived of aphasia as an impairment of the power to formulate and use symbols. Any act of external or internal verbal expression (speech or thought) which demands symbolic formulation therefore tends to be defective, and the difficulties accumulate as the propositional values of the symbols required increased. Head recognized 4 types of aphasia, as follows:

(1) **Verbal aphasia**, characterized by a defect in the power to form individual words, whether for external or internal use. In severe cases, the subject may be able to produce only one or two words aside from "automatic speech."

(2) **Syntactic aphasia**, characterized by disturbances of balance and rhythm of words or phrases spoken in sequence, with faulty phrases or misprounced words. The subject can write better than he can speak, and understands single words well. He can obey commands except when they demand the precise recall of a spoken phrase.

(3) **Nominal aphasia**, characterized by impairment of the ability to name objects and to understand the nominal significance of words.

(4) **Semantic aphasia**, characterized by inability to appreciate the metaphorical significance or "coloration" of words and phrases (connotation) apart from their immediate meaning (denotation). There is loss of the power to arrive at logical conclusions from a given sequence of ideas or series of actions.

The patient can read, but the full meaning is liable to be misinterpreted or inadequately grasped. He can write, but the results are unsatisfactory. In general, semantic defects tend to impair understanding of the connected sequence of what is written even when the individual verbal forms are sufficiently clear.

Goldstein states that all disturbances of language may be designated as aphasia. He distinguishes between those language difficulties due to "disturbances of instrumentalities" and those due to "impairment of abstract attitude" and other nonlanguage mental phenomena. His classification of language disturbances includes the following:

(1) Disturbances of the expressive side of language due to cortical lesions: **Dysarthria** is due to paresis of the muscles used in speaking. **Peripheral motor aphasia** is a defect of the learned and specialized motor speech performances. **Central motor aphasia** consists of disintegration of motor speech due to impairment of abstract attitude and impaired function of motor modalities.

(2) Disturbances of language due to impairment of nonlanguage mental processes: May be due to impairment of abstract attitude or of "basic functions of the brain."

(3) Disturbances of language due to the receptive side of language due to cortical lesions: **Cortical deafness** is a disturbance of acoustic perception due to a cortical lesion. **Noise and musical cortical deafness** is a disturbance of perception of the characteristic sounds of noise and music, although hearing is not impaired. **Sensory aphasia** may be **peripheral** (pure sensory aphasia) or **central** (cortical sensory aphasia).

(4) **Central aphasia**: Aphasia occurring without any definite motor or perceptual changes.

(5) **Amnesic aphasia**: Lack of nouns, adjectives, verbs, and especially names for concrete objects with impairment of abstract attitude.

(6) **Transcortical aphasias**: Characterized by better preservation of repetition than of understanding and spontaneous speech; classified as transcortical motor symptom complexes, transcortical sensory symptom complexes, and mixed.

(7) **Agraphia**: Disturbances in writing. **Primary** agraphia consists of inability to build letters without disturbances in the spheres of speech and vision. **Secondary** agraphia is due to defects in language.

(8) **Alexia**: Disturbances in reading. **Primary** alexia is also called visual agnostic alexia. **Secondary** alexia is due to defects in language.

(9) **Echolalia**: The subject is able to repeat heard language but does not understand the words he hears.

Nielsen believes that language or performance difficulty is related to a specific site of cerebral pathology. In right-handed persons the left cerebral hemisphere is usually dominant (major); in left-handed persons, the right hemisphere. (Exceptions to these general rules are more common among left-handed persons.) In either case, the other cerebral hemisphere is referred to as the recessive (minor) hemisphere. Nielsen's conclusions may be summarized as follows:

(1) A lesion in the isthmus of the major temporal lobe incapacitates the major language area entirely.

(2) Some varieties of aphasia have localizing value. In **motor aphasia**, the lesion affects fibers from the major convolution of Broca on their way to the ipsilateral precentral gyrus. The lesion of **Wernicke's aphasia** affects the major temporal lobe, especially the superior temporal convolution in its posterior half. **Aphasic alexia** is referable to a lesion in the major temporal lobe. **Formulation aphasia** and **jargon aphasia** are caused by lesions in the major temporal lobe at area 37.

(3) **Agraphia** has no localizing value unless it is the only symptom present, in which case it may be caused by a lesion at the border between the major angular gyrus and the occipital lobe or by a lesion of the major second frontal convolution.

(4) Certain **agnosias** (difficulties in identification or recognition) are highly specific in localization.

Studies made upon human subjects at the time of cerebral operation under local anesthesia have indicated that certain portions of the cerebral cortex of the dominant cerebral hemisphere may be intimately related to speech function. Penfield has published a cerebral map indicating those areas where electric stimulation is highly effective in altering voluntary speech in the conscious patient.

Diagnosis.

Speech function may be systematically and elaborately examined and detailed observations recorded. Abnormalities of speech associated with defective or disordered function of the muscles of phonation (as in diseases of the cerebellum, basal ganglia, medulla, or motor cortex) must be distinguished from purely aphasic disorders. In **bulbar palsy**, the speech of the patient is thick, nasal, and feeble. In **cerebellar disorders**, the speech

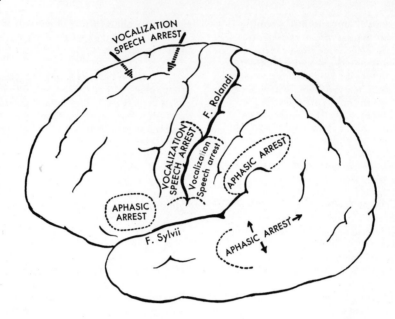

Summary of Areas in Which Stimulation May Interfere With Speech or Produce Vocalization in the Dominant Hemisphere. Speech interference produced by stimulation of the superior intermediate frontal area within the longitudinal fissure has in certain cases produced evidence of aphasia rather than simple arrest, an observation that calls for further study. (Reproduced, with permission, from Penfield and Rasmussen: The Cerebral Cortex of Man. Macmillan, 1950.)

Some Classifications of Aphasia (after Weisenburg and McBride)

Broca	Wernicke	Marie	Pick	Goldstein	Head
Aphemia	Motor aphasia	Anarthria	Expressive aphasia	Peripheral form of motor aphasia	
		Broca's aphasia		Transcortical form motor aphasia	
				Central form of motor aphasia (cortical motor)	Verbal aphasia
Verbal amnesia	Sensory aphasia	Wernicke's, or the true aphasia	Impressive aphasia	"Pure" word deafness	Different aspects introduced in nominal, syntactical, and semantic aphasia
				Sensory aphasia (cortical sensory)	
	Conduction aphasia			Central aphasia Amnesic aphasia	
			Amnesic aphasia		
	Total aphasia		Total aphasia		

may be explosive and intermittent. In **multiple sclerosis**, a scanning type of speech with a monotonous, sing-song quality is characteristically found. In **basal ganglia disorders**, speech may be slurred and very feeble, reduced in volume, and monotonous. **Stammering and stuttering**, which involve hesitation in the pronunciation of some words, sounds, or syllables, and involuntary repetitions lasting as long as several minutes, frequently have a psychogenic component.

Analysis of aphasic disorders involves the following types of tests:

(1) Ability to comprehend spoken language: The capacity of the patient to understand simple questions and commands is evaluated. Commands of increasing complexity, involving 3 or more separate acts, may be necessary before a defect can be suitably demonstrated.

(2) Ability to comprehend written language: A series of written commands of increasing complexity is shown to the patient and his responses noted. The ability to read printed items in a book or newspaper is tested and the grasp of the essential items therein is assessed. A passage should be chosen whose meaning the subject would ordinarily understand.

(3) Ability to express oneself in spoken language: The ability of the patient to speak in ordinary conversation is noted together with the patient's associated behavior. Automatic responses, as in counting numbers, enumerating days of weeks or months of the year, and recital of the alphabet may be relatively well preserved in the presence of otherwise serious difficulties with motor speech. Difficulty in writing is frequently associated with difficulty in motor speech. **Paraphasia** refers to a defect of expression in which a different word (perhaps a word of similar sound) is substituted for the exact word required.

(4) Ability to name objects: The capacity of the patient to name familiar objects such as a watch, pen, coins, buttons, or knife is tested and his ability to explain the specific use of particular items is noted. Ability of the patient to identify and recognize parts of the body should be verified.

Batteries of tests are usually required for formal testing of language function, and such tests vary widely among different clinical investigators. Among the types of tests listed by Weisenburg and McBride are the following: Spontaneous speaking, naming, repeating, understanding spoken language, following directions, reading, arithmetic, language intelligence, reproduction of verbal material, nonlinguistic tests, and handedness.

In most aphasic persons, alteration of nonlanguage capacities may also be demonstrated (as in the reactions to situations of daily life, social responses, and attitudes).

Amobarbital sodium (Amytal®) aphasia test. - In certain cases, especially where surgery is contemplated, it may be useful to establish which cerebral hemisphere is dominant with respect to speech. Amobarbital is injected into a carotid artery while the patient is counting aloud and making rapidly alternating movements of fingers of both hands. When the carotid artery of the dominant side is injected, a much greater and prolonged relative interference with speech function occurs than after similar injection of the other side.

APRAXIA

By apraxia is meant the inability to carry out, on request, a complex or skilled movement not due to paralysis, ataxia, sensory changes, or deficiencies of understanding (confusion).

Ideational apraxia is believed to be due to loss of the power to formulate the ideational concepts necessary to the performance of the act; the subject cannot grasp or retain the idea of the desired act. Simple and isolated movements may be unaffected, but more complicated acts are impossible. Ideational apraxia occurs as a manifestation of certain diffuse brain disorders (e.g., cerebral arteriosclerosis).

Motor apraxia is believed to represent the loss of the kinesthetic memory patterns necessary to the performance of the act. The purpose of the movements is usually apparent to the patient, but execution remains defective. Motor apraxia is usually associated with a lesion of the precentral gyrus.

Ideomotor apraxia is a state in which the patient cannot perform a given act correctly although old habitual motor acts can be performed spontaneously or repetitiously (often with perseveration). Ideomotor apraxia is associated with lesions of the dominant cerebral hemisphere (supramarginal gyrus).

In testing for apraxia, the responses, failures, and reactions upon testing are noted. Examples of tests for apraxia include requesting the patient to show how to use a toothbrush, light a cigarette, place a letter in an envelope, pretend to drive a car, and construct a square from toothpicks.

AGNOSIA

Agnosia generally refers to the failure to recognize familiar objects perceived by the senses. It is the loss of ability to recognize objects or symbols by one sense organ with recognition of the same object or symbol by other sense organs. In tests for agnosia, the patient may be required to identify his hands, eyes, feet, etc., or those of the examiner; to show awareness of his disease or deficit; to distinguish right from left; to identify himself as a person and to orient himself in space and time. He may be asked to imagine himself performing such acts as walking, sitting, or standing. More specific tests including numerical relationships, body scheme, and revisualization tests may be used.

Agnosias are usually considered to be caused by disturbances in the association function of the cerebral cortex. **Astereognosis** refers to failure of tactile recognition of objects. Agnosia for body parts may occur as well as disturbances in concepts of the patient's body scheme. **Anosognosia**, the lack of aware-ness of disease or denial of disease, may occur with disease of the parietal lobe in the area of the supramarginal gyrus. **Autotopagnosia**, the impaired recognition of body parts, may occur with lesions of the posteroinferior portion of the parietal lobe.

Visual agnosia may occur with or without hemianopsia on the dominant side as a result of parieto-occipital lesions, with loss of visual recognition of objects, pictures, persons, and spatial relationships.

Charcot-Wilbrand syndrome consists of visual agnosia and loss of ability to revisualize images. It may be associated with occlusion of the posterior cerebral artery of the dominant cerebral hemisphere.

Anton's syndrome is a form of anosognosia in which the patient denies his blindness. The patient usually confabulates, claiming to see objects in the blind field.

Gerstmann's syndrome is characterized by disability in calculation (acalculia), finger agnosia, and right-left disorientation and writing disability, and is usually associated with a focal lesion of the dominant cerebral hemisphere in the region of the angular gyrus.

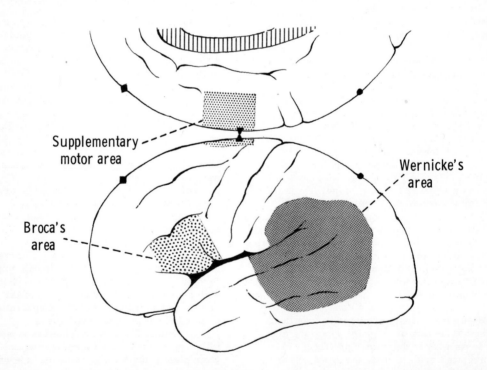

Three Speech Areas of Dominant Cerebral Hemisphere. (1) The posterior or parieto-temporal area (Wernicke's area) is most important. (2) The anterior, or Broca's area, is next most important but is dispensable in some patients at least. (3) The superior, or supplementary motor, area is dispensable but may be important after damage to other speech areas. (Redrawn and reproduced, with permission, from Penfield and Roberts: Speech and Brain-Mechanisms. Princeton, 1959.)

14 . . .

Trophic Changes

Nutritional or trophic changes form an important part of the symptomatology in many neurologic disorders. They may appear in the skin, nails, subcutaneous tissues, muscles, bones, and joints.

Classification.

A. Skin and Nails: Glossy, smooth skin; hyperhidrosis (excessive sweating), hypohidrosis or anhidrosis (reduced or absent sweating); white, leathery skin; cyanosis or discoloration, hypertrichosis (excess of hair), hypotrichosis (loss of hair), edema of the skin; brittle, ridged nails; and trophic ulcers, or mal perforans, which heal very slowly.

B. Joints: Joint changes are seen in tabes dorsalis. So-called Charcot joints are painless in spite of the marked destruction of cartilage, ligaments, and joint surfaces; bone fragments and excess fluid fill the joint cavity and mobility is increased. The larger joints, e.g., at the knee, hip, and ankle, are most often affected.

C. Bone atrophy or osteoporosis accompanies paralyses and disuse.

D. Muscle atrophy is discussed below.

Causes of Trophic Change.

Although a neurologic basis has usually been stressed as a prime factor in the causation of trophic changes, other factors apparently also play a role. These include activity, blood supply, nutritional elements (vitamins), lymph drainage, and endocrine activities.

A. Inactivity: Muscle "atrophy of disuse" follows any prolonged immobilization and is characterized by a reduction in the amount of sarcoplasm without loss of striation, degeneration of muscle fibers, or change in electric response. No degeneration of intramuscular nerves or their endings occurs. Atrophy of other tissues, including bone, also results from disuse.

B. Neurogenic Control: Denervated tissues soon lose the vitality of normal tissues; muscles, in addition to a reduction in the amount of sarcoplasm, show a loss of striation and an alteration in electric responses. Gerard has suggested that "neurogenic metabolites" are transmitted along the axons and mediate trophic functions. The motor nerves (from cells of the anterior gray column) are essential to normal muscle metabolism since their degeneration is accompanied by a rapid loss of motor end-plates and muscle striations. The sympathetic nerves (from the cells of the intermediolateral cell column) affect the trophic state of tissues through their vasomotor activities and, according to the results of some workers, also exert a specific effect on the metabolism of muscles and other tissues. Poliomyelitis, which is characterized by marked trophic dysfunction in the involved tissues, shows a lesion of both motor and sympathetic neurons. There is little evidence that fibers of the sensory nerves (from cells of the dorsal root ganglia) have any direct trophic function. Loss of pain sensibility predisposes to ulcerations from trauma and burns, as frequently occur in analgesic extremities in syringomyelia and peripheral nerve injuries. The skin lesions in herpes zoster occur in the distribution of spinal roots involved in the inflammatory process.

C. Blood Supply: Adequate blood supply is essential to nutrition and oxygenation of tissues. Vascular disturbances, such as Volkmann's ischemic contracture, are characterized by severe damage to the affected muscles and other tissues. Trophic skin and nail changes as well as the angioneuroses are probably the result of disturbances in the innervation of blood vessels.

D. Other Factors Affecting the Trophic State of Tissues:
1. Food intake must be sufficient to balance tissue catabolism in order to prevent cachexia and general weight loss.

2. Avitaminoses cause specific trophic changes seen in beriberi, pellagra, scurvy, xerophthalmia, etc.

3. Glandular disturbances - Thyroid deficiency results in myxedema. Pituitary dysfunction is responsible for rare growth disturbances, e. g., acromegaly, pituitary cachexia, and possibly adiposis dolorosa.

4. Lymph drainage - The trophic importance of an adequate lymph supply is not well understood. Obstruction results in marked edema and skin changes, as seen in elephantiasis. Toxins of various types may act locally or systemically to produce marked atrophy or wasting of tissue, as, for example, in carcinoma and infections.

DISEASES SHOWING MARKED TROPHIC CHANGES

Neurologic Disorders.

A. Syringomyelia (e. g., Morvan's disease) shows trophic disturbances of the skin, subcutaneous tissues, and bones, usually of the upper extremity. Glossiness of the skin, deep fissures, and nail changes are common. Progressive atrophy beginning in the small muscles of the hands and gradually involving the arms and shoulders is usually seen. Perforating ulcers from trauma to the analgesic fingers and hands may occur, and joint changes are occasionally seen.

B. Tabes Dorsalis: Freely movable, swollen, painless "Charcot" joints are often seen late in the course of tabes. Perforating ulcers of the ball of the foot are occasionally found, and the marked muscular hypotonia is accompanied by some atrophy, probably from relative disuse.

C. Herpes zoster (shingles) is characterized by pain and vesicle formation (blisters) in the cutaneous distribution of the sensory roots involved by the viral inflammation. These areas may become anesthetic later.

D. Lower motor neuron disease, either in the anterior gray column of the spinal cord or in the peripheral nerves, is characterized by marked atrophy of the paralyzed muscles as well as the associated bones and skin. In this group are included poliomyelitis, amyotrophic lateral sclerosis, primary muscular atrophies, and peripheral nerve lesions. **Peripheral neuritis** is a lower motor neuron disorder in which trophic changes are usually quite marked.

E. Causalgia is a painful disorder of an arm or leg which is usually associated with median, sciatic, or tibial nerve injury and accompanied by trophic changes in the affected skin and nails. Osteoporosis of the bones of the affected extremity is occasionally present.

F. Neurogenic Arthropathy (Charcot's Joint): Joint destruction may result from impaired perception of proprioception, pain, and temperature. Although clinically seen in tabes dorsalis, it may also occur with diabetic neuropathy, syringomyelia, spinal cord disorders, and peripheral nerve injuries. Prolonged administration of intra-articular hydrocortisone may also cause Charcot's joint. Treatment is directed against the underlying disease, with the use of devices to assist in weight bearing and to prevent further trauma to joints.

Vascular Disorders.

Various diseases of the blood vessels, such as thromboangiitis obliterans (Buerger's disease), endarteritis obliterans, arteriosclerosis, varicose veins, and Volkmann's ischemic contracture may produce trophic ulcers, skin changes, and gangrene in the dependent tissues because of the reduced blood supply to these parts.

Trophoneuroses.

These are thought to be due to dysfunction of the sympathetic innervation and are defined on p. 149. The association of trophic disorders with lesions of the hypothalamic region suggests that this part of the brain may be the central representation of the autonomic system.

Other Trophic Disorders.

Trophic disorders associated with various skin infections, malignancies, glandular disorders, and similar conditions are not within the scope of neurology.

SWEATING

The various types of sweating have been classified on the basis of the mechanism involved in their production. Thermoregulatory sweating is generalized and centrally induced and can be produced by ingestion of fluids or antipyretics and exposure to heat. Emotional sweating is localized. It is most commonly seen on the flexor surfaces of the hands and feet and in the axillas, and may be elicited by emotional or painful stimuli. Drugs such as the cholinergic substances pilocarpine and methacholine (Mecholyl®) may induce a variable amount of sweating by a presumed effect on the sweat glands or on cholinergic nerve endings. In some normal individuals, eating spicy foods can induce localized facial sweating (gustation sweating). In pathologic circumstances, this kind of sweating may become pronounced. In subjects with transverse lesions of the spinal cord, an appropriate local stimulus applied to an area below the level of the lesion may induce automatic reflex sweating as part of a mass reflex response (spinal reflex sweating). Sweating is frequently associated with peripheral vasodilatation.

Anatomy. (See p. 218.)

Anatomic pathways involved in thermoregulatory sweating have been suggested, as follows: Crossed and uncrossed fibers from the hypothalamus travel via the tegmentum of the pons and the lateral reticular substance of the medulla to the lower brain stem and cervical spinal cord. They then descend farther as uncrossed fibers in the anterolateral and lateral tracts of the spinal cord to the intermediolateral gray column of the spinal cord. From here fibers emerge via the anterior roots to join the sympathetic chain and peripheral nerves.

Two sets of cholinergic fibers have been postulated on the basis of sweat responses to injection of pilocarpine or methacholine (Mecholyl®): postganglionic sympathetic and parasympathetic cholinergic fibers. Most of the cholinergic fibers to the trunk and extremities emerge via the thoracolumbar sympathetic system. Most of the cholinergic fibers to the head travel via the cranial parasympathetic nerves.

Sweat glands are believed to possess a predominantly sympathetic nerve supply. While the sympathetic innervation of sweat glands in humans is cholinergic, species differences have been noted. In cats (as in humans), epinephrine causes little or no sweat secretion and the secretion obtained by stimu-lation of the sympathetics is blocked by atropine. In horses, epinephrine evokes sweat secretion and the secretion obtained by sympathetic stimulation is not blocked by atropine.

Tests for Lesions of the Sympathetic Nervous System.

A. Thermoregulatory sweating may be used to demonstrate lesions of the sympathetic nervous system since it is dependent upon the thoracolumbar sympathetic system. The **sweat test of Minor** is commonly employed. The subject takes 0.5 Gm. of aspirin one-half hour prior to the test and his skin is then painted with an iodine solution. After the skin dries, it is dusted with fine rice starch powder. The subject then drinks a large quantity of hot tea, is exposed to the heat of a large electric cabinet and is covered carefully with blankets draped over a frame. The moisture of the sweat secretion facilitates the reaction between the iodine and starch, producing a blue-black color change on the skin in the sweating areas. In lesions of the sympathetic system, local loss of thermoregulatory sweating occurs. The immediately adjacent skin area may show increased sweating.

B. Skin Resistance to Electric Current: The resistance of the skin to the passage of an electric current is greatly influenced by activity of the sweat glands and may be measured with a dermometer. Areas of skin with impaired or absent autonomic nerve supply show greatly increased resistance to the passage of small currents. If sweat glands are active, skin resistance is low; if sweat glands are inactive, skin resistance is high, the affected zones being similar in configuration to those demonstrated by the sweat test of Minor. A small current is passed between an ear electrode and an exploring skin electrode. Whereas dampness of normal skin permits the passage of a small current which is registered on a sensitive ammeter, a dry area has a high resistance and allows little or no current to pass.

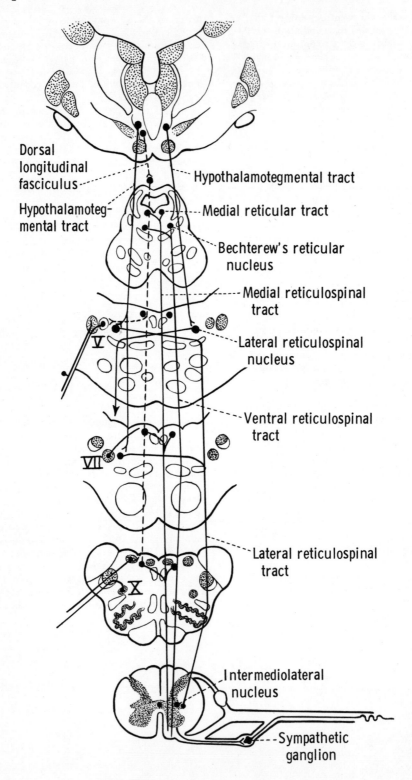

Dorsal longitudinal fasciculus

Hypothalamotegmental tract

Hypothalamotegmental tract

Medial reticular tract

Bechterew's reticular nucleus

Medial reticulospinal tract

Lateral reticulospinal nucleus

Ventral reticulospinal tract

Lateral reticulospinal tract

Intermediolateral nucleus

Sympathetic ganglion

The Probable Pathways of Thermoregulatory Sweating (Hypothalamotegmental and Reticulospinal Connections). (Reproduced, with permission, from List and Peet: Sweat secretion in man. A.M.A. Arch. Neurol. & Psychiat. 42:1098, 1939.)

15...

The Cerebrospinal Fluid

Normal cerebrospinal fluid (CSF) is clear, colorless, and odorless. Some of the more important average normal values are as follows:

Specific gravity: 1.007
pH: 7.35
Chlorides (as NaCl): 720 mg./100 ml.

Glucose: 65 mg./100 ml.
Total base: 157 mEq./L.

Total protein:
Lumbar: 15-45 mg./100 ml.
Cisternal: 10-25 mg./100 ml.
Ventricular: 5-15 mg./100 ml.

Circulation of Cerebrospinal Fluid. (Redrawn from original drawing by Frank H. Netter, M.D., which first appeared in Ciba Clinical Symposia, copyright 1950.)

The CSF is present for the most part in a system which may be considered as composed of 2 communicating portions: The **internal** system consists of the 2 lateral ventricles, their interventricular foramens (of Monro), the third ventricle, the cerebral (sylvian) aqueduct, and the fourth ventricle. The **external** system consists of the subarachnoid spaces, including the dilated portions known as cisterns. Communication of the internal and external systems occurs through the 2 lateral apertures of the fourth ventricle (foramens of Luschka) and the medial foramen of the fourth ventricle (foramen of Magendie).

Formation.

The choroid plexuses are believed to be the principal sources of the CSF. Fluid may also be formed by diffusion through the ependymal and pial vessels. It is estimated that 95% of the fluid is formed in the lateral ventricles. Most of the remainder is formed in the third and fourth ventricles.

It is probable that much of the CSF is formed by dialysis across the walls of the choroid plexuses. Studies using tracer substances indicate that the CSF may not be fully formed when it appears and that exchanges of particular constituents between the CSF and the blood may occur at more or less characteristic rates. Water and electrolytes enter and leave the CSF rapidly, both in the ventricular and subarachnoid spaces, and not exclusively through the choroid plexuses. Protein is absorbed largely from the arachnoid villi. The rate and site of protein reabsorption significantly affects the direction and rate of CSF flow. Although the formation of CSF is predominantly in the cerebral ventricles, it may also be formed in the subarachnoid spaces. There is evidence to suggest that CSF may come from the brain as well as from the choroid plexuses. Usually the CSF is hypertonic to blood, and changes in CSF osmotic pressure usually follow changes in blood osmotic pressure.

Wide variations in the amount of fluid formed daily are believed to occur. Estimates of as much as 6000 ml./day have been made. The average normal amount probably does not exceed 1500 ml./day. The over-all addition of CSF beyond the volumes exchanged has been estimated to be as little as 10-20 ml./day via the choroid plexuses of the ventricles. Factors influencing the bulk formation of CSF may operate independently of each other and thus change in relative importance. Cerebral metabolism, hydrodynamic forces of blood flow, and changes in blood osmotic pressure influence the fluctuating rate of CSF flow, although there may be an irreducible minimum of CSF produced related to the arterial blood pressure.

Circulation.

The existence of an active circulation of CSF has been postulated. According to this concept, fluid is formed in the lateral ventricles, circulates through the interventricular foramens into the third ventricle, and then via the cerebral aqueduct into the fourth ventricle. Here the fluid escapes via the lateral apertures of the fourth ventricle and the medial foramen of the fourth ventricle into the subarachnoid spaces, where it diffuses over the brain and spinal cord. Respiratory and circulatory changes are believed to change the pressure within the closed system and promote the mixing and diffusion of fluid.

Absorption.

The site of greatest absorption of CSF is believed to be the subarachnoid villi which project into the dural venous sinuses. The pacchionian bodies are relatively large arachnoid villi distributed along the superior longitudinal sinus. Absorption into the pial veins may also occur.

Functions.

The CSF probably acts as a cushion for the brain, preventing or diminishing the transmission of jarring or shocking forces to the brain and spinal cord. Its role in metabolism is conjectural. It might conceivably convey nutritive materials to the CNS and carry away metabolites. Changes in the intracranial volume are sometimes compensated for by the production of CSF. This is apparent in destructive or postoperative lesions.

Evidence from studies with deuterium and tritium suggest that water may enter at many points other than the choroid plexus, although isotope studies with solutes suggest that most enter the cerebral ventricles via the choroid plexus. In the same way, CSF may exit by routes other than the arachnoidal villi. This rapid transfer of water into and out of the cerebrospinal compartments permits the extracellular fluids of the CNS to remain isotonic with other body fluids. Experimental studies indicate that heavy water enters the subarachnoid space faster than it enters a similar volume of ventricle. Flow out of the ventricles accounts for less than $1/25$ of the total water that leaves the 4 ventricles. Most monovalent electrolyte and protein can enter the subarachnoid space as well as the ventricles directly.

Hydrodynamics.

Because the CSF is contained within a closed system, the bony spine and the skull, forces which tend to increase the volume of the CSF are apt to increase its pressure. Increased blood circulation or blood pressure within the arterioles and capillaries of the choroid plexus tends to increase the amount of CSF formed and its pressure. Obstruction to the flow of venous blood in the sinuses blocks the free absorption of fluid and also increases the amount and pressure of the fluid. Anesthesia may produce primary or secondary changes in CSF pressure. Those administered via semiclosed systems produce rises in CSF pressure proportional to carbon dioxide retention, and these rises can be prevented by previous hyperventilation. Rise in CSF pressure also occurs with administration of anesthetics that cause excitement, cough, laryngospasm, or respiratory obstruction. Barbiturate anesthesia tends to lower CSF pressure, whereas halothane raises it. Ether, trichloroethylene, nitrous oxide, and cyclopropane have no primary effect but tend to raise CSF pressure because of secondary effects.

Lumbar Puncture.

Lumbar puncture is usually performed with the patient lying down; in this position the pressure is normally 70-200 mm. water (average, 125 mm. water). If the puncture is done with the patient sitting upright, the fluid will normally rise to about the level of the mid-cervical spine. Coughing or straining will usually cause a prompt rise and subsequent fall in pressure. This is due to congestion of the spinal veins and the resultant increase of pressure on the contents of the subarachnoid space.

A. Technic: After the initial pressure has been determined and found to be normal, 3-4 specimens of 2-3 ml. each are usually withdrawn in sterile tubes for laboratory examination. Cultures and special tests, such as those for sugar and chlorides, are done when indicated. Routine examination usually includes cell counts, total protein, colloidal gold curve, and Wassermann reaction. The pressure is routinely measured also after the fluid is removed. In cases of spinal subarachnoid block, a normal initial pressure will suffer a profound drop after the removal of 7-10 ml. of fluid.

The Ayala index is sometimes helpful in the diagnosis of subarachnoid block, hydrocephalus, etc.

$$\text{Ayala index} = \frac{\text{Quantity of fluid removed (10 ml.)} \times \text{final pressure}}{\text{Initial pressure}}$$

A normal Ayala index is 5.5-6.5. An index greater than 7.0 is interpreted to mean a large reservoir, as in hydrocephalus or serous meningitis. An index of less than 5.0 means a small reservoir, as in subarachnoid block.

B. After-effects: Severe headache may occur following lumbar puncture. This may be due to the loss of the fluid or the leakage of fluid through the puncture site. Lumbar puncture headaches are characterized by relief on lying down and exacerbation upon raising the head. The injection of saline solution into the subarachnoid spaces may give partial or complete relief.

C. Contraindications to lumbar puncture are relatively few. In cases of brain tumor, especially of the posterior fossa, spinal puncture should be done carefully, since herniation of the cerebellum and medullary compression may follow removal of fluid.

D. The Queckenstedt Test or Maneuver: Queckenstedt's test is performed by compressing the jugular veins during lumbar puncture. Normally there is a prompt rise in CSF pressure which is maintained as long as compression is maintained. A moderate rise in pressure occurs if one jugular vein is compressed, and a further rise occurs when the second jugular vein is compressed. On release of compression of the jugular veins, the CSF pressure promptly returns to normal levels. If the pressure fails to rise and fall promptly, a block in the system is presumed to be present between the site of the puncture and the site of the compression of the jugular vein. Absence of pressure rise on compression of one jugular vein can be caused by thrombosis of the lateral sinus on the same side. Absence of pressure rise - or a slow rise and slow fall - upon compression of both jugular veins implies a complete or partial block in the spinal subarachnoid pathway; further definitive studies, such as iophendylate (Pantopaque®) myelography, are then usually indicated.

Queckenstedt's test is contraindicated in the presence or suspicion of intracranial tumor or bleeding since it may abruptly precipitate further bleeding or cause herniation of the cerebellar tonsils with medullary compression.

E. Froin's Syndrome: Yellow spinal fluid (xanthochromia) which is high in globulin and practically free of cells and which clots spontaneously on standing may be associated with subarachnoid block.

Cerebrospinal Fluid Findings

Entity	Appearance	Pressure (in mm. of water)	Cells (per cu. mm.)	Protein	Miscellaneous CSF Findings
Normal lumbar Normal ventricular	Clear and colorless Clear and colorless	70-200 70-190	0-5 0-5 (lymphocytes)	15-45 mg./100 ml. 5-15 mg./100 ml.	Glucose 50-75 mg./100 ml. NPN 10-35 mg./100 ml. Kahn and Wassermann negative; Lange curve 0000110000.
Traumatic tap	Bloody; supernatant fluid clear.	Normal	Red blood cells	4 mg./100 ml. rise per 5000 red cells.	Bloody; supernatant fluid clear.
Cerebral hemorrhage Ventricular Subarachnoid	Bloody; supernatant fluid yellow.	Slightly increased	Red blood cells	As above	Blood equal in all three specimens.
Meningitis Acute purulent	Clear, cloudy, milky or xanthochromic; occasional clot formation.	Greatly increased (250-700)	Polymorpho-nuclear cells, usually over 1000.	Increased	Glucose decreased early; chlorides decreased late; organisms on smear and culture.
Acute tuberculous	Opalescent to turbid; faint fibrin web or pellicle formation.	Moderately increased (200-450)	10-500 (lymphocytes)	Increased	Chlorides decreased early, often before decrease of glucose. Smear, culture, and guinea pig inoculation for organisms.
Acute syphilitic	Clear to turbid; fibrin clot.	Moderately increased (200-350)	100-1000 (mostly lymphocytes)	Slightly increased	Positive Wassermann; syphilitic zone curve.
Syphilis Meningovascular Parenchymatous	Clear and colorless	Normal	Normal or increased	Slightly increased	Positive Wassermann; positive gold curve.
Brain tumor	Usually clear and colorless	Increased	Normal or increased	Increased	Findings depend on location and type of tumor.
Brain abscess	Clear and colorless	Greatly increased	Polymorpho-nuclear cells normal or increased.	Increased	Pressure may go as high as 600-700 mm. water.
Subdural hematoma	Classically yellow, but often clear and colorless.	Usually increased	Normal	Normal or slightly increased	
Encephalitis	Clear and colorless	Normal	Normal or increased (mostly lymphocytes)	Normal or slightly increased	Serologic tests of value in virus infections.
Uremia	Clear and colorless	Slightly increased	Normal	Normal or slightly increased	Spinal fluid NPN increased; gold curve may be paretic.
Lead encephalopathy	Clear or slightly cloudy	Increased	Lymphocytes	Normal or slightly increased	Lead in spinal fluid.
Arterial hypertension	Clear	Normal or increased	Normal	Normal or slightly increased	Choked disk may suggest brain tumor.
Epilepsy (idiopathic)	Normal fluid	Normal	Normal	Normal	
Multiple sclerosis	Normal fluid	Normal or low	Normal or increased	Normal or increased	Paretic, tabetic, or normal gold curve. Negative serolo
Poliomyelitis, acute	Opalescent, may be faintly yellow; delicate fibrin web.	Slightly increased	Slightly increased	Slightly increased (for a few weeks)	Pre-paralytic stage, 80% polymorphonuclear cells; paralytic state, mononuclears.
Spinal cord tumor Partial block	Clear and colorless	Normal	Normal	Slightly increased	
Complete block (Froin's syndrome)	Yellow	Normal or low	Slightly increased	Marked rise (200-600 mg./100 ml.)	Coagulation may occur.
Diabetic coma	Clear and colorless	Decreased	Normal	Normal or slightly increased	Glucose elevated; may reach 200-300 mg./100 ml.
Acute alcoholic coma	Clear and colorless	Slightly increased	May be slightly increased	Normal	Alcohol content parallels that of blood.

16...

Electroencephalography

Electroencephalography is the study of the electric activity of the brain. Variations exist in the electric activity of the brains of humans. By comparing records from standardized positions on the head, valid interpretations may be made.

The average amplitude of electric activity in the brain is about 1% of that obtained from the heart. Sensitive but stable amplification is necessary, therefore, to produce an undistorted record of brain activity. The potentials of the brain which are recorded in an electroencephalogram (EEG) appear in wave form ranging from 1-100 cycles/second and an amplitude ranging from 5 to several 100 microvolts.

Electroencephalography provides useful information in organic disease of the brain; its value in nonorganic diseases is questionable. Epilepsy, brain tumor, brain abscess, cerebral trauma, subdural hematoma, meningitis, encephalitis, cerebral vascular accident, and congenital defects of the brain represent types of conditions in which electroencephalography is useful. Focal changes may furnish considerable aid in the localization of cerebral damage. The electroencephalogram is widely used as a guide in surgery of the epileptic. In post-traumatic epilepsy, a cerebral scar may be present which is electrically inactive and which is surrounded by a zone of hyperexcitable cortex. The hyperactive foci, as determined by spontaneous and electrically evoked technic, may be excised. Surgical extirpation of the anterior temporal lobe is sometimes performed in those patients with psychomotor epilepsy in whom a prominent spike focus in this area is demonstrable in the electroencephalogram. Depth electrography - localization of a focus by depth recording - may be advisable in certain cases.

Serial recordings are helpful in distinguishing expanding from vascular lesions and in following the clinical course after head injury, cerebrovascular accident, and inflammatory and other brain disorders.

Electroencephalography has its limitations, however, and normal appearing records may be obtained in spite of clinical evidence of severe organic brain disease.

Technic.

Records are taken simultaneously, when possible, from multiple analogous areas of the brain in order to detect changes in activity which may be of diagnostic importance. Electrodes, usually solder pellets covered with electrolyte paste or jelly, are ordinarily attached by means of collodion to the scalp over the frontal, parietal, occipital, and temporal areas, and are attached also to the ears.

With the subject recumbent or seated in a grounded, wire-shielded cage and his eyes closed, a record is taken for at least a 20-minute period. Hyperventilation, during which the patient takes 40-50 deep breaths per minute for 2 minutes, is routinely employed since it frequently accentuates abnormal findings and may disclose latent abnormalities. "Scalp to ear" and "scalp to scalp" leads are routinely used, with the addition of further electrodes as necessary in order to accurately localize abnormalities in the graph. Rhythmic light flash stimulation (1-30/second) is carried out for 2 or more minutes.

Interpretation. (See Glossary, p. 226.)

The interpretation of the EEG depends on the frequency, amplitude, form, and distribution of the wave activity present. In the **Davis system**, each record is graded from 1-5 on the basis of stability of the pattern. Rating 1 is given to any normal type of pattern which is stable and whose fluctuations of frequency and voltage lie within fairly narrow limits without sharp transitions. Rating 2 includes normal records which are slightly less stable or regular than those rated 1 and which may fluctuate in a somewhat atypical manner or which have an alpha rhythm that is regular but unusual in wave form. Rating 3 includes normal records in which some feature may be exaggerated which cannot in itself be regarded as abnormal. Rating 4 is given to any dysrhythmic and suspicious record in which abnormalities are clear but not diagnostic. Rating 5 is given to

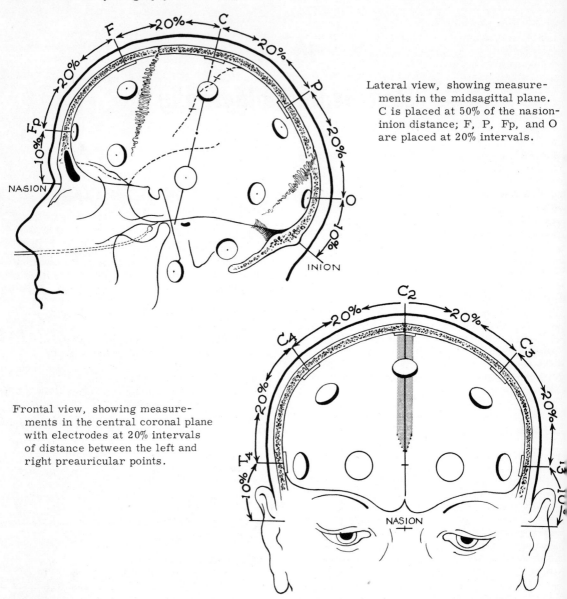

Lateral view, showing measurements in the midsagittal plane. C is placed at 50% of the nasion-inion distance; F, P, Fp, and O are placed at 20% intervals.

Frontal view, showing measurements in the central coronal plane with electrodes at 20% intervals of distance between the left and right preauricular points.

Electrode Placements in the "Ten Twenty" Electrode System. (Fp = frontal pole. F = frontal. C = central. P = parietal. O = occipital.) (Redrawn and reproduced, with permission, from EEG. Clin. Neurophysiol. **10**:372, 1958.)

any record which reveals well-recognized abnormal dysrhythmias, such as those found in epilepsy.

The pattern of electric activity is further evaluated in the Davis system as either A, B, M, MF or MS. The A type pattern has a regular alpha rhythm with proportioned distribution over the occipital, precentral, and frontal areas when recorded simultaneously. The B type of pattern, under standard conditions and at a resting level of activity, is made up pre-dominantly of fast frequencies of 14-20 cycles/second. The M type is composed of mixed frequencies, none clearly dominant, and contains slow, alpha, and fast frequencies. The MF type contains mixtures of frequencies in the alpha and fast frequency ranges. The MS type includes records whose frequencies are in the alpha and slow frequency range.

In the **Gibbs classification**, emphasis is upon the dominant frequency or significant wave form present. With one exception, all records not classified as paroxysmal, slow, or fast are normal and are classified according to the frequency of the dominant rhythm (8.5/second, 9, 9.5, etc., up to 12/second). A low voltage record with no countable frequency is classified "low voltage fast" and is considered normal. Records containing activity slower than 8.5 cycles/second and with voltages of more than 20 microvolts are classified as "slow" and subclassified as "moderately slow" (S1) and "very slow" (S2). If there is much activity with a frequency greater than 12/second and a voltage of more than 15 microvolts, the record is classified as "fast" and subclassified as "moderately fast" (F1) and "very fast" (F2). Records containing a mixture of fast and slow waves are classified according to which predominates, or both.

Moderately slow and fast records are considered mildly abnormal; very slow and very fast records are definitely abnormal.

Paroxysmal records are classified by Gibbs according to the type of clinical seizure with which he believes they are associated and are subclassified as "petit mal variant" (PMV), "petit mal" (PM), "psychomotor" (PSY), "spikes" (SP) and "grand mal" (GM) records.

Hypsarrhythmia is a striking pattern consisting of high voltage activity of the slow, sharp, and polyspike type in all regions. It is seen in infants and young children who usually have massive spasms and generalized tonic-clonic seizures which are difficult to control.

Fourteen and six positive spikes is a pattern in which positive spikes repeat at a frequency of 14 or 6/second. It is most pronounced in the occipitotemporal region, and is believed to have its origin in the hypothalamus or thalamus. This pattern is most frequently encountered in children and adolescents with clinical histories of autonomic or visceral manifestations, headache, or behavior disturbances.

Jasper and his co-workers have based their classification primarily on the location of abnormal wave forms. The types they recognize are as follows: (1) Localized unilateral: Random spike focus (L1), random sharp waves (L2), delta foci (L3), and local paroxysmal rhythm (L4) (10 cycles or more/second, localized to a discrete cortical area). (2) Diffuse: Multiple spikes (D1) (usually associated with diffuse fast rhythm, 14-25 cycles/second), multiple sharp waves (D2), and multiple delta (D3). (3) Bilaterally synchronous: Wave and spike (B3 and 1), 3/second (B3), 6/second (B4), and sharp waves (B2). Combined forms may occur.

It has been demonstrated that with the use of nasopharyngeal electrodes inserted through the nasal passages, additional information concerning the electric activity at the base of the brain may be obtained. Such an electrode may serve also as a convenient "reference" or localizing electrode. The use of "tympanic leads" placed in contact with the tympanic membranes, in conjunction with nasopharyngeal and other electrodes, may more conveniently demonstrate deep lesions or foci.

Electroencephalograms may be made during sleep or in circumstances simulating those most apt to precipitate clinical seizures or electric abnormalities. Chemical activation with drugs such as pentylenetetrazol (Metrazol®) may be used. Sleep records made during normal or drug-induced sleep may disclose abnormalities in patients whose patterns would otherwise be considered normal. "Photic driving" refers to the phenomenon in which some cerebral frequencies may be controlled by the intermittent illumination of the retina. This procedure may induce convulsive seizures in some epileptic patients.

Asymmetries between normal rhythms due to suppression or augmentation of the rhythm on one side may reflect cerebral pathologic changes, e.g., partial or complete suppression of alpha rhythm may occur on the side of an acute destructive lesion or subdural hematoma.

Delta rhythms - complex, irregular, slow waves with little tendency to repetition of the same wave forms and usually unaffected by alerting, hyperventilation, or eye opening - are seen with tumors, vascular occlusion, and inflammations. Dysrhythmias (3-7/second) - more repetitive and rhythmic than normal, at times with a characteristic wave form - may be accentuated by hyperventilation and inhibited by eye opening or mental activity, with a tendency to be synchronized in different parts of the cerebral hemisphere.

A recording of electric activity of an operatively exposed brain is designated as an **electrocorticogram**. Needle electrodes may be introduced into the brain for recording from multiple subcortical areas at operation or postoperatively. Stereotaxic instruments for the more accurate placement of small needle electrodes into the human brain are available.

Frequency analyzers which depend upon mechanical or electric devices are employed to give a quantitative measurement of the specific frequencies present and permit the recognition of frequencies whose presence otherwise might be difficult to determine.

Microelectrode Studies.

Fine microelectrodes inserted within animal brain may record the action potential spikes of single neurons. These unit spikes last less than 1 msec. Recorded outside of cells, they range in amplitude from 0.5-10 mv. With ultrafine intracellular electrodes, spikes of 40-80 mv. may be recorded as well as the resting membrane potential of individual cells. Epileptic neurons are characterized by very high rates of repetitive discharge, reaching 500-1000/second (in contrast with normal cell rates of about 10-15/second). These epileptic neurons are also found to have a very unsteady membrane potential, being rapidly depolarized and remaining depolarized presumably because of defective recovery processes. Under certain conditions, inhibitory effects have also been noted, a cell becoming "hyperpolarized" with arrest of its discharge.

When unit discharges are recorded with microelectrodes simultaneously with the surface activity with gross electrodes, the relationship between surface waves and cell discharges appears variable. Very active unit discharge may be recorded during a relatively flat "desynchronized" surface EEG. The surface waves are made up largely of "dendritic" or synaptic potentials very loosely coupled to the unitary cellular activity of the cortex, except under certain conditions of massive synchronization. Some of the waves appear to have an inhibitory rather than an excitatory effect upon repetitive cell discharge during an epileptiform discharge.

A variety of patterns of neuronal hyperactivity may occur in monkeys made epileptic by alumina cream treatment of the cerebral cortex. Most frequently, rhythmically recurrent bursts of high frequency discharges occur in the epileptic cortical neuron interseizure patterns. Random bursts with varying frequencies of soma discharge may also occur over long periods. In other cases, interseizure hyperactivity of the neurons may consist of long trains of high-frequency discharges of variable frequency. Brief bursts of high-frequency discharges of 800/second or more and brief silences may occur.

There is no apparent relationship between the surface electrode recording and that from within the epileptic cells. At times, surface electrode "spikes" occur either associated or unassociated with bursts of discharges of cell bodies. Surface cortical electrodes of epileptic monkeys reveal that spontaneous electric seizures originate in the region of the cortical scar and spread to involve the ipsilateral as well as the contralateral cortex, and seizure discharges recorded in EEG show a tonic-clonic sequence like that of man. Microelectrode studies of single cells during seizures show that before the onset of the propagated disturbance spontaneous activity will be increased, with very high frequency discharges at rates up to 1000/second. The cortical standing potential develops a negative base-line shift of about 3 mv. after the seizure is started, and this direct current shift slowly progresses to a peak value. It then shifts more quickly in the positive direction toward the original value as the tonic phase of the seizure ends. The cessation of the seizure may be the result of local metabolic exhaustion, but active inhibition by involvement of inhibitory interneurons may also play a role.

Spread of a seizure discharge from an epileptic focus can occur either by local spread through the cortical feltwork and involve mechanisms similar to those of spreading depression or via spread of seizure discharges to other portions of the cortex and subcortex via conventional neuronal pathways. "Mirror foci," cortical and subcortical, showing spontaneous paroxysmal abnormalities as well as hypersensitivity to various activating agents, may occur in association with an experimentally induced cortical epileptic focus.

GLOSSARY OF TERMS
(EEG. Clin. Neurophysiol. 13:646-8, 1961.)

Abundance: Amount of activity, in terms of amplitude and number of waves, with respect to time.

Activity: Any sequence of waves.

Alpha rhythm: Rhythm, usually with frequency of 8-13 c/second, of almost sinusoidal form, in the posterior areas, present during relaxation when the eyes are closed; attenuated during attention, particularly visual.

Alpha variant rhythm: Rhythm with frequency simply related to, and with the same location and reactivity as, the alpha rhythm. Fast: The frequency is harmonically related to the alpha rhythm. Slow: The frequency is subharmonically related to the alpha rhythm.

Alpha wave: A component wave of the alpha rhythm.

Amplitude: Voltage of wave from peak to peak.

Attenuation: Decrease of amplitude of the waves.

Background activity: More or less general and continuous activity, in contrast with paroxysmal and focal activities. Not synchronous with alpha rhythm.

Beta rhythm: Rhythm with frequency higher than 13 c/seconds.

Beta wave: Wave with a duration of less than 75 msec. and usually forming part of a beta rhythm.

Burst: See Paroxysm.

Complex: Group of 2 or more waves, clearly distinguished from background activity and recurring either with consistent form (as in subacute encephalitis) or with a well recognized form (e.g., spike and wave).

Cycle: A complete series of changes undergone by a wave or a complex before the series of changes is repeated.

Delta activity: Sequence of waves with frequency of less than 4 c/second or with durations of more than 250 msec.

Delta rhythm: Rhythm with frequency of less than 4 c/second.

Delta wave: Wave with a duration of more than 250 msec.

Diffuse: Occurring over large areas without constant location.

Diphasic: See Phase.

Driving: Waves occurring at the same, or harmonically related, frequency as rhythmic stimuli, when phase locked, are said to show driving.

Duration: See Period.

Focus: A limited region involved by, or the point of maximal potential of, a specified wave or activity (e.g., spike focus, delta focus).

Frequency: The number of complete cycles of a rhythm in 1 second.

Index: The percentage time occupied by the waves specified (alpha index, delta index, etc.) with more than minimal amplitude (usually 10 microvolts) in a given sample, usually of 1 minute's duration.

Intermittent delta rhythm: 1-4 c/second rhythm, in paroxysms, usually frontal or occipito-temporal and usually sinusoidal or sawtoothed in form.

Isolated slow wave: Single slow wave.

K-complex: Combination of vertex sharp wave and sigma paroxysm, occurring spontaneously and especially in response to sudden stimuli during sleep.

Lambda wave: Sharp wave, mainly surface positive, in occipital areas, commonly associated with pattern vision.

Location: Frontal, parietal, etc.; refers to brain areas.

Low voltage fast record: See Low voltage record.

Low voltage record: No rhythmic activity above 10 microvolts; no activity above 20 microvolts.

Morphology: The shape of a wave or complex.

Mu rhythm: Rhythm at 7-11 c/second in central region, often with arcade or comb form and associated with beta rhythm, attenuated by real or imagined movement or tactile stimulation, particularly of the hands. (Synonyms: "Rhythme en arceaux," "wicket," and "comb" rhythm.)

Paroxysm: Series of waves of same or mixed periods appearing and disappearing abruptly (burst).

Period: Time interval in seconds from beginning to end of a wave. If the wave is a component of a rhythm, then the period is the reciprocal of the frequency.

Phase: Strictly: Amplitude time relations of sinusoidal waves. Loosely: Time relations of different parts of a wave in a single trace or of a wave as recorded in several channels.

Monophasic (wave): Deflected to one side of the baseline.

Diphasic (wave): Deflected first to one side, then to the other, of the baseline.

Polyphasic (wave): Deflected several times in opposite senses.

Poly-spike and wave: Spike and wave complex with more than one spike. (Synonym: Poly-pointe onde.)

Random: Recurring at inconstant time intervals.

Reactivity: Changeability of the EEG following change of environment.

Rhythm: Waves recurring with some constancy of period and form. A rhythm can be more or less stable in frequency, more or less constant in form, and more or less modulated in amplitude.

Sharp and slow wave: Complex with spike and wave form but with durations of, respectively: 80-200 msec. and 500-1000 msec.

Sharp wave: Isolated wave with triangular form: arbitrarily, with a duration of more than 80 msec. and less than 200 msec.

Sigma rhythm: Episodic rhythm at about 14 c/second, usually diffuse, usually occurring during certain stages of sleep. (Synonym: sleep spindles.)

Slow wave: Wave with period of more than 250 msec. Includes theta and delta waves.

Slow wave complex: Group of 2 or more slow waves recurring with constant form (as in subacute encephalitis).

Spike: Isolated wave; arbitrarily, with a duration of less than 80 msec.

Spike and wave complex: Complex of 2 waves, one having a duration of less than 80 msec. (spike), the other having a duration of 200-500 msec. (wave).

Spike and wave rhythm: Bilaterally synchronous spike and wave complexes, recurring rhythmically with frequency of 2.5-3.5 c/second, closely associated with clinical petit mal seizures.

Theta rhythm: Rhythm with frequency of 4 to less than 8 c/second.

Theta wave: Wave with duration of more than 125 but less than 250 msec.

Topology: Distribution of activity with respect to anatomic landmarks (see location).

Transient: Any single wave (spike, sharp wave, etc.) or brief complex, notably different from the background activity.

Unilateral: Occurring on one side of the head.

Vertex sharp wave: Sharp wave, mainly surface negative, maximal at the vertex, associated with arousal stimuli.

Wave: Any single transient change of potential difference in the EEG.

Wave complex: See Complex.

REPRESENTATIVE ELECTROENCEPHALOGRAMS

R = RIGHT F = FRONTAL   P = PARIETAL   AT = ANTERIOR TEMPORAL T = TEMPORAL
L = LEFT   O = OCCIPITAL Pc = PRECENTRAL Pf = POSTERIOR FRONTAL   E = EAR

Calibration: 50 microvolts (vertical) and 1 second (horizontal).

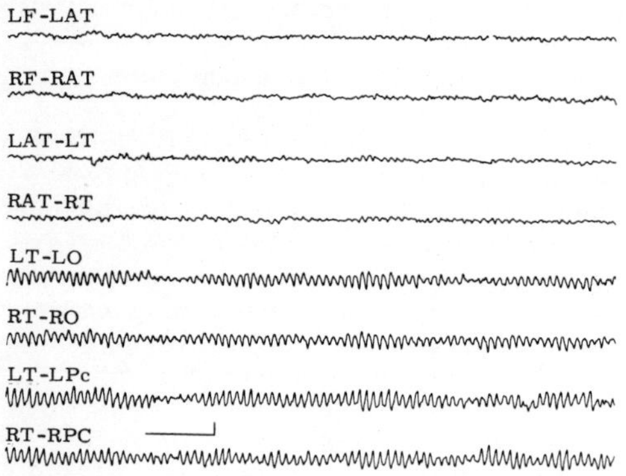

LF-LAT

RF-RAT

LAT-LT

RAT-RT

LT-LO

RT-RO

LT-LPc

RT-RPC

Normal Adult

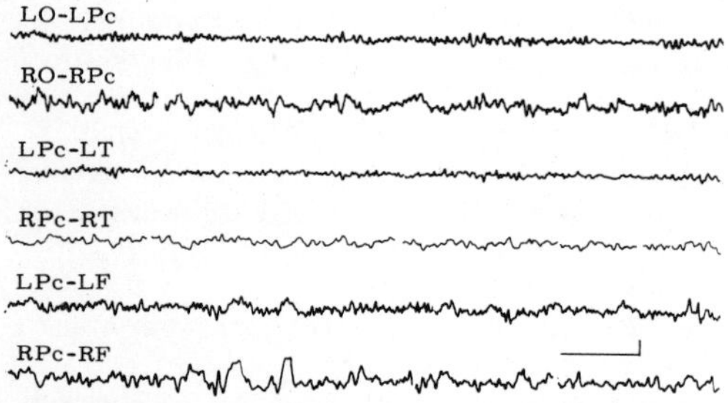

LO-LPc

RO-RPc

LPc-LT

RPc-RT

LPc-LF

RPc-RF

Cerebral Thrombosis. Tracing of a 71-year-old woman who showed moderate improvement one month after the onset of a left hemiplegia.

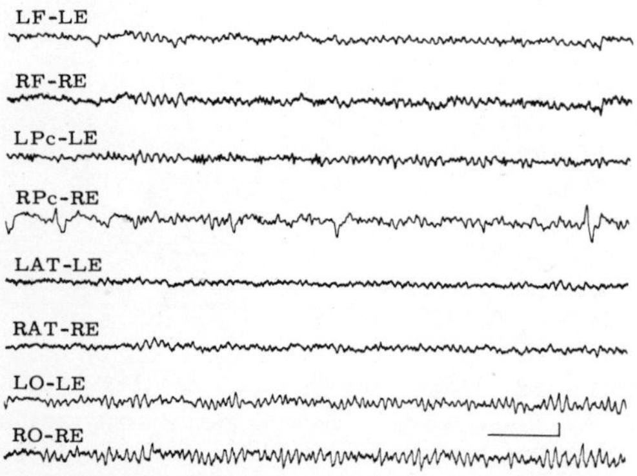

LF-LE

RF-RE

LPc-LE

RPc-RE

LAT-LE

RAT-RE

LO-LE

RO-RE

Hypertensive Encephalopathy. A 66-year-old hypertensive woman 5 days after acute onset of left hemiparesis and left focal motor seizures starting in the foot.

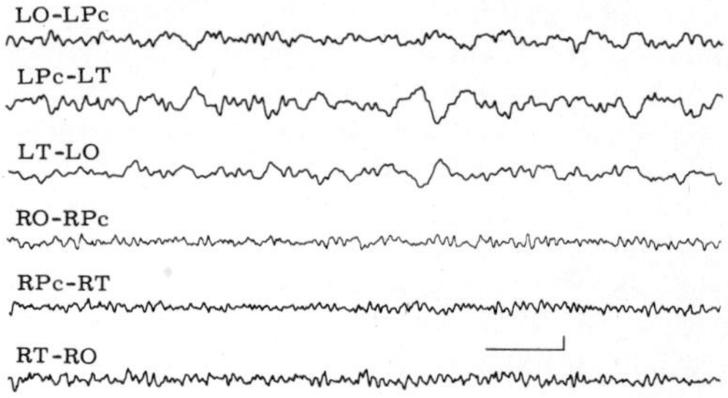

LO-LPc

LPc-LT

LT-LO

RO-RPc

RPc-RT

RT-RO

Cerebral Embolism. Record made one month after onset of aphasia and right hemiplegia which occurred 4 days after acute anterior myocardial infarct.

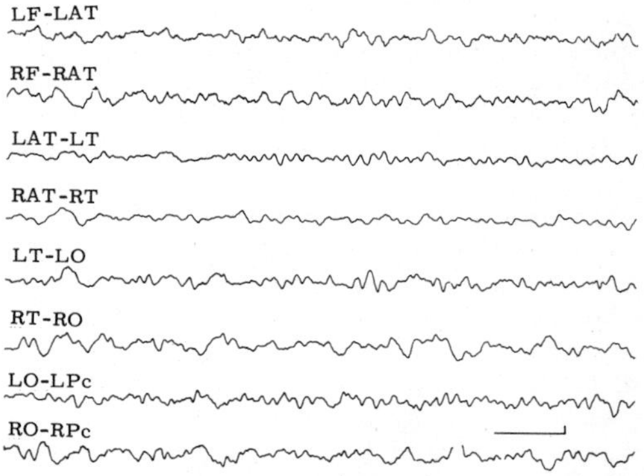

LF-LAT

RF-RAT

LAT-LT

RAT-RT

LT-LO

RT-RO

LO-LPc

RO-RPc

Chronic Right Subdural Hematoma. A lethargic 17-year-old boy with a history of head injury 3 months previously, followed by increasing headaches, diplopia, and left extensor plantar response.

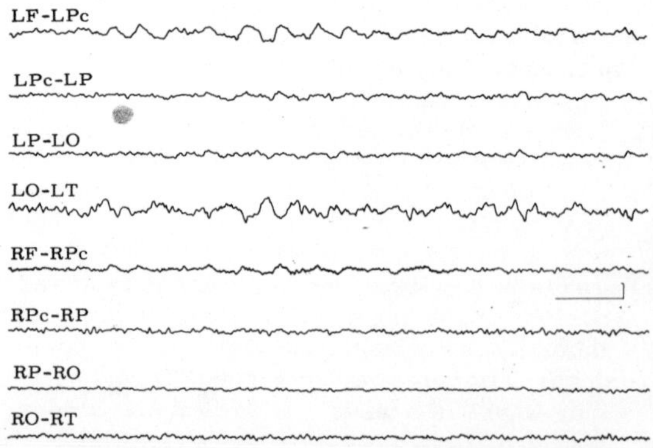

LF-LPc

LPc-LP

LP-LO

LO-LT

RF-RPc

RPc-RP

RP-RO

RO-RT

Thrombosis Left Internal Carotid Artery. Disorientation, euphoria, impaired mentation, and acalculia began suddenly in this 41-year-old man 2 weeks earlier.

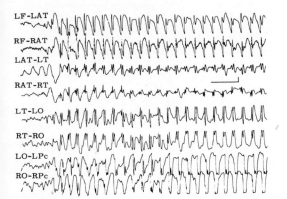

Petit Mal Epilepsy. This six-year-old boy had one of his "blank spells," in which he was transiently unaware of surroundings and blinked his eyelids, during the recording.

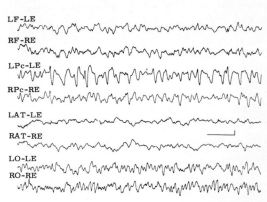

Epilepsy. Record of a six-year-old girl with frequent nocturnal major convulsions as well as daily seizures in which she became stiff, stared, and shook slightly.

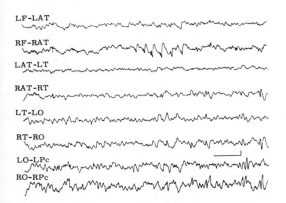

Epilepsy. This six-year-old child had suffered 3 major convulsions, 2 of which appeared to start in the left extremities.

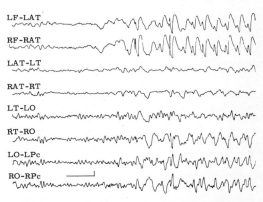

Epilepsy. Record of a 34-year-old man with history of recurrent nightmares and major and minor seizures since the age of 12 years.

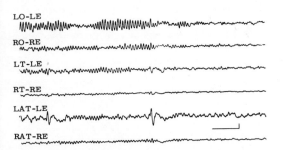

Psychomotor Epilepsy. This 20-year-old man had monthly episodes for the previous 6 years characterized by motor automatisms and frequently followed by generalized tonic-clonic convulsions.

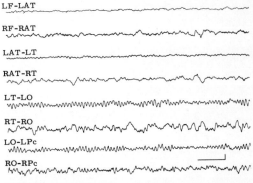

Focal Motor Epilepsy. This 47-year-old man with focal motor seizures beginning in the left hand stated his seizures began 20 years previously, approximately one year after a severe head injury.

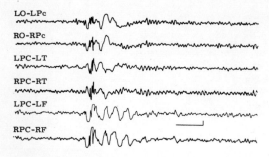

LO-LPc

RO-RPc

LPC-LT

RPC-RT

LPC-LF

RPC-RF

Epilepsy. Tracing of a 24-year-old man with generalized tonic-clonic convulsions and aura of nausea.

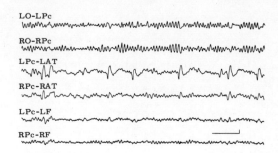

LO-LPc

RO-RPc

LPc-LAT

RPc-RAT

LPc-LF

RPc-RF

Epilepsy. Tracing of a 27-year-old woman with history of meningitis at age of 15 months and generalized tonic-clonic seizures since the age of 12 years.

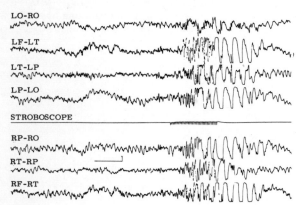

LO-RO

LF-LT

LT-LP

LP-LO

STROBOSCOPE

RP-RO

RT-RP

RF-RT

Epilepsy. This 13-year-old girl had brief episodes characterized by blinking of the eyes and absences over the past 3 years. Activation of an electric cerebral seizure was produced by photic stimulation at 20 cycles/sec. frequency.

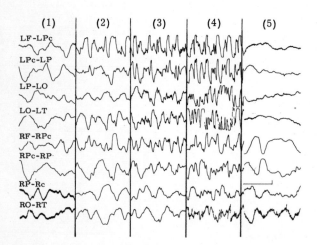

(1)   (2)   (3)   (4)   (5)

LF-LPc

LPc-LP

LP-LO

LO-LT

RF-RPc

RPc-RP

RP-Rc

RO-RT

Status Epilepticus. Excerpts from the record of a five-year-old comatose boy whose seizures began 5 days previously in association with a febrile illness: (1) Resting record. (2) Beginning of electric seizure (LF). (3) Clinical seizure apparent in right arm and face. (4) Height of clinical seizure. (5) Postconvulsive period.

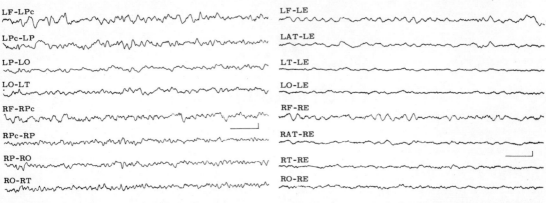

LF-LPc
LPc-LP
LP-LO
LO-LT
RF-RPc
RPc-RP
RP-RO
RO-RT

LF-LE
LAT-LE
LT-LE
LO-LE
RF-RE
RAT-RE
RT-RE
RO-RE

Left Cerebral Brain Abscess. Severe headaches, progressive right hemiparesis, and
aphasia occurred in this 50-year-old woman
with left temporofrontal abscess.

Skull Fracture and Brain Contusion. This 45-
year-old man was found wandering on the
streets in a disoriented and confused state one
week earlier, at which time skull x-rays re-
vealed left parietotemporal fracture and lumbar puncture disclosed xanthochromic CSF
under mildly increased pressure.

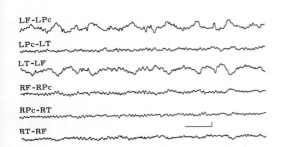

LF-LPc
LPc-LT
LT-LF
RF-RPc
RPc-RT
RT-RF

Left Frontal Tumor. A left frontal glioblastoma multiforme was found in this 58-year-
old man with onset of seizures, right hemiparesis, and aphasia 2 years previously.

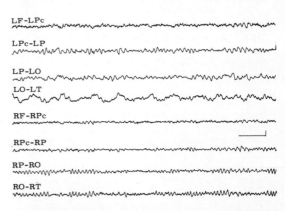

LF-LPc
LPc-LP
LP-LO
LO-LT
RF-RPc
RPc-RP
RP-RO
RO-RT

Left Temporal Tumor. Astrocytoma was found
in this 66-year-old man with a history of
headaches and aphasia of 3 weeks' duration.

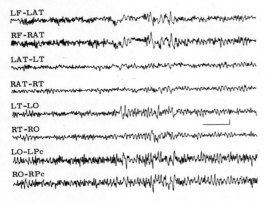

LF-LAT
RF-RAT
LAT-LT
RAT-RT
LT-LO
RT-RO
LO-LPc
RO-RPc

Barbiturate Intoxication. Tracing of a 32-year-
old woman, a barbiturate drug addict, during
a period in which she suffered intermittent
confusion, amnesia, and generalized motor
seizures.

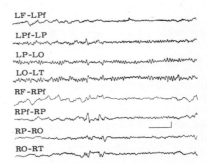

LF-LPf
LPf-LP
LP-LO
LO-LT
RF-RPf
RPf-RP
RP-RO
RO-RT

Infarct, Right Posterior Cerebral. Tracing
5 weeks after acute onset of transient left
hemiparesis, left homonymous hemianopsia,
left motor seizures with visual aura in a 52-
year-old man with normal right carotid
angiogram and pneumoencephalogram.

17...

Electromyography

Electromyography is concerned with the study of the electric activity arising from muscles and associated with muscle activity. Variations of potential are detected by needle electrodes inserted into skeletal muscle; the electric activity may be displayed on a cathode ray oscilloscope and played on a loudspeaker for simultaneous visual and auditory analysis.

The striated muscle of man is composed functionally of motor units in which the axons of single motor (anterior horn) cells innervate many muscle fibers. Hundreds of muscle fibers may be innervated by a single axon. All the fibers innervated by a single motor unit respond immediately in an "all-or-none" pattern to adequate stimulation. The interaction of many motor units can produce relatively smooth motor performance. Increased motor power results from activation of a greater number of motor units or from repeated activation of a given number of motor units. The action potential of a muscle consists of the sum of the action potentials of many motor units. The action potential of normal muscle fibers originates at the motor end-plates and is triggered by an incoming nerve impulse at the myoneural junction. It then spreads along muscle fibers, exciting contraction. The contraction itself produces no electric activity.

Electric potentials may be recorded, after amplification, by a cathode ray oscillograph. Inkwriting oscillographs, such as are used in electroencephalography, may be used in clinical studies and permit simultaneous recording from many muscles. However, the use of a cathode ray oscillograph recording as a control is advisable. Surface electrodes attached over the muscle with collodion may be used for recording muscle action potentials. With micro-electrodes or coaxial needle electrodes the discharges of single motor units may be recorded. The amplitude of single motor unit discharges (diphasic or triphasic waves) ranges from 20-2000 microvolts; duration of discharge is usually 0.003-0.015 seconds; frequency varies usually from 6-30/second.

They produce a knocking or thumping sound over the loudspeaker.

Clinical studies indicate that normal muscle at rest shows no action potentials. In simple movements, the contracting muscle gives rise to action potentials while its antagonist relaxes and gives rise to no potentials. During contraction, different portions of the same muscle may discharge at different rates and parts may appear to be transiently inactive; in strong contractions many motor units are active, producing numerous action potentials. Passive stretching of a muscle is associated with action potentials from the stretched muscle; further stretching produces the additional finding of action potentials in the antagonistic muscle. In each area of muscle tested, observations may be made of "insertion potentials" evoked by movement of the needle, resting muscle activity, and electric activity during voluntary muscle contraction.

Although the majority of motor unit potentials have a simple biphasic or triphasic form with an amplitude of 0.5-2 millivolts and a duration of 3-15 milliseconds, smaller potentials may be found in the face and external ocular muscles. The appearance of an active motor unit may be greatly influenced by its position relative to the recording electrode. During strong contraction, a concentric needle electrode may not be suitable for following single units, since it may record from too large an area. Therefore, micro-electrode technics have been devised which indicate that in the initiation of voluntary contractions the first motor units to discharge are apparently smaller than those which follow at higher tensions.

Clinical Applications.

In diseases where the lower motor neuron and the muscle innervated by it become atrophied, fasciculations and, later, fibrillations may occur in the muscles. Fibrillations are believed to represent the contractions of single muscle fibers and are associated with irregular potentials of low voltage and high frequency.

In **anterior poliomyelitis**, the presence of synchronous motor unit discharges in partially functioning muscles and their antagonists is interpreted to indicate a disturbance of reciprocal innervation. In clinical conditions associated with **spasticity**, the resting muscle may show no action potentials. In such cases, however, minimal stimuli may set off strong muscle contractions (associated with action potentials) in antagonistic muscle groups.

In **parkinsonism**, with rigidity, persistent simultaneous activity occurs in antagonistic muscles despite attempted relaxation. With diseases characterized by irregular involuntary movements (athetosis, dystonia), irregular, asynchronous patterns of discharge occur in the muscles.

Fibrillation potentials are simple monophasic or biphasic spikes less than 200 microvolts in amplitude and less than 2 milliseconds in duration. Fibrillation potentials produce a sharp clicking sound in the loudspeaker and are clearly distinguishable from normal motor unit potentials by their small size, brief duration, and sharp sound.

In a complete nerve lesion fibrillation potentials occur without motor unit potentials, whereas partial nerve lesions show both fibrillation and motor unit activity or voluntary muscle contraction. Diminution or cessation of fibrillation potentials and the appearance of small disintegrated motor unit action potentials occur with nerve regeneration. Fibrillations in a paretic muscle are increased by warmth, activity, and neostigmine, and decreased by cold or immobilization.

After **complete section of a nerve**, denervation fibrillation potentials are evident in all areas of the muscles supplied by a peripheral nerve after about 18 days. In **partial nerve injuries**, despite the clinical appearance of complete paralysis, some motor unit discharges persist. By mapping the areas in which denervation fibrillation potentials are present, single nerve root disorders may be diagnosed. Spinal nerve root compression can be recognized with the aid of such a technic. Extramedullary **cord tumors** are characterized by the frequent associated involvement of nerve roots with consequent local denervation fibrillation potentials.

Alterations in the electromyogram are commonly encountered in the **myopathies.** In the myotonias (myotonia congenita, atrophica, and acquisita) there is accentuation of the electromyographic response upon voluntary muscle contraction or insertion of the needle. The repetitive discharge of single muscle fibers or groups is initially high in frequency and declines rapidly, the discharge ceasing within a few seconds; this gives rise to the so-called "dive-bomber" sound in the loudspeaker. Denervation muscle potentials are not seen. In the muscular dystrophies, voluntary

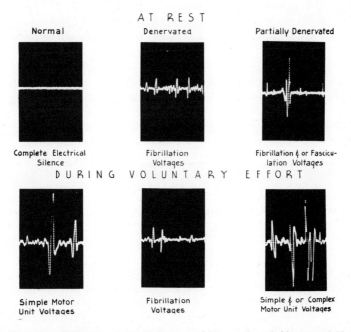

Electromyograms, Showing Characteristic Voltages of Normal and Abnormal Voluntary Muscle.
(Reproduced, with permission, from Golseth: Diagnostic contributions of the electromyogram. California Med. **73**:355, 1950.)

muscle contraction produces electric patterns of diminished amplitude and frequency. In myasthenia gravis, with continued muscle contraction, there is a gradual diminution in amplitude and frequency of motor unit discharges. In progressive muscular atrophy and amyotrophic lateral sclerosis there are usually diffuse denervation fibrillation and fasciculation discharges, even in cases which upon clinical examination appear to be anatomically limited to the distal portion of the upper extremities.

The electromyogram produced after appropriate motor nerve stimulation provides a useful clinical means of studying **neuromuscular diseases and disorders.** The response to single nerve stimuli or to repeated nerve stimulation may be studied in pathologic states and under modifications produced by therapy. Thus the effectiveness of medication in modifying the reaction of muscles in conditions like myasthenia gravis may be readily evaluated. The **conduction velocities** of motor nerves may be readily estimated by this technic. Conduction velocity may be markedly slowed in conditions affecting the peripheral nerves, and evidenced by increase in conduction time from point of stimulation to the muscle and increase in duration of action potentials of the muscle. The time and manner of reinnervation of muscles supplied by an injured or sectioned nerve can also be observed and correlated with clinically detectable movements during voluntary motion. In a functional disorder, such as hysteria, a normal pattern is demonstrable.

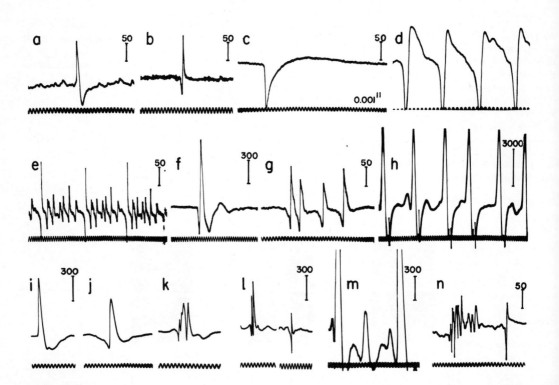

Action Potentials in Electromyography. (a) "Nerve potential" from normal muscle; (b) fibrillation potential and (c) positive wave from denervated muscle; (d) high-frequency discharge in myotonia; (e) bizarre high-frequency discharge; (f) fasciculation potential, single discharge; (g) fasciculation potential, repetitive or grouped discharge; (h) synchronized repetitive discharge in muscle cramp; (i) diphasic, (j) triphasic and (k) polyphasic motor unit action potentials from normal muscle; (l) short-duration motor unit action potentials in progressive muscular dystrophy; (m) large motor unit action potentials in progressive muscular atrophy; (n) highly polyphasic motor unit action potential and short-duration motor unit action potential during reinnervation. Calibration scales are in microvolts. All time scales are 1000 cycles per second. An upward deflection indicates a change of potential in the negative direction at the needle electrode. (Reproduced, with permission, from Clinical Examinations in Neurology. Members of the Sections of Neurology and Section of Physiology, Mayo Clinic and Mayo Foundation for Medical Education and Research, Graduate School, University of Minnesota, Rochester, Minnesota. Saunders, 1956.)

18 . . .

Electrodiagnostic Examinations

Electric stimulation of muscles and nerves is of clinical value in the diagnosis and prognosis of motor disorders. Galvanic (direct or continuous) current normally produces momentary contraction of a muscle upon "making" or "breaking" the circuit. It may be used to stimulate the nerve or the muscle directly. Faradic (induced or interrupted) current normally produces a continuous tetanic contraction due to the rapidly repeated stimuli. It is ordinarily used in stimulating the nerve only. Interrupted currents whose component electric pulses are measurable in terms of duration of pulse, form of pulse (square wave, saw-tooth, etc.), and electric energy may also be used.

In the muscle-nerve complex a variation is noted in the excitability of different parts. The nerve is most sensitive to stimulation; the myoneural junction is intermediate in sensitivity; and the muscle itself is the least sensitive. Clinically, stimulation is usually applied over the course of the nerve or at the **motor point** of the muscle being tested. The motor point is normally the most excitable point of a muscle and represents the greatest concentration of nerve endings. It is located on the skin over the muscle, and corresponds approximately to the level at which the nerve enters the muscle belly. Since some muscle fibers may be affected differently than others, it is often necessary to test different portions of the same muscle. Muscles should always be tested at the motor point; denervated muscles should be tested at the former motor point and in the neighborhood of the motor point.

A minimum amount of time is necessary for an electric current to produce stimulation of a nerve or muscle. This is expressed by the **chronaxie**, the time necessary for a current which is twice the rheobase to produce a response. The **rheobase** is the minimum amount of current necessary to stimulate a nerve or muscle.

Electric skin resistance (see p. 217) may be greatly increased in disorders which impair peripheral or autonomic nerve function with associated decrease in sweat secretion.

Normal Formula of Response (NFR).

In the use of galvanic current, 2 electrodes are needed. The indifferent electrode is broad and is placed against a large flat surface, e.g., the patient's back. This is necessary to afford good contact. The stimulating electrode is small and is placed over the nerve or motor point of the muscle being tested. Either electrode may be used as the anode, the other as the cathode. Ordinarily only closing or "make" shocks are used, since opening or "break" shocks usually require a painful amount of current to produce a response. With the cathode as stimulating electrode less current is needed to produce a response than when the anode is used. In other words, CCC (cathode closing contraction) exceeds ACC (anode closing contraction); the NFR, therefore, can be written CCC > ACC.

A "reversal of polarity" occurs when an injured nerve has undergone degeneration. A greater amount of current is needed to produce a response, and ACC > CCC. This polar inversion has never been satisfactorily explained.

The response of denervated muscle to galvanic current or interrupted current with pulses of long duration (0.5 seconds or longer) is retained but altered. In severe injuries galvanic stimulation of the nerve produces no response, and stimulation of the muscle causes a vermicular (worm-like) contraction instead of the normal quick reaction. Furthermore, the motor point disappears and the muscle becomes isosensitive throughout. The best response is then obtained by "longitudinal reaction," in which the lines of current are directed through the whole muscle instead of being concentrated at one point.

Degeneration of motor neurons may cause denervated muscles to fail to contract upon stimulation with interrupted current of electric pulses of short duration (less than 0.0005 seconds, or faradic). This change, which occurs after a delay of 2-3 weeks, is comparable in significance to the appearance of fibrillation denervation potentials in the electromyogram.

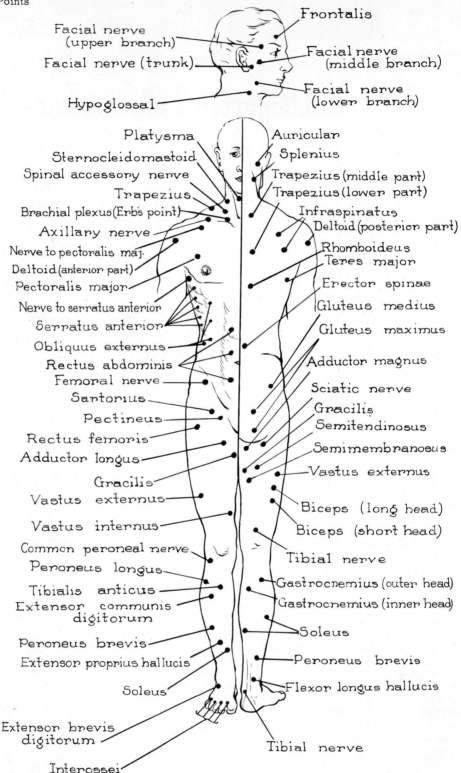

Facial nerve
(upper branch)
Frontalis
Facial nerve (trunk)
Facial nerve
(middle branch)
Facial nerve
(lower branch)
Hypoglossal

Platysma
Auricular
Sternocleidomastoid
Splenius
Spinal accessory nerve
Trapezius (middle part)
Trapezius
Trapezius (lower part)
Brachial plexus (Erb's point)
Infraspinatus
Deltoid (posterior part)
Axillary nerve
Nerve to pectoralis maj.
Rhomboideus
Teres major
Deltoid (anterior part)
Erector spinae
Pectoralis major
Gluteus medius
Nerve to serratus anterior
Gluteus maximus
Serratus anterior
Obliquus externus
Adductor magnus
Rectus abdominis
Sciatic nerve
Femoral nerve
Gracilis
Sartorius
Semitendinosus
Pectineus
Semimembranosus
Rectus femoris
Vastus externus
Adductor longus
Gracilis
Biceps (long head)
Vastus externus
Biceps (short head)
Vastus internus
Tibial nerve
Common peroneal nerve
Gastrocnemius (outer head)
Peroneus longus
Gastrocnemius (inner head)
Tibialis anticus
Extensor communis
digitorum
Soleus
Peroneus brevis
Peroneus brevis
Extensor proprius hallucis
Flexor longus hallucis
Soleus
Extensor brevis
digitorum
Tibial nerve
Interossei

Points for Electric Stimulation of Muscles and Nerves

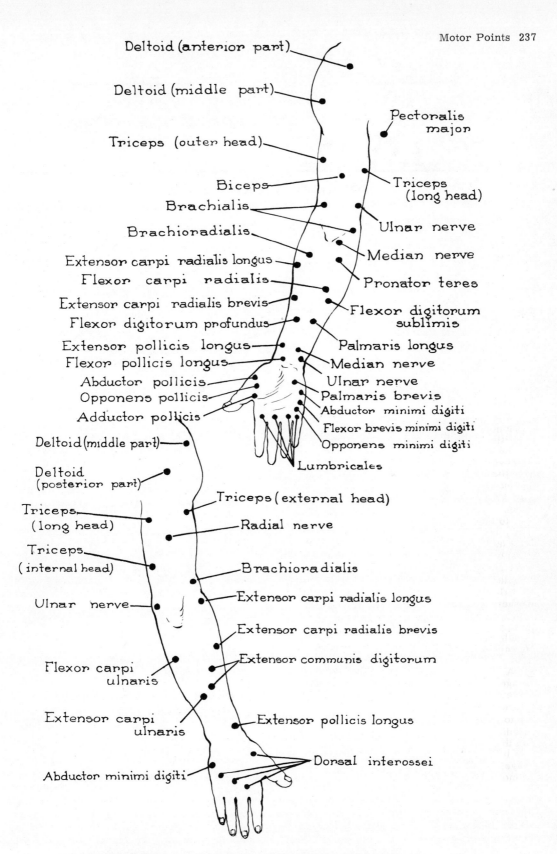

Deltoid (anterior part)

Deltoid (middle part)

Pectoralis major

Triceps (outer head)

Triceps (long head)

Biceps

Brachialis

Brachioradialis

Ulnar nerve

Median nerve

Extensor carpi radialis longus

Pronator teres

Flexor carpi radialis

Extensor carpi radialis brevis

Flexor digitorum sublimis

Flexor digitorum profundus

Extensor pollicis longus

Palmaris longus

Flexor pollicis longus

Median nerve

Abductor pollicis

Ulnar nerve

Opponens pollicis

Palmaris brevis

Abductor minimi digiti

Adductor pollicis

Flexor brevis minimi digiti

Opponens minimi digiti

Deltoid (middle part)

Lumbricales

Deltoid (posterior part)

Triceps (external head)

Triceps (long head)

Radial nerve

Triceps (internal head)

Brachioradialis

Extensor carpi radialis longus

Ulnar nerve

Extensor carpi radialis brevis

Extensor communis digitorum

Flexor carpi ulnaris

Extensor carpi ulnaris

Extensor pollicis longus

Dorsal interossei

Abductor minimi digiti

Points for Electric Stimulation of Muscles and Nerves

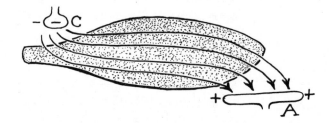

The Normal Formula of Response (NFR)

Longitudinal Reaction

Reaction of Degeneration (R. D.).

The characteristic electric changes in lower motor neuron lesions are known as the "reaction of degeneration." This reaction may be partial or complete, depending upon the severity of the injury. It is always necessary to wait 10-14 days after the injury before testing the R. D., since that much time is required for degeneration of an injured nerve to occur. Both galvanic and faradic currents are used to test the degree of R. D. In **mild partial R. D.**, faradic stimulation of nerve requires more current than normal and galvanic stimulation of nerve and muscle produces normal response. In **severe partial R. D.**, faradic stimulation of nerve produces no contraction and galvanic stimulation of nerve and muscle produces a normal response. In **complete R. D.**, faradic or galvanic stimulation of nerve produces no response and galvanic stimulation of muscle produces vermicular contractions.

A. Prognostic Significance of R. D. : Changes in the reaction of degeneration were at one time advocated as a prognostic guide to recovery of function. Experience has shown this to be a limited and unreliable index. Faradic excitability may return much later than the disappearance of fibrillation potentials in the electromyogram and is sometimes delayed until after the return of voluntary muscle movement.

The following claims for the prognostic significance of reaction of degeneration have been made: mild partial R. D., recovery expected in 6 weeks; severe partial R. D., recovery expected in 6 months; complete R. D., recovery not expected for 1-2 years or may never occur. The time required for recovery depends somewhat upon how far the regenerating fibers must grow. The rate of growth is about 1 mm. /day or 1 inch/month.

B. Diagnostic Significance of R. D. : R. D. is absent in upper motor neuron lesions and functional paralysis; present in lower motor neuron lesions and true organic lower motor neuron paralysis. R. D. is not present in cases of motor loss resulting from cut tendons and hence is useful in differentiating such lesions from motor loss due to lower motor neuron changes.

Chronaxie.

The chronaxie of denervated muscle (see p. 235) may be greatly increased; the value for normal human skeletal muscle usually does not exceed 0.7 msec. After section of a motor nerve, electric stimulation of a distal portion of the nerve and motor point chronaxie may remain normal for 2 days. On about the third day, stimulation of the distal portion of the sectioned nerve may produce no response. Motor point chronaxie may be increased but muscle response may appear normal, the muscle contracting and relaxing abruptly.

Chronaxie continues to rise thereafter. In about one week, slowness in relaxation of muscle following electrically induced contraction may be evident. About a month after nerve section, motor point chronaxie may have increased 100 times. Upon galvanic stimulation, muscle contraction and relaxation are slowed.

With nerve regeneration and muscle reinnervation, progressive decrease in chronaxie may occur. The muscle then begins to contract rapidly on electric stimulation of the nerve.

Galvanic-tetanus Ratio.

The ratio of current strength required for a minimal visible muscle contraction to that required for a sustained contraction when long constant (galvanic) currents are used is called the galvanic-tetanus ratio. In normal muscle the ratio is 1:4; in denervated muscle, 1:1. Although the gradual change in this ratio toward normal has been described as a more sensitive index of reinnervation than the return of faradic excitability, the method has been criticized because it does not yield constant results. Increased responsiveness to constant currents may also be shown by the use of slowly rising currents which may cause tetanic contractions in denervated muscle without affecting normal muscles at comparable current strengths.

Strength-duration Curves.

The excitability of nerve and muscle may be measured with the help of stimulators which provide interrupted current with pulses varying from 0.0001-1 second. In general, the shorter the pulses used, the greater the strength of current required to reach the threshold of excitation. A strength-duration curve may be plotted to show the excitation time characteristics and chronaxie of a particular locus. Although this method is not as sensitive as electromyography, such curves may show evidence of denervation following nerve injury or chronic lower motor neuron disease at times when spontaneous fibrillations are difficult to detect. In normal muscle, the nerves remain the most excitable component and the curve reflects the excitability characteristic of nerve; in denervated muscle, the curve reflects the excitability of denervated muscle fibers rather than of the nerve components.

Electric Stimulation of Nerve Trunks.

The presence, absence, or reduction of innervation may be determined by electric stimulation of peripheral nerves. The location of a nerve block may be demonstrated. Anomalies of innervation may be detected by noting which muscles respond to nerve stimulation. Abnormal fatigability following repeated stimulation of the nerve may be noted.

In the presence of paralysis, stimulation of the peripheral nerve with a normal response of innervated muscles shows that the cause of paralysis is proximal to the stimulated point. On the other hand, an absent or weak response suggests that further testing is desirable to detect the site and nature of the defect.

In diseases affecting peripheral nerves, there may be a reduction in conduction velocity of motor nerves. This may be evident in the increase in conduction time from the point of stimulation of the nerve to the muscle and by increase in duration of the muscle action potential. Marked slowing in conduction velocity occurs in diseases which affect peripheral nerves, as in chronic neuropathies, during regeneration following nerve injuries, and in Charcot-Marie-Tooth atrophy. No slowing in conduction occurs in progressive muscular dystrophy or polymyositis; in diseases affecting the anterior horn cells, such as amyotrophic lateral sclerosis and progressive muscular atrophy, there is no slowing or very mild slowing in conduction velocity.

Other Clinical Applications of Electric Examinations.

A. Jolly's Myasthenic Reaction: In myasthenia gravis and in some other types of neural disorders, involved muscles show rapid fatigue upon repeated faradic stimulation and finally do not respond at all. Excitability usually returns after a rest period.

Repetitive supramaximal stimulation of a peripheral nerve may reveal abnormal fatigability of the peripheral neuromuscular system. The action potential of muscle may be recorded as a measure of the response; in myasthenia gravis the characteristic response is most evident in severely affected muscle.

B. Myotonic Reaction: In disorders characterized by myotonia (e.g., myotonia congenita or myotonia atrophica), affected muscles may show a prolonged response to a single stimulation.

C. Tetanic Reaction: In tetany, muscles may be hyperexcitable (Erb's sign). However, the chronaxie of muscles may be significantly increased.

D. Cadaveric Reaction: In an acute attack of familial periodic paralysis, complete absence of electric excitability may occur. Normal excitability may return after the attack.

E. Miscellaneous: Muscular dystrophy may be characterized by a disparity between the feeble muscle contraction elicited on electric stimulation and the apparent mass of pseudohypertrophic muscle. Vascular disorders which produce impaired circulation (e. g., Buerger's disease) may produce increased chronaxie in muscles of affected extremities. In atrophies of disuse and in paralysis not due to lower motor neuron disease, the chronaxie of motor points is usually normal.

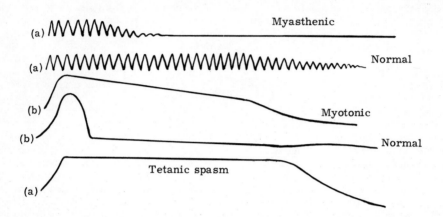

(a) Myasthenic

(a) Normal

(b) Myotonic

(b) Normal

Tetanic spasm

(a)

Normal and Abnormal Forms of Muscular Reaction to (a) Repetitive and (b) Single Electric Stimulation

•   •   •

19 . . .

Radiologic Examination

ROENTGENOGRAPHY OF THE SKULL

A complete roentgenographic study of the skull may require 6-7 different views. For most routine studies, however, a right and left lateral view, a posteroanterior view, and an oblique anteroposterior (Towne) view are adequate.

The skull is slightly asymmetric, and one half is usually slightly larger in the postero-anterior view (see p. 243). In this view the frontal sinuses may appear to be of different shape and size and the septum slightly to the right or left of center. The right and left nasal cavities may also be of different shape and size.

In the lateral view, one can get a general impression of the convexity of the skull and its size and relationship to the facial bones (see p. 244). The cranial wall varies in thickness in different individuals as well as in different regions of the skull; it usually appears to be either homogeneous or granular. In elderly persons coarse mottling or pronounced osteoporosis may occur. The cranial wall varies in thickness from 3-5 mm. in the frontoparietal regions to 15 mm. in the area of the occipital protuberance. The sphenoidal sinuses vary considerably in size and extension; the petrous bone is seen as a dense triangular shadow.

The cranial sutures are usually easily recognized in skull roentgenograms, particularly the coronal, lambdoid, and temporoparietal sutures. The coronal suture is especially evident near the vertex in the lateral view. Occasionally, sutures ossify in later life and may be difficult to identify. Suture lines, especially in children, may be readily mistaken for fractures. The infant skull often shows sutures and bones not seen in the adult skull.

Skull roentgenograms of normal adults frequently show dense shadows of various size, shape, and position. These correspond to deposits of calcium in certain intracranial structures such as the pineal body, the falx cerebri, the tentorium cerebelli, the choroid plexuses, the pacchionian granulations, and the habenular commissure. **Reid's base line** (see p. 244) passes through the center of the external auditory meatus and the lower orbital margin. It is sometimes more convenient to use the orbito-meatal line, which joins the external auditory meatus to the outer canthus of the eye, as a line of reference.

Roentgenograms of the skull may show abnormal features in association with neurologic disorders. These include the following:

(1) Skull deformities: Congenital malformations, hydrocephalus, basilar impression.

(2) Head injuries: Skull fractures, bony skull defects, subdural hematoma.

(3) Skull lesions: Osteitis, hyperostosis, osteomas, skull tumor, vascular lesions of the scalp.

(4) Systemic disease: Xanthomatosis, osteitis deformans, marble bones, hyperparathyroidism, rickets, chondrodystrophy, erythroblastic anemia, senile atrophy, tuberous sclerosis, cretinism, mongolism.

(5) Brain calcifications: Toxoplasmosis, Sturge-Weber syndrome, endocrine disorders.

(6) Increased intracranial pressure: Brain tumor, brain abscess, hydrocephalus, intracranial hematoma.

(7) Vascular anomalies: Cerebral aneurysm, vascular malformations of the brain.

Plain x-rays may reveal significant information in a variety of disorders and diseases of the CNS. Skull roentgenograms may disclose typical changes suggestive of an intracranial tumor. In children, these include suture diastasis or separation, sellar changes, and increased convolutional markings of the cranial vault. In adults, there may be sellar changes ranging from demineralization and thinning of the dorsum sellae to actual erosion or pineal displacement.

Intracranial calcifications may occur with a variety of neurologic disorders. Among brain tumors, calcification may be seen in (1) gliomas, especially slow-growing ones such as oligodendrogliomas; (2) meningiomas,

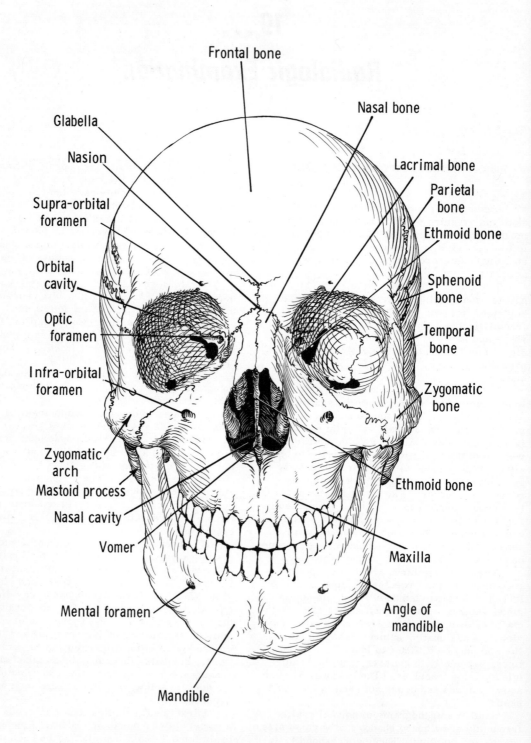

Frontal bone

Nasal bone

Glabella

Lacrimal bone

Nasion

Parietal bone

Supra-orbital foramen

Ethmoid bone

Orbital cavity

Sphenoid bone

Optic foramen

Temporal bone

Infra-orbital foramen

Zygomatic bone

Zygomatic arch

Ethmoid bone

Mastoid process

Nasal cavity

Vomer

Maxilla

Mental foramen

Angle of mandible

Mandible

Anterior View of Skull

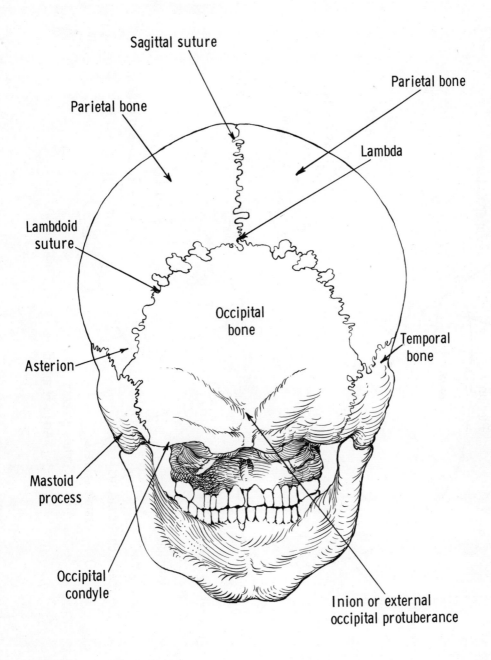

Sagittal suture

Parietal bone

Parietal bone

Lambda

Lambdoid suture

Occipital bone

Temporal bone

Asterion

Mastoid process

Occipital condyle

Inion or external occipital protuberance

Posterior View of Skull

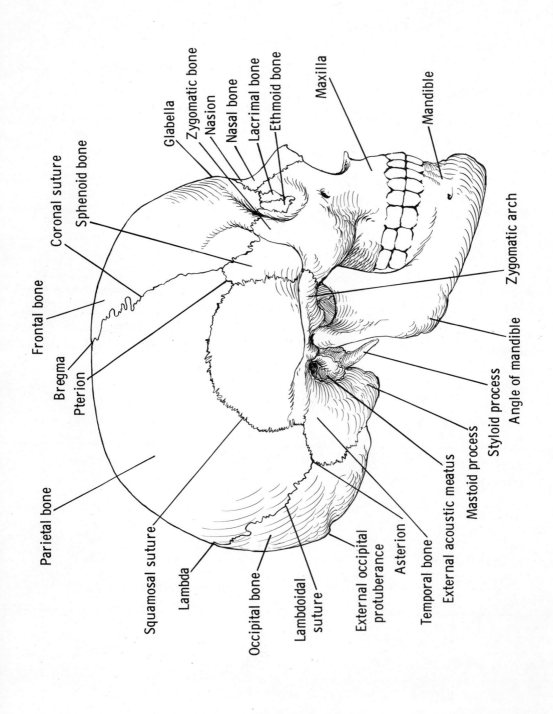

Lateral View of Skull

Parietal bone

Frontal bone

Coronal suture

Sphenoid bone

Bregma

Pterion

Glabella

Zygomatic bone

Nasion

Nasal bone

Lacrimal bone

Ethmoid bone

Maxilla

Mandible

Zygomatic arch

Styloid process

Angle of mandible

Squamosal suture

Lambda

Occipital bone

Lambdoidal suture

External occipital protuberance

Asterion

Temporal bone

External acoustic meatus

Mastoid process

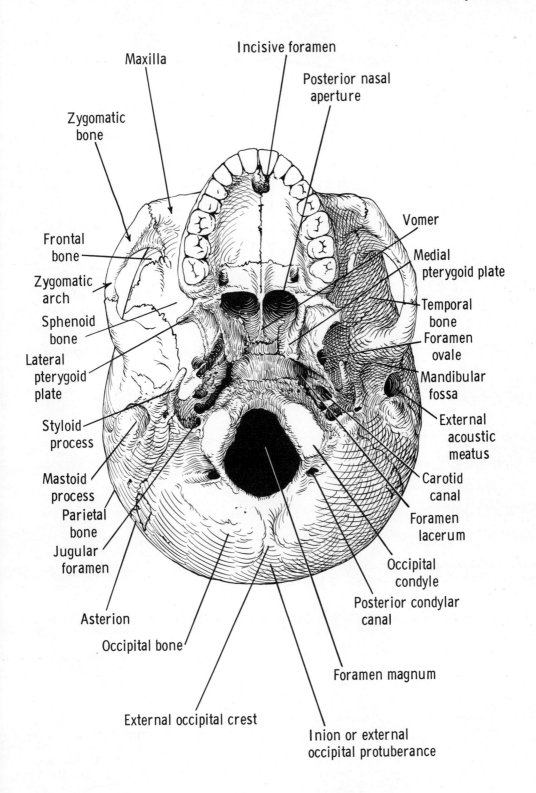

Maxilla

Incisive foramen

Posterior nasal
aperture

Zygomatic
bone

Vomer

Medial
pterygoid plate

Frontal
bone

Temporal
bone

Zygomatic
arch

Foramen
ovale

Sphenoid
bone

Mandibular
fossa

Lateral
pterygoid
plate

External
acoustic
meatus

Styloid
process

Carotid
canal

Mastoid
process

Foramen
lacerum

Parietal
bone

Jugular
foramen

Occipital
condyle

Asterion

Posterior condylar
canal

Occipital bone

Foramen magnum

External occipital crest

Inion or external
occipital protuberance

Basal View of Skull

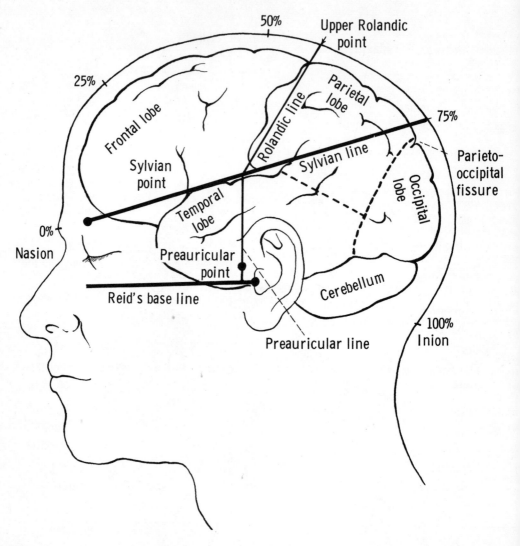

Determination of the Rolandic and Sylvian Fissures. (Reproduced, with permission, from Taylor and Haughton, Tr. Roy. Acad. Med. in Ireland **18**:511, 1900.)

especially those which are parasagittal or along the sphenoid ridge; and (3) craniopharyngiomas, usually suprasellar and in children.

Vascular calcification commonly occurs in cerebral arteriosclerosis and is usually situated in the carotid artery (carotid siphon) as it lies in the cavernous sinus. Walls of cerebral aneurysms may show circular or arcuate calcifications. Basal ganglia calcification may occur with hypoparathyroidism or pseudohypoparathyroidism.

In Sturge-Weber syndrome (trigeminal angiomatosis), typical "railroad track" calcification (double-linear) may be seen. This is due to calcification or opacification of atro-

phic cerebral cortex, usually in the occipital regions. Intracranial calcification in tuberous sclerosis tends to be subcortical and paraventricular and is more marked after puberty.

Local erosions, or enlargements of foramens, occur with some intracranial masses. In acoustic neurinoma, enlargement of the internal auditory meatus, producing funnel-shaped or fish-mouth deformity, may be detected on routine x-rays. A glioma of the optic nerve may enlarge the optic foramen. Superior orbital fissure may enlarge with retro-orbital aneurysm or meningioma. Ballooning of the sella turcica is usually due to chromophobe and, more rarely, to eosinophilic ade-oma of the pituitary.   The foramen spinosum may be enlarged unilaterally with meningiomas because of the enlarged meningeal vessels on the affected side.

Hyperostosis of local type may be caused by meningioma.   Characteristic sites of meningioma formation include the parasaggital area, the sphenoid ridge, the olfactory groove, and the base of the skull.   A more benign form of hyperostosis is hyperostosis frontalis interna, which is usually bilateral, sparing the midline, affects only the inner table of the skull, and occurs with high frequency in postmenopausal women.

Increased vascular markings, if generalized, pronounced, and symmetric, may be associated with intracranial vascular malformation.   Locally increased meningeal or diploic markings often occur with angioma or meningioma.

INTRACRANIAL PNEUMOGRAPHY

Intracranial pneumography has become one of the most valuable diagnostic aids at the disposal of the neurologist or neurologic surgeon.   Its purpose is to localize intracranial disease.   The procedure is based upon the principle that a gaseous replacement of the fluid within the ventricular and subarachnoid systems offers a contrast medium, air being much less dense than fluid to roentgen rays. In this manner the convolutions and ventricles can be visualized.

An encephalogram is a roentgenogram of the skull following replacement of CSF by air or oxygen by means of lumbar puncture.   The subarachnoid spaces, including the cisterns and ventricles, can usually be visualized by this method.   It is contraindicated whenever lumbar puncture is not safe.

A ventriculogram is a roentgenogram of the skull following replacement of CSF by air or oxygen by means of ventricular puncture. This is an operating room procedure.   Ventricular puncture drains only the ventricular system; the subarachnoid spaces and cisterns are not visible in this film.   Ventriculography is usually considered safer than encephalography in the diagnosis of expanding intracranial lesions.

In patients with posterior fossa lesions or obstructive hydrocephalus, it is sometimes desirable and helpful to perform ventriculography with a positive contrast medium.   Iophendylate (Pantopaque®) is usually injected into a lateral ventricle with the patient's head

so positioned that the contrast medium will fall into an anterior horn.   The head is then manipulated carefully so that the medium enters the third ventricle and thence the cerebral aqueduct and the fourth ventricle.

PNEUMOENCEPHALOGRAPHY

Pneumoencephalography is widely used for demonstrating cerebral structures.   The technic is to replace measured quantities of CSF with air or some other suitable gas introduced by means of lumbar puncture (or, more rarely, by cisternal puncture).   It is used mainly in those cases in which intracranial CSF pressure is not increased.

Air is believed to enter the ventricular system mainly through the medial foramen of the fourth ventricle (foramen of Magendie), situated at the top of the funnel-shaped cisterna magna.

Failure of filling of the ventricular system may be due to increased intracranial pressure, to the valve-like action of the pia arachnoid at the medial foramen of the fourth ventricle, or to other mechanical causes of obstruction at this site.

It is usually best to wait about 10 days after a previous lumbar puncture before attempting pneumoencephalography.   This is to avoid entering a fluid-distended subdural space instead of subarachnoid space.   Although air may be injected by the cisternal as well as the lumbar route, the latter is preferred for technical reasons.

Indications.

Pneumoencephalography has been useful in the study of patients with epilepsy, cerebral atrophies, congenital brain lesions, and post-traumatic cerebral disorders.

Brain tumors may produce relatively characteristic alterations in ventricular pattern, suggesting tumor location and type.   These tumors may be classed radiographically as follows:

A. Supratentorial:
1. Lateral - Produce displacement of septum pellucidum and third ventricle away from side of lesion.   Usually can estimate height, size, and location of lesion.
2. Midline - Includes tumors of corpus callosum, septum pellucidum, third ventricle, and adjacent region, most of which have characteristic appearances on pneumoencephalography.   Suprasellar tumors may be considered

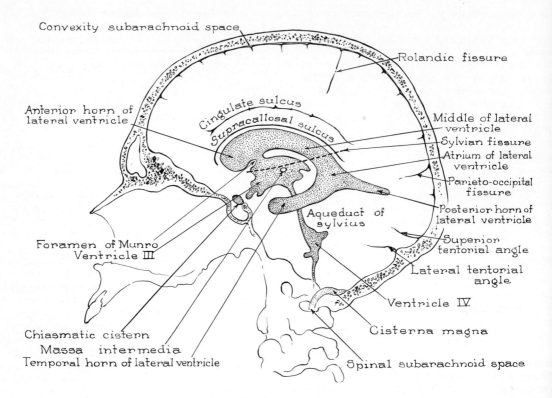

Convexity subarachnoid space

Rolandic fissure

Anterior horn of lateral ventricle

Cingulate sulcus

Supracallosal sulcus

Middle of lateral ventricle

Sylvian fissure

Atrium of lateral ventricle

Parieto-occipital fissure

Posterior horn of lateral ventricle

Aqueduct of sylvius

Superior tentorial angle

Foramen of Munro
Ventricle III

Lateral tentorial angle

Ventricle IV

Chiasmatic cistern
Massa intermedia
Temporal horn of lateral ventricle

Cisterna magna

Spinal subarachnoid space

Lateral Encephalogram

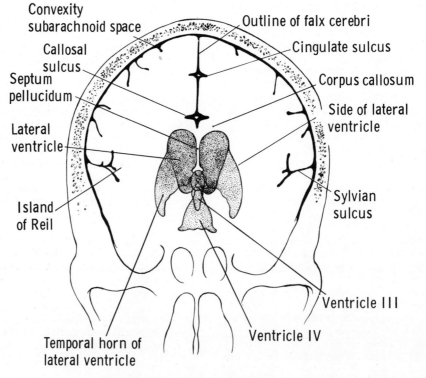

Convexity subarachnoid space

Outline of falx cerebri

Callosal sulcus

Cingulate sulcus

Septum pellucidum

Corpus callosum

Side of lateral ventricle

Lateral ventricle

Island of Reil

Sylvian sulcus

Ventricle III

Temporal horn of lateral ventricle

Ventricle IV

Anteroposterior Encephalogram

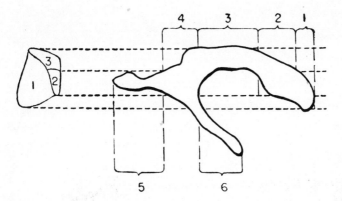

The lateral ventricle divided into 6 portions which are visible as units in anteroposterior views. The dotted horizontal lines serve to project portions 1, 2, and
3 on an imaginary plate. These lines would be approximately parallel to the base
of the skull.

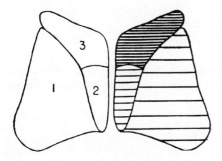

Outlines of portions 1, 2, and 3
in an anteroposterior view.

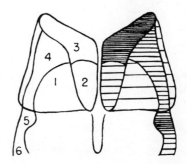

Superposition of ventricular shadow
in an anteroposterior plate.

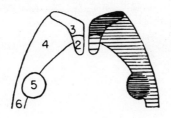

Superposition of ventricular shadow
in a posteroanterior plate.

Normal Anatomy of the Lateral Ventricle as Determined by Ventriculographic Studies. (Re-
arranged and reproduced, with permission, from Peele: The Neuroanatomical Basis for
Clinical Neurology. Blakiston-McGraw, 1954.)

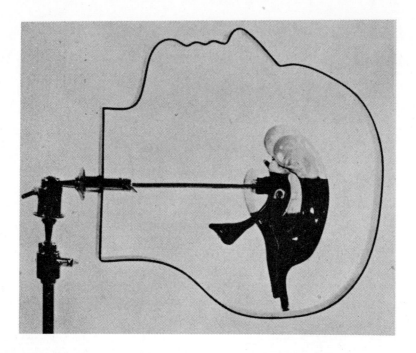

Front-up Position of a Model of the Ventricular System Partially Filled with Air. (Reproduced, with permission, from De Vet: Translucent glass model of the cerebral ventricular system. J. Neurosurg. 8:454, 1951.)

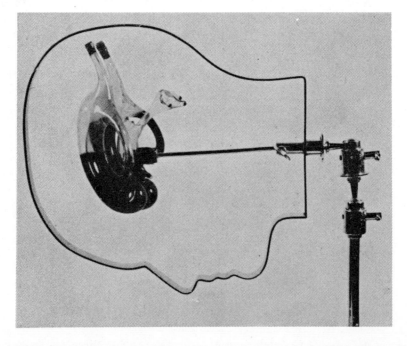

Occiput-up Position of a Model of the Ventricular System Partially Filled with Air. (Reproduced, with permission, from De Vet: Ibid.)

part of this group, and include craniopharyngioma, extensions of pituitary adenomas, meningioma of tuberculum sellae, chiasmatic gliomas, and aneurysms.

B. Infratentorial: These can often be precisely localized, especially with the use of added technics such as autotomography. Useful radiographic landmarks in this group include:

1. Twining's line - The midpoint of a line joining the tuberculum sellae to the internal occipital protuberance (in lateral view) normally lies in the fourth ventricle.

2. Lysholm's line - The aqueduct of Sylvius lies below the junction of the first and second thirds of a line from the clivus through the aqueduct to the skull vault.

Technic.

Simple replacement of CSF by air without the use of elaborate apparatus is widely used. A manometric reading of the CSF pressure prior to the injection of air is always indicated. Lumbar puncture is made under local anesthesia (in children, a general anesthetic is used). When large quantities of gas are injected, about 5% less gas than the volume of CSF withdrawn is injected; this is to allow for expansion of the injected gas at body temperature. CSF should not be aspirated but should be allowed to escape spontaneously. The rate of escape of fluid and injection of the gas should not exceed 5 ml. or cc. in one minute. The quantity of gas injected varies. Fifty to 70 cc. are usually sufficient to adequately fill the ventricles and subarachnoid spaces. The normal capacity of the ventricular system is 18-20 cc. of gas. In marked hydrocephalus, 120-150 cc. of gas may be required.

Modified Robertson's Technic (Fractional Encephalography).

With the subject seated and his head slightly flexed, 5 cc. of filtered air are slowly injected at a rate of 1 cc./minute. A posteroanterior x-ray is then taken; this usually shows air in the fourth ventricle, the aqueduct, and the third ventricle. CSF is allowed to drip slowly through the needle until the manometer indicates approximately initial pressure; another 5 cc. of gas are then injected and another posteroanterior x-ray taken. After injection of another 5 cc. of gas, a lateral view (with the patient still sitting) is taken; this view should show air in the fourth ventricle, the aqueduct, the posterosuperior part of the third ventricle, the posterior horns, and the posterior parts of the bodies of the lateral ventricles. Alternate introduction of air and re-

moval of CSF is continued until a satisfactory filling of the ventricles is obtained. In normal subjects about 20 cc. of air are sufficient to fill the ventricles. To outline the basal cisterns, the head and neck are slightly extended and, after introduction of a further quantity of air, a lateral x-ray taken. After removal of the needle, the patient is placed in the supine position, which brings air into the anterior parts of the lateral and third ventricles. An anteroposterior x-ray is then taken in this position. The subject then is placed in a prone position and a posteroanterior x-ray made. Supplementary views, including lateral and oblique, may then be made to complete the study.

Absorption of Air.

Air is absorbed most rapidly from the subarachnoid spaces over the convexity of the cerebral hemispheres, frequently within 24 hours. Air in the cisterns may absorb in 48 hours. Air in the ventricles may be absorbed for the most part in 72 hours.

Complications.

Headache and nausea and vomiting are relatively minor complications which may occur after pneumoencephalography and usually respond well to symptomatic therapy and rest flat in bed. Disturbances of intracranial pressure and beginning tentorial or medullary pressure cones may lead to grave consequences. Ventricular tap and prompt decompression may be immediately necessary in this group.

In the presence of elevated CSF pressure, a pneumoencephalogram is hazardous. The risk is reduced by controlled encephalography using small quantities of air.

ANGIOGRAPHY

Iodopyracet (Diodrast®) and, less frequently, Thorotrast® (thorium dioxide, 25% suspension) were first used as contrast media in angiographic studies. Diodrast®, when used in 35% concentration, is relatively nontoxic. Thorotrast® carries the threat of delayed reactions because of its persistent radioactivity and its prolonged retention in significant amounts by the reticuloendothelial system. Contrast media such as acetrizoate (Urokon®), diatrizoate (Hypaque®), and Renografin® have proved to be quite satisfactory also and are now more widely used.

The injection may be made through the intact skin or following operative exposure of a suitable vessel. After injection of the selected artery, roentgenograms may be made of the arterial and venous phases of circulation through the brain and head.

Normal Findings.

Internal carotid injections may disclose the arterial vessels of the cerebral hemispheres. The internal carotid artery may be visualized as it penetrates the skull, usually in a single or double S-curve. The ophthalmic artery branch is the first major branch and enters the orbit through the optic foramen. The posterior communicating artery is seldom seen. The small anterior choroidal artery is frequently seen and passes posteriorly to enter the choroid plexuses of the lateral ventricles.

The anterior cerebral artery, which passes anteriorly and medially and curves around the genu of the corpus callosum, is readily visualized. The frontopolar artery is a branch which passes toward the frontal pole. The pericallosal artery is a branch which curves posteriorly and remains adjacent to the corpus callosum. The callosomarginal artery also extends posteriorly and supplies the uppermost medial portion of the cerebral hemispheres.

The middle cerebral artery is readily seen in normal subjects and curves posteriorly into the lateral cerebral fissure. The ascending frontoparietal artery is a branch which supplies the inferior frontoparietal area. The terminal branches of the middle cerebral artery are known as the sylvian group and consist of the posterior parietal artery, which supplies the convexity of the parietal lobe; the angular artery, which supplies the angular gyrus and the adjacent parieto-occipital area; and the posterior temporal artery, which supplies the superoposterior portion of the temporal lobe.

Vertebral arteriograms disclose the circulation of the structures of the posterior fossa and the posterior portions of the cerebral hemispheres. The course of the vertebral artery may be seen as it passes upward. The posterior inferior cerebellar artery may be visualized as the first intracranial branch and supplies the ventrolateral portion of the cerebellum and medulla. The basilar artery is formed by the 2 vertebral arteries at the junction of the pons and medulla. The anterior inferior cerebellar and the superior cerebellar arteries, supplying the dorsum of the cerebellum and midbrain, may be visualized. The 2 posterior cerebral arteries are the terminal branches of the basilar artery; they supply the basilar portions of the temporal and occipital lobes.

Visualization of the **venous passages** following internal carotid artery injection demonstrates 3 major collecting systems: (1) The superficial cerebral veins are variable in number and empty into the superior longitudinal sinus and the transverse sinus. (2) The deep cerebral veins drain the basal ganglia. The internal cerebral vein (located in the tela choroidea on the dorsal surface of each thalamus) drains the basal vein of Rosenthal, which comes from the base of the brain around the cerebral peduncle. The junction of the 2 internal cerebral veins forms the great cerebral vein of Galen, a short midline vessel which enters the straight sinus. (3) The venous sinuses include the superior longitudinal sinus, which terminates in the confluence of sinuses by joining the lateral and straight sinuses; and the inferior longitudinal sinus, located at the inferior edges of the falx cerebri, which forms the straight sinus by joining with the great cerebral vein of Galen.

Clinical Applications.

Angiography is of value in demonstrating intracranial aneurysms, vascular malformations, hematomas, and tumors. **Meningiomas** usually obtain their vascular supply chiefly from branches of the external carotid artery and are most readily seen in the venous phase of the angiogram. Cerebral **gliomas** may present typical vascular patterns in addition to displacing adjacent vessels. Frontal gliomas may dislocate the anterior cerebral artery toward the opposite side and may depress the sylvian group of vessels. Parietal gliomas may push the anterior cerebral artery to the opposite side; occasionally there may also be depression of the terminal portions of the anterior cerebral artery. Temporal gliomas characteristically displace the vessels of the sylvian group upward, especially if they are near the tip of the temporal lobe. Increased vascularity is typical of glioblastoma multiforme and metastatic carcinomas. **Hematomas are** characterized by avascular local areas with displacement of adjacent vessel trunks. Alterations may be demonstrated in intracranial and extracranial arteries to the brain and head, including occlusion, stenosis, angulation, distortion, malformation, and anomalous course and distribution.

Cerebral angiography often provides localization and clues to pathologic types of tumor. The blood supply and vascularity to a mass can thus be clearly defined. Tumors of the cerebral hemispheres usually displace the anterior cerebral artery across the midline. Local stretching of arteries near the tumor may disclose the exact site of the tumor. Characteristic deformities and displacement of deep cerebral veins may help localize tumors of the midline and the basal ganglia area. Highly vascular tumors such as glioblastoma multiforme, meningioma, and metastatic tumor may be visualized by a tumor stain or blush.

Vascular lesions such as intracranial aneurysms and angiomatous malformations usually require study by angiography before adequate therapy can be planned. Angiography has stimulated increased interest and efforts to improve morbidity and mortality associated with bleeding aneurysms. In relatively small accessible arteriovenous malformations, angiography has led to increasing use of extirpation and allied types of therapy.

Subdural hematoma usually can be readily diagnosed by angiography. A characteristic avascular area between the brain and adjacent skull vault may be seen on anteroposterior skull x-rays.

Internal carotid artery thrombosis often occurs within 1 cm. of the origin of this artery in the neck from the common carotid artery and is readily demonstrable by angiography. Anastomosis between the ophthalmic artery and the external carotid artery (via the maxillary artery) may be demonstrable, as well as increased blood supply to the affected cerebral hemisphere from occipital vertebral anastomoses.

In selected patients, the association of stenosis of the internal carotid artery in the neck has led to endarterectomy in the belief that such vessels are precursors to local internal carotid artery thrombosis. In such cases pre- and postoperative angiography are essential for adequate clinical management and evaluation.

Vertebral angiography, by a variety of technics, may disclose evidence of expanding masses or vascular lesions of the posterior fossa. A characteristic vascular stain may occur with hemangioblastoma or meningioma of the posterior fossa; however, pneumography may be more effective in demonstrating pontine and cerebellopontine angle masses. Vascular lesions of the posterior fossa (aneurysm, angioma, stenosis, etc.) usually require vertebral angiography for adequate visualization.

RADIOISOTOPIC ENCEPHALOGRAPHY

Recent technical improvements and new radioisotopic compounds have increased the reliability and accuracy of radioisotopic encephalography.

Hg^{203}-labeled chlormerodrin (Neohydrin®) has been used in many centers. Hg^{203} has physical properties which make it useful in brain scanning. To reduce renal uptake, 1-1.5 ml. of mercuhydrin may be given intravenously the day before administration of the chlormerodrin-Hg^{203}.

On the day of examination, the patient receives 600 microcuries of chlormerodrin-Hg^{203} intravenously approximately 4 hours before scanning. If clinical findings suggest a vascular malformation, an earlier scan is performed 15-45 minutes after the intravenous injection.

The patient's head is immobilized and appropriate landmarks (vertex of skull, nasion, external auditory meatus, and glabella) are recorded before scanning. Scans are obtained first in the anteroposterior and then in the lateral position with the side with the suspected lesion toward the probe. With a posteriorly situated lesion, posteroanterior scan is substituted for anteroposterior scan.

Positive brain scans (increased focal uptake) may be obtained with brain tumor, subdural hematoma, brain abscess, and cerebral infarct. Among neoplasms, meningiomas stand out particularly in scans.

More recently Hg^{197}-tagged chlormerodrin has been advocated and used for brain scanning. The kidney dose is considerably reduced ($1/12$ that of Hg^{203}) because of its shorter physical half-life and the absence of β-ray emission.

ECHOENCEPHALOGRAPHY

A diagnostic technic of value in neurologic diagnosis involves the use of ultrasound generator and receiver, displaying echoes on an oscilloscope with camera attachment for permanent recording. The same transducers used for generation of ultrasound (1-10 megacycles per second) are used for reception. The region of the skull to be investigated is wet with water, mineral oil, or maple syrup, and the tip of the transducer is immersed in the same solution before firm application to the side of the head at right angles to the skull. Optimal detection of midline echo comes from application of the transducer 4-5 cm. vertically above the external auditory meatus. For detection of tumor echoes, the transducer may be placed at right angles at any locus of the head above the level of the inion and zygoma.

The significance of a shift in the midline echo is analogous to that of a shift of the pineal in plain skull x-rays. The source of a midline echo may be pineal and midline structures such as the third ventricle, septum pellucidum, longitudinal fissure, and falx cerebri.

Intracerebral echoes have also been obtained from the lateral ventricles, the sylvian fissure, and in some cases space-occupying masses.

ROENTGENOGRAPHY OF SPINE

Plain x-rays of the spine are often useful and informative in evaluation of neurologic disorders. They should be made in all cases of suspected spinal cord and spinal root compressions. Evidence of the underlying disease may be demonstrated in congenital lesions such as spina bifida, Klippel-Feil deformity, occipito-atlantal fusion, congenital hemivertebra, and bony dystrophies. Signs of tuberculosis of the spine, primary or secondary neoplasms, and trauma to the spine may be readily disclosed on routine films.

Intraspinal tumor may be noted or suspected because of widening or erosion of the vertebral pedicles, local erosion of the intervertebral foramen, erosion of the posterior surface of a vertebral body; or associated paraspinal mass.

Intervertebral disk disease may be noted on plain x-rays by the narrowing of the intervertebral disk space. Osteophytosis or sclerosis or adjacent vertebral margins may also occur. Disk calcification may occasionally be demonstrated. Local immobility or fixation of the spine associated with intervertebral disk disease may also be seen in appropriate views.

The results of trauma to the spinal column may also be seen on plain x-rays. Compression of vertebral bodies, dislocation of the spine, fractures of vertebrae, alterations of normal curvature, or narrowing of intervertebral foramens may be demonstrated. Evidence of coexisting narrowing of intervertebral disk space can also be seen.

MYELOGRAPHY

X-rays made after the introduction of a radiopaque substance into the spinal subarachnoid space are sometimes helpful in diagnostic problems. Iophendylate (Pantopaque®), a liquid of relatively low viscosity, is the contrast medium of choice. It should be aspirated at the termination of the myelographic examination, although reactions following its use are minimal even in those instances where it has been left in the spinal canal for prolonged periods.

Air injection into the spinal subarachnoid space was formerly used but is technically inferior to Pantopaque® myelography. However, air myelography may be very useful when used with autotomography and especially in the study of the upper cervical portion of the spinal cord.

Technic.

The site of injection depends upon the suspected site of the lesion. Since artifacts may be produced by the needle puncture, the spinal subarachnoid space is usually entered at other than the suspected level. Similarly, spinal dynamics (Queckenstedt's test) may be performed prior to the injection of the Pantopaque® to determine the existence of a partial or complete block in the spinal subarachnoid space. The CSF removed prior to the injection may be useful for diagnostic tests.

Following the injection of Pantopaque®, fluoroscopic examination of the spine and spot x-ray films are made on a tilting table.

Clinical Applications.

Pantopaque® myelography is used most widely for the demonstration of evidence of herniations or protrusions of the intervertebral disks. The myelogram should be interpreted in terms of the clinical findings. Relatively minor or minimal filling defects at an appropriate level may be significant. On the other hand, "characteristic" filling defects are sometimes demonstrated in individuals without symptoms. The myelographic abnormalities due to herniated disks may be medially or laterally situated, usually at the level of the intervertebral disk.

A complete block in the flow of Pantopaque® may be due to the presence of a tumor, adhesions, mechanical constriction as by a bony lesion, or a herniated intervertebral disk. If the presence of a block is determined, introduction of media at a higher spinal or cisternal level may succeed in defining the physical extent of the block.

With spinal tumors, myelography often provides information regarding the location, nature, and anatomic features of the mass. Intramedullary tumors may show diffuse enlargement of the spinal cord on myelography, and this is characteristically noted with ependymoma and syringomyelia. Extramedullary intradural masses characteristically produce deviation or displacement of the cord by the tumor. Extramedullary extradural masses are apt to be associated with abrupt cut-off of the contrast column with an irregular "paintbrush" border appearance.

Angiomatous lesions of the spinal cord may be suspected from the negative shadows in the contrast column produced by the characteristic worm-like enlarged vessels.

A variety of other lesions that cause spinal cord compression may be demonstrated by myelography. These include extradural spinal abscess, scoliosis and kyphosis of the spine, meningeal adhesions, and spinal column or vertebral compression, fracture, or dislocation.

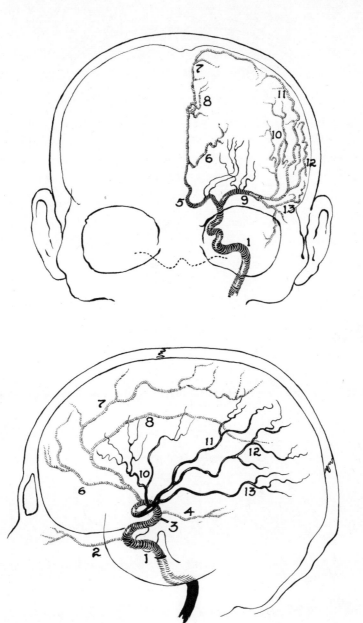

1. Internal carotid artery.
2. Ophthalmic artery.
3. Posterior communicating artery.
4. Anterior choroidal artery.
5. Anterior cerebral artery.
6. Frontopolar artery.
7. Callosomarginal artery.
8. Pericallosal artery.
9. Middle cerebral artery.
10. Ascending frontoparietal artery.
11. Posterior parietal artery.
12. Angular artery.
13. Posterior temporal artery.

Schematic Drawings of Normal Arteriograms of the Internal Carotid Artery. Above, anteroposterior projection. Below, lateral projection. (Redrawn and reproduced, with permission, from List, Burge, and Hodges: Intracranial angiography. Radiology **45**:1-14, 1945.)

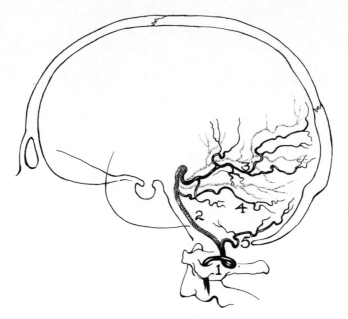

1. Vertebral artery.
2. Basilar artery.
3. Posterior cerebral artery.

4. Superior cerebellar artery.
5. Posterior inferior cerebellar artery.

Schematic Drawing of a Normal Vertebral Arteriogram in Lateral Projection. (Redrawn and reproduced, with permission, from List, Burge, and Hodges: Ibid.)

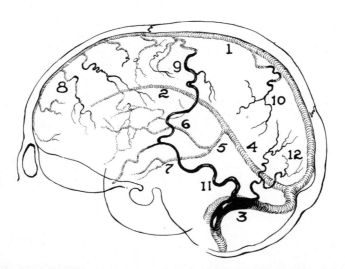

1. Superior sagittal sinus.
2. Inferior sagittal sinus.
3. Transverse sinus.
4. Straight sinus.
5. Great cerebral vein of Galen.
6. Internal cerebral vein.

7. Basal vein of Rosenthal.
8. Frontal ascending vein.
9. Rolandic vein of Trolard.
10. Parietal ascending vein.
11. Communicating temporal vein of Labbé.
12. Descending temporo-occipital vein.

Schematic Drawing of Normal Venogram in Lateral Projection, Obtained by Carotid Injection. Superficial veins are shaded more darkly than the sinuses and deep veins. (Redrawn and reproduced, with permission, from List, Burge, and Hodges: Ibid.)

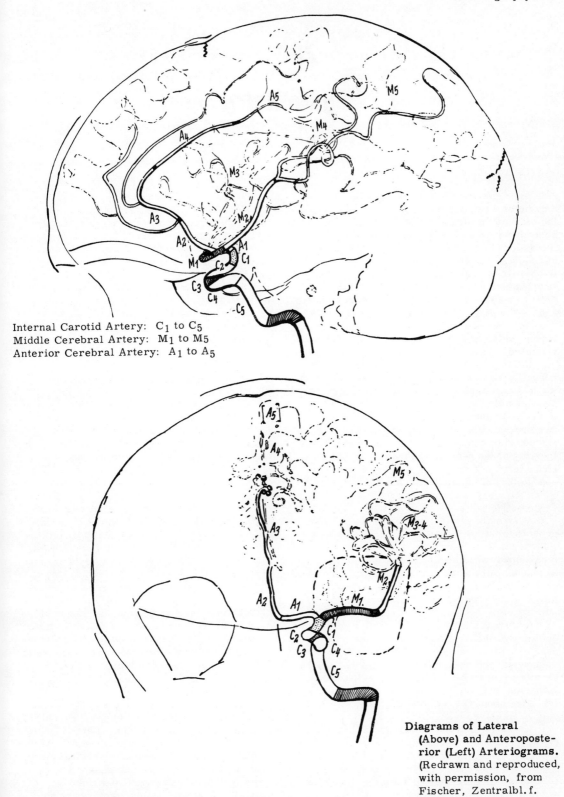

Internal Carotid Artery: C_1 to C_5
Middle Cerebral Artery: M_1 to M5
Anterior Cerebral Artery: A_1 to A_5

Diagrams of Lateral (Above) and Anteroposterior (Left) Arteriograms. (Redrawn and reproduced, with permission, from Fischer, Zentralbl. f. Neurochirurgie 3:300, 1938.)

20 ...

Cystometry

When the urinary bladder is filled through a catheter with successive increments of fluid, the detrusor musculature of the bladder will contract, producing a measurable increase of intravesical pressure. As 50 ml. increments of fluid are introduced, notations are made of the patient's responses: (1) ability to perceive temperature and entrance of fluid; (2) the point at which "desire to void" is experienced; and (3) the stage at which pain or distress is first felt, as well as the point of severe pain beyond which no further vesical filling can be tolerated.

Urinary bladder filling and emptying is normally an automatic process dependent upon the fact that distention beyond a certain point produces bladder contractions which increase in intensity until a massive contraction empties the bladder. Normally this reaction is postponed by the action of the higher centers. Because of the neural arrangement at the sphincter, its function may be considered to oppose that of the bladder muscle (detrusor).

Cystometrograms.

A normal cystometrogram records little or no tone initially. As 50 ml. increments of fluid are added, the intravesical pressure rises slowly until about 500 ml. of solution have been introduced. At this stage, a marked contraction usually occurs with a sharp rise of intravesical pressure to about 15 mm. Hg (21 cm. water).

A normal bladder can usually perceive the entrance of the first fluid injected and can usually interpret temperature. The desire to void, apparently a muscle stretch phenomenon, usually occurs when the bladder is distended with about 200 ml. of fluid. Distress may be felt after about 400 ml. of filling and severe pain at about 500 ml.

There are 2 types of **neurogenic bladder**: (1) efferent (hypertonic bladder with small capacity, presumably due to lack of inhibition from higher levels upon lower spinal cord segments); and (2) afferent (hypotonic bladder of large capacity).

A. Patients with efferent neurogenic bladder may show a desire to void with the first or second filling (50-100 ml. of fluid), and moderate distention of the bladder causes severe pain. This type of bladder is commonly associated with disorders involving the pyramidal tracts; lesions involving a single pyramidal tract have been claimed to produce hypertonic bladders. The internal sphincter also becomes hypertonic, but not sufficiently so to withstand the effect of the hypertonic detrusor; dribbling and perhaps incontinence result.

B. Patients with afferent neurogenic bladder may tolerate up to 2 L. of fluid added in 50 ml. quantities. Desire to void, distress, and pain are produced only when greater than usual amounts of fluid have been added. Hyposensitivity or complete lack of sensitivity may be associated, in which case the desire to void may not occur until 500 ml. have been introduced and distress and severe pain may be delayed until up to 800 ml. have been introduced. The internal sphincter pressure remains normal despite a hypotonic detrusor muscle. The aid of the voluntary abdominal muscles is therefore frequently required in micturition. This type of bladder is associated with disorders affecting the afferent pathway (end organs, posterior roots, or posterior spinal columns). Hyposensitivity of the bladder may lead to delayed awareness of the need to empty the bladder. Atrophy of the detrusor muscle due to prolonged overdistention plus inability of the internal sphincter to relax at the proper time may result.

Sphincterometry.

When the detrusor muscle of the bladder contracts, the internal sphincter of the bladder relaxes from its normal tonic state. As soon as urine enters the posterior urethra, the external sphincter (compressor urethrae) may relax to allow the stream to pass. The external sphincter, however, can voluntarily restrain the stream unless the urge to void is too great. Normally, internal sphincter tone is about 15 mm. Hg; the external sphincter tone, about 23 mm. Hg.

The external (dominant) sphincter is rarely affected by disease. If its fibers are surgically divided, incontinence results.

The internal sphincter is rarely paralyzed; it may be severely damaged surgically without resultant incontinence.

Incontinence of urine may be of the overflow or the hypertonic type. Normally, the detrusor does not force urine through the internal sphincter. If the detrusor is markedly hypertonic, a normal or even hypertonic sphincter may be overcome.

In overflow incontinence associated with hypotonic, hyposensitive bladders, the incontinence is not due to a defect in function of the internal sphincter. Overflow occurs when intravesical pressure exceeds internal sphincter pressure. When the atonic, atrophic bladder collects a large quantity of urine, intravesical pressure gradually rises (helped by muscle stretch reflex, elasticity of bladder, and contractions of abdominal musculature). Large amounts of residual urine may occur because the internal sphincter has not lost its tone and may close down after a portion of the urine in the bladder has been expelled.

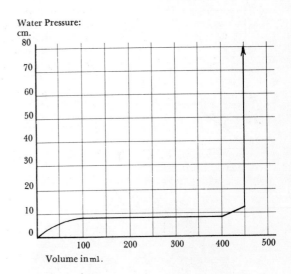

CYSTOMETROGRAM

Water Pressure: cm.

Volume in ml.

Motor Power:
    Uninhibited contractions - absent
    Capacity   - 450 ml.
    Voiding stream   - normal
    Residual urine   - none
Sensation:
    First desire to void - 150 ml.
    Perception of fulness - 400 ml.

Diagram labels: 1000 ml. · Hoffman clamp · Murphy drip bulb · Metric rule marked in cm. · Glass tube 5 cm. diam. · 6 Feet · Level of symphysis pubis · Catheter to bladder

Cystometer and Normal Cystometrogram. The pressure in the normal bladder remains at about 8 to 15 cm. of water until capacity (350 to 500 ml.) is reached, at which time the intravesical pressure rises sharply to or above 100 cm. of water. Involuntary voiding then occurs around the catheter. No uninhibited contractions occur, and there is no residual urine. (Reproduced, with permission, from Smith: General Urology, 4th Ed. Lange, 1963.)

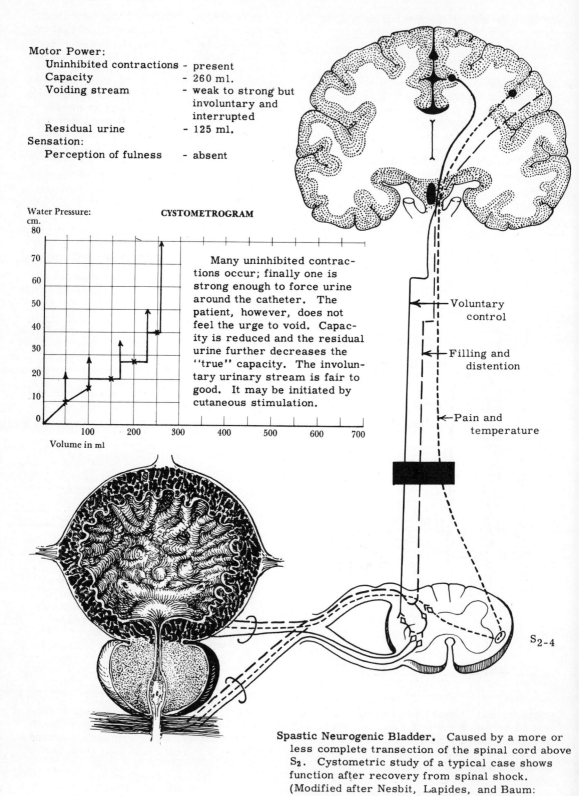

Motor Power:
 Uninhibited contractions - present
 Capacity   - 260 ml.
 Voiding stream   - weak to strong but
                            involuntary and
                            interrupted
 Residual urine   - 125 ml.
Sensation:
 Perception of fulness   - absent

Water Pressure:
cm.

CYSTOMETROGRAM

Many uninhibited contractions occur; finally one is strong enough to force urine around the catheter. The patient, however, does not feel the urge to void. Capacity is reduced and the residual urine further decreases the "true" capacity. The involuntary urinary stream is fair to good. It may be initiated by cutaneous stimulation.

Volume in ml

Voluntary control

Filling and distention

Pain and temperature

S$_{2-4}$

Spastic Neurogenic Bladder. Caused by a more or less complete transection of the spinal cord above S$_2$. Cystometric study of a typical case shows function after recovery from spinal shock. (Modified after Nesbit, Lapides, and Baum: Fundamentals of Urology. Edwards, 1953.)

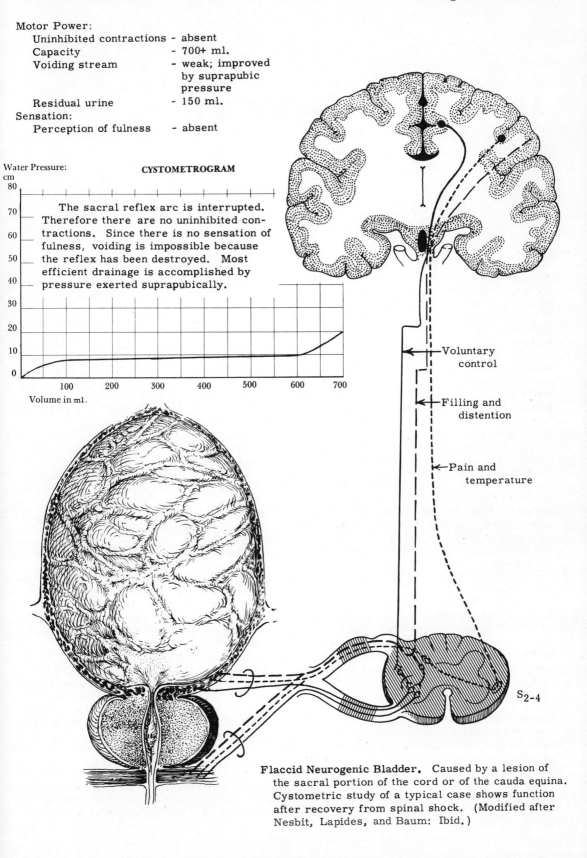

Motor Power:
    Uninhibited contractions - absent
    Capacity   - 700+ ml.
    Voiding stream   - weak; improved
                         by suprapubic
                         pressure
    Residual urine   - 150 ml.
Sensation:
    Perception of fulness - absent

Water Pressure:

CYSTOMETROGRAM

cm

The sacral reflex arc is interrupted. Therefore there are no uninhibited contractions. Since there is no sensation of fulness, voiding is impossible because the reflex has been destroyed. Most efficient drainage is accomplished by pressure exerted suprapubically.

Volume in ml.

Voluntary control

Filling and distention

Pain and temperature

S_{2-4}

Flaccid Neurogenic Bladder. Caused by a lesion of the sacral portion of the cord or of the cauda equina. Cystometric study of a typical case shows function after recovery from spinal shock. (Modified after Nesbit, Lapides, and Baum: Ibid.)

21...

Audiometry

Hearing loss becomes a significant handicap when there is difficulty in communication by speech. Beginning impairment has been defined as an average hearing level loss of 16 decibels at frequencies of 500, 1000, and 2000 cycles/second. A person is usually considered to be deaf when his average hearing level loss for these 3 frequencies is at or above 82 decibels. Early hearing loss often appears initially at 4000 cycles/second, both in children with conduction impairment and in adults with presbycusis.

The incidence of hearing loss rises sharply with age and is generally greatest among persons 65 years of age and older. However, loss of hearing is also notable among younger people. The most common cause of deafness in active adult life is otosclerosis, which is frequently first noticed in late adolescence. Twice as many women as men have otosclerosis, although hearing impairments due to all causes are more common in males. Continuous exposure to intense noise can produce permanent damage of the inner ear. Among children, severe or total deafness may be associated with hereditary nerve deafness, birth trauma, brain defects, cerebrospinal meningitis, mental retardation, and early infections.

Voice Tests.

The patient's perception of whispered or spoken words provides a quick rough estimate of loss of hearing. However, voice tests are apt to be inaccurate because of variations in intensity of voice even when test words are spoken by trained personnel. In unilateral loss of hearing, the better ear should be "masked" or tightly closed.

Tuning Fork Tests.

Tuning forks should be used whose vibrations fade gradually and which are free of overtones. The fork should be struck against the pad of the palm or a piece of rubber.

A. Weber's Test: When hearing is normal there is no lateralization of sound to either ear when the stem of the vibrating tuning fork is held against the midline vertex portion of the skull. If the sound is referred to the poorer hearing ear, loss of hearing is due to impaired conduction in the external or internal ear. If the sound is referred to the better hearing ear, loss of hearing is attributable to poor function of the auditory nerve or the cochlea.

B. Schwabach's Test: The bone conduction hearing of the patient is compared with that of the examiner (normal ear), and time in seconds is recorded. The vibrating tuning fork is usually applied behind the ear to the mastoid area.

C. Rinne's Test: The ability to hear a tuning fork by air conduction is compared with the ability to hear by bone conduction. The vibrating tuning fork is alternately held in front of the ear and pressed against the mastoid process. In the normal ear, a fully vibrating fork of 256 or 512 vibrations/second is heard about twice as long by air conduction as by bone conduction (positive test). Impaired function of the middle ear is indicated if hearing by bone conduction is equal to or greater than hearing by air conduction (negative test).

Watch Tick Test.

Testing the patient's perception of a watch tick provides a crude estimate for hearing of frequencies of more than 2000 double vibrations/second. Results are recorded as a fraction indicating the distance at which the test watch is heard by the patient compared to the distance at which it is heard by normal ears. Ears with a high-frequency perceptive loss may be detected by this test; however, reduced hearing for watch tick may be of little clinical significance.

Electronic Audiometer Tests.

These tests depend upon the use of an electronic instrument which can deliver pure tones at controlled intensities. Some instruments also contain a circuit capable of delivering speech signals from a live voice or phonograph recordings at controlled intensities. Air conduction and bone conduction receivers are provided.

Audiometers used for general clinical purposes usually deliver tones at octave and half-octave intervals. To produce a tone one octave higher than a preceding tone, it is necessary to double the frequency of vibrations. The range of frequencies tested usually is from 125-8000 vibrations/second.

Intensities are calibrated in decibels, a physical unit based on sound pressure energy. Each decibel approximates a barely perceptible increase in loudness of the tone for a normal ear. The average loudness of the conversational voice is about 60 decibels.

Pure tone threshold audiometric results may be charted, with frequencies as abscissa and intensity as ordinate. Air conduction is frequently recorded in black and bone conduction in red. Right ear results may be recorded as circles joined by a solid line and left ear results as crosses joined by a broken line. Tests for loudness recruitment may corroborate bone conduction findings or provide information on the site of the disorder in perceptive deafness.

Speech audiometry provides a measure of the ear hearing of frequencies and sounds above threshold intensities. Spondaic words used for determining speech reception thresholds consist of two-syllable words which give approximately equal emphasis to each syllable (e.g., "railroad," "baseball"). The speech reception threshold is the intensity at which an individual can correctly repeat half of the spondaic words; this usually corresponds with the average of pure tone thresholds for the speech frequencies of 500, 1000, and 2000 cycles/second.

Phonetically balanced words are lists of monosyllables. Selected lists of 50 words each cover the phonetic range of the English language. The test is believed to measure the ability of the ear to discriminate speech, and the results may be graphed, with intensity as the abscissa and percentage of words repeated correctly as the ordinate. Results of this test do not always correlate well with the results of threshold tests.

Characteristic Examples.

A. Middle Ear or Conduction Deafness:

1. Air conduction - Pure tone threshold moderately or severely impaired, particularly in the lower frequencies, with much less impairment in higher frequencies.

2. Bone conduction - Approximately normal curve.

3. Speech reception threshold impaired to an extent similar to average of pure tone thresholds in speech frequencies.

B. Perception or Nerve Deafness:

1. Air conduction - Air conduction threshold for pure tones impaired with greatest deficit in the higher frequencies.

2. Bone conduction - Bone conduction threshold for pure tones impaired in fashion similar to that for air conduction.

3. Speech reception threshold deficit approximates the pure tone threshold deficit in the speech frequencies.

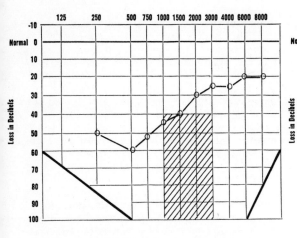

Middle Ear or Conduction Deafness
Representative air conduction curve, showing greatest impairment of pure tone thresholds in lower frequencies.

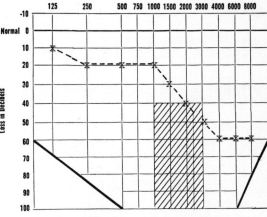

Perception or Nerve Deafness
Representative air and bone conduction curve of pure tone thresholds with greatest deficit in higher frequencies.

22 . . .

Psychometric Tests

Psychologic tests are sometimes used to help evaluate the status of neurologic patients. Results must be considered in terms of the clinical history and findings of the particular subject tested. Psychologic tests are best used in combination or in a battery of tests so that individual test weaknesses are minimized.

Efficiency of intellectual function may be impaired with cerebral disease, but the degree is not necessarily related to the severity of the organic disorder, especially where the lesions are small. No test specific for brain disease exists as such, although subjects with brain injuries may have intellectual impairment and increased emotional lability. Greater relative deficiency in tests involving memory, speed, or new learning than in tests involving vocabulary and information is regarded as evidence of intellectual deterioration. Patients with deterioration from organic brain lesions, as well as schizophrenic patients, show a tendency to be rigid, stereotyped, and concrete in their concepts, with inability to perform adequately tests involving classification, categorization, or induction. Tests of intellectual performance may sometimes give the best evidence of organic brain disorder. A variety of tests may be used, testing the subject's ability to abstract, use symbols, and evaluate new experiences on the basis of past experience. Diffuse brain disorders and those with bilateral frontal lobe changes are most commonly associated with intellectual performance impairment. The patient with organic brain disease is apt to show diminished capacities to grasp the essence of a situation and to detect slight differences or changes, difficulty in remembering 2 or more commands or to follow directions, limited attention span, faulty judgement, impaired memory, and, in severe cases, gross memory loss and confusion.

Obvious mental or language dysfunction may require specific tests to define the nature and severity of the disorder. Indications for such formal testing may be evident from the history or examination. For instance, simple testing of intellectual performance during neurologic examination may indicate defects in memory, calculation, judgement, or general information.

Two general types of psychometric tests are recognized. **Objective tests** are standardized from representative portions of the population and used for "quantitative" evaluation of personality traits in relation to established norms. Standard intelligence tests and personality inventories are typical examples. **Projective tests** are designed to evaluate the subject's responses to "amorphous," ambiguous, or unstructured stimuli or tasks. The responses are considered to be significantly influenced by the subject's personality. Although the responses may be compared with previously established norms, a significant variable factor is the subjective interpretation placed upon them by the examiner. The Rorschach, thematic apperception, and sentence completion tests are examples of this type.

OBJECTIVE TESTS

Wechsler-Bellevue Intelligence Test.

This test is used widely for measurement of intelligence of the adult population and has the reputed advantage that past formal education background does not greatly modify test results. Intelligence quotients may be computed with due regard for anticipated decline in intelligence with advanced aging. "Global intelligence" is measured by use of 11 diversified subtests. Six of these form a verbal intelligence scale, and measure abilities in verbal area, arithmetical area, and those areas dependent upon abstract reasoning (e.g., ability to perceive logical relations and use of symbols). The remaining 5 subtests comprise the performance intelligence scale and depend upon the subject's ability to handle practical situations calling for performance and manipulative abilities.

A revision known as the Wechsler Adult Intelligence Scale (WAIS) was published in 1955 and a scale for children (WISC) in 1949.

Stanford-Binet Intelligence Test.

This is one of the most widely used intelligence tests and is particularly suitable for children. It consists of a selection of short problems arranged for ages 2-14 years by one-half and one-year levels, with 3 "adult" levels of difficulty. A wide range of psychologic functions are checked, with verbal and language functions predominating. Test items vary at different age levels or appear in more difficult forms at higher levels. Performance is indicated in terms of mental age and intelligence quotient. Because of its standardization and the character of the items contained in it, the test appears to be appropriate for children of grade school years and adolescence.

Bender Gestalt Test.

This is considered to be a test of visual motor function and depends upon the responses (pattern or Gestalt) elicited by 9 standard patterns. The patterns are presented to the subject singly, and he is requested to copy them on a sheet of paper. Interpretation of the test results depends on many factors, including the manner in which patterns are reproduced, their relationships to each other, spatial background, and temporal patterning.

Porteus Maze Test.

A performance test in which the subject is asked to trace his way through a series of mazes graded by year levels with increasing difficulty. Performance in this test appears to be related to traditional intelligence quotient. The complexity of the mazes successfully solved indicates ability; the manner in which the test is done is related to aspects of personality.

Goodenough Draw-a-Man Test.

A performance test of the ability of a subject to draw a picture of a man. The drawing is scored according to prescribed standards.

Minnesota Multiphasic Personality Index.

A widely used standardized objective personality test consisting of several 100 diverse statements about feelings, family matters, attitudes, events, and reactions which the subject is asked to classify as "true," "false," or "cannot say" with regard to himself. A personality profile may be derived on the basis of 9 categories: hypochondriasis, depression, hysteria, psychopathic deviates, masculinity-feminity, paranoia, psychasthenia, schizophrenia, and hypomania. Interpretation is usually based on the profile as a whole.

PROJECTIVE TESTS

Rorschach Test.

This projective test is administered by having the patient examine 10 standard cards, each of which contains an ink blot. Various aspects of the subject's responses contribute to the interpretation: content of associations to ink blots; factors such as shape, color, or shading; and whether all or part of a blot is employed. Each ink blot has minimal conventionalized meanings; the individual subject's responses represent functions of his own personality. Feelings and motivations which are deep or unconscious may stimulate distorted responses to the test. Claims for the value of such a projection technic for evaluating organic brain damage rest upon the findings of repetition, perplexity, stereotyped responses, and confusion in such patients.

Thematic Apperception Test (TAT).

This is a projective test which depends upon the story told by the subject on viewing test material consisting of 20 picture cards appropriately selected for age and sex. Pictures differ among themselves and are intentionally unclear and ambiguous. For each picture, the subject constructs a plot or story which is the product of his own imagination. The themes of these plots may reveal his attitude, drives, and conflicts, for the themes projected into the stories often are related to analogous themes in the subject's life. The content of the stories provides clues to the manner in which the subject perceives and thinks as well as his fears, needs, and hopes.

For use with children, a variation known as the Children's Apperception Test (CAT) has been developed.

Sentence Completion Test.

The subject is asked to complete a number of incomplete sentences. The subject's completions are felt to reveal his wishes, needs, and feelings. Since different personalities show characteristic performance differences and the test itself is simple, brief, and flexible, it enjoys wide use as a corroborative test.

The Make-A-Picture-Story Test (MAPS).

The test materials consist of large numbers of cut-out figures and various backdrops. The patient is asked to select figures and arrange them before a backdrop he selects. He is then asked to tell a story about the arrangement he has made. The patient's selection and arrangement of materials and the stories he invents may reveal his conscious and unconscious needs and feelings.

•   •   •

Section IV: Central Nervous System Disorders

23...

Congenital Defects

Several factors, singly or in combination, may contribute to the development of a congenital CNS anomaly or malformation: (1) Heredity: A tendency to develop abnormally may exist in the fertilized egg, and this tendency may be related to the existence of the same tendency in the parents or other relatives. (2) Intrinsic factors: The growth in complexity and the differentiation of some portions of the embryo are under the control of the chemical and metabolic environment of that portion of the tissue. (3) Extrinsic factors: The host or parent in which an embryo grows affects the growth of the embryo in many ways. Thus it is assumed that for normal development to occur there should be normal uterine mucosa, adequate circulation, and proper temperature. In the developing fetus, the nervous system is particularly vulnerable to anoxia, ionizing radiations, and certain infectious diseases of the mother (German measles, mumps). (4) Critical periods: At certain phases in the early development of tissue and organs, relatively minor variations may give rise to severe abnormalities.

Genetic diseases may be inherited, characteristically along classical mendelian lines. The chromosome defect is usually considered to be at the molecular level (as a mutant gene) and thus produces no visible structural chromosomal change.

Deoxyribonucleic acid (DNA), important in transmission of hereditary characteristics, is found in the chromosomes of all cells and in some viruses. Models have been constructed from x-ray diffraction studies of DNA extracted from chromosomes or viruses. DNA is believed to consist of 2 helical chains of alternate phosphate and sugar (deoxyribose) molecules linked by pairs of nitrogen bases which project from the sugar molecules on each chain. The base pair, one a purine (usually adenine and guanine) and the other a pyrimidine (thymine and cytosine), are bound by weak hydrogen bonds. It has been suggested that adenine is always paired with thymine and that guanine is always paired with cytosine.

It has been further suggested that the particular arrangement of base pairs along the chains of the long, thin molecule of DNA constitutes a genetic code, passed on via replication of DNA. Just before mitosis of somatic cells or meiosis (reduction division) of gametic cells, DNA is thought to be present in double helical form. During the mitosis or meiosis, the DNA melts and the 2 unwound chains then attract from their environment the proper basis to build 2 copies which duplicate exactly the original helix.

Genes and their subdivisions, gene particles, have not yet been precisely identified chemically. It is quite possible that they represent a nucleotide or several nucleotides. If this is so, then one DNA molecule may have many thousands of genes or gene particles.

Abnormalities of cell division may occur during human gametogenesis or during early division of the fertilized egg, leading to development of individuals with an abnormal chromosome constitution. Cytologic technics have established that normally there are 46 chromosomes in humans, and improved technics have made possible more accurate analysis and study of the normal human chromosome. Cells from normal human tissues or peripheral blood may be grown in a medium containing minute amounts of colchicine. By this treatment, mitosis is stopped at the metaphase and many such cells accumulate in the culture. Exposure of the colchicine-treated cells to the osmotic effects of hypotonic solution for several minutes before fixation causes them to swell and thus disperses the chromosomes within. Squash or smear preparations spread the chromosomes in one optical plane, which allows accurate counting and photography. Preparations are then stained and examined under oil-immersion lens.

Chromosomes in metaphase of mitosis appear as rod-shaped structures split longitudinally into 2 chromatids, lying side by side and held together at a constricted area, the centromere, the site of spindle fiber attachment. Chromosomes vary in length and centromere position, so that individual characteristics occur. Chromosome analysis depends upon classifying them into 7 groups based on their total length and arm ratios.

There are 22 pairs of identical nonsex chromosomes, or autosomes, and, in the male, one pair of sex chromosomes of unequal length. One of the sex chromosomes, the X, is usually the seventh largest chromosome, and the other, the Y, is frequently the largest of the smallest group. The normal female has what appears to be an identical pair of X chromosomes and no Y chromosomes.

Two main types of human chromosome abnormalities have been described: (1) an irregular number of chromosomes, and (2) altered structure of individual chromosomes. An irregular number of chromosomes may occur, e.g., if one of a pair is missing or if there are more than 2 of a given pair. Altered structure of individual chromosomes includes chromosome deletion, e.g., if one arm of a chromosome is broken off and subsequently lost, and translocation, if 2 chromosomes exchange unequal fragments.

Autosomal trisomy syndromes occur when 3 instead of 2 chromosomes of a particular autosomal pair are present. In mongolism, trisomy of chromosome No. 21 occurs, so that the total number of chromosomes is 47 instead of the normal 46. Other trisomy conditions involving chromosomes of group IV (Nos. 13, 14, and 15) are associated with mental defects and multiple congenital anomalies. Patients with trisomy of group V (No. 17 or No. 18) show spasticity, ear anomalies, flexion of the fingers, deformed feet, and congenital heart disease; they usually do not survive past infancy.

Sex chromosome anomalies may also occur. **Klinefelter's syndrome** is characterized by an abnormal number of chromosomes (47) with an extra X chromosome, so that sex chromosome constitution is XXY. Small testes, sterility, eunuchoidism, and gynecomastia may occur.

Patients with **Turner's syndrome** have 45 chromosomes with a single X chromosome. They are short females who fail to develop secondary sex characteristics and may have multiple congenital defects, including webbing of the neck, peripheral lymphedema, coarctation of the aorta, and hypoplasia of the nails.

Mental retardates with XXX female sex chromosomes (47 total) or with XXXY male (48 total) have also been described. In the male these patients resemble those with Klinefelter's syndrome.

Other unusual examples reported have included sex chromosome constitutions such as XXYY, XXXX, and XXXXY.

Most classifications of congenital CNS lesions are based on the location and time of occurrence of a malformation. In general, there may be a primary defect involving cells, tissues, organs, embryonal layers, and organ systems, or combinations of these. Clinically important malformations are discussed in the following paragraphs.

SPINA BIFIDA GROUP

Spina bifida results from failure of the vertebral canal to close normally because of a defect in the development of vertebrae. Other abnormalities affecting the development of the spinal cord, brain stem, cerebrum, or cerebellum may be associated, as well as meningoceles, meningomyeloceles, congenital tumors, hydrocephalus, or other somatic developmental defects. Since the bony spinal column closes by the twelfth week of intra-uterine life, these defects are concerned with early intra-uterine life. In general, 2 large groups may be defined: (1) spina bifida occulta, in which there is a simple defect in the closure of the vertebra; and (2) spina bifida with meningocele or meningomyelocele, where the defect is associated with sac-like protrusions of the overlying meninges and skin, which may contain portions of the spinal cord or nerve roots. Simple failure of closure of one or more vertebral arches in the lumbosacral region is a common finding on routine x-ray or autopsy examination of the spine. A slight tendency for familial incidence of this defect has been noted.

Spina Bifida Occulta.

This type of defect occurs relatively frequently and is sometimes noticed as an incidental finding on x-ray examinations of the vertebral column. The bony defect, which is present usually in the lumbar or sacral spine, is due to a failure of closure of the laminas of the affected vertebrae. The defect in the spine may be palpated. Associated abnormalities, such as hypertrichosis over the affected area, fat deposits, dimpling of the skin, and telangiectases of the overlying skin may occur. Symptoms may be due to the presence of intraspinal lipomas, adhesions, bony spicules, or maldevelopment of the spinal cord. Maldevelopment and deformities of the feet (valgus, varus, or cavus) and scoliosis are commonly associated.

Symptoms may not occur until late and are proportionate to functional impairment of the affected sacral spinal cord and cauda equina. Bladder and bowel dysfunction, radicular

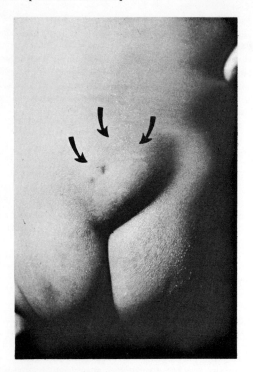

Spina Bifida Occulta. Fat deposit and dimpling of skin overlying spina bifida occulta of lumbosacral spine in infant.

motor and sensory symptoms, and skin and vasomotor changes may occur. Muscles of one or both lower extremities may be atrophied, and alteration of tendon reflexes may occur. The finding of a spinal defect on x-ray does not necessarily imply that the patient's symptoms are due to this defect, especially since there is a likelihood of associated congenital or developmental defects. The course of patients with this disorder depends upon the extent and nature of the lesion and the associated congenital defects. Spina bifida occulta as such is compatible with a relatively normal life.

Meningocele.

Herniation of the meningeal membranes through the bony vertebral defect usually causes the appearance, low in the midline of the back, of a cystic, soft, translucent tumor.

Meningomyelocele.

Nerve roots and spinal cord protrude through the bony vertebral defect and are usually adherent to the inner wall of the meningeal sac. Symptomatically there is apt to be bladder and bowel incontinence, sexual impotence, and sensory and motor loss of function of the involved spinal cord and nerve roots. At higher levels there may be the clinical picture of complete or incomplete transection of the cord, or combined root and spinal cord symptoms similar to those of syringomyelia.

The threat of meningitis from extension of local infection is always present in meningocele and meningomyelocele. Prophylactic repair of the sac and supportive closure of the tissues over the bony defect may be performed early in life. Excision of spinal sacs which contain neural elements is usually followed by poor results. The closure of a sac, particularly a large one, may be followed by progressive hydrocephalus.

Types of Closure Defects*

Embryonic Origin	Type of Dysplasia	Resultant Condition
Cutaneous; somatic ectodermal	Cutaneous	Cutaneous defect, hypertrichosis, hypoplasia of skin, pilonidal cysts, congenital dermal sinuses
Mesodermal	Vertebral	Absence of spinous process, split spinous process, cleft in vertebral neural arch, rachischisis
	Dural	Nonfusion of dura mater
Neural; neuroectodermal	Neural tube	Myelodysplasia, intramedullary and extramedullary growth associated with dysraphia
	Neural crest	Ectopia of spinal ganglion

*Reproduced, with permission, from Lichtenstein: Spinal dysraphism. Arch. Neurol. & Psychiat. **44**:792, 1940.

CRANIUM BIFIDUM

Midline defects of fusion of the cranial bone, most commonly occipital, usually accompanied by sac-like protrusions of the overlying skin, may occur. The sac contains meninges (meningocele), or meninges and nervous tissue (encephalocele). When the defect is in the occipital region, hydrocephalus is apt to occur. The symptoms and signs depend upon the presence or absence of hydrocephalus or other associated congenital neural malformations. Treatment consists of excision of the sac and its contents, with firm closure of the dura where possible. Prognosis is poor in those cases where the sac contains large amounts of cerebral tissue in the presence of hydrocephalus or other serious neural defects.

CONGENITAL HYDROCEPHALUS

Enlargement of the head, associated with the accumulation of CSF within or without the ventricles of the brain, may occur before birth

Head Circumference of Normal Children (After Stuart and Meredith)

Boys, Percentile			Age	Girls, Percentile		
10	50	90		10	50	90
33.5	35.3	37.0	Birth	33.4	34.7	36.0
39.2	40.9	42.1	3 months	38.5	40.0	41.7
42.7	43.9	45.4	6 months	41.4	42.8	44.5
44.5	46.0	47.1	9 months	43.2	44.6	46.3
45.5	47.3	48.4	12 months	44.3	45.8	47.7
47.0	48.7	49.9	18 months	45.5	47.1	49.0
48.0	49.7	51.0	24 months	46.4	48.1	50.1
48.9	50.4	51.9	36 months	47.5	49.3	51.1

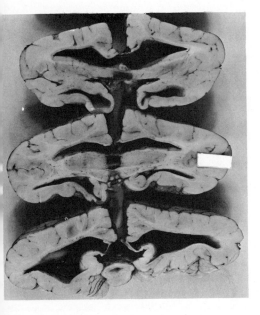

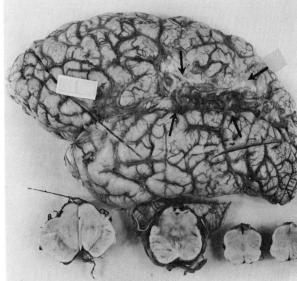

Coronal Sections of Brain of Infant with Congenital Communicating Hydrocephalus Showing Symmetric Dilatation of Ventricles

Cerebral Palsy. Left fronto-parietal cystic atrophy of brain of 33-year old woman with right hemiparesis since birth.

or soon after. Congenital hydrocephalus may be communicating or noncommunicating, depending upon the presence of free flow of CSF from the ventricles into the lumbar subarachnoid space. This may be determined by use of a test in which dye is injected into the lateral ventricle and its absence or presence in lumbar subarachnoid CSF determined.

Head circumference is measured by passing a tape measure over the most prominent part of the occiput and just above the supraorbital ridges. The average of normal children at birth is about 35 cm. (13.75 in.), ± 1.2 cm. In the first 4 months of life, the head increases by 5 cm. (about 1.2 cm./month); during the next 8 months it increases another 5 cm. (10 cm. increase at the end of one year). The average circumference at 2 years is 49 cm.; at 3 years, 50 cm.; at 4 years, 50.5 cm.; at 5 years, 50.8 cm.; and at 6 years, 51.2 cm.

It is assumed that defective absorption of the CSF into the venous sinuses occurs in some cases. Obstruction in the midbrain as a consequence of a malformed aqueduct of Sylvius occurs in others. The functional obstruction of the foramens of Luschka and Magendie may also occur secondary to intra-uterine meningitis with meningeal adhesions, congenital absence, or congenital abnormality.

Symmetric dilatation of the cerebral ventricles and atrophy of the brain are usually present. Other malformations which may be associated include porencephaly, microgyria, macrogyria, absence of corpus callosum, spina bifida, syringomyelia, Arnold-Chiari malformation, and meningocele. Separation of the suture lines of the skull and bulging of the fontanelles may be evident. The scalp appears thin and stretched; the lower face appears small by contrast with the upper head. Optic atrophy, mental deficiency, and spastic paralysis of extremities are frequently seen.

The heads of infants may be "transilluminated" with a flashlight held at right angles against the head in a darkened room. In cases of hydrocephalus, porencephaly, hydranencephaly, and subdural hygroma, transillumination may be pronounced. In other cases, where there is increased space between the brain and the undersurface of the cranium, a defect of the cranium or scalp, and subdural effusion, an unusual glowing of a side or part of the head may be noted.

In the Dandy-Walker syndrome hydrocephalus is caused by atresia of the foramen of Magendie. The skull may enlarge principally in the occipital region because of the relatively large fourth ventricle, and the bitemporal diameter may remain normal.

Macewen's sign is the presence of tympany on percussion over the lateral ventricle of an infant with increased intracranial pressure and hydrocephalus.

The course of congenital hydrocephalus is usually progressively downhill, with death in the first or second year of life due to intercurrent infections. Occasionally hydrocephalus may be "arrested," and the child develops into adult life with few symptoms beyond enlargement of the head. Surgery is often required, and the outcome may depend upon the success of the operation as well as the presence of other serious malformations of the nervous system. Operations for relief of hydrocephalus include excision or cauterization of the choroid plexuses and shunting procedures by which artifical connections are made between the ventricular system and cisterns or veins, or between subarachnoid spaces and body cavities.

CEREBRAL PALSY
(Little's Disease, Infantile Cerebral Palsy)

Broadly used, the term "cerebral palsy" includes disorders of the nervous system characterized by paralytic symptoms in infancy or childhood. This heterogeneous group includes disorders and damage to the nervous system incurred in utero, at birth, or in early postnatal life, and caused by developmental defects, trauma of labor, postnatal anoxia, intrauterine meningitis or encephalitis, cerebrovascular accidents of infancy, and kernicterus.

Various clinical types of cerebral palsy have been noted: spastic, athetoid, ataxic, rigid, and tremorous. Combinations of these groups are common, and other significant neural defects may be associated, such as speech disorders, dysphasia, apraxia, hemianopsia, and mental retardation. Brain injury may be suspected at birth because of listlessness, feeding difficulties, and poverty of movements. The rate of development of motor, speech, and intellectual faculties may be delayed. In mild cases, the defect may not be recognized for several years until it is obvious that the child is physically and intellectually inferior to others of the same age group.

The relative incidence of clinical types of cerebral palsy, classified on the basis of major motor complaints, is as follows: spastic, 65%; athetoid, 25%; rigid, tremulous, ataxic, 10%.

Infantile spastic hemiplegia is the most common form of cerebral palsy, accounting for about one-third of all cases. **Prenatal** spastic hemiplegia is uncommon (less than 5%) and is caused by brain malformations or prenatal "stroke" due to toxemia. **Natal** spastic hemiplegia is the most common type (65%). Predisposing factors include prematurity and heavy birth weight, and perhaps also debility of the newborn or bleeding diathesis. Forceps trauma may injure the brain, and physiologic hazards of birth may cause injury to the fetal head, which acts as a battering ram during labor; pelvic disproportion, dystocia, or pituitrin induction may aggravate physiologic trauma. **Postnatal** infantile spastic hemiplegia is common (over 30%). It comprises over 90% of all postnatal cerebral palsies, since most postnatal brain injuries are unilateral. It is usually caused by head trauma, infection and encephalitis, and vascular damage. Motor aphasia is common only in postnatal right hemiplegia.

Mental retardation and convulsive seizures are common in all forms of infantile spastic hemiplegia. The upper extremity is usually more involved than the lower. The sensory handicap may be more disabling than the motor, because proprioception and form discrimination are lost. Failure of growth may be of cerebral origin due to involvement of the postcentral gyrus. Hemianopsia may follow damage to the occipital lobe.

Good results have been reported in treatment of patients with athetosis with diazepam (Valium®), 2-20 mg. daily.

MENTAL RETARDATION

Mental retardation or mental deficiency is characterized by incomplete or slow intellectual maturation from early years. It may be caused by genetic, biologic, or other factors and usually results in social maladjustment. Poor attention span, inability to concentrate on a single activity, hyperactivity, distractability, and anxiety may increase the problems of adjustment. Overt evidence of organic brain damage is variably present. Sometimes there are associated convulsive disorders, paralyses, ataxias, deformities, etc. Patients with organic brain damage are more likely to exhibit behavior of unpredictable nature, distractability or inability to concentrate, hyperkinesis, impulsiveness, overreaction to environmental stimuli, and difficulties in abstract thinking.

The degree of deficiency may be assessed by psychometric tests and clinical evaluation, and may vary from borderline to severe. Mental retardation is ordinarily considered to be present if the Intelligence Quotient (I. Q.) is less than 70. Morons are those with I. Q. 's between 70 and 50, and correspond in intelligence to the average normal ten-year-old child. They can often learn to read and write and may possibly be self-supporting. Imbeciles are those with I. Q. 's between 50 and 20, and correspond in intelligence to the average normal seven-year-old child. They are trainable and can be taught a certain degree of self care. Idiots have I. Q. 's of less than 20, correspond in intelligence to the average normal three-year-old child, and often present a severe custodial problem throughout life. Asphyxia, anoxia, and cerebral hemorrhage during prolonged labor or associated with prematurity, prenatal infections, and childhood encephalitides are etiologically accountable for a large segment of this group. A family history of mental deficiency may be present in others. Associated neurologic syndromes such as tuberous sclerosis, neurofibromatosis, amaurotic family idiocy, metabolic disorders, and mongolism are commonly present.

Among the conditions apt to be confused with mental retardation is childhood schizophrenia or infantile autism. This condition usually develops gradually, and a child may exhibit unusual behavior for a long time before he is brought to the doctor. He loses interest in siblings, parents, playmates, and school, and seems to live in a world of his own, sitting inactive and apparently preoccupied for hours at a time. He is emotionally cold and shows no emotional response to stimuli and environment. He often shows motor awkwardness, mannerisms, and habit spasms, and his voice may have a flat mechanical quality. As he becomes older, the clinical features of adult schizophrenia may become apparent.

Children with neuroses are sometimes thought to be mentally retarded. In this group, however, the child uses his neurotic symptoms as a defense against environmental stress, or as an outlet for emotional conflicts. Usually no evidence of brain damage can be found or inferred in the child's birth history or early life. Hyperactivity and tics are common. Stereotyped repetitions and purposeless, abrupt, involuntary tic movements are prone to occur in older children of this type.

The association of mental retardation with remediable defects in some disorders has led to a more optimistic outlook for selected patients. Thus the adequate early surgical treatment of craniosynostosis may prevent or favorably modify associated mental retardation. The early recognition and prompt treatment of metabolic disorders such as phenylketonuria, galactosemia, and cretinism may prevent or halt the manifestations of mental retardation in these patients.

The following are among the clinical syndromes associated with mental retardation.

Laurence-Moon-Biedl Syndrome.

Mental retardation, adiposogenital dystrophy, retinal pigmentary degeneration, and, sometimes, polydactylism in afflicted families.

Sturge-Weber Syndrome.

Localized calcification and cortical atrophy with an ipsilateral port wine nevus of the face or scalp, characterized clinically by convulsions. Mental retardation, hemiplegia, or hemianopsia may also occur. A characteristic pattern (cortical calcification) may be demonstrated on skull x-ray.

Lindau-Von Hippel Syndrome.

Hemangioblastomas of the cerebellar hemispheres, often associated with angiomatosis of the retina, cysts of the kidney and pancreas, and a tendency to familial distribution.

Morquio's Syndrome.

A familial type of osseous dystrophy characterized by mental deficiency, dwarfism, kyphosis, and impaired joint action. Onset frequently is in the first year of life.

MONGOLISM (Mongolian Idiocy)

Mental deficiency in infants with facial and body features superficially resembling those of Mongolian origin is called mongolism. Physical and mental development is retarded. Brachycephaly, flattening of the face, narrowing and slanting of palpebral fissures, epicanthus, broadening and coarsening of the tongue, shortening of stature, and congenital skeletal and visceral anomalies are frequently associated. There is often a single crease across the hand. Trisomy of chromosome No. 21 occurs in mongolism, which is one of the most common causes of mental retardation in children.

TUBEROUS SCLEROSIS
(Epiloia, Bourneville's Disease)

This congenital, sometimes familial disease begins in early childhood and is characterized by progressive mental deterioration, convulsions, and the appearance of tumors of the skin and viscera. Within the brain are numerous glial nodules, and those projecting from the walls of the lateral ventricles may sometimes be seen in air studies of the brain. The skin tumors, which resemble adenoma sebaceum, are scattered all over the body but are characteristically found about the face,

nose, and lips. These skin lesions are small yellow or red-brown nodules in butterfly distribution over the nose and cheeks.

CRANIOSTENOSIS
(Craniosynostosis)

Premature closure of the skull sutures may result in malformation of the skull with secondary effects upon the brain and eyes. Familial incidence and developmental defects of other bones (particularly of the upper extremities) may be associated. Early operation is usually advisable; the operation of choice is linear craniectomy parallel to the suture which is prematurely fused, with insertion of polyethylene film over the edges to delay closure.

Oxycephaly is characterized by a dome-shaped skull (tower skull), exophthalmos, optic atrophy, and developmental retardation. The skull is of great height, forehead receding, face narrow and elongated, eyeballs prominent and protruding. Headaches, papilledema from increased pressure, and secondary optic atrophy are common; mental retardation, convulsive seizures, and deafness sometimes also occur. **Scaphocephaly** results from premature closure of the sagittal suture. Deformity in shape of skull is characterized by lateral flattening, high vertex, increased anteroposterior diameter, and bulging forehead. Clinically, scaphocephaly resembles mild oxycephaly. **Brachycephaly** results from premature closure of coronal suture so that the head is flattened in the anteroposterior plane and the vault is abnormally high. The forehead is broad, nose flattened, eyes widely separated. Brachycephaly resembles oxycephaly clinically.

KLIPPEL-FEIL SYNDROME

In this congenital condition, there is a fusion and reduction in number of the upper cervical vertebrae, producing a short neck, a low hairline, and limitation of motion of the neck. Developmental anomalies of the cervical spinal cord may also be present, such as syringomyelia, spina bifida, and other congenital defects.

NEUROFIBROMATOSIS
(Von Recklinghausen's Disease)

This congenital disorder is characterized by development of multiple tumors of the spinal or cranial nerves, tumors of the skin, and cutaneous pigmentation. Changes in the skin include plexiform neurofibromas, pedunculated or sessile polyps, café-au-lait spots, and port wine or anemic nevi. Bone changes and local overgrowth of tissue, causing hypertrophy of the tongue, face, and extremities, may occur. Meningioma and gliomas of the CNS may be associated. The cutaneous manifestations together with overgrowth of skin and other tissues may produce characteristic deformities and disfigurements. The course is often relatively benign, with no shortening of life span. However, in patients with cranial nerve or spinal root lesions, disabling symptoms requiring surgery may occur.

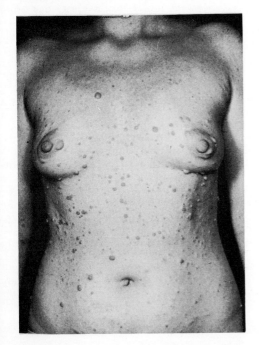

Neurofibromatosis (Von Recklinghausen's Disease). Multiple cutaneous and subcutaneous nodules.

ARNOLD-CHIARI MALFORMATION

In this anomaly, a projection of medulla and cerebellum extends through the foramen magnum and into the cervical spinal canal. It is frequently associated with spina bifida. Presumably during fetal life, fixation of the lower spinal cord or its nerve roots exerts traction on the upper cervical cord and brain stem, thus causing the medulla and cerebellum to herniate through the foramen magnum. Hydrocephalus is usually present. Other developmental defects may be associated, such

as defects in bones of skull, spinal column, spinal cord, and meninges.

Signs and symptoms usually are evident in the first few months of life and are related to the associated hydrocephalus and other developmental neural defects. Prognosis is poor in these. Hydrocephalus is attributed to basal cistern obstruction; compression of brain stem and stretching of cranial and cervical nerves produce other signs and symptoms. Rarely, onset of symptoms may be delayed until adult life and may simulate symptoms produced by posterior fossa tumor, syringomyelia, disseminated sclerosis, or platybasia.

Treatment of infants includes decompression of the posterior fossa and excision of the sac of the spinal region; in adults, decompression of posterior fossa is performed.

SYRINGOMYELIA

Syringomyelia, a disease of the spinal cord and brain stem of unknown cause associated with gliosis and cavitation of spinal cord and brain stem, is characterized clinically by muscular wasting and weakness, varying types of sensory defects, signs of injury to the long tracts, and trophic disturbances. It is considered by many to be the result of imperfect closure of the neural tube, the persistence of embryonic rests giving rise to a proliferation of glial cells in the central portion of the spinal cord about the central canal.

Lower cervical cord segments are usually affected, although the disease may similarly affect the lumbar cord and brain stem. Constitutional or developmental defects are frequently associated, such as "pigeon breast," scoliosis, cervical rib, or hydrocephalus. Pathologically, there is central gliosis of the affected portion of the cord and often associated cystic cavitation with the presence of thick yellow fluid. A coincidence of syringomyelia and intramedullary tumors (gliomas, hemangiomas) has been noted.

Symptoms usually occur in the second or third decade of life and are characterized by the early loss of pain and temperature sense, with preservation of touch and deep pressure sense in the lower cervical dermatomes. The classical and most common form is that in which the cervical spinal cord is involved. Presenting symptoms may be wasting of small muscles of the hand and painless burns of the fingers or forearm. Weakness and atrophy of the shoulder girdle muscles may be associated, as well as Horner's syndrome, nystagmus, and vasomotor and trophic disturbances of the upper extremities. Loss of pain and temperature sensation in the cervical and thoracic dermatomes is apt to be in a shawl-like distribution (see p. 195). Deep reflexes of upper extremities may be absent. As a result of long tract spinal cord damage, spasticity and ataxia of lower extremities and impaired bladder function may be present. Charcot joints are common in this disorder. **Morvan's syndrome** consists of the formation of slowly healing, painless infections of the fingers or toes in an anesthetic extremity, as in syringomyelia.

When the lumbosacral region alone is involved in syringomyelia, the clinical picture may be characterized by weakness and atrophy of the lower extremities and pelvic girdle, dissociated sensory loss in lumbosacral segments, bladder paralysis, and vasomotor and trophic disturbances of the lower extremities. When the medulla is involved (syringobulbia), atrophy and fibrillation of the tongue, loss of pain and temperature sense in the face, nystagmus, dysphonia, or respiratory stridor may occur.

After an initial rapid progression, the disease usually progresses slowly for years. New clinical signs and symptoms reflect the further involvement of CNS tissue. In spinal cases, death usually is the result of intercurrent infection; in syringobulbia, death may occur within a few months due to destruction of medullary nuclei.

Myelography discloses in many cases a partial or complete block in the zone of the syringomyelia, or a characteristic deformity of the contrast column may be detected. Treatment varies with the degree of clinical involvement and the evidence of block on myelographic study. Laminectomy and decompression may be performed, with needle aspiration or myelotomy through the posterior median fissure of the spinal cord in selected cases. Roentgen therapy of the affected area of the spinal cord has been advocated, but the results of such treatment are generally poor.

PLATYBASIA (Basilar Impression)

Platybasia is a deformity of the occipital bone and upper end of the cervical spine resulting from defective development. It is sometimes characterized by fusion of the atlas with the basioccipital bone and accompanied by abnormalities of the odontoid process of the axis. Signs of compression of the medulla, complete obstruction of the subarachnoid space, and hydrocephalus may occur. Symptomatically the disease may resemble syringomyelia, multiple sclerosis, or progressive spastic paralysis. When lateral x-ray of the skull shows the dens extending above Chamberlain's line (a straight line drawn from the posterior lip of the foramen magnum to the posterior border of the hard palate), platybasia should be suspected. Surgical decompression of the foramen magnum, freeing of adhesions, and occasionally amputation of the cerebellar tonsils are sometimes indicated for treatment.

CERVICAL RIB SYNDROME

The brachial plexus and subclavian artery may be compressed in the neck by a rudimentary cervical rib, fibrous band, first thoracic rib, or tight scalene muscle giving rise to sensory, motor, or vascular symptoms in one or both upper extremities. The onset of symptoms has been related by some to the loss of tone in shoulder girdle muscles with age or excessive trauma to these parts incurred by lifting or straining.

Cervical ribs, rudimentary or fully developed, are relatively common although frequently asymptomatic. Although they are frequently bilateral, cervical ribs may give rise to unilateral complaints. Prominence of the lower neck above the clavicle on one or both sides may be obvious on inspection. Pressure in this region will give rise to local pain as well as pain referred to the hand and arm. Pain and paresthesia, particularly in the ulnar portion of the hand and forearm, most commonly occur. Impaired perception of pain and light touch in the hand or forearm, and muscular weakness of small hand muscles, may also be present. Coldness and blueness of the hand and diminished pulsation in radial and ulnar arteries may be noted. Horner's syndrome, resulting from damage to cervical sympathetics, has occurred. **Adson's test** or maneuver is usually positive on the affected side. The patient, seated with hands resting on thighs, takes a rapid deep inspiration, holds his breath, hyperextends his neck, and turns his head as far as possible first to one side and then the other. Obliteration of the pulse on one side is considered a positive test. **Naffziger's syndrome** (scalenus anticus syndrome) is characterized by pain in the arm, shoulder, and neck, and is associated with atrophy of the small muscles of the hand and numbness of the hand in ulnar distribution. It is caused by compression of the lowermost cord of the brachial plexus by the scalenus anticus muscle.

The clinical course is subject to considerable variations. Frequent remissions or slow progression occur. Temporary relief may be obtained by wearing a sling support on the affected extremity. Rest in bed, traction on the neck, and the use of pillows to support the shoulders are also helpful. Surgical removal of cervical ribs, division of fibrous bands, or section of the scalenus anticus muscles may give permanent relief.

24 ...

Disorders Due to Vascular Disease of the Central Nervous System

ARTERIOSCLEROSIS OF THE BRAIN

The primary pathologic change in arteriosclerosis of the brain occurs in the cerebral blood vasculature, although similar changes may be present in other systemic vessels also. The disease is predominantly one of old age, and is considered by many to be a normal manifestation of the aging process in man. Disturbances in metabolism, especially of fats, are believed to be a prominent associated change.

Pathology.

Atheromatous changes in the arterial system are found relatively frequently at postmortem examination of the bodies of people who have reached middle age. Vessels of all sizes may be affected. Microscopically, one sees a combination of degenerative and proliferative changes. The muscularis is the main site of degeneration; the intima the main site of proliferation. Disseminated areas of softening of the brain, generalized atrophy, and senile plaques in the cortex are frequently found.

The most frequent and severe atherosclerotic lesions noted in an analysis of 1175 consecutive autopsies were located in 4 areas of the circle of Willis: the upper and lower basilar artery, the internal carotid artery at its trifurcation, the first third of the middle cerebral artery, and the first part of the posterior cerebral artery. Severe narrowing of vessels sufficient to cause vascular insufficiency oc-

➤

Distribution of Degenerative Lesions in Large Cerebral Arteries of the Circle of Willis in 1175 Consecutive Autopsies. Severity of lesions is illustrated by intensity of shaded areas, the darkest areas showing the most severe lesions. (Reproduced, with permission, from Baker and Iannone, Neurology 11:23-32, 1961.)

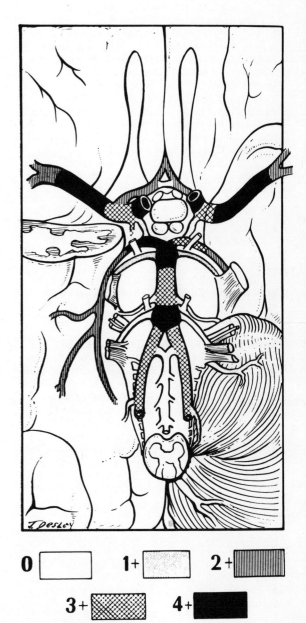

0   1+   2+

3+   4+

curred in 2% of cases as early as age 30-40 and in as many as 6-8% in patients from 60-70. In younger patients vessel narrowing in the anterior part of the circle of Willis occurred in the internal carotid artery or the first part of the middle cerebral arteries. In older patients, narrowing was almost exclusively present in the posterior part of the circle of Willis in the basilar artery, the vertebral arteries, or the first part of the posterior cerebral arteries.

Clinical Findings.

Headache, dizziness, tinnitus and insomnia are common, and memory may be impaired. Personality changes are well recognized, and judgment is apt to be impaired; aphasia, delusions, hallucinations, behavior disorders, and dementia may occur in the later stages. Paralysis agitans and apoplectic syndromes are common complications. Evidence of arteriosclerosis of other parts, such as the retina or the extremities, may coexist.

Treatment and Prognosis.

There is no specific therapy for the prevention or cure of this disease. Symptomatic therapy is employed as necessary.

HYPERTENSIVE ENCEPHALOPATHY

Hypertensive encephalopathy syndromes affecting the CNS are frequently encountered in essential hypertension as well as in glomerulonephritis associated with hypertension.

Pathology (Cerebrovascular Accidents).

The findings usually associated with cerebral arteriosclerosis are noted, i.e., thickening and hyalinization of the muscularis with narrowing of the lumens of the vessels and hyaline deposits beneath the endothelium. Recurrent arterial spasms associated with altered permeability of the blood-brain barrier are believed to occur prior to the onset of severe arteriosclerotic changes. Brain edema or swelling is commonly noted; many small infarcts and petechial hemorrhages may be found.

Clinical Findings.

Anorexia, weakness, vomiting, headache, and dizziness are common. Transitory focal motor or sensory signs may occur, presumably as a result of temporarily altered local cerebral function. Symptoms may be accentuated by rises in blood pressure following emotional disturbances.

Convulsive seizures preceded by an aura are frequently associated with abrupt increases in blood pressure. Variable degrees of changes in the fundus are noted: narrowing of arteries, evidence of old and recent retinal hemorrhages, papilledema, exudates, and arteriovenous nicking. CSF pressure is usually elevated and protein increased, with values up to 200 mg./100 ml. Blood NPN may be normal or only slightly elevated.

Treatment.

Medical management may include the use of sedatives, salt restriction, hypotensive drugs, psychotherapy, anticonvulsant drugs, and autonomic ganglionic blocking agents. Surgical treatment, usually the removal of portion of the lumbodorsal sympathetic chains, has been advocated in some clinics for patients with early malignant hypertension and good renal function.

CEREBROVASCULAR ACCIDENTS

The acute onset of apoplexy or a "stroke" is usually associated with disease of the intracranial vascular tree or of the blood or is due to trauma. The commonest causes of generalized or focal disturbance of brain function are cerebral vascular lesions.

The main types of spontaneous cerebrovascular accidents may be classified as (1) cerebral thrombosis, (2) cerebral hemorrhage, (3) cerebral embolism, or (4) subarachnoid hemorrhage.

Etiology.

Cerebrovascular accidents may occur at any age, but intracerebral hemorrhage and thrombosis are rare before 40 years. Peak incidence for cerebral thrombosis is at 50-70 years; for cerebral hemorrhage, 40-70 years. Cerebral thrombosis is the commonest cause of strokes (approximately 60%); hemorrhage and embolism cause about 20% each.

Pathology.

A. **Cerebral thrombosis** is usually associated with softening of the brain (encephalomalacia); occasionally softening of the brain occurs without demonstrable thrombosis of a cerebral vessel. By far the commonest cause is arteriosclerosis. Other causes include vasculitis, meningitis, encephalitis, thromboangiitis obliterans, periarteritis nodosa, polycythemia, dehydration, mechanical obstruction by masses, and systemic acute infections of childhood. In

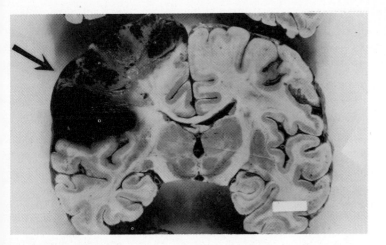

Hemorrhagic (Red) Infarct of Right Cerebral Hemisphere in 67-year-old Hypertensive Man

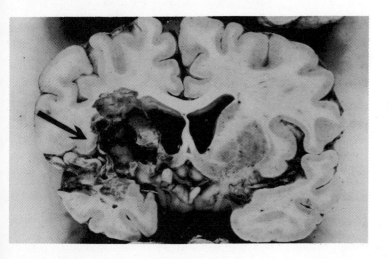

Postencephalomalacic Cyst of Right Cerebral Hemisphere

patients with arteriosclerosis, cerebral thrombosis is believed to follow clotting of the blood at a site where its flow is impeded by a sclerotic plaque on the vessel wall. Ischemia and infarction of brain tissue in the area supplied may follow occlusion of the cerebral artery, with congestion and edema of neighboring zones. After a few days edema diminishes; ischemic brain may undergo necrosis **(pale infarct)**. Necrotic brain tissue is liquefied and removed by macrophages; a glial and vascular scar partially replaces the destroyed brain tissue, producing shrinking of brain tissue or formation of small multilocular cysts filled with clear fluid. Occasionally red blood cells invade the necrotic tissue area to form a **red infarct**; in these cases it has been felt that the obstructing clot (or embolus) moves distally, permitting hemorrhage through the necrotic vessel wall.

B. **Cerebral Hemorrhage:** Hemorrhage into the brain or meninges results from rupture of one of the cerebral vessels, and in the great majority of cases is from a ruptured arteriosclerotic vessel. Other causes include rupture of congenital and mycotic aneurysms, acute infections, toxic agents, blood dyscrasias, trauma, and systemic disease. Hemorrhage deep into the substance of the brain - especially the pons and midbrain - may result from head trauma or in association with supratentorial brain tumor. Diffusely scattered hemorrhages of various sizes may result from damage to brain vessels by acute infection, toxins or drugs, acute leukemia, polycythemia, thrombocytopenic purpura, and scurvy. The mechanism of rupture of diseased vessels remains obscure. Some hemorrhages are of arterial and others of venous origin. Softening of the brain tissue about a blood vessel probably facilitates rupture of that vessel. Rupture of the vasa vasorum of medium-sized vessels may precipitate cerebral hemorrhage. Changes in caliber and tension within the vessel may contribute to rupture of a vessel.

The blood clot destroys and replaces adjacent brain tissue; neighboring brain tissue is usually softened. In large hemorrhages, the site of the ruptured vessel may not be apparent. The most common site for simple hemorrhages is the basal ganglia extending to involve the internal capsule and frequently rupturing into the lateral ventricles, where blood spreads throughout the ventricular system and into the subarachnoid space of convexity and base of the brain. In cases where recovery ensues, blood and necrotic brain tissue are removed by macrophages. Blood is removed and destroyed brain tissue is completely replaced by connective tissue, glia, and new blood vessels, producing a shrunken, fluid-filled area.

C. Cerebral Embolism: Cerebral embolism is the occlusion of a cerebral vessel by a small piece of blood clot, tumor, fat, air, or other substance, or a clump of bacteria. Following occlusion of the vessel, necrosis of the area supplied by the vessel occurs. Most cerebral emboli are sterile, although emboli of patients with pulmonary infections or bacterial endocarditis may contain bacteria and may give rise to encephalitis, abscess, or meningitis.

The most common source of cerebral embolism is heart disease, although embolism may occur with thrombotic or suppurative processes of any part of the body. Air embolism may follow lung injuries. Fat embolism may be associated with fractures of long bones. In children, cerebral emboli occur with rheumatic heart disease or bacterial endocarditis; in middle-aged and elderly patients, cerebral embolism frequently occurs with atrial fibrillation or coronary thrombosis. Embolus may completely or partially occlude a cerebral vessel. The area of brain tissue supplied by this vessel becomes infarcted and resolves in somewhat the same way in which resolution of a thrombotic infarct occurs. Red infarcts of the brain often occur with cerebral embolism. If the embolism is septic, encephalitis or abscess or, if infection is confined to the vessel, mycotic aneurysmal dilatation may occur. This may later rupture, giving rise to cerebral hemorrhage. Emboli to the brain are frequently multiple, and there may be infarcts to lungs, spleen, kidneys, and other viscera and peripheral vessels.

D. Subarachnoid Hemorrhage: This may be caused by head trauma, blood dyscrasias, intracranial tumor, vascular anomalies, intracerebral hemorrhages, or infectious disease. Primary subarachnoid hemorrhage refers to bleeding due to rupture of a vessel in the subarachnoid space. The vast majority are due to congenital weakness of the vessel. Maldevelopment of the media, especially at the area of bifurcation, has often been noted. In older age groups, arteriosclerosis is a contributing factor. Septic emboli with mycotic aneurysms and syphilis are occasionally significant factors.

E. Recurrent Cerebral Ischemia: Recurrent cerebral ischemia with transient impairment of cerebral circulation may produce recurring attacks of approximately the same pattern depending upon which artery is chiefly affected. These ischemic episodes, formerly called "vasospasm," are considered to be a warning of impending or threatening stroke. Attacks may last a few seconds or minutes and may vary in number from a few to hundreds. These attacks appear to be closely related to atherosclerosis and thrombosis, and are apt to occur when local cerebral circulation is about to fail completely. Although precipitation of attacks has been attributed to transient fall in blood pressure, this is often difficult to confirm objectively. Anticoagulants may abolish the attacks in many cases, but their specific mode of action is not known.

F. Progressive Cerebral Ischemia: Narrowing of the extracranial arteries, particularly the internal carotid artery at its origin in the neck, by arterosclerotic patches has been incriminated in some cases of transient cerebral ischemias and infarction. Routine postmortem studies have disclosed that in patients over 50 years of age about 40% have at least one major cervical carotid or vertebral artery reduced by more than half. In patients whose history is consistent with cerebral ischemia, high-grade cervical arterial stenosis was present in about 70%. The many patients who have cervical arterial stenosis without ischemic symptoms emphasize the importance of interpreting angiograms of stenosis or occlusion with due regard for the clinical features presented.

Pulseless disease (Takayasu's syndrome) is produced by progressive stenosis of the major arteries arising from the aortic arch, with consequent obliteration of peripheral radial pulses. Cerebral infarction is apt to be associated. The etiology is obscure, although syphilis has been noted in some cases.

Clinical Findings.
The general clinical picture is apt to be similar for "strokes" of varying etiology.

remonitory symptoms are infrequent. These nclude headache, dizziness, drowsiness, and nental confusion. Local premonitory signs re most likely to be indicative of thrombosis. nset is usually sudden, and maximum intenity is reached within a few hours at most. Ieadache commonly occurs, and stupor or oma is present during the acute phase. Focal eurologic signs (paralysis, sensory loss, and peech defects) are common. Generalized eurologic signs include headache, vomiting, onvulsions, and coma; these are most common with cerebral hemorrhage. Nuchal riidity is common with intracerebral or subrachnoid hemorrhage. In the period following a stroke, mental signs and symptoms (conusion, disorientation, and memory defects) re common. Early symptoms and signs vary onsiderably. The onset of a stroke may be iolent, with the patient falling to the ground nd lying inert like a person in deep sleep, ith flushed face, stertorous or Cheynetokes respirations, full and slow pulse, and ne arm and leg usually flaccid. Lesser rades of stroke may consist of slight deangement of speech, thought, motion, sensaion, or vision. Consciousness need not be ltered. Symptoms may last seconds to mintes or longer, and may persist indefinitely. ome degree of recovery is usual.

Survivors of the acute phase of a stroke ften enter a convalescent or chronic recovery hase. Varied signs and symptoms may be resent, usually resembling the acute maniestations and related to the location and deree of brain damage. Recovery is sometimes emarkably complete, so that altered brain unction may be hardly demonstrable even with pecial tests (EEG, psychometrics, pneumoncephalograms, etc.). Generally, however, atients have lesser grades of their initial deects (e.g., hemiparesis, numbness, aphasia, emianopsia, impaired mentation). Paralyzed imbs and parts in this later phase usually show igns of upper motor neuron disease: spastic eak muscles with little muscle atrophy, hyperctive deep reflexes, diminished or absent uperficial reflexes, and pathologic reflexes uch as a positive Babinski sign.

Pseudobulbar palsy is characterized by eakness of muscles supplied by the medulla blongata (bulb), which controls talking, swalowing, and pharyngeal and tongue movements. t is caused by multiple lesions in both cereral hemispheres, particularly thromboses in erebral arteriosclerosis. It may occur without paralysis of the extremities, and is often ssociated with loss of emotional control and pontaneous outbursts of laughing and crying.

Specific focal signs are associated with cclusion of particular arteries. These are utlined below:

A. Common and Internal Carotid Artery: Occlusion may be asymptomatic in young persons with a normal circle of Willis. In middleaged or elderly patients, any of the following may occur: (1) transient attacks of hemiplegia at first, with persistent hemiparesis thereafter; (2) unilateral loss of vision (ophthalmic artery occlusion); and (3) aphasia when the dominant hemisphere is affected.

Internal Carotid Artery Thrombosis. Occlusion of first portion of internal carotid artery just beyond bifurcation of common carotid artery with filling of external carotid artery and branches in carotid angiogram.

B. Anterior Cerebral Artery: This artery supplies the medial aspect of the anterior twothirds of the cerebral hemisphere. It arises from the internal carotid artery. Its branches include the following: (1) the frontopolar artery, to the anterior portion of the medial surface of the frontal lobe; (2) the callosomarginal artery, to the posterior portion of the medial surface of the frontal lobe; (3) the pericallosal artery, to the corpus callosum and the posterior portion of the medial surface of the frontal lobe; and (4) the recurrent artery of Heubner, which appears at about the level of the anterior communicating artery and supplies the most anterior portion of the basal ganglia and the adjacent internal and external capsules.

Occlusion of the main trunk of the anterior cerebral artery may cause contralateral hemiplegia, affecting chiefly the lower extremity; mild sensory deficits in the contralateral lower extremity; mental confusion, and clouding of consciousness.

C. Middle Cerebral Artery: This artery supplies the greater portion of the convexity of the cerebral hemisphere. It is the largest branch of the internal carotid artery and initially lies deep within the fissure of Sylvius. Its branches include the following: (1) perforating branches to the basal ganglia, internal capsule, and thalamus (lenticular, lenticulostriate arteries); (2) the ascending frontoparietal artery, to the lateroposterior portion of the frontal lobe and the lateral portion of the parietal lobe; (3) the posterior parietal artery, to the parietal lobe; (4) the angular artery, to the posterior parietal lobe and the superior posterior temporal lobe; and (5) the posterior temporal artery, to the superior and posterior portions of the temporal lobe.

Occlusion of the main trunk of the middle cerebral artery may cause coma, contralateral flaccid hemiplegia, hemianesthesia, and hemianopsia, and profound motor and sensory aphasia if the dominant side is involved.

Occlusion of perforating branches may cause contralateral hemiplegia. Contralateral rigidity and tremor may follow.

Occlusion of the posterior parietal, angular, or posterior temporal artery may cause contralateral hemiparesis, contralateral astereognosis, contralateral homonymous hemianopsia, and sensory aphasia, agnosia, apraxia, and alexia if the dominant side is involved.

D. Posterior Cerebral Artery: This artery supplies the posterior pole and the medial portion (posterior third) of the cerebral hemisphere and the inferior portion of the temporal lobe. It usually takes its origin from the basilar artery, occasionally from the internal carotid artery. Its branches include (1) the anterior temporal artery, to the inferior surface of the temporal lobe; (2) the posterior temporal artery, to the inferior surface of the temporal lobe; (3) the posterior occipital artery, to the inferior and posteromedial portion of the occipital lobe and the posterior corpus callosum; (4) the calcarine artery, to the pericalcarine cortex; and (5) collateral arteries (thalamo-geniculate and thalamo-perforating branches), to the basal ganglia and midbrain.

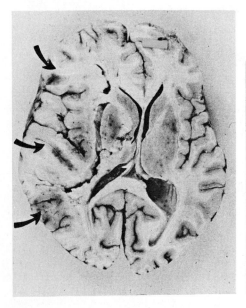

Middle Cerebral Artery Thrombosis.
Massive infarction of the cerebral hemisphere with a shift of ventricles to the opposite side simulating the effects of intracerebral mass lesion.

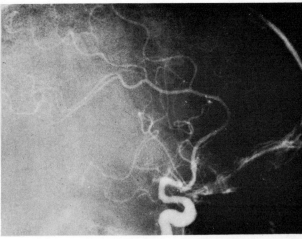

Middle Cerebral Artery Thrombosis. Carotid angiogram showing filling of the carotid siphon and anterior cerebral artery and branches. The middle cerebral artery does not fill because of thrombosis at its origin.

Occlusion of the main trunk of the posterior cerebral artery may cause contralateral hemiplegia, usually transient; contralateral hemianesthesia; contralateral homonymous hemianopsia; and sensory aphasia if the dominant side is involved. Less often, occlusion also causes ipsilateral cerebellar signs, contralateral rigidity, tremors, and choreiform movements.

Occlusion of the posterior occipital artery may cause thalamic syndrome with contralateral hemianalgesia (pain and temperature) and contralateral spontaneous dysesthesia and pain.

Occlusion of the calcarine artery may cause contralateral homonymous hemianopsia with loss of half of macular vision, and visual agnosia, if the dominant side is involved.

The retrolenticular capsule syndrome consists of hemiplegia, hemihypalgesia, hemianesthesia, and hemianopsia resulting from occlusion of that branch of the posterior cerebral artery which supplies the posterior portion of the internal capsule.

E. Posterior Inferior Cerebellar Artery: This artery supplies the posterior inferior portion of the cerebellum and the lateral portion of the medulla. It arises from the vertebral artery just posterior to the basilar artery. Its branches include (1) the medial branch, to the posterior inferior portion of the cerebellum; and (2) the lateral branch, to the posterior inferior portion of the cerebellum and the lateral portion of the medulla.

Occlusion of the main trunk of the posterior inferior cerebellar artery may cause ipsilateral facial analgesia, ipsilateral Horner's syndrome, ipsilateral ataxia, and contralateral analgesia. Ipsilateral weakness of the vocal cords or tongue with contralateral hemiparesis may also be present.

F. Superior Cerebellar Artery: This artery supplies the superior surface of the cerebellum and sends a few branches to the pons and midbrain. It arises from the anterior part of the basilar artery. Occlusion may cause ipsilateral ataxia and contralateral hemianalgesia and hemianesthesia.

G. Basilar Artery: This artery supplies the brain stem and midbrain via short paramedian and long circumferential branches. Occlusion of the main trunk of the basilar artery may cause headache, dizziness, and coma; flaccid quadriplegia, areflexia, complete anesthesia, pinpoint pupils, and hyperpyrexia.

H. Anterior Spinal Artery: Occlusion of this vessel is associated with a characteristic clinical picture and with softening of the spinal cord (myelomalacia). Symptoms include sudden paraplegia, depending on the spinal level of softening; disturbance in bowel and bladder function, and sensory disturbances (impaired perception of pain and temperature).

Differential Diagnosis.

It is sometimes not possible to identify the type of vascular accident which has occurred during an individual attack. In general, however, the following criteria may be used to arrive at a probable diagnosis:

1. Mode of onset - A relatively slow onset favors the diagnosis of thrombosis.

2. Precipitating cause - Apoplexy occurring during or soon after exertion or emotional upset favors cerebral hemorrhage or subarachnoid hemorrhage.

3. Pre-existing diseases - A known history of hypertension favors cerebral hemorrhage. Bacterial endocarditis, atrial fibrillation, or previous myocardial infarction favors embolism.

4. Associated clinical findings - Cranial nerve palsies and evidence of meningeal irritation favor subarachnoid hemorrhage.

5. Laboratory findings - Evidence of massive bleeding into the CSF usually favors subarachnoid or cerebral hemorrhage.

6. Cerebral angiography may disclose characteristic x-ray patterns.

Treatment and Prognosis.

Immediate treatment involves bed rest with the head elevated, sedation, supportive measures, and nursing care. Place the patient at complete rest and handle him carefully to avoid injury. If he is agitated, give tranquilizers or sedatives as necessary. If he is unconscious or unable to swallow, do not attempt to give oral feedings. Maintain nutrition with tube feedings or by parenteral means. Catheterization may be required. Lumbar puncture may be performed cautiously, removing a small quantity of CSF for diagnostic and therapeutic purposes.

Cerebral hemorrhage is usually fatal. The clot is large and acts like an intracranial mass, absorbing slowly. For this reason operative removal of the blood clot may be indicated in patients who withstand the initial shock of hemorrhage and show evidence of continued increased intracranial pressure by lumbar puncture or in patients who show evidence of development of papilledema.

Anticoagulant therapy has been advocated for the prevention of recurrences in cerebral

Diagnosis of Cerebrovascular Disorders

	Intracerebral Hemorrhage	Cerebral Thrombosis	Cerebral Embolism	Subarachnoid Hemorrhage	Vascular Malformation and Intracranial Bleeding
Onset	Generally during activity. Severe headache (if patient is able to report findings).	Prodromal episode of dizziness, aphasia, etc., often with improvement between attacks. Unrelated to activity.	Onset usually within seconds or minutes. No headache. Usually no prodrome. Unrelated to activity.	Sudden onset of severe headache unrelated to activity.	Sudden "stroke" in young patient. No headache. Unrelated to activity.
Course	Rapid hemiplegia and other phenomena over minutes to one hour.	Gradual progression over minutes to hours. Rapid improvement at times.	Rapid improvement may occur.	Variable; apt to be at worst in initial few days after onset.	Most critical period is usually in early stages.
History and related disorders	Suspect diagnosis especially if other hemorrhagic manifestations are present and in acute leukemia, aplastic anemia, thrombopenic purpura, and cirrhosis of the liver.	Evidence of arteriosclerosis, especially coronary, peripheral vessels, aorta. Associated disorders: diabetes mellitus, xanthomatosis.	Evidence of recent emboli: (1) other organs (spleen, kidneys, lungs), extremities, intestines; (2) several regions of brain in different cerebrovascular areas.	History of recurrent stiff neck, headaches, subarachnoid bleeding.	History of repeated subarachnoid hemorrhages, epilepsy.
Sensorium	Rapid progression to coma.	Relative preservation of consciousness.	Relative preservation of consciousness.	Relatively brief disturbance of consciousness.	Relatively brief disturbance of consciousness.
Neurologic exam.	Focal neurologic signs or special arterial syndromes; nuchal rigidity.	Focal neurologic signs or special arterial syndromes.	Focal neurologic signs or special arterial syndromes.	Focal neurologic signs frequently absent; nuchal rigidity, positive Kernig and Brudzinski signs.	Focal neurologic signs; cranial bruit.
Special findings	Hypertensive retinopathy, cardiac hypertrophy, and other evidences of hypertensive cerebrovascular disease may be present.	Evidence of arteriosclerotic cardiovascular disease frequently present.	Cardiac arrhythmias or infarction (source of emboli usually in the heart).	Subhyaloid (preretinal) hemorrhages.	Subhyaloid (preretinal) hemorrhages and retinal angioma.
BP	Arterial hypertension.	Arterial hypertension frequent.	Normotensive.	Arterial hypertension frequent.	Normotensive.
CSF	Grossly bloody.	Clear.	Clear.	Grossly bloody.	Grossly bloody.
Skull x-ray	Shift of pineal to opposite side.	Calcification of internal carotid artery siphon visible; shift of pineal to opposite side may occur.	Pineal apt to show little if any displacement.	Partial calcification of walls of aneurysm sometimes noted.	Characteristic calcifications in skull x-rays may be present.
Cerebral angiography	Hemorrhagic area seen as avascular zone surrounded by stretched and displaced arteries and veins.	Arterial obstruction or narrowing of circle of Willis (internal carotid, etc.).	Arterial obstruction of circle of Willis branches (internal carotid, etc.).	Typical aneurysmal pattern in circle of Willis arteries (internal carotid, middle cerebral, anterior cerebral, etc.)	Characteristic pattern showing cerebral arteriovenous malformation.

thrombosis or cerebral embolism, and for the treatment of carotid or basilar insufficiency. Recent studies by several groups suggest that anticoagulant therapy helps only a few individuals in any large series of patients with the clinical picture of stroke. The evidence is most promising for cerebral ischemia. The risk of hemorrhage is particularly great in hypertensive patients.

Narrowing of the extracranial arteries, especially the cervical portions of the internal carotid artery, is now being evaluated, and operative measures to correct the affected vessels are being studied.

Prognosis is usually difficult to evaluate in the early stages. The prognosis for life should be guarded; residual disability (hemiplegia, etc.) is the rule. The rehabilitation of the patient with hemiplegia due to cerebrovascular accident should start early and should be intensive.

The outcome in cerebral thrombosis is determined to a great extent by the location and extent of the infarct as well as the general condition of the patient. In general, the greater the delay in improvement, the poorer the prognosis. In cerebral embolism, the underlying condition and the presence of emboli in other organs are significant factors. In intracerebral hemorrhage, the prognosis is poor, particularly in the presence of hypertension and arteriosclerosis. Intraventricular or brain stem hemorrhage is a discouraging sign.

If the patient survives the acute attack the prognosis for life may be good. With active rehabilitation many patients are able to walk and care for themselves. Return of useful function to the upper extremity occurs less often. Patients can be trained to achieve some degree of recovery. The prognosis for functional recovery is poor in those patients with severe residual organic mental syndrome or sensory aphasia, and in those patients with profound, irreversible, or massive infarction or hemorrhage.

INTRACRANIAL ANEURYSM

Aneurysmal dilatation of blood vessels may occur as a result of arteriosclerosis, congenital abnormalities, or embolism. Intracranial aneurysms vary from the size of a pea to that of an orange, and individual aneurysms may vary in size from time to time. Larger aneurysms may erode the bones of the skull and sella turcica and compress adjacent cerebral tissue and cranial nerves. Most are located near the basilar surface of the skull, and almost half arise from the internal carotid or middle cerebral arteries. They are usually single but occasionally are multiple. A coincidence of congenital intracranial aneurysms and polycystic kidneys and coarctation of the aorta has been noted.

Pathology.
Fusiform dilatation of the basilar arteries or the terminal portions of the internal carotids may occur as a consequence of diffuse arteriosclerotic changes. Miliary, saccular aneurysms frequently occur near the bifurcation of a vessel in the circle of Willis and are associated with congenital abnormalities of the muscularis. A mycotic aneurysm, the result of an arteritis produced by bacterial emboli, is relatively infrequent. Larger aneurysms may be partially or completely clot-filled; occasionally they may be calcified.

Clinical Findings.
Prior to rupture, aneurysms may be asymptomatic or may cause symptoms depending upon the location and size of the aneurysm. Headache on effort and involvement of cranial nerves II, III, and V are apt to be present. Bruit on stethoscopic auscultation over the affected site is sometimes heard.

Following rupture, the symptoms are those of acute subarachnoid hemorrhage. Recurrent unilateral headaches which clinically resemble those of migraine sometimes occur.

Diagnosis.
By use of carotid or vertebral angiography with injections of iodopyracet (Diodrast®), sodium acetrizoate (Urokon®), or other contrast media, an aneurysm may be demonstrated on x-ray.

Treatment and Prognosis.
Because of the high mortality rate associated with spontaneous subarachnoid bleeding and the probability of recurrence of subarachnoid hemorrhage, intracranial aneurysms are considered a serious pathologic entity. The choice of surgical treatment as opposed to medical treatment rests upon many circumstances, including the size and location of the aneurysm, the clinical status of the patient, the skill and experience of the surgeon, and the enthusiasm for a particular therapeutic regimen. Various surgical procedures including "trapping" the aneurysm by applying clips on either side of the aneurysm, clipping the neck of the sac of the aneurysm, packing muscle around the aneurysm, etc., have been successfully performed in some cases.

More recently, methods have been applied for preventing rupture of a cerebral aneurysm by use of plastics sprayed directly on the aneurysm and the surrounding vessels, with the reported advantage that operative sacrifice of a major cerebral vessel can thus be avoided.

Incidence of Signs and Symptoms in the Variously Located Aneurysms and Vascular Anomalies

	Before Rupture			Chance of Rupture	After Rupture in Subarachnoid Space									
					Involvement of Cranial Nerves							Coma	Hemiparesis	Convulsions
	Asymptomatic	Headache	Paresis of Cran. N. III		II	III	IV	V	VI	VII	VIII			
Supratentorial vascular anomalies	+(*)	+	0	+	0	0	0	0	0	0	0	++	++	+
Aneurysm of internal carotid artery														
Infraclinoid	0	0	++++	+	+	++++	+++	+	+++	0	0	+	0	0
Carotid cavernous fistula	0	+	+(**)	0										
Supraclinoid	++	++	++	+++	+	++	+	0	0	0	0	+	+	+
Aneurysm of anterior cerebral and communicating arteries	++	++	0	+++	+	0	0	0	0	0	0	+++	+	+
Aneurysm of middle cerebral artery	+	+	0	+++	0	0	0	0	0	0	0	++	++	+
Aneurysm of posterior communicating and cerebral arteries	+	+++	+	+++	0	++	+	+	+	0	0	+	+	+
Aneurysm of vertebral and basilar arteries	++	+	0	+++	0	0	0	0	0	+	+	+++	+	0

*Convulsions common.

**Syndrome of pulsating exophthalmos, bruit, and at times ocular palsies.   Rating: 0 = 0.5%   ++ = 35.1-65%
(Reproduced, with permission, from Walker, Neurology 6:88, 1956.)   + = 5.1-35%   +++ = 65.1-95%
++++ = 95.1-100%

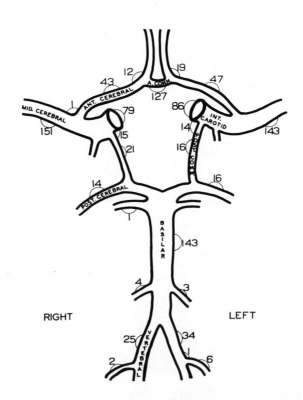

Location of Intracranial Aneurysms in 1,023 Cases. (Reproduced, with permission, from McDonald and Korb, A.M.A.Arch.Neurol. & Psychiat. 42:298, 1939.)

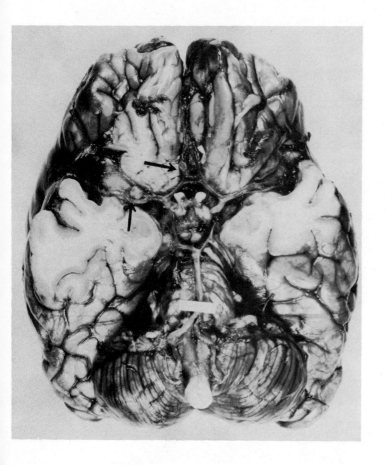

Multiple Aneurysms (Right Middle Cerebral and Anterior Cerebral Arteries) in a Woman With Coarctation of Aorta

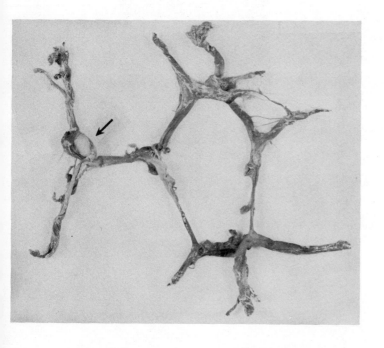

Right Middle Cerebral Arterial Aneurysm Which Ruptured and Produced Intracerebral Hemorrhage

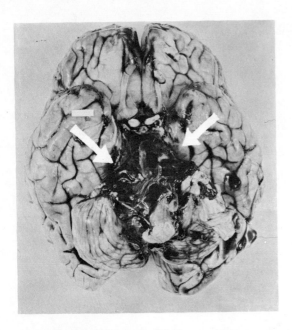

Severe Subarachnoid Hemorrhage
Secondary to Intracerebral Hemorrhage

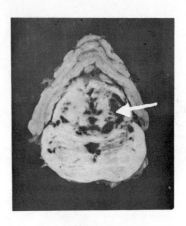

Pontine Hemorrhage

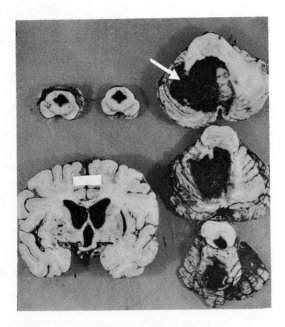

Cerebellar Hemorrhage
With Intraventricular Rupture

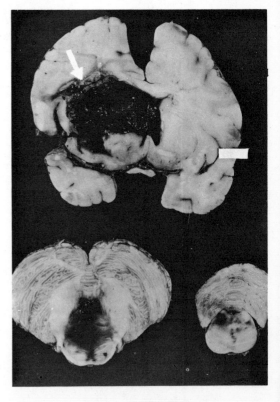

Cerebral Hemorrhage
With Intraventricular Rupture and
Associated Pontine Hemorrhage

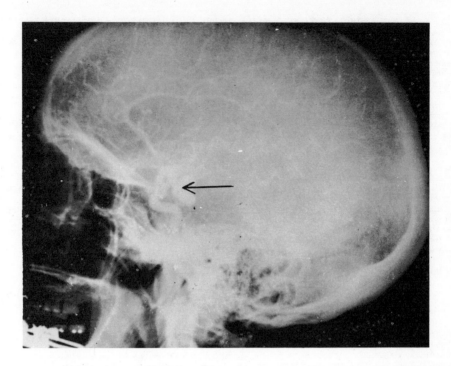

Aneurysm of the Posterior Communicating Artery Demonstrated by Carotid Angiogram

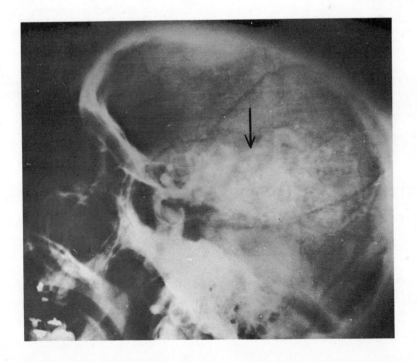

Arteriovenous Aneurysm (Malformation) of Middle Cerebral Artery and Vein

A CLASSIFICATION AND OUTLINE OF THE CEREBROVASCULAR DISEASES*

I. CEREBRAL INFARCTION [pale, red (hemorrhagic) and mixed types]
  A. Thrombosis with atherosclerosis
  B. Cerebral embolism
    1. Of cardiac origin
       (a) Atrial fibrillation and other arrhythmias (with rheumatic, atherosclerotic, hypertensive, congenital heart disease)
       (b) Myocardial infarction with mural thrombus
       (c) Acute and subacute bacterial endocarditis
       (d) Heart disease without arrhythmia or mural thrombus
       (e) Complications of cardiac surgery
       (f) Nonbacterial thrombotic ("marantic") endocardial vegetations
       (g) Paradoxical embolism with congenital heart disease
    2. Of noncardiac origin
       (a) Atherosclerosis of aorta and carotid arteries (mural thrombus, atheromatous material)
       (b) From sites of cerebral artery thrombosis
       (c) Thrombus in pulmonary veins
       (d) Fat
       (e) Tumor
       (f) Air
       (g) Complications of neck and thoracic surgery
       (h) Miscellaneous: rare types
       (i) Of undetermined origin
  C. Other conditions causing cerebral infarction
    1. Cerebral venous thrombosis
    2. Systemic hypotension
    3. Complications of arteriography
    4. Arteritis (see VI)
    5. Hematologic disorders (polycythemia, sickle-cell disease, thrombotic thrombopenia, etc.)
    6. Dissecting aortic aneurysm
    7. Trauma to carotid
    8. Anoxia
    9. Radioactive or x-ray radiation
    10. With tentorial, foramen magnum, and subfalcial herniations
    11. Miscellaneous: rare types
  D. Cerebral infarction of undetermined cause

II. TRANSIENT CEREBRAL ISCHEMIA WITHOUT INFARCTION
  A. Recurrent focal cerebral ischemic attacks (previously called vasospasm, usually associated with thrombosis and atherosclerosis)
  B. Systemic hypotension ("simple faint," acute blood loss, myocardial infarction, Stokes-Adams syndrome, traumatic and surgical shock, sensitive carotid sinus, severe postural hypotension)
    1. With focal neurologic deficit
    2. With syncope
  C. Migraine

III. INTRACRANIAL HEMORRHAGE (including intracerebral, subarachnoid, ventricular, rarely subdural)
  A. Hypertensive intracerebral hemorrhage
  B. Ruptured saccular aneurysm (if unruptured see IV A)
  C. Angioma (if unruptured see IV B)
  D. Trauma
  E. Hemorrhagic disorders (leukemia, aplastic anemia, thrombopenic purpura, liver disease, complication of anticoagulant therapy, etc.)
  F. Of undetermined cause (normal blood pressure and no angioma)
  G. Hemorrhage into primary and secondary brain tumors

III. INTRACRANIAL HEMORRHAGE, Cont'd.
  H. Septic embolism, mycotic aneurysm
  I. With hemorrhagic infarction, arterial or venous (see under I and VII)
  J. Secondary brainstem hemorrhage (temporal lobe herniation)
  K. Hypertensive encephalopathy
  L. Idiopathic brain purpura
  M. With inflammatory disease of arteries and veins (see under VI, VII)
  N. Miscellaneous: rare types

IV. VASCULAR MALFORMATIONS AND DEVELOPMENTAL ABNORMALITIES
  A. Aneurysm - saccular, fusiform, globular, diffuse (if ruptured see III B)
  B. Angioma (including familial telangiectasis, trigeminal encephalo-angiomatosis (Sturge-Weber-Dimitri), retinal-pontine hemangiomas) (if ruptured see III C)
  C. Absence, hypoplasia, or other abnormality of vessels (including variations in pattern of circle of Willis)

V. INFLAMMATORY DISEASES OF ARTERIES
  A. Infections and infestations
    1. Meningovascular syphilis
    2. Septic embolism
    3. Arteritis secondary to pyogenic and tuberculous meningitis
    4. Rare types (typhus, schistosomiasis mansoni, malaria, trichinosis, etc.)
  B. Diseases of undetermined origin
    1. Lupus erythematosus
    2. Rheumatic arteritis
    3. Polyarteritis nodosa (necrotizing and granulomatous forms)
    4. Cranial arteritis (temporal)
    5. Idiopathic granulomatous arteritis of aorta and its major branches

VI. VASCULAR DISEASES WITHOUT CHANGES IN THE BRAIN
  A. Atherosclerosis
  B. Hypertensive arterio- and arteriolosclerosis
  C. Hyaline arterio- and arteriolosclerosis
  D. Calcification and ferruginization of vessels
  E. Capillary sclerosis, etc.

VII. HYPERTENSIVE ENCEPHALOPATHY
  A. Malignant hypertension (essential, chronic renal disease, pheochromocytoma, etc.)
  B. Acute glomerulonephritis
  C. Eclampsia

VIII. DURAL SINUS AND CEREBRAL VENOUS THROMBOSIS
  A. Secondary to infection of ear, paranasal sinus, face, or other cranial structures
  B. With meningitis and subdural empyema
  C. Debilitating states (marantic)
  D. Postpartum
  E. Postoperative
  F. Hematologic disease (polycythemia, sickle-cell anemia)
  G. Cardiac failure and congestive heart disease
  H. Miscellaneous; rare types
  I. Of undetermined cause

IX. STROKES OF UNDETERMINED ORIGIN

*Reproduced, with permission, from Neurology 8:405-8, 1958.

25...

Infectious Diseases of the Central Nervous System

PYOGENIC LEPTOMENINGITIS

Classifications of leptomeningitis may be made on the basis of the specific etiologic agent. Among the commoner causes are meningococcic, pneumococcic, streptococcic, and Hemophilus influenzae infections. Less frequently, staphylococcic and gonococcic organisms are isolated. Neisseria meningitidis (meningococcus) is the causative agent in about 40% of all cases of meningitis.

Pathogenesis and Pathology.

Access to the subarachnoid space may be gained by an invading pyogen following a systemic and blood stream infection. More rarely, extension from an adjacent infected area may take place.

Characteristically, the subarachnoid space contains a cloudy or milky CSF. An exudate, containing great numbers of polymorphonuclear leukocytes, and tissue undergoing destruction are present in the subarachnoid space. Degenerative neuronal changes, perivascular leukocytic collections, and congestion of adjacent tissues are frequent. Evidence in the brain and spinal cord of encephalitis, brain abscess or petechial hemorrhage is not unusual.

Clinical Findings.

At onset, violent headache, severely stiff and painful neck, greatly elevated temperature, and clouding of sensorium, with stupor and delirium, are common. As the disease progresses, nausea, vomiting, photophobia, and convulsions frequently occur. Cranial nerve palsies with diplopia, tinnitus, and choking of optic disks are well recognized occurrences. Rigid spine, head retraction, and positive Kernig's and Brudzinski's signs are prominent features. Petechial skin hemorrhages and arthritis are commonly present; endocarditis and nephritis are rare complications.

Brudzinski's "neck" sign is positive when forcible flexion of the neck on the chest causes flexion of both legs and thighs. **Kernig's sign** is demonstrated when the recumbent patient's leg cannot be extended with the hip joint flexed at a right angle. Brudzinski's contralateral "leg" signs may be present: (1) When one thigh is flexed at the hip, the other also becomes flexed; (2) when one leg and thigh are fully flexed and the other extended, lowering of the flexed leg causes flexion of the extended one.

Diagnosis. (See chart on p. 222.)

Blood culture, nasopharyngeal smear and culture of CSF will usually indicate the specific pyogen causing the meningitis. The presence of co-existing or preceding infections, such as otitis media, points to potential meningitis. Exposure or contact with known meningitis cases raises probability of occurrence.

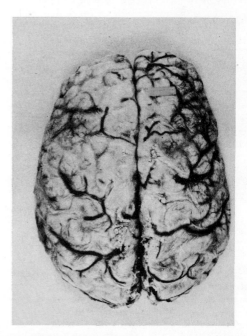

Pneumococcic Meningitis. Convexity of brain covered by thick green exudate in subarachnoid space.

Bacterial meningitis should be considered in all newborn infants who appear ill or do not thrive; signs of the disease are vague and non-specific, particularly in premature infants. Anorexia, vomiting, lethargy, irritability, jaundice, respiratory distress, diarrhea, bulging fontanel, convulsions, nuchal rigidity, fever, pyoderma, and omphalitis may occur, and pneumonitis, gastroenteritis, or other infection increases the possibility of meningitis.

Treatment and Prognosis.

Sensitivity tests are of value in determining the drug of choice in treatment, but treatment should not be withheld pending the results of the tests. Occasionally, however, it is necessary to use combinations of drugs for proper treatment. Although bacteriologic studies are necessary, initial treatment cannot await final results. Since treatment must be directed toward both gram-positive and gram-negative organisms, 2 and perhaps 3 drugs should be used.

A. Meningococcic Meningitis: Sulfonamides are the agents of choice. In addition, give penicillin. Antibacterial therapy need be continued only one week.

Chlortetracycline, chloramphenicol, and oxytetracycline have also been used successfully in small series of cases.

Prophylactic sulfadiazine by mouth to exposed persons may abort an epidemic and control its spread.

B. Pneumococcic, Streptococcic, and Staphylococcic Meningitis: Pneumococcic and streptococcic meningitis are treated specifically with penicillin. Treat staphylococcic meningitis with combined penicillin, bacitracin, erythromycin, novobiocin, and chloramphenicol pending results of sensitivity tests, or with methicillin (Staphcillin®).

With adequate and at times very large doses of antibiotics, the mortality rate is strikingly reduced. Staphylococcic meningitis carries the gravest prognosis.

The primary focus of infection should be eradicated by surgery if necessary, especially in recurrent or persistent pneumococcic meningitis.

C. Hemophilus influenzae Meningitis: Give streptomycin I.M. and intrathecally. In severe cases give also sulfadiazine, sulfamerazine, sulfamethazine, or a mixture of equal parts of each. Tetracycline drugs are of value. Chloramphenicol is also effective. In untreated infants the mortality rate is over 90%. Subdural effusion is commonly seen in infants with in-

fluenzal meningitis and is characterized by persistent vomiting, bulging fontanelles, convulsions, and persistent fever. Prompt relief follows evacuation of the effusion via subdural tap through the fontanelles.

D. Supportive therapy, including blood transfusions and other infusions, should be employed as necessary. Subdural effusions are a common complication of purulent meningitis, and should be ruled out if fever recurs after an afebrile period. Convulsions, irritability, fever, lethargy, and coma may also be associated. Subdural taps in children with open fontanelles are advantageous, and should be repeated, removing 15-30 ml. at a time until the subdural space is dry.

With the advent of chemotherapy, the prognosis for the pyogenic leptomeningitides is relatively good for life.

BRAIN ABSCESS

Localized suppurations may occur within the brain as in other portions of the body. Following acute purulent infection, pus in brain tissue may be free or encapsulated. Abscesses vary from microscopic size to an area covering most of a cerebral hemisphere.

Brain abscess is usually caused by staphylococci and pneumococci, although any of the common pyogenic bacteria may be found. The organism may gain access to the brain by direct extension from otitis media, mastoiditis, sinusitis, and infected head injuries, or, more rarely, via the blood stream from distant sources, such as lung infections and bacteremias.

Pathology.

The abscess consists of a central necrotic and purulent area surrounded by a capsule. The central area contains debris and leukocytes. The capsule, which may take weeks to form, may have 3 layers: (1) an inner layer adjacent to the pus cavity, characterized by presence of collagenous connective tissue fibers; (2) a broader middle layer, rich in connective tissue repair elements such as capillaries and fibroblasts; and (3) an external layer of connective tissue containing vessels and more phagocytes than the middle layer.

Abscesses occurring by extension from infections of the middle ear or mastoid are usually located within the temporal lobe or cerebellum. Abscesses occurring by extension from paranasal sinuses usually occur in the frontal lobe. Abscesses following bacteremia are apt to be multiple. Metastatic abscesses are commonly secondary to pulmonary suppurations.

Clinical Findings.

A history or evidence of preceding infection is usual. Otitis media, mastoiditis, sinusitis, bronchiectasis, or pneumonia is frequently present. Focalizing manifestations may occur, producing visual field defects, motor and other sensory changes, aphasia, and cranial nerve palsies similar to those caused by any other intracranial mass.

Signs of increased intracranial pressure may occur, such as papilledema, headache, and slowed pulse and respirations. Mild meningeal signs may be present, such as a mild rigidity of the neck and a positive Kernig sign. Somnolence and slowing of mental processes are common. The temperature is mildly elevated and rarely exceeds 102° F. (39°C.) if complications such as meningitis do not occur.

Diagnosis.

Brain abscesses may be confused with other clinical entities, such as brain tumors, leptomeningitis, or encephalitis. In brain tumor, history or evidence of preceding infection is usually absent, and the CSF cell count is usually normal. Leptomeningitis can usually be differentiated through a positive culture of the CSF. Acute fulminating leptomeningitis is easily distinguished clinically from brain abscess; mild leptomeningitis, such as tuberculous and syphilitic leptomeningitis, may be clinically indistinguishable. Encephalitis usually fails to exhibit the focalizing signs of brain abscess and usually provokes more profound and severe changes in the sensorium and personality.

Air ventriculography, pneumoencephalography, or cerebral angiography is frequently necessary to determine the site of abscess.

Brain abscesses may be located at operation with the use of needle aspiration.

Treatment and Prognosis.

Treatment consists of operative drainage of pus. Operation is usually delayed until the abscess is firmly encapsulated. If the abscess is well encapsulated and if it is practicable, excision in toto is sometimes performed. Marsupialization of the cavity, packing of the cavity, and various types of incision and drainage are commonly employed. After surgical drainage has been induced, irrigations of the abscess cavity with antibiotic solutions are helpful. Treatment of the original focus of infection, such as a chronic mastoiditis, is

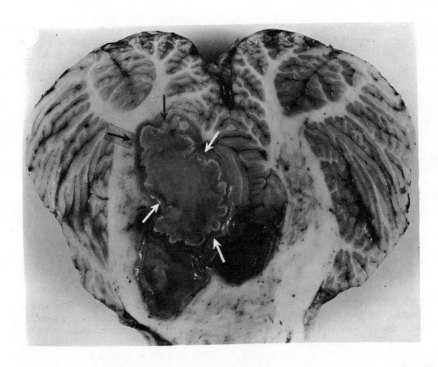

Cerebellar Abscess

sometimes necessary before a brain abscess will heal completely.

The use of chemotherapy has greatly improved the outlook for brain abscess. It has even been maintained that the formation of brain abscesses - e.g., in debilitated patients with pyogenic infections elsewhere - can be aborted with the use of appropriate antibiotic and sulfonamide drugs. Without treatment, brain abscess usually has a fatal outcome.

LESS COMMON PYOGENIC INFECTIONS

Subdural Abscess.

Cerebral subdural abscess is a relatively rare form of intracranial infection which may result from extension directly from the middle ear, nasal sinuses, or meninges, or as a complication of skull fracture or septicemia. Pyogenic bacteria, particularly staphylococci, are the usual causative agents. Subdural effusions, with or without bacteria, may complicate influenzal and other types of meningitis of infancy. Symptomatology includes that of the focus of origin (nasal sinus, ear, etc.) and that of intracranial extension. If untreated, the mortality rate is high; with prompt evacuation of pus and chemotherapy, recovery is possible.

Spinal Epidural Abscess.

Spinal epidural space infections, characterized by fever, headache, pain in the back, and paraparesis or complete paraplegia, may result from direct extension of local skin infections, perforating wounds, or lumbar puncture, or by metastasis through the blood stream from remote infected areas. The usual infective organism is Staphylococcus aureus, although other pyogens may be causative. The mid-thoracic vertebral zone is the most common site, and pus is usually posterior to the spinal cord. Localized granulomatous collections may result when the organism is of low virulence.

Symptoms develop abruptly: severe pain in back or lower extremities, followed by stiff neck, headache, malaise, and fever. Paralysis of the lower extremities may develop at any time; flaccid paraplegia may develop secondary to thrombosis of infected spinal vessels. Treatment consists of prompt surgical drainage by laminectomy and the use of appropriate antibiotics. Delay in drainage may result in permanent paralysis; in cases with transverse myelitis, little if any improvement occurs following delayed operation.

Lateral Sinus Thrombophlebitis.

This is much less frequently seen since antibiotics have come into wide use. It occurs principally in infants and children and usually is secondary to otitis media and mastoiditis of hemolytic streptococcus origin. Classical clinical features include fever, headache, nausea and vomiting, swelling over the mastoid area, and distention of local superficial veins. Papilledema, bulging of the fontanelles, and separation of sutures in infants, drowsiness, coma, and convulsive seizures may also occur. Chemotherapy and surgery are indicated, with removal of infected bone, exposure and drainage of the sinus, and jugular vein ligation.

In normal persons it is necessary to compress both jugular veins to produce engorgement of the retinal veins. In unilateral sinus thrombosis, compression of the healthy side only will suffice to produce engorgement (Crowe's sign).

Cavernous Sinus Thrombophlebitis.

Cavernous sinus thrombophlebitis is usually secondary to suppuration in the orbit, nasal sinuses, or upper face zone and usually spreads via the circular sinus to involve the opposite cavernous sinus. Acute onset with febrile reaction, proptosis of the eyeball, edema and chemosis of the conjunctiva and eyelids, diplopia, ptosis, and papilledema may develop. This disorder usually responds well to antibiotic treatment.

Most infections are due to Staphylococcus aureus. In other cases, S. albus, streptococci, pneumococci, or Proteus bacilli may be responsible. Penicillin G and synthetic penicillin (Staphcillin®) should be given until sensitivity studies are reported. Penicillin G should be effective against streptococci and pneumococci, and the synthetic drug should eradicate resistant staphylococcic infections. Adjunct therapy with steroids may be necessary where functional derangement of the hypophysis is associated.

Longitudinal Sinus Thrombophlebitis.

Thrombophlebitis of the superior sagittal (longitudinal) sinus may cause fever, prostration, elevated intracranial pressure, edema of forehead and anterior scalp, and engorgement of the vertex veins. There may be extension to local tributary cerebral veins, with convulsive seizures, hemiplegia, aphasia, or hemianopsia. Nonseptic thrombosis may occur, particularly in infants with dehydration and marasmus. Obstruction may be demonstrated by injection of radiopaque dye directly into the anterior superior longitudinal sinus. Antibiotics are indicated in the septic type.

Nonseptic or primary thrombosis may occur in debilitating illness. Treatment is aimed at reducing intracranial pressure, and may include the use of 30% solution of intravenous urea.

ACUTE INFANTILE HEMIPLEGIA

Acute infantile hemiplegia is believed to be due to inflammation of the branches of the middle cerebral artery, with resultant thrombosis and motor involvement. It affects both sexes equally, and often occurs in children who have been well. The seizure occurs suddenly, with profound loss of consciousness and abrupt temperature elevation. Convulsions may recur and coma may persist for days. The child slowly recovers, but residual hemiplegia may persist, often associated with language disturbances and hemianopsia. CSF studies are usually normal.

Symptomatic treatment and rehabilitation measures may be required.

CYTOMEGALIC INCLUSION BODY DISEASE

This disorder is a viral infection, usually latent, in infants and children. Clinically obvious infections may occur in newborn infants following transplacental transmission and are manifested by jaundice, anemia, thrombocytopenia and hemorrhages, hepatosplenomegaly, chorioretinitis, encephalitis, and microcephaly. The disease may affect older debilitated children. Typical cytomegalic cells may be isolated from urine or adenoids in clinical and latent cases. No specific treatment is effective, and the active clinical disease is usually fatal.

NEUROSYPHILIS

Infection of the CNS by Treponema pallidum may occur early or late in the course of syphilis. The hypothesis that a neurotropic form of this organism exists remains to be proved. In general, patients with mild early manifestations of syphilis are more apt to develop tabes and general paresis.

The clinical syndromes resulting from neurologic infection with Treponema pallidum

depend upon the extent of involvement of the parenchyma, blood vessels, and meninges. Although the CNS is involved by Treponema pallidum within a few weeks or months of the original infection, clinical evidence of involvement may be delayed for many years.

On the basis of clinical and pathologic data, CNS syphilis may be classified as (1) **nonparenchymatous or interstitial neurosyphilis** (syphilitic leptomeningitis, vascular neurosyphilis), or (2) **parenchymatous neurosyphilis** (general paresis, tabes dorsalis). Combinations of the main features of two or more types may occur. **Argyll Robertson pupil** (common with neurosyphilis; occasionally present in epidemic encephalitis and alcoholism) consists of loss of light reflex, retention of accommodation reflex, loss of ciliospinal reflex, and imperfect dilatation of the pupil with atropine. Miosis is usually present.

Asymptomatic neurosyphilis may occur in which abnormalities of CSF indicative of CNS infection are present without clinical signs or symptoms. In untreated cases, the incidence of asymptomatic neurosyphilis varies according to the duration of the infection; highest incidence occurs in the first or second years after infection. Prognosis is good with adequate treatment.

ACUTE SYPHILITIC MENINGITIS

Acute syphilitic meningitis is often the earliest form of neurosyphilis present in a particular patient and is a frequent concomitant of early secondary syphilis. Involvement of the meninges may be diffuse or focal in type. The incubation period varies from a few months to many years, but usually occurs within the first year of infection.

On pathologic examination the pia is found to be moderately congested, and lymphocytes are collected around the blood vessels.

In severe, fully developed cases the patient may exhibit the classical findings of acute leptomeningitis such as headache, stupor, convulsions, fever; stiff, painful neck; cranial nerve palsies, and positive Kernig's and Brudzinski's signs.

A strongly positive blood and CSF Wassermann is usually present. The CSF usually exhibits a marked lymphocytic pleocytosis.

The treatment of choice is penicillin, 15-20 million units I.M. in a two- to three-week period. The disease is usually influenced favorably by the prompt use of penicillin, bismuth, and the arsenicals.

VASCULAR NEUROSYPHILIS

The blood vessels of the CNS are frequently affected by syphilis. The consequences of involvement of these vessels are generally more serious than similar involvement elsewhere in the body. Thrombosis of arteries and encephalomalacia with appearance of various focal signs are characteristic.

Proliferation of the intima, cellular infiltration of the adventitia and media, and splitting of the elastica generally make up the pathologic picture of **Heubner's endarteritis.** Some degree of associated meningitis or meningoencephalitis is usually present. Infarction of the brain occurs following occlusion or thrombosis of affected vessels.

Early in vascular neurosyphilis few if any symptoms may be recognized. With increasing vascular involvement and subsequent parenchymal damage, headache, convulsions, stupor, and personality changes may occur. When relatively large vessels are affected in the brain, occlusion or rupture with gross cerebral hemorrhage may occur (see p. 276).

Symptomatic treatment as for similar cerebrovascular lesions is indicated. Penicillin, 15-20 million units I.M. in a period of 2-3 weeks, is necessary.

GENERAL PARESIS

General paresis is not as common as it formerly was because of the earlier and more frequent recognition and more effective treatment of syphilis. It usually appears many years after the primary lesion, and is therefore more common in the fourth and fifth decades of life.

The frontal lobes are predominantly affected; the cerebral convolutions are atrophied and the sulci widened. The cerebral cortex is thin, and the ventricles appear enlarged. There is distortion of the normal structure of the cortex, produced by a degeneration and disappearance of ganglion cells, and great increase in interstitial glial elements and blood vessels. The leptomeninges over the atrophic areas are opaque, thickened, and adherent to the underlying cortex.

Mental symptoms are believed to be primarily a reflection of frontal lobe dysfunction. Dementia, delusions, emotional changes, defective judgment, and clouding of consciousness are common. General paresis may mimic any of the classical mental and psychiatric disorders and syndromes. Tremors of fingers, lips, and tongue; slurred speech,

ataxia, Argyll Robertson pupils, a positive Babinski sign, and exaggerated deep tendon reflexes are frequent findings.

The CSF and blood Wassermann reactions are strongly positive. The CSF usually shows a moderate increase in cells (lymphocytes) and globulin, and a first zone colloidal gold curve.

Penicillin, 20-30 million units, is injected I.M. in a period of 3-4 weeks. If considered desirable, fever therapy (8-14 febrile bouts) by inoculation of malaria parasites or with an artificial fever cabinet may be given.

Without treatment, death occurs in a few years. The use of antibiotics or fever therapy (malaria or artificial fever) may retard or halt the progression of the disease.

TABES DORSALIS
(Locomotor Ataxia)

This common syndrome appears as a relatively late manifestation of syphilis. The primary lesion and the early mild signs are frequently not evident to the patient. Tabes dorsalis is relatively uncommon at present. It is much more frequent in males and whites and commonly develops 10-25 years after the initial infection.

The syndrome is more readily understood when it is remembered that it results from syphilitic infection of the posterior roots and the root entrance zone of the spinal cord, with secondary degeneration of the dorsal columns. Grossly, the spinal cord may appear smaller and atrophic, and the posterior roots are likely to be smaller than average. Microscopically, a decrease in number of normal nerve fibers of the lumbosacral roots, a cellular infiltration of the dorsal root ganglia, and degeneration of the posterior columns is evident.

Clinical Findings.

Root symptoms such as shooting and girdle pains, paresthesias, and hypesthesias occur. Periodic, irregular, severely painful episodes, known as crises, sometimes occur. Ataxia and bladder disturbances are common.

Loss of sense of position and vibration, ataxia, and a positive Romberg sign are a result usually of posterior column degeneration. Hypotonia of skeletal musculature, Argyll Robertson pupils, optic atrophy, and decreased or absent deep tendon reflexes are commonly found. Other signs include disorders involving the bladder and rectum, cranial nerve palsies, Charcot joints, and mal perforans (painless perforating foot ulcers). Abadie's sign (presumptive evidence of tabes) is loss of the sense of pain on squeezing the Achilles tendon. Biernacki's sign (of tabes) is loss of deep pressure pain when pressure is exerted over the ulnar nerve behind the elbow. **Westphal's sign** is characteristic of tabes, but it may occur with any lesion which completely interrupts the motor or sensory neurons of the femoral nerve; it consists of absence of the knee jerk reflex. **Romberg's sign** (of posterior column disease or polyneuritis) is positive if when the patient stands with his feet together and closes his eyes he begins to sway and perhaps loses his balance and falls, indicating a loss of proprioceptive sense in the legs.

Diagnosis.

The blood and CSF Wassermann is positive in about half of known cases. Increased cell count and total protein of the CSF may be present. CSF is abnormal in the early stage but may be normal in the late stage.

Treatment and Prognosis.

Treatment with antibiotic chemotherapy is usually effective. In resistant cases, heavy metals (arsenicals and bismuth) or fever therapy may be useful. Cordotomy may be necessary as a last resort for relief of excruciating pains. Penicillin, 15-20 million units I. M. over a two- to three-week period, is effective in arresting the course of the disease and in reversing the CSF abnormalities. Persistence of lightning pains and crises, ataxia, bladder disturbances, and Charcot joints is usual despite antiluetic treatment.

If tabes dorsalis is untreated, progression occurs with severe disability and suffering.

• • •

TUBERCULOUS MENINGITIS

Tuberculous meningitis differs from most other common meningitides since the course is more prolonged, the mortality rate much higher, and the CSF changes less severe. It occurs most commonly in childhood and ranks next to meningococcic meningitis in incidence. It may be referable to a focus of tuberculosis elsewhere in the body, most commonly in the peritracheal, peribronchial, or mesenteric lymph nodes, lungs, or other organs. Discharge of bacilli into CSF from adjacent foci of caseation in the brain has been considered by Rich to occur in the majority of cases.

Pathology.

Tubercles may be found scattered through the brain and spinal cord. Exudate is usually found over the base of the brain, and is usually thick, tough, and adherent. Microscopically, the brain shows miliary tubercles whose structure is like that of tubercles found elsewhere in the body.

Clinical Findings.

The presence of tuberculous lesions elsewhere in the body may sometimes be demonstrated. In children, evidence of contact with tuberculous family members should be sought.

The onset is usually gradual, with listlessness, irritability, loss of appetite, and mild fever.

During the progression of the disease, headache, vomiting, extra-ocular palsies, night cries, convulsions; stiff, painful neck; and positive Kernig's and Brudzinski's signs usually appear. In infants, bulging of fontanelles and peculiar shrill "meningeal" cries are apt to occur. Opisthotonos, choked disks, paralysis, and coma soon follow.

Diagnosis.

The CSF is frequently xanthochromic, cloudy or opaque, under increased tension, and may form a pellicle and web on standing. Smear, culture, and guinea pig inoculation of the pellicle and web will demonstrate tubercle bacilli. Increased cells (lymphocytes) and total protein occur. Glucose and chlorides are usually markedly reduced in amount.

Demonstration of tuberculous infection or exposure may be better judged after chest x-rays and tuberculin skin testing.

Intracranial tuberculoma occasionally occurs and is characterized by symptomatic progression, focal signs, and evidence of increased intracranial pressure so as to resemble an expanding intracranial neoplasm.

Tuberculous meningitis must be considered in the differential diagnosis of fever of unknown origin, especially in children 1-2 years of age. Confusion with viral infections of the CNS may occur, especially where symptoms of encephalitis predominate. Careful study of CSF can usually rule out uncommon infections, e.g., torulosis. Rarely, malignant disease may simulate tuberculous meningitis.

The prognosis is better in older than in younger children. Serial lumbar punctures are helpful in evaluation. A persistently abnormal EEG usually indicates a poor outlook, even without clinical convulsions. A normal pneumoencephalogram early in the course of tuberculous meningitis is a favorable prognostic sign. Obstruction at basilar cisterns may sometimes be noted with hydrocephalus. Ultimate recovery of survivors can be determined only after prolonged clinical observation, with EEG and psychometric studies providing useful aid.

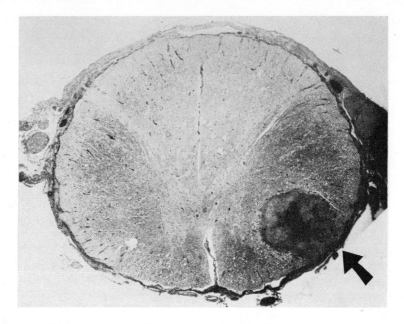

Tuberculoma of the Anterolateral Region of the Spinal Cord. The tumor had caused
analgesia and thermoanesthesia on the opposite side of the body below the level of the
lesion. It was this case particularly that led Spiller to recommend chordotomy as a
practical surgical procedure for the relief of pain. (Reproduced, with permission, from
Cadwalader: Diseases of the Spinal Cord. Williams & Wilkins, 1932.)

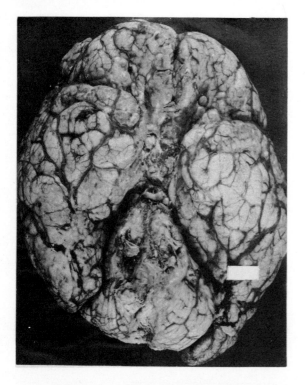

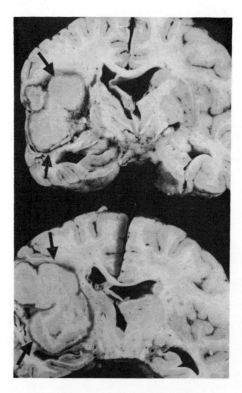

Tuberculous Meningitis, Basal View

Tuberculoma of the Brain

Treatment and Prognosis.

Give streptomycin I.M. and intrathecally. Give also isoniazid (INH), and aminosalicylic acid (PAS) or sodium para-aminosalicylate. (Intrathecal streptomycin is probably not necessary if isoniazid is used.)

Treat symptoms as they arise and maintain good nutrition and adequate fluids. Treatment with corticosteroids in the early phases needs further evaluation.

In untreated cases, death may occur within 3 weeks of onset of symptoms. Recovery may occur with proper prolonged treatment, but severe residuals (deafness, blindness, paralysis, hemiplegia, mental retardation, and convulsions) may occur.

YEAST MENINGITIS

The clinical picture of the usual case of yeast meningitis may resemble that of tuberculous meningitis. Onset of nervous system signs is gradual, and meningeal signs predominate. Occasionally, focal neurologic signs or mental syndromes are prominent. Diagnosis is established by culture of organisms [Cryptococcus (Torula), Saccharomyces, or Blastomyces] on Sabouraud's medium or identification of organisms in CSF or centrifuged sediment. The CSF changes in yeast meningitis are like those of tuberculous meningitis: fluid is under increased pressure, with mild to moderate pleocytosis, increased protein, and decreased glucose and chlorides.

Although there is no specific therapy for yeast meningitis, amphotericin B (Fungizone®) has been successful, especially when therapy was begun before extensive involvement of the CNS by Cryptococcus or Blastomyces has occurred.

EPIDEMIC ENCEPHALITIS
(Von Economo's Disease, Encephalitis Lethargica)

This disease is characterized by an acute onset of clinical manifestations of diffuse brain involvement and various sequelae. It occurred in epidemic form between 1916 and 1926, but is now quite rare. The inference has been drawn that a filtrable virus related to the virus of influenza causes this disease since the pandemic of influenza of 1919 to 1920 was associated with and followed by many cases of epidemic encephalitis. However, no valid proof exists that epidemic encephalitis is caused by a virus.

Pathology.

Severe acute damage to nerve cells, perivascular round cell infiltration, glial proliferation, and congestion occur. Damage is especially prone to occur to nerve cells of periaqueductal gray matter and adjacent cranial nerve nuclei, substantia nigra, ventromedial nucleus of thalamus, and the medial geniculate body.

Clinical Findings.

Onset may be sudden and violent or insidious. Initially, headache, tinnitus, malaise, and mild fever, such as are commonly associated with upper respiratory tract infections, are apt to be present. After about 2 weeks, diplopia, sleepiness, lethargy, insomnia, and weakness of muscles may be evident. In the acute phase, progression to severe coma and death is possible.

Following apparent recovery, further symptoms may appear. Forms of parkinsonism may appear later in life. Severe behavioral disturbances, especially in children, may ensue. These personality changes sometimes require institutionalization of the patient. Epilepsy, narcolepsy, and fat and water metabolic disturbances have occurred.

Diagnosis.

The specific type of encephalitis present in a particular patient may not be identified for weeks and perhaps never. CSF examination usually shows completely normal reactions, although a slight increase in cells or protein is not unusual. Isolation of a virus from the spinal fluid or blood must be attempted very early in the disease if it is to have any chance of success. The titer of spinal fluid and blood as determined by neutralization tests on animals inoculated with specific viruses may give a clue to the presence of that particular virus infection. A rise in titer with clinical progression of the disease or upon recovery is usually a positive reaction. In times of epidemic less error is apt to be made concerning the specific etiology of a case.

Accompanying infections in the spinal cord are common in encephalitic virus infections, and these signs and symptoms sometimes predominate and mask the features of the brain infection.

Differential Diagnosis.

A. Other Encephalitides: Other types of encephalitis may be clinically indistinguishable from epidemic encephalitis, so that immunologic reactions are of primary importance in establishing specific etiology. In **St. Louis encephalitis** a specific virus, transmissible to mice and able to be neutralized by the serum of convalescent patients, can be isolated from the spinal fluid. Diagnosis is made by isolation of the virus from brain tissue or development of specific neutralizing antibodies.

Two types of **equine encephalomyelitis**, eastern and western, occur in the United States and produce immunologically specific reactions. Epidemics of this equine infection occur primarily in the summer. The virus of the western type of equine encephalomyelitis has been isolated from human blood and spinal fluid. Diagnosis can be made by neutralization tests. The virus can be isolated from the brains of fatal cases. The virus of eastern equine encephalitis has been recovered also from the blood of laboratory animals, wild and laboratory-bred birds, and from human blood. Eastern equine encephalitis is spread by infected birds and transmitted by a mosquito that feeds on these birds and may also bite humans and other mammals. People and horses can be immunized against the disease. The mortality rate is believed to be 5-20%, and survivors may have permanent brain damage. Immune bodies in the serum can be detected in the blood of infected persons.

B. Systemic Infections: Encephalitis may occur as a complication of systemic virus disease. Under these circumstances, the possibility of activation of a latent virus infection by the original infection must be considered in measles, chickenpox, and mumps. Encephalitis has been known to occur following vaccination for smallpox, but this is rare. Herpes simplex, infectious mononucleosis, typhus, scrub typhus, herpes zoster, rabies, trichinosis, malaria, and schistosomiasis may be associated with severe encephalitis. Administration of ACTH, corticosteroids, or both to patients with encephalitis such as measles encephalitis does not prevent CNS sequelae. Some deaths may be averted by constant, intensive therapy. Supportive measures include correction of dehydration and electrolyte imbalance by intravenous administration of appropriate fluids. In addition, tracheostomy to avoid respiratory distress, treatment of bacterial complications with antibiotics, oxygen administration, anticonvulsants as necessary, and adequate nursing attention are required.

C. Toxoplasmic Encephalitis: This entity is well defined. It is caused by a protozoon, the Toxoplasma. It usually occurs in very young infants and may be fatal in the congenital type. Findings include convulsions, internal hydrocephalus, chorioretinitis, and cerebral calcifications demonstrable by x-ray. Diagnosis can be confirmed by intracerebral or intraperitoneal transmission of the parasite from the blood or spinal fluid of a patient into mice or rabbits, by demonstration of neutralizing bodies in blood of the infant, or by skin test.

D. Lymphocytic Choriomeningitis: This disease frequently resembles a mild attack of influenza, and the virus that causes it affects other tissues as well as the CNS and the meninges. The virus is easily obtainable from the spinal fluid and blood, and clinical diagnosis is confirmed by complement fixation and neutralization tests. The CSF characteristically contains many lymphocytes but shows no change in sugar or chloride content.

E. Inclusion Body Encephalitis: This subacute encephalitis of children and adolescents, of unknown etiology, is characterized by progressive dementia, incoordination, ataxia, myoclonic jerks, and other focal signs. Children under 12 years of age are predominantly affected, with gradual onset without fever. Although CSF shows little remarkable change, the EEG usually shows widespread abnormalities with two- to four-per-second wave and spike complexes. Intranuclear and intracytoplasmic inclusion bodies are found in the neurons, and occasionally in oligodendroglia of the brain. Beginning with mental deterioration, the disorder progresses to hallucinations, a stage of involuntary movements occurring at intervals of 5-10 seconds, akinetic mutism, and death. The disease usually lasts about 2 years, although survival for 8 years has been reported.

F. Coxsackie Virus Infection: Symptoms and signs of meningeal involvement may occur with acute or subacute fever, headache, malaise, nausea, abdominal pain, and stiff neck. As a rule no sensory, motor, or reflex changes occur; a coincidental infection with the virus of acute anterior poliomyelitis may occur. The course is self-limited and benign; herpangina and epidemic pleurodynia may also be caused by this type of virus. Diagnosis can be established by recovery of virus from feces or pharynx or by the demonstration of an increase in specific neutralizing antibodies in the sera. Enteroviruses which infect the human intestinal tract now include over 60 immunologically different agents. Thirty Coxsackie virus types (24 Group A and 6 Group B), 28 ECHO virus types, and 3 poliovirus types comprising this group may produce CNS involvement which is clinically indistinguishable from that produced by nonenteric viruses such as mumps and herpes simplex.

G. Herpes Simplex Meningoencephalitis: Severe asymmetric necrotizing inflammation, strikingly predominant in the limbic system, produces behavioral disturbances, memory loss, disorientation, olfactory and gustatory hallucinations, and focal neurologic defects including hemiparesis, hemianopsia, aphasia, and adversive and jacksonian seizures. The disease usually progresses rapidly and terminates fatally early. Characteristic intranuclear inclusions occur in affected neurons of the brain.

Treatment and Prognosis.

Treatment in the acute stage is supportive and symptomatic and directed at keeping the patient alive. Later treatment is modified to fit the most prominent symptoms.

Repeated lumbar punctures may relieve symptoms. Prevention or early treatment of decubiti, pneumonia, and urinary tract infections is important. Give anticonvulsants as needed.

The prognosis for life is usually good, but the prognosis for complete recovery must always be guarded since complications may occur at relatively long intervals following the acute illness.

ACUTE ANTERIOR POLIOMYELITIS
(Heine-Medin Disease)

This widely distributed, acute generalized disease may occur in sporadic or epidemic forms. Several strains of virus have been isolated which may be transmitted to mice, monkeys, and chimpanzees, in whom relatively specific pathologic and immunologic reactions occur.

A gastrointestinal portal and an insect vector have been implicated as likely modes of transmission. There is some question as to the exact manner in which infection occurs. Experimentally, infection via the gastrointestinal and upper respiratory tracts can be effected. Multiplication of the virus in the gastrointestinal tract may continue for weeks or months after the acute infection.

The disease is most prevalent during the summer and warm periods, when flies are especially abundant. Invasion of the nervous system occurs as a relatively late manifestation. A stage of early viremia precedes invasion of the nervous system, which may occur from the gastrointestinal tract to the nervous system by way of the axis cylinders of the nerves.

There are 3 antigenic virus strains. Complement-fixing antigens are known for each of the 3 types of virus and they may be prepared from tissue culture or the CNS of infected infant mice or hamsters. Inactivation of the virus by formalin, heat, or ultraviolet light liberates a soluble complement-fixing antigen. A type-specific precipitin reaction occurs when virus in sufficient concentration is used with immune animal or convalescent human serum.

Pathology.

There is a predilection for gray matter damage to occur. Changes in ganglion cells, varying in severity from mild to severe degeneration, occur especially in the anterior horn cells of the spinal cord. The lumbar and cervical enlargements of the cord are most affected. Microglia are increased early; later, remaining glial elements partake in glial scar formation.

Round cell infiltration of the spinal root ganglia may occur. Congestion and hemorrhage of the pia and arachnoid as well as the parenchyma of the cord may be present.

Clinical Findings.

A. Prodromal Stage: In the prodromal or preparalytic phase, this disease resembles many other mild infections. One usually cannot predict which of a group of ill patients in an epidemic will develop the severe permanent paralyses and which ones will never be severely affected. During the preparalytic phase, irritability, drowsiness, diarrhea, abdominal distress, headache, and fever of mild degree may be present. The CSF examination at this time may indicate a mild increase in the number of cells, most of which are polymorphonuclear leukocytes.

B. Paralytic Stage: The paralytic phase may come on soon after, and may be accompanied by severe general symptoms, collapse, coma, and fever of 103-105° F. Usually 1-3 days after severe symptoms have been present, the fever drops and motor paralysis is apparent. Stiff, painful and retracted neck and a positive Kernig sign are present early. In the acute phase there may be tenderness of muscles, with painful contractions precipitated by movement or exposure to cold. Retention of urine is common in the earlier acute phases, but soon disappears. When paralysis of muscles occurs it may be severe and generalized and function returns slowly in the weeks after.

C. Convalescent Stage: In general, maximum recovery occurs in the first few months after onset of paralysis, although it may require as long as 2 years.

Differential Diagnosis.

The diagnosis of acute anterior poliomyelitis frequently cannot be made in the early phases of the disease. Especially in times of

epidemic outbreaks, other diseases are confused with it. The major entities apt to be
confused with poliomyelitis are meningitis,
which can usually be diagnosed by adequate
CSF smear, culture and cell counts; diphtheria,
which can be detected by early nasopharyngeal
smear and culture; and Guillain-Barré syndrome, which usually causes sensory changes,
symmetric involvement and characteristically albumino-cytologic dissociation, and is
usually milder. Other virus infections of
nervous system may be identified by virus and
immunologic studies. Osteomyelitis of extremities may be excluded by CSF studies.

Landry's paralysis is characterized clinically by a rapid ascending paralysis usually
terminating in death. It is believed to be a
fulminating type of acute anterior poliomyelitis,
although other etiologies cannot be excluded.
Because of the rapid course of the disease,
demonstrable pathologic changes are minimal
or absent. The **Guillain-Barré syndrome** may
last for weeks or months, but recovery is the
rule and is often complete, without paralytic
sequelae or muscular atrophy. The components
of this syndrome are as follows: (1) Motor disturbances: Progressive weakness or paralysis
beginning in the lower extremities and ascending to involve the trunk, upper extremities,
and occasionally the cranial nerves. Deep reflexes are lost, but the cutaneous reflexes are
preserved. (2) Sensory disturbances, including paresthesias and marked tenderness on
pressure over the affected muscles; objective
sensibility is only slightly disturbed. (3) Al-
buminocytologic dissociation: Hyperalbumino-
sis of the spinal fluid in the absence of an increase in the number of cells is a constant
diagnostic finding.

Treatment and Prognosis.

The patient should be kept in bed on a firm
mattress with a padded foot board. Therapy
in the acute phase is aimed at keeping the patient comfortable. To this end, hot applications by means of packs are beneficial. When
painful contractions of the muscles are no
longer present, muscle re-education should be
vigorously pursued. The use of a body respirator may be a necessary life-saving measure
in the acute phase when central paralysis has
occurred. The patient should be watched
carefully and, if signs of respiratory embarrassment develop, placed in a body respirator
immediately. Tracheostomy may be desirable
or necessary when air passages are occluded
by mucus or laryngospasm, particularly in
patients in respirators. Application of re-
movable splints may assist in prevention of
stretching or injury to weak or paralyzed muscles.

The prognosis varies for different epidemics and localities. In the individual patient, the degree of functional recovery cannot
be predicted in the acute phase. The early return of a mild or very slight degree of function
in a muscle is a good prognostic sign for that
particular muscle.

Use of vaccine, such as Salk vaccine, is
desirable prophylactically, since the incidence
of paralytic poliomyelitis is much lower in
vaccinated groups. When intramuscular poliomyelitis vaccine (Salk) is used, 2 injections of
1 ml. are given at intervals of one month and
repeated after 7 months and again after one
year. Oral vaccine of the Sabin type is recommended as 3 doses of trivalent vaccine at intervals of 4-6 weeks, followed by one dose a
year later.

RABIES

Rabies is an acute encephalomyelitis with
characteristic neuronal inclusion bodies transmitted by infected saliva of a rabid animal. In
the U.S.A., human rabies usually results from
the bite of an infected dog, although cats, bats,
squirrels, wolves, and other warm-blooded
animals may also carry the virus. The incubation period in man ranges from 10 days to
2 years. Pain appears at the site of the bite
followed by tingling; the skin becomes hypersensitive to temperature change and air currents. Periods of rage may alternate with
calm intervals. Attempts at drinking cause
painful laryngeal spasms, so that the patient
refuses to drink (hydrophobia). The patient
becomes restless, with muscle spasms, laryngospasm, and extreme excitability. Convulsions occur finally, followed by death from
cardiac or respiratory failure or generalized
paralysis in 2-3 days. Once symptoms have
appeared, therapy is of little or no value. After a positive diagnosis of rabies in the biting
animal or after the bite of suspected animal
when the animal cannot be observed, immuni-
zation with rabies vaccine (duck embryo), 1 ml
subcut. daily for 14 days, is recommended.
In facial or severe head bites, rabies hyper-
immune serum may be administered in addition to vaccine.

CHOREA
(Sydenham's Chorea)

Sydenham's chorea occurs in young individuals, and is characterized by involuntary

irregular movements, incoordination of voluntary movement, mild muscle weakness, and, occasionally, mental disturbances. It is generally linked with and regarded as one of the manifestations of rheumatic fever. Other clinical evidences of rheumatic fever are apt to be present.

Clinical Findings.

The child becomes irritable, excitable, restless, and sleepless. Parents and friends describe the patient as being unable to keep still. He may grimace, become clumsy in movement, and stumble frequently. Involuntary irregular and dysrhythmic movements are the outstanding feature of this disease. Movements - especially of the extremities - are abrupt, sudden, short, quick, and jerky. Speech and trunk muscles may also be affected. Voluntary movements of affected parts are modified by the superimposed involuntary movements, which are made worse in attempted movement. Affected limbs are weaker in motor power and are hypotonic.

Diagnosis.

Sydenham's chorea usually runs a limited course with maximum disability 2-3 weeks after onset, then subsides slowly to disappear in 2-3 months. Recurrences occasionally occur. It must be differentiated from tics or habit spasms, which are characterized by stereotyped facial grimacing, blinking, smacking of the lips, and clicking noises without difficulty in articulation. There is no associated muscle weakness or evidence of rheumatic fever. Multiple tics may persist for months undiminished.

Treatment.

Sedation with phenobarbital is usually helpful. Treatment with corticotropin (ACTH), cortisone, or amphetamine has also been reported to be useful.

BACTERIAL NEUROTOXINS

The toxins elaborated by some pathogenic bacteria have an affinity for the nervous system.

Botulism.

The poisoning which may follow ingestion of contaminated food containing the toxin of Clostridium botulinum is characterized by weakness of striated and smooth muscles. Clostridium botulinum, a gram-positive an-

aerobe, has spores which are heat-resistant and which may be introduced by contamination during canning and subsequently flourish, forming gas and giving a rancid taste and odor to food. Twelve to 48 hours after ingestion of contaminated food, symptoms of acute bulbar palsy may occur. Difficulty in convergence, ptosis of eyelids, paralysis of extraocular muscles, dilated pupils, difficulty in swallowing, and dysarthria are characteristic. Weakness of the muscles of the trunk and extremities may follow; the sensorium remains clear until convulsions and coma develop terminally.

Treatment should include early use of intravenous antitoxin (20,000-40,000 units 2-3 times daily). Gastrointestinal lavage, purgation, artificial respiration, and other supportive measures may also be necessary.

Diphtheria.

The earliest neurologic complications of diphtheria may occur in the second or third week after the onset of infection. Paralysis of the palate and laryngopharyngeal muscles and nerves is believed to be due to local action of the toxin, producing characteristic nasal speech, regurgitation of fluid through the nose, and swallowing difficulties. Blurred vision develops due to accommodation paresis. About 2-3 weeks later, manifestations of generalized polyneuritis may occur, including motor weakness, peripheral sensory changes, and tenderness of muscles and nerves to pressure.

Symptomatic treatment and use of rehabilitation measures may be required.

Tetanus.

Tetanus or lockjaw results from infection of wounds with Clostridium tetani, an anaerobic spore-former whose toxin may produce local or generalized muscle spasms. In the localized form, muscular spasms and contractions are limited to an involved extremity. In the generalized form, stiffness of the jaw (trismus) occurs early. Thereafter neck stiffness, irritability and restlessness, rigidity of back muscles, and opisthotonos may occur. Rigidity of facial muscles, recurrent tonic muscle spasms, and generalized convulsions may occur spontaneously or may be elicited by external stimuli. Dysphagia, cyanosis, respiratory distress, and asphyxia may occur. Consciousness is usually preserved except in convulsions.

Prompt and adequate use of tetanus antitoxin, debridement of wounds, general anesthetics and muscle relaxants, and continuous nursing care are essential features of the treatment program.

•   •   •

26...

Trauma to the Central Nervous System

HEAD INJURY

Emergency Evaluation.

Any patient who gives a history of head injury followed by unconsciousness, and any unconscious patient who may have sustained a head injury, should receive careful neurologic evaluation. Particular effort should be made to detect focal or progressive neurologic changes. Skull x-rays should be taken as soon as possible.

The following are the most important features of the examination:

A. State of Consciousness: The depth and duration of unconsciousness usually reflect the degree of trauma. However, an initially alert and well-oriented patient may become drowsy, stuporous, and comatose as a result of progressive intracranial hemorrhage. During the first 24-48 hours it may be necessary to awaken the patient hourly to evaluate his degree of orientation, alertness, and general response to stimulation. **Caution:** Do not discharge the patient to home care unless it is certain that a responsible person will be on hand to awaken him from "sleep" every hour and to summon aid if he cannot be completely aroused.

B. Vital Signs: Temperature, pulse, respirations, and blood pressure should be observed at intervals of one-half to 12 hours, depending upon the extent of injury.

C. Paralysis: In the stuporous or unconscious patient, paralysis can be demonstrated only by careful examination. Loss of strength and motion, although of minimal grade, may indicate intracranial hemorrhage.

D. Ocular Signs: The pupils should be observed regularly along with the vital signs. A fixed dilated pupil often means an ipsilateral epidural or subdural hemorrhage or ipsilateral brain damage. Ophthalmoscopic examination may reveal evidence of papilledema (due to intracranial pressure) or retinal hemorrhage.

E. Convulsions are apt to occur soon after a head injury; focal (jacksonian) convulsions suggest an irritative lesion of the contralateral cerebral hemisphere. Cerebral contusion and laceration, often in association with epidural, subdural, or intracranial hemorrhage causes focal convulsions.

F. Nuchal Rigidity: Although nuchal rigidity may result from the subarachnoid bleeding often associated with head injuries, cervical spine injury must be ruled out by appropriate x-ray and clinical examinations.

G. Bleeding From the Ear: Otorrhagia suggests basilar fracture through the petrous pyramid of the temporal bone, but it may also occur as a result of traumatic rupture of the tympanic membrane or laceration of the mucous membranes without perforation of the drum.

General Considerations.

Craniocerebral injuries are frequently classified on the basis of the nature of the injury to the skull, although the prognosis for recovery depends primarily upon the nature and severity of the damage to the brain.

Closed head injuries are those in which there is no injury to the skull or in which the skull injury is limited to simple undisplaced fracture of the skull. They may be considered clinically as mild, moderate, or severe. Mild head injuries are characterized by brief loss of consciousness (seconds to minutes) without demonstrable neurologic changes (usually the same as cerebral concussion). CSF findings are usually normal. Retrograde amnesia may be present. Moderate head injuries are characterized by longer periods of unconsciousness, frequently with abnormal neurologic signs, and are often associated with cerebral edema and contusion. Severe head injuries cause prolonged unconsciousness and abnormal neurologic signs and are usually associated with cerebral contusion and laceration.

Open head injuries include scalp lacerations, compound fractures of the skull, and various degrees of cerebral destruction. If fragmentation of bone occurs, there will be extensive associated contusion and laceration of the brain. Consciousness may not be impaired at first, although depression of consciousness may occur later if progressive intracranial bleeding or edema occurs. Scalp lacerations should be sutured immediately unless they overlie a depressed fracture or penetrating would of the skull, in which case the skin wound is treated in conjunction with the fracture in the operating room.

Fractures may be simple or compound, and linear (with no displacement of fragments), comminuted, or depressed.

Cerebral edema ("wet brain") following head injury is believed to be due to brain swelling. Clinically, there is considerable variation in the severity of the findings. Focalizing signs such as convulsions, hemiplegia, and aphasia are not uncommon. CSF pressure is usually slightly increased. At operation, the brain looks very pale and swollen.

Contusion or bruising of the brain at or directly contralateral to the zone of impact (contrecoup injury) may be limited to superficial cortex, or associated hemorrhage into the underlying brain may also occur. Contusions frequently occur along the base of the posterior frontal lobes and the adjacent temporal lobe tips. Brain contusion is often clinically indistinguishable from concussion or laceration of the brain.

Brain laceration (a tear in the substance of the brain) usually occurs at the point of application of great force to the head or directly opposite (contrecoup-effect). Lacerations involving the base of the brain usually cause death in a short time. Focal neurologic signs may persist after the acute episode has subsided. Associated subarachnoid or intracerebral hemorrhage is usually present, and the CSF is bloody. Brain laceration (or contusion) may occur with no injury (or minimal injury) to the skull. The frontal and temporal lobes are common sites. Minor injuries may cause tearing of the brain and meninges and extensive hemorrhagic necrosis of the cortex and subcortical white matter. Associated hemorrhage of the basal ganglia and brain stem may also occur. Laceration of arachnoidal vessels may result in subarachnoid bleeding or the formation of subdural hematoma. Tearing of the middle meningeal artery or the dural sinuses or veins may be followed by bleeding into the extradural spaces.

Clinical Findings.

A. Symptoms and Signs: Transient loss of consciousness from seconds to minutes occurs classically with concussion of the brain. In coma which lasts for several hours or days there is a likelihood of edema or of contusion and laceration of the brain. The period of coma depends upon the extent and site of injury; in severe cases it may last for several hours, days, or weeks.

After the patient recovers consciousness, symptoms and signs are related to the severity and nature of associated brain injury. With mild concussion, the patient may be normal within a few minutes; with laceration or contusion of the brain, mental confusion is apt to be present. Hemiplegia, aphasia, cranial nerve paralysis, and other focal neurologic signs may also be noted depending upon the nature and extent of the brain injury. The ipsilateral pupil is often dilated in dural hemorrhage.

In the recovery phase and for months thereafter there may be complaints of headache, dizziness, and personality changes ("post-traumatic cerebral syndrome").

Loss of memory for the period immediately after recovery of consciousness (post-traumatic amnesia) and for the period immediately preceding the injury (pretraumatic or retrograde amnesia) may occur and is often related to the extent of brain damage.

If the patient remains unconscious, diagnosis of a progressive intracranial hemorrhagic lesion is difficult. Vital signs (pulse rate, respirations, blood pressure) may change, although these are not reliable. In case of deepening or unusually prolonged coma, exploratory trephination is indicated; cerebral angiography may show pathognomonic features of subdural, epidural, or intracerebral hemorrhage. Prolonged unconsciousness is believed to indicate severe damage to the brain stem, usually due to secondary hemorrhage or compression of the brain stem.

B. Laboratory Findings:

1. Lumbar puncture is advisable to establish the presence of subarachnoid hemorrhage and to establish a base-line appearance and pressure of the CSF. CSF is frequently normal in all respects in brain concussion or cerebral edema. With contusion or laceration of the brain, bloody CSF under increased pressure may be found.

2. Skull x-rays should be taken as soon as the patient's physical condition permits. Cerebral angiography may help demonstrate subdural or intracerebral hematoma. A pneumogram often is useful in demonstrating ven-

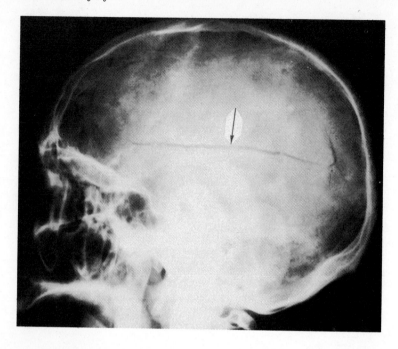

Roentgenogram Showing a
Skull Fracture

tricular distortion, shift, or dilatation following head injury.

3. EEG may be of diagnostic and prognostic aid in selected cases.

Differential Diagnosis.

The history of a blow to the head makes
the etiology of the unconsciousness evident;
however, especially where a history of trauma
is lacking, it is necessary to differentiate head
injury from other causes of unconsciousness
such as diabetic, hepatic, or alcoholic coma,
cerebrovascular accident, and epilepsy (where
trauma to the head may actually occur during
the attack).

Differentiate the neurologic findings following head injury from those caused by epidural hematoma, subdural hematoma, brain
tumor, etc.

Complications and Sequelae.

The complications of head injuries include
vascular lesions (hemorrhage, thrombosis,
aneurysm formation), infections (meningitis,
abscess, osteomyelitis), rhinorrhea and otorrhea, pneumatocele, leptomeningeal cysts,
cranial nerve injuries, and focal brain lesions.
The sequelae include convulsive seizures,
psychoses, mental disturbances, and the post-
traumatic cerebral syndrome.

A. **Subarachnoid Hemorrhage:** Bleeding
into the subarachnoid space is often associated
with other types of brain injury and is relatively common in traumatized patients who
have been unconscious for one hour or more.
The clinical and diagnostic features of traumatic and spontaneous subarachnoid hemorrhage are similar. Painful stiffness of the
neck and the presence of fresh blood in the CSF
are the usual findings.

B. **Subdural Hemorrhage:** Bleeding into
the subdural space, which lies between the
dura mater and the arachnoid, may follow relatively minor head injuries. This space is ordinarily filled with small amounts of lymph-like
material and has little capacity to absorb
blood. Acute subdural hemorrhage of minor
degree may occur in association with other
brain damage or injury and may not require
surgical relief. Chronic subdural hemorrhage
or hematoma usually requires operative relief.
Bleeding usually occurs originally from a subdural vein rupture. Subsequently the hematoma increases in size and may be enveloped
in a capsular mesothelial membrane. Increasing intracranial pressure and personality
changes may appear weeks or months after the
precipitating injury. X-rays frequently show a
pineal shift to the opposite side. Specific
patterns may be seen in angiograms. Evacuation of the hematoma through exploratory
trephine openings may be necessary.

C. **Extradural Hemorrhage:** Extradural
hemorrhage classically follows traumatic
rupture of the middle meningeal artery or vein,

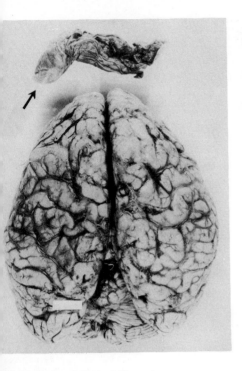

eft Chronic Subdural Hematoma.
Membranes with part of contents
placed in front of brain.

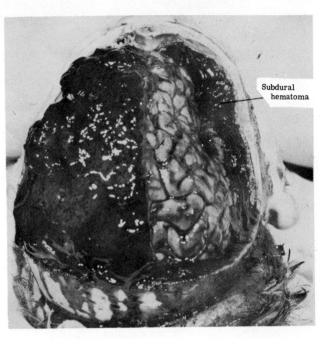

Chronic Right Subdural Hematoma. Part of dura
mater and hematoma has been reflected over
left cerebral hemisphere.

Subdural
hematoma

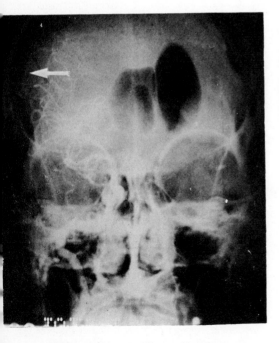

Subdural Hematoma. A combined pneumoencephalogram and arteriogram to
demonstrate a chronic subdural hematoma.

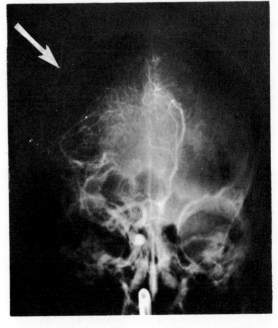

Subdural Hematoma. Carotid angiogram
revealing avascular space occupied by
subdural hematoma.

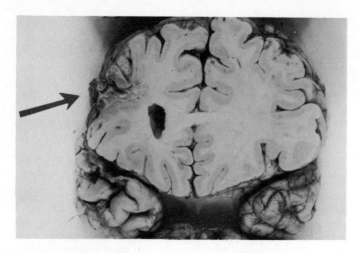

Post-traumatic Epilepsy.
Cerebral scar 15 years
after skull fracture.

and may be difficult to detect early. A transient loss of consciousness and apparent quick return to normal, usually occurs. A "lucid interval," lasting as long as a day or more in extreme cases, customarily follows ; during this time the patient develops signs of increased intracranial pressure. This is caused by the continued steady accumulation of blood in the extradural space from the bleeding middle meningeal vessel.

Trephining of the skull is frequently necessary to make the diagnosis. Blood may then be evacuated through the trephine openings.

A fracture which by x-ray is found to cross the middle meningeal groove should raise the suspicion that this syndrome may be present.

D. Intracerebral Hemorrhage: A large subcortical hematoma may develop, but the most common findings are multiple small intracerebral hemorrhages near the contused area. The angiographic pattern is characteristic.

E. Rhinorrhea and Otorrhea: Rhinorrhea (leakage of CSF from the nose) may follow fracture of the frontal bone with associated tearing of the dura mater and arachnoid. Erect posture, straining, and coughing usually cause an increase in the flow of fluid. Replacement of lost fluid by air entering the cranial vault through the same (or a similar) pathway may give rise to an aerocele. Otorrhea (leakage of CSF from the ear) is usually of serious prognostic importance since it is caused by injuries to the more vital areas of the base of the brain.

Infection and meningitis are potential hazards in both instances and may be prevented by the early use of prophylactic antibiotic ther-

apy. In the case of rhinorrhea, surgical repair of the dural tear may be necessary to stop the flow of CSF and to close off a potential route of infection.

F. Cranial Nerve Paralysis: Injury to the cranial nerves may occur. Commonly affected nerves are the olfactory (anosmia), facial (paralysis), auditory (tinnitus and deafness), and optic (atrophy).

G. Post-traumatic Syndrome: The post-traumatic syndrome is more common after serious head injuries, but severe symptoms may be produced by relatively minor injuries. Headache, giddiness, easy fatigability, memory defects, and impaired ability to concentrate are common complaints. Personality changes are not uncommon. Changes of posture, exposure to sunlight or heat, exercise, and alcohol ingestion are apt to make the symptoms worse.

On pathologic examination the brain may appear normal or may show severe cortical atrophy and ventricular dilatation.

H. Post-traumatic Epilepsy: The exact incidence of seizures following head injuries is not known. In general, the more severe the injury, the greater the possibility of seizures. EEG studies are important in establishing the diagnosis.

I. Other Complications of Head Injuries:
1. Increased intracranial pressure may be manifested by changes in the level of consciousness, headache, restlessness, unequal pupils, a slowly falling respiratory rate, a falling pulse rate, a slowly rising blood pressure, papilledema, hemiparesis, and elevated

CSF pressure. Intracranial bleeding (subdural, epidural, or intracerebral) must be ruled out.

2. Wound infection or osteomyelitis may be prevented by prophylactic antibiotic therapy in patients with compound or depressed fractures of the skull, rhinorrhea, otorrhea, or extensive scalp lacerations, and by meticulous aseptic technic for all dressings.

3. Pulmonary infections or atelectasis may be prevented or treated by the proper use of suction, positioning on the side, or, if necessary, intubation or tracheostomy.

4. Hyperthermia may result from injury of the hypothalamus or brain stem, local or general infection, or marked dehydration.

5. Shock usually occurs in patients with head injuries complicated by other severe injuries to the trunk and extremities, and must be treated at once.

Treatment.

A. Emergency Measures:

1. Treat shock if present; parenterally administered fluids and blood may be required.

2. Maintenance of an adequate airway and pulmonary ventilation is vital. The patient should be placed prone, with head turned to one side to facilitate drainage of secretions from mouth and to keep the tongue from obstructing the pharynx. Intratracheal intubation or tracheostomy may be necessary to maintain an open airway. Give oxygen if necessary.

B. General Measures:

1. During the acute or initial phases, restlessness may be a disturbing factor. Special nursing care and paraldehyde may be required. Avoid morphine because of its medullary depressant effects. Catheterization of a full bladder may ameliorate restlessness. Lumbar puncture and removal of a small amount of bloody CSF may also relieve an agitated patient.

2. Antibiotic treatment is always indicated if there is active bleeding or discharge from the nose or ears. Give procaine penicillin G, 600,000 units b.i.d., or broad-spectrum antibiotics, until the danger of infection is past.

3. Continued careful observation is essential.

Course and Prognosis.

Prognosis and course are related to the severity and site of cranial injury. With simple concussion recovery is usually rapid. With laceration of the brain, mortality may be 40-50%.

Subdural or epidural hematoma ordinarily requires prompt surgical evacuation in order to prevent death or serious neurologic complications.

In general, residual symptoms and signs in patients with head trauma are likely to be more extensive and incapacitating in those with the more severe types of brain injury. It is not uncommon, however, for patients to remain symptomatic (headache, dizziness, impaired memory, personality changes) even though neurologic diagnostic studies are negative.

Predictions regarding the clinical outcome are more accurate when made 6-12 months after the injury or when the clinical status of the patient has stabilized. Great variations occur in individual cases. A patient in whom subdural hematoma has been successfully removed may recovery completely. On the other hand, many patients continue to have severe complaints after an apparently trivial head injury. A complicating factor in many cases is the role played by the "secondary gain" for the patient via lawsuits, insurance, and other types of compensation.

BIRTH INJURIES

Normal or prolonged labor may cause a variety of brain injuries. Subdural hemor-

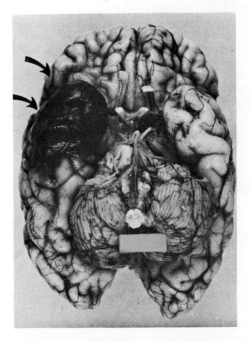

Birth Injury. Hematoma of right anterior temporal lobe associated clinically with status epilepticus in a newborn infant.

rhage and tears of the dural membrane are relatively common. Following manipulation, depressed skull fracture with damage of underlying cerebral tissue may occur. Children who die within the first few months of life sometimes are found to have cortical lacerations and intracerebral bleeding.

Bloody CSF is often found in normal newborn infants. This is thought to be due to mild subarachnoid hemorrhage caused by rupture of superficial brain veins.

Massive focal subarachnoid hemorrhage associated with hemorrhagic lesions in the brain parenchyma, intraventricular hemorrhages, hemorrhagic infarction, and direct traumatic bruising of the brain with local hemorrhagic diathesis have been noted in infants who died from acute birth injury. Minor extravasations of blood in the subarachnoid space and isolated petechial hemorrhages in the brain were also seen. A possible asphyxial basis for hemorrhagic lesions has been suggested under certain circumstances.

SPINAL CORD INJURIES

In general, the sequelae of spinal cord injuries are more dangerous and disabling than those of head injuries.

Concussion of the Spinal Cord.

Concussion of the spinal cord is a rare disorder which is believed to be analogous to concussion of the brain. Loss of function in the spinal cord causes motor paralysis, loss of sensation, and sphincter paralysis with subsequent return of function. The signs are believed to be due to reversible alterations of the neural tissue of the spinal cord. Edema and petechial hemorrhage with altered spinal cord circulation may occur. Assessment of ultimate disability requires an adequate post-traumatic observation period.

Contusion of the Spinal Cord.

Contusion of the spinal cord may occur following fractures and dislocations of the vertebral column. Edema and mild evidence of bleeding of the pia and arachnoid may be found on pathologic examination. Severe symptoms of loss of function of the cord are present early,

but the final degree of improvement can only be assessed after prolonged observation. In the acute stage, contusion of the spinal cord is associated with bloody CSF. **Jolly's sign** or position indicates a unilateral lesion of the seventh cervical root segment. The patient holds his forearm in flexion with the shoulder abducted. When bilateral, the sign is called Bradburne's or Thorburn's sign.

Compression of the Spinal Cord.

Fracture dislocations of the vertebral column are particularly apt to cause transverse compression, which may be complete when any severe degree of bony injury has occurred. The CSF is bloody in the acute phase. It later becomes xanthochromic and may thereafter have an increased amount of protein. Partial or complete block of the subarachnoid channels may occur. Permanent severe residua are common, and significant improvement is rare. Loss of function below the level of the lesion may be complete. Severe and irreversible parenchymal damage with replacement of functioning neural elements by glial and fibrotic scars and formation of meningeal adhesions is the usual result.

Urinary tract infection is a common complication and may be fatal. Prevention of urologic infections and decubitus ulcers is an important aspect of the total care of the patient.

Treatment in the acute stage usually consists of correction of the dislocation with laminectomy and removal of compressing bone fragments. Orthopedic devices and braces should be used as soon as possible to encourage locomotion with the aid of crutches.

HERNIATION OF INTERVERTEBRAL DISK

In most cases rupture or herniation of an intervertebral disk is caused by trauma. Sudden straining with the back in an "odd" position and lifting in the trunk-flexed posture are commonly recognized precipitating causes. The defect may occur immediately after an injury or following an interval of months to years.

The lumbosacral intervertebral disks (L5-S1 or L4-5) are most commonly affected, producing the clinical picture of sciatica. Herniation occasionally occurs in the cervical region (characterized by cervical radicular complaints); rarely in the thoracic region.

Clinical Findings.

A. Symptoms and Signs: These usually depend upon the location and size of the herniated or extruded disk material. Compression of a nerve root by a disk may be confined to a single nerve root; however, several roots may be compressed (e.g., cauda equina by disk at L5-S1). Larger lesions may even compress the spinal cord and produce symptoms commonly associated with tumors.

1. Lumbosacral disk - In the great majority (over 90%), rupture of the disk occurs at the level of the fourth or fifth lumbar interspace. This is characterized by straightening of the normal lumbar curve, scoliosis toward the side opposite the sciatic pain, limitation of motion of the lumbar spine, impaired straight-leg raising on the painful side, tenderness to palpation in the sciatic notch and along the course of the sciatic nerve, mild weakness of the foot or great toe extensors, impaired perception of pain and touch over the dorsum of the foot and leg (in L5 or S1 distribution), decreased or absent ankle jerk, and radiation of pain along the course of the sciatic nerve to the calf or ankle on coughing, sneezing, or straining.

2. Cervical disk herniation (5-10% of herniated disks) - The cervical disks most commonly involved are between C5-C6 and C6-C7. Paresthesias and pain occur in the upper extremities (hands, forearms, and arms) in the affected cervical root distribution (C6 or C7). Slight weakness and atrophy of the biceps or triceps may be present, with diminution of biceps or triceps jerk. The mobility of the neck is restricted with accentuation of radicular and neck pains by neck motion, coughing, sneezing, or straining. Long tract signs (extensor plantar response, sensory or motor impairment of lower levels, etc.) occasionally occur, indicating compression of the spinal cord by the disk.

B. Laboratory Findings: CSF protein may be elevated, and complete or partial CSF block is occasionally demonstrated.

C. X-ray Findings: Spine x-rays may show loss of normal curvature, scoliosis, and narrowing of the intervertebral disk. A characteristic roentgenologic defect in the subarachnoid space is usually produced by a herniated disk and is readily demonstrable by myelography. Electromyography (EMG) may be of value in localizing the site of a ruptured disk if characteristic denervation potentials can be demonstrated in muscles of a particular root distribution.

Differential Diagnosis.

In tumors of the spinal cord the course is progressive, CSF proteins are elevated, par-

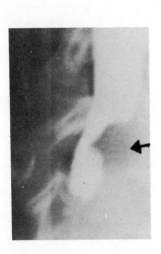

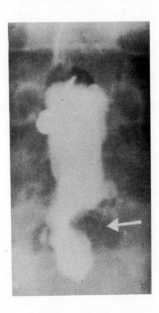

Iophendylate (Pantopaque®) Myelogram Showing the Defect Caused by Herniation of a Lumbosacral Intervertebral Disk. (Left, lateral view. Right, posteroanterior view.)

tial or complete spinal subarachnoid block is present, and the myelographic pattern is distinctive.

In arthritis neurologic findings are usually minimal or absent, and the myelogram is usually negative.

Spinal column anomalies show characteristic x-ray findings, CSF findings are negative, and myelographic changes are dissimilar or absent.

Treatment.

A. General Measures:

1. Lumbosacral disk - In the acute phase, bed rest, heat applied locally to the back, salicylate analgesics, and the use of a bed board under the mattress are indicated. Traction to the lower extremities is frequently beneficial. The avoidance of severe physical effort and strain is essential to minimize recurrence of symptoms after the initial episode. Low back belts, braces, or supports may be beneficial. It is important to instruct the patient in the proper methods of bending, lifting (with knees flexed), and carrying (with the object held close to the body).

2. Cervical disk - In acute exacerbations of herniated cervical disks, bed rest with cervical halter traction is indicated. In subacute or mild episodes, intermittent cervical halter traction with various devices may be employed on an outpatient basis or at home. The use of a light collar may be helpful. Local application of heat, diathermy, and similar measures may be of temporary value.

B. Surgical Measures: If the response to conservative measures is poor or recurrences are disabling, diskectomy is indicated.

Prognosis.

Conservative management with or without traction may bring about improvement to the point of "practical" recovery. Relief of pain usually follows removal of the damaged disk. Reversal of motor dysfunction, muscle atrophy, and skin sensory changes may occur.

LOW BACK PAIN

Low back pain may be associated with a variety of causes, and careful examination of such a patient may yield important clues regarding the site and etiology of the disorders. Such a patient may be subjected to a larger number of laboratory, x-ray, and diagnostic procedures with ambiguous or disappointing results. This may in turn often reflect the inadequate clinical evaluation of the patient, and commonly results from failure to utilize the information which a properly conducted physical and neurologic examination may supply. The increasing over-dependence of the clinician upon the laboratory is unnecessarily exaggerated when the physician fails to obtain vital information available at the bedside examination.

Inspection and palpation of the painful area is important. Since pain from nerve roots or nerves is commonly referred toward the periphery, the entire nerve lengths leading from the area should be explored, noting the presence of any masses or tenderness and, where possible, the size and consistency of nerves.

Rectal and vaginal examination should be included so that local lesions and involvement of accessible lumbodorsal plexuses can be ruled out if possible.

Muscle spasm and tenderness to percussion and deep pressure may give evidence suggesting radicular irritation, particularly when associated with local deformity or restriction of spinal motion.

The range of motion of joints and the effect of movement on the pain should be determined, since pain from areas such as the hip may be referred distally and severe distal peripheral pain may be referred to the entire limb.

The regional blood vessels and those of the extremity should be checked for adequacy of pulsation and aneurysmal dilatation.

The straight leg raising test (**Lasegue's** sign) should be elicited. The relaxed, extended lower extremity is gently lifted from the bed or table with the patient supine. The presence and amount of pain and the extent to which the straight leg may be raised are noted. Pain and limitation of motion often accompany radiculopathy, especially that which occurs with herniated lumbar or lumbosacral disks.

The "f-ab-er-e" sign (**Patrick's sign**) is tested for. The patient lies supine, and the heel of the lower extremity being tested is passively placed on the opposite knee. Then the knee on the side being tested is pressed laterally and downward by the examiner as far as it will go. The test is considered positive if motion is involuntarily restricted and pain frequently accompanies this limitation of motion. The test is positive in hip joint disease and negative in sciatica. "F-ab-er-e" is a mnemonic formula: "f" for flexion, "ab" for abduction, "er" for external rotation and "e" for extension motions of the hip.

Kernig's sign is elicited with the patient supine. The examiner flexes the hip and then extends the knee as far as possible without producing significant pain. A positive Kernig test consists of an involuntary spasm of the hamstring muscles which limits extension of the knee and often causes pain. Its clinical significance is similar to that of a positive straight leg raising test.

Lumbar paraspinal muscle spasm frequently is noted with local radiculitis, which is due to many causes including herniated lumbar intervertebral disk.

Passive flexion of the neck so that the chin rests on the chest may induce ascension of the spinal cord within the spinal canal. This then puts tension on the various spinal roots, causing excessive pain and indicating disease of particular nerve roots - provided motion of the spinal column was not induced and the patient was relaxed.

With the patient standing with his back toward the examiner, the presence of lordosis, scoliosis, or list affecting the lumbar region is noted. The effect of flexion, hyperextension, and lateral flexion of the trunk on the pelvis is observed.

Psoas muscle spasm usually indicates disease of the psoas muscle or of the lumbar vertebrae and soft tissue adjacent to this muscle. It may be tested with the patient prone and the pelvis firmly pressed against the table with one hand by the examiner. With the other hand grasping the ankle, the leg is moved to the vertical position with the knee flexed at a right angle. The hip is passively hyperextended by lifting up on the ankle. Limitation of motion is produced by involuntary psoas muscle spasm.

Limitation of passive lumbar flexion and resulting pain often accompany disease of the lumbar or lumbosacral articulations. With the patient supine, the examiner grasps one lower extremity with both hands and moves the thigh to a position of maximal flexion. Then he presses firmly downward toward the table and upward toward the patient's head, passively flexing the lumbar spinal column.

CERVICAL SPONDYLOSIS

Radicular symptoms and myelopathy may result from cervical spondylosis. Symptoms develop because of direct cord and root compression and angulation by ridges on the posterior margins of the vertebral bodies, ischemia due to compression of the anterior spinal artery and veins, vascular and soft tissue changes, and trauma - although the initiating vertebral disturbance may be unknown. Spondylosis usually affects several levels, being confined to a single level in only one-fifth of cases.

The onset is variable. A high proportion of cases occur in males who report a long duration of symptoms, and the average age at onset is in the mid-fifties. Paresis, dysesthesia, and numbness of the upper extremities as well as fasciculations, atrophy, and weakness of the affected upper limbs may occur. Hyperreflexia in the lower limbs, extensor plantar responses, and gait disturbances may also be noted in severe cases.

Loss of cervical lordotic curvature, subluxation, narrowing of intervertebral spaces, and osteophytosis may be detected in lateral cervical spine x-rays. Myelographic examination frequently demonstrates anterior indentation of the spinal cord, although complete block is infrequent.

Conservative measures include heat, massage, cervical traction, and a Minerva jacket or immobilization in a cervical collar for several months. If the response to conservative measures is poor or if there is rapid progression of neurologic signs, wide laminectomy of the affected cervical spine and section of the dentate ligaments may prove beneficial.

SHOULDER-HAND SYNDROME

This syndrome may result from reflex mechanisms in which shoulder pain is associated with swelling of the hand and wrist. The shoulder pain may be secondary to local trauma or may be referred from myocardial infarction, osteoarthritis of the cervical spine, cervical radiculitis, etc. In some cases, no obvious cause can be established. The vasomotor disturbance and swelling in the hand may suggest scleroderma. The shoulder difficulty may be confused with bursitis, arthritis, and gout. Treatment of underlying disease, analgesics, and physical therapy are usually necessary. Stellate ganglion block and systemic corticosteroids may be required.

ACUTE SPRAIN OF CERVICAL SPINE
(Whiplash Injury)

Whiplash refers to an injury in which the spine is suddenly and unexpectedly violently forced in one direction and then with a returning force and motion in the opposite direction. It is often associated with rear-end automobile collisions. It may be manifested by rapid onset of neck pain and headache, stiff neck with increased pain on motion, nervousness, and apprehension. The pain may be intensified by motion and improved by rest. Nausea, vomiting, and radiating pains and numbness in the upper extremities may occur. In severe cases, headaches may persist for several weeks and neck stiffness for several months. Loss of normal neck motion is often striking. Forward flexion of the neck is attempted slowly and cautiously.

Muscle spasm of the neck muscles may be evident on palpation. X-rays of the cervical spine often show straightening or reversal of normal cervical spine curvature. Treatment may require analgesics, sedatives, tranquilizers, rest, heat, and massage. Cervical traction may be useful and necessary, particularly in the early phases. Neck support with a cervical collar, cast, etc. may be required.

•　　•　　•

27 . . .

Tumors of the Central Nervous System

INTRACRANIAL TUMORS

Primary tumors generally do not resemble the carcinomas and sarcomas that are found outside the CNS and rarely metastasize outside of the CNS. The CNS is fertile soil for the growth of metastatic carcinomas and sarcomas from extraneural foci. Experimentally, certain carcinogenic agents may induce gliomas of the brain in some strains of mice.

If one includes all tumors (both primary and metastatic) of the brain, skull, and scalp in the term intracranial tumors, a convenient classification may be made, as follows: congenital, mesodermal, ectodermal, metastatic, and miscellaneous.

Pathology.

A. Congenital: **Dermoids** are frequently cystic and may contain sebaceous caseous material, hair, etc. The tumor cavity is usually lined with squamous epithelium. **Teratomas** are developmental tumors which usually contain a greater variety of structures such as bone, muscle, fat, and nerve tissue, and are calcified so that they are readily seen in x-ray. They tend to lie in the midline. **Epidermoids**, also known as cholesteatomas or pearly tumors, occur in the bones of the skull, and are made up of masses of crystalline cholesterine enclosed within a capsule of stratified squamous epithelium. **Chordomas** are soft tumors containing much mucoid intercellular material and cords of highly vacuolated large cells. They arise from remnants of the primitive notochord. **Craniopharyngiomas** occur mainly in children and arise from the pars tuberalis of the hypophysis. They are usually cystic, and calcifications above the sella turcica may be seen on x-ray. The tumor mass and cyst frequently become quite large and slowly compress the adjacent tissue. It contains cells arranged in stratified squamous epithelial layers or in a syncytial mass.

B. Mesodermal: Many types of **meningiomas** are recognized. Characteristically the tumor is encapsulated and easily separated from nervous tissue. Calcified psammoma bodies and whorl-like collections of cells are commonly found. Mitoses are rare. The nuclei tend to be ovoid and vesicular. **Neurinomas** are thought to arise from neurilemma sheath cells of the vestibular portion of the eighth cranial nerve, within the auditory meatus, where they grow and expand to fill the cerebellopontine angle. They are apt to be yellowish, soft, and cystic, and are composed of elongated, spindle-shaped cells with ovoid nuclei which seem to run in parallel streams with the nuclei showing a tendency to lie side by side in "palisade" formation. Mitoses are uncommon.

Tumors growing from nerves are of 2 types: **True neuromas** (rare) arise from actual nerve tissue, usually in connection with the sympathetic system. They are distributed beneath the skin, and are often multiple. **False neuromas** arise from the connective tissue of the nerve trunk, usually on the spinal nerves and often in large numbers. They usually appear in the first half of life, and are often hereditary. Various types include plexiform neuromas, pachydermatocele, and multiple neurofibromatosis (Von Recklinghausen's disease). A common symptom of nerve tumors is pain, usually intermittent and radiating to the periphery of the nerve. Paresthesias may occur. Treatment is by excision. In nerves which may be examined directly by inspection and palpation, abnormal masses may be seen or felt, and there may be tenderness to palpation or percussion.

Vascular tumors may occur as angiomas or hemangioblastomas. **Angiomas** are usually associated with vascular malformation elsewhere in the body and are regarded as malformations by some writers. A bruit is sometimes audible, especially if the angioma lies between relatively large arterial and venous elements. **Hemangioblastomas**, usually cystic, are apt to occur in the cerebellar hemispheres and are sometimes present in association with angiomas of the retina and other organs.

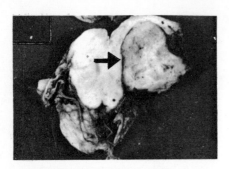

**Compression of the Brain Stem
by Acoustic Neurinoma**

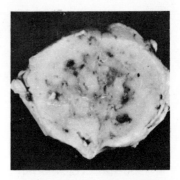

**Glioblastoma Multiforme
of Brain Stem**

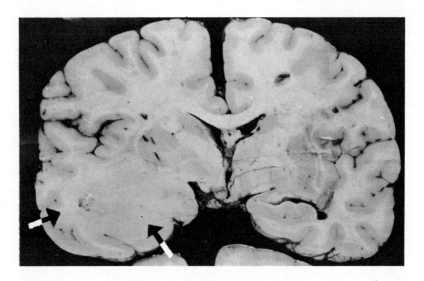

Astrocytoma of Left Temporal Lobe

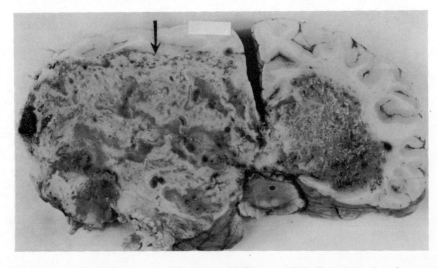

**Glioblastoma Multiforme in a 65-year-old Woman With Extensive Involvement
of Both Cerebral Hemispheres and Corpus Callosum**

The tumor usually is a relatively small nodule in the wall of the cyst cavity and is composed of many capillaries and extremely vacuolated cellular tissue arranged in small groups or cords. Reticulin stains reveal many reticulin fibers about the capillaries.

C. Ectodermal:

1. Gliomas - Glioblastoma multiforme is an infiltrative, rapidly growing cerebral tumor which occurs most frequently in middle-aged persons and is apt to invade both cerebral hemispheres via the corpus callosum. It is a multicolored tumor with grossly visible hemorrhagic, yellow, and brown areas. Microscopically, the tumor is quite cellular, with many mitoses, giant cells, and young glial forms (spongioblasts). Areas of necrosis are characteristic, with pseudopalisading of cells about the necrotic foci. The blood vessels within the tumor show severe proliferation of the intima and hyaline degeneration. The average survival period is about one year.

Medulloblastoma is a rapidly growing tumor of the vermis of the cerebellum occurring usually in children. It characteristically metastasizes to the surfaces of the remaining CNS via the subarachnoid spaces. It is grossly red and soft and is composed of many closely packed cells, with oval nuclei and many mitoses.

Pseudorosette formations in which nuclei of the cells tend to group themselves in circles or semicircles are common. The average survival period with x-ray treatment is 15 months.

Astrocytoma usually occurs in the cerebrum of adults and the cerebellum of children, although it may occur in the cerebellum of adults. It grows slowly, and usually becomes cystic. It is composed of astrocytes with densely staining nuclei and scanty cytoplasm and is usually relatively acellular. Fibrillary and protoplasmic astrocytomas may be distinguished by the presence of fibrillary or protoplasmic astrocytes. The survival period averages about 6 years.

Oligodendrogliomas are slowly growing, solid, calcified tumors usually found in the cerebral hemispheres of adults. They are grossly firm and red, with areas of calcification, and are composed of cells with deeply staining nuclei within polyhedral spaces where the cytoplasm is hardly discernible. Mitoses are uncommon. The average survival period is about 5 years.

Astroblastoma is a relatively rare glioma which occurs in the cerebral hemispheres of middle-aged adults. It looks grossly and behaves clinically like glioblastoma multiforme. It contains astroblasts which arrange them-

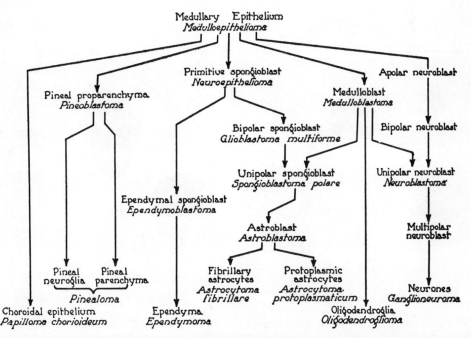

Scheme to Relate Types of Gliomas According to the Predominant Cellular Constitution of Each Group. (Reproduced, with permission, from Bailey: Intracranial Tumors, 2nd Ed. Thomas, 1948.)

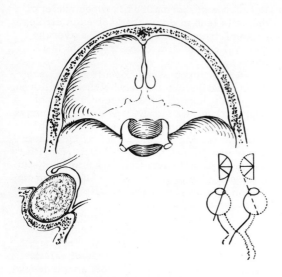

**Pituitary Adenoma
(Chromophobe Type)**

Failing vision, primary optic atrophy, and bitemporal hemianopsia; endocrine disturbances and enlargement of sella turcica.

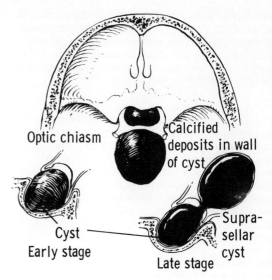

Craniopharyngioma

Early Stage: Failing vision, primary optic atrophy, bitemporal field defects, endocrine disturbances (hypopituitarism), suprasellar calcification (80%) in children and adolescents. **Late Stage:** Headache, nausea and vomiting, papilledema.

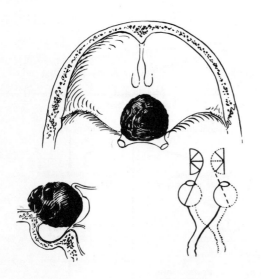

Meningioma of Tuberculum Sellae

Failing vision, primary optic atrophy and bitemporal hemianopsia, BUT no endocrine disturbance and no enlargement of the sella turcica in middle-aged persons.

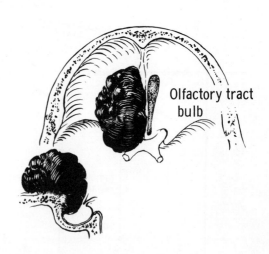

Olfactory Groove Meningioma

Ipsilateral anosmia and primary optic atrophy; contralateral papilledema (optic nerve

(Reproduced, with permission, from Scarff: Classic Syndromes of Brain Tumor:

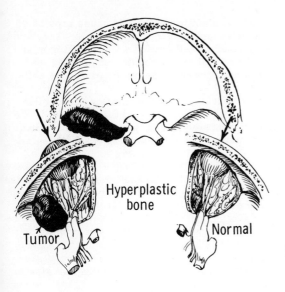

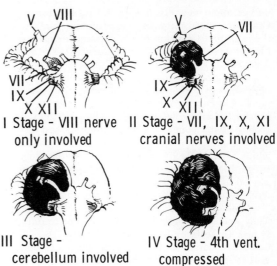

Retro-orbital Meningioma

Early Stage: Unilateral exophthalmos, slowly progressing (months-years). Increased density (in x-rays): retro-orbital plate, ipsilateral side.

Acoustic Neurinoma

First Stage: Tinnitus; later, deafness and disturbances of equilibrium.
Second Stage: Weakness of facial muscles, pain in face, dysphasia and dysarthria.
Third Stage: Ataxia and incoordination.
Fourth Stage: Ventricles compressed. Evidence of increased intracranial pressure.

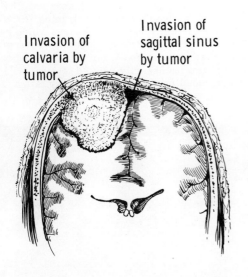

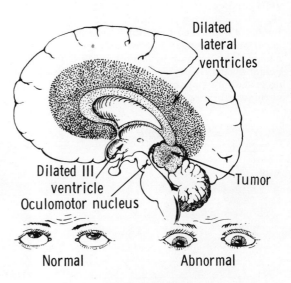

Parasagittal Meningioma

Disturbances of cerebral function, depending on localization. Focal hyperplasia and hypervascularization of the overlying bones.

Pinealoma

Symptoms and signs of increased intracranial pressure, without lateralizing signs. Limitation of upward gaze. Abnormal pupillary reactions.

Annual Clinical Conference of the Chicago Medical Society, 1953.)

selves about vessels in a radiating fashion. Giant cells and mitoses are common, and there is proliferation of the intima of smaller blood vessels. The average survival period is 3 years.

Spongioblastomas occur predominantly near the optic chiasm of children and in the pons, where they are apt to cause uniform enlargement and give the appearance of "hypertrophy of the pons." They are composed of spindle-shaped cells of the spongioblast series, which tend to lie in parallel rows and have large thick processes. The average survival period of patients with spongioblastomas occurring in the brain stem is about one year.

Ependymomas occur chiefly in children. They are slowly growing, and are apt to calcify and arise in or near ventricular walls. They are more common in the fourth ventricle than elsewhere, and are composed of adult ependymal cells or younger ependymoblasts. Pseudo-rosette formation, in which the cells are arranged about a clear space or a blood vessel, is common, and blepharoplasts (small round or rod shaped intracytoplasmic bodies) may be demonstrated. The survival period is short due to the usual location in fourth ventricle.

2. Pituitary tumors - Chromophobe tumors are relatively common in the anterior pituitary glands of adults. They usually cause erosion and expansion of the sella turcica and give the appearance on x-ray of "ballooning" of the sella turcica. Compression of the adjacent optic chiasm and hypothalamus is common. The tumor is composed of uniform appearing polygonal cells arranged in rows along strands of connective tissue or in alveoli. The cytoplasm stains lightly eosinophilic, but contains no granules comparable to those seen in chromophil cells. Chromophil tumors are

much less apt to expand and cause erosion of the sella turcica and "ballooning." They are composed of cells which are less uniform and not arranged in any regular or specific manner, and give the appearance of a loose cell mass. The cytoplasm contains acidophilic or alpha granules, and there is less connective tissue and vascularization than is found in the chromophobe type. It is highly doubtful that beta cells or cells containing basophilic granules form pituitary tumors.

D. Metastatic: These tumors usually arise from carcinomas, more rarely sarcomas, and only occasionally from melanoblastomas, hypernephromas, and retinal tumors. The most common source of metastatic tumor to the brain is bronchogenic carcinoma. Carcinomas of the breast, thyroid gland, and gastrointestinal tract also frequently give rise to brain metastases.

E. Miscellaneous: Aneurysms, tuberculomas, syphilomas, gummas, and parasitic formations are among those included.

Clinical Findings.

A. Generalized Symptoms: The presence of a tumor may give rise to early effects mechanically, either through displacement of brain tissue or by causing a mild block in CSF circulation. Headache is commonly present and is intensified or precipitated by any activity which tends to raise the intracranial CSF pressure, such as stooping, straining, or exercising. Conversely, measures which reduce intracranial CSF pressure may relieve headache. Nausea and vomiting are common and are not necessarily related to meals. Mental clouding, lethargy, and easy fatiga-

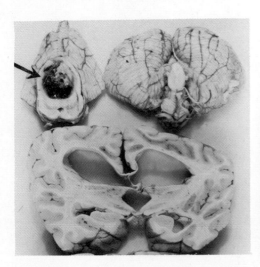

Ependymoma Causing Occlusion of Aqueduct of Sylvius and Obstructive Hydrocephalus

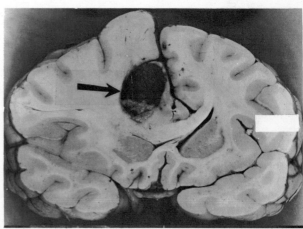

Metastatic Carcinoma of Right Frontal Parasagittal Region in a 40-year-old Woman

bility are not unusual. As the intracranial
CSF pressure increases, papilledema occurs.

B. Focal Signs and Symptoms: As a tumor
grows, progressively greater destruction or
dysfunction of tissue may occur, causing
locally referable signs. In this way involvement of the cerebrum, brain stem, cranial
nerves, etc., may soon be evident through the
loss of alteration of function of these parts.
Tumors involving the frontal lobe tend to produce a disturbed mental state with defective
memory, impaired judgment, irritability,
mood changes, and facetiousness. Convulsive
seizures may occur as well as loss of speech
in left-sided (dominant hemisphere) tumor.
Anosmia may occur with tumors at the base of
the frontal lobe.

Sensory and motor abnormalities are common in parietal lobe tumors. Motor or sensory
focal seizures, contralateral hemiparesis,
hyperreflexia, impaired sensory perception,
astereognosis, and a positive extensor plantar
responses may be present. Aphasic and ag-
nosic components may be demonstrable when
the dominant side is involved.

Visual alterations and seizures preceded
by an aura of lights and visual hallucinations
are characteristic. Contralateral homonymous
hemianopsia, frequently with sparing of the
macular area, occurs. Agnosia may be noted.

Psychomotor seizures and automatisms
occur with temporal lobe tumors. If the dominant side is involved, sensory aphasia may be
pronounced. A contralateral homonymous
field defect may occur.

Cerebellar tumors are characterized by
disturbances of equilibrium and coordination
and the early development of increased intracranial pressure and papilledema.

RIGHT

LEFT

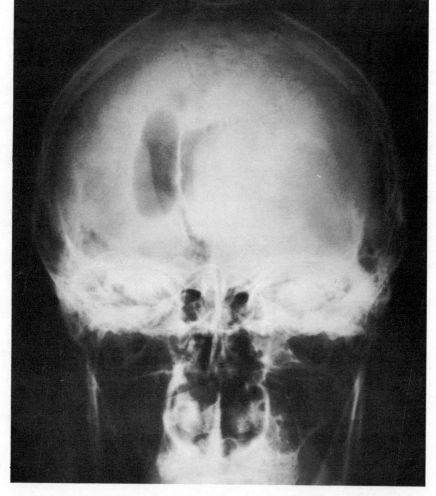

**Ventriculogram of a Left Parieto-temporal Tumor Showing Shift of the
Lateral and Third Ventricles to the Right**

Diagnosis.

A. X-rays: X-ray of the skull may show the shift of a calcified pineal gland, local erosions or hypercalcifications, and ballooning of the sella turcica. Digital markings on the inner table of the skull may be apparent following prolonged (at least 6 months) increase of CSF pressure. In children, abnormal separation of the sutures is apt to occur. **Lumbar puncture** usually shows increased CSF pressure (over 200 mm. water), and the total protein content is apt to be increased. **Visual field examinations** may disclose classic defects caused by involvement of the optic nerve, optic tract, or radiations. (See p. 83.) **Air ventriculography** (introduction of air directly into the ventricles) may indicate obstruction, deformity, dilatation, shift, and other changes of the ventricular system produced by an intracranial neoplasm. **Air encephalography** (introduction of air via the lumbar subarachnoid spaces) is usually contraindicated when there is a strong suspicion of intracranial neoplasm. **Electroencephalography** often shows focal abnormalities (especially a delta focus) in association with cerebral neoplasm. **Arteriography,** the injection of diatrizoate (Hypaque®) or iodopyracet (Diodrast®) into the internal carotid or vertebral artery, may show displacement or obliteration of major vessels or may outline the presence of a neoplasm. In serial angiography glioblastomas appear in the arterial and capillary phase; astrocytomas and oligodendrogliomas are more apt to appear in the venous phase. Meningiomas appear in the arterial phases and reach greatest contrast at the end of the venous phase. **Radioactive isotope studies,** e.g., with iodinated serum albumin, Hg^{203} labelled chlormerodrin, etc., have been used to lateralize intracranial masses on the theory that cellular tumors, metastatic carcinomas, sarcomas, and recurrent tumors give high local concentrations and uptake which can be detected with the aid of radiation localizers.

Ultrasonic encephalography, in which ultrasonic signals are sent into the brain, may be helpful as a simple screening test to detect shift of midline structures. The ultrasonic transducer is placed against the patient's moistened temple, and waves that are reflected back are transmitted to an oscilloscope. Three equidistant spikes, representing the 2 sides of the skull and the center of the brain, are usually noted. A shift of the middle spike may result from a shift of the cerebral hemisphere, as with tumor, intracerebral or subdural hematoma, etc.

B. Histopathologic Methods:

1. Frozen section preparations are often used for the rapid survey of pathologic material removed at the time of operation or at postmorten examination. Using suitable methods, cells and nuclei, metachromatic substances, axis cylinders and myelin sheaths, glial fibers, microglia, oligodendroglia, and fat may be identified. Tissue fixed in formalin ammonium bromide shows astrocytes very well with the Cajal gold sublimate method, and microglia can be demonstrated in similarly fixed tissue by Hortega's method. Oligodendroglia can frequently be shown by the methods of Hortega or Penfield.

2. Paraffin sections - These orinarily are employed for routine work in most laboratories and are quite suitable for making thin sections, for rapid surveys of blocks of tissue, and for handling soft or disintegrating specimens. Basic methods include (1) survey stains such as hematoxylin and eosin, cresyl violet, Van Gieson, Masson trichome, and Mallory's phosphotungstic acid—hematoxylin; (2) glial methods (Holzer, Mallory); (3) myelin sheath stains (Weil, Heidenhain); (4) axons (Bodian); and (5) connective tissue (Perdrau, Foot, Masson, Van Gieson).

3. Celloidin sections - These are useful for preparation of large blocks of tissue and for serial and interval sections. The natural structure of tissue is best preserved with this method, and various stains can be readily applied to successive sections of tissue. Contrasts in such slides facilitate study; for example, on celloidin-prepared tissue successive sections can be stained by the Nissl method for nerve cells, the Weil method for myelin sheaths, the Holzer method for glia, and the Van Gieson method for connective tissue.

Treatment and Prognosis.

Cure may be achieved in some tumors, e.g., meningiomas, neurinomas, dermoids, and astrocytomas, by early diagnosis and operative removal of the neoplasm. On the other hand, a deep-seated tumor such as glioblastoma multiforme, medulloblastoma, or ependymoma may be entirely unaffected and even unfavorably influenced by operation.

Prognosis varies with the type and location of the tumor. A favorable response to intensive x-ray therapy may occur with a variety of tumors, and in some cases (e.g., pituitary tumors) a cure may be achieved. Reduction of increased intracranial pressure for periods of 3-10 hours may be obtained by intravenous administration of urea (30% solution in 10% invert sugar).

The use of newer experimental methods such as proton beam radiation of tumors, boron[10] slow neutron captive therapy, antimetabolites, etc., have shown promising results in the hands of various investigators and experts; however, these methods are as yet not available or applicable for use on most patients.

PSEUDOTUMOR CEREBRI
(Benign Intracranial Hypertension)

Pseudotumor cerebri is a syndrome characterized by increased intracranial pressure, usually in the absence of other neurologic manifestations other than headache or papilledema. Pneumoencephalograms and CSF protein and cell count are normal. In some cases this syndrome follows ear infections and/or may be associated with thrombi in the superior longitudinal or lateral sinus. Prognosis is usually good, although complete recovery may be delayed for months or years.

TUMORS WITHIN THE SPINAL CANAL

The onset of individual tumors has sometimes been related to traumatic episodes. In general, however, there is no known relationship between the presence of primary tumors and any specific factor.

On the basis of the location within the spinal canal, neoplasms are classified as extradural (outside of the dura mater) or intradural (within the dura mater). Intradural neoplasms are either extramedullary (outside of the spinal cord) or intramedullary (within the spinal cord).

Pathology.
There is a distinct relationship between the pathologic nature of a neoplasm and its location within the spinal canal.

A. Extradural: Sarcomas and carcinomas, invasive from adjacent vertebrae or metastatic from a distant source, are commonly found. Hodgkin's disease is also common. Lipomas, fibromas, neurinomas, chondromas, and angiomas also occur.

B. Intradural:
1. Extramedullary tumors - These are relatively benign in that they usually have their origin from the pia-arachnoid and the sheaths of roots of spinal nerves. **Neurinomas** are especially common in the thoracocervical area and may occur as part of a generalized neurofibromatosis. They are encapsulated and well circumscribed and arise from the sheath of a spinal nerve. Microscopically they resemble intracranial neurinomas. **Meningiomas** may occur in many forms. They are usually circumscribed and encapsulated and are nearly twice as common as neurinomas. They usually arise from arachnoid membrane and are microscopically similar to those within the intracranial cavity. Rarely, a diffuse **sarcoma** occurs as part of a diffuse invasion of the intracranial and intraspinal pia and subarachnoid spaces.

2. Intramedullary tumors - Gliomas, particularly ependymomas, are the commonest intramedullary tumors. Hemangiomas and lipomas occur more rarely.

Clinical Findings.
The location of the tumor largely determines its clinical manifestations. In general, as with intracranial neoplasms, slow progression and focalization of signs is the rule.

Signs and symptoms referable to the spinal nerve roots are common, e.g., radicular pains and paresthesias which are made worse by exertion, coughing, or straining. Localized motor weakness, paralysis, and muscle atrophy following involvement of motor roots or anterior horns of the spinal cord also occur.

Symptoms may be related to compression of the cord, producing paraplegia, sensory loss, bowel and bladder sphincter disturbances, and similar abnormalities. The early loss of sensation occurs in intramedullary tumors, but the perianal area is apt not to become involved until late.

Diagnosis.
The following diagnostic measures are of value in establishing a diagnosis of intraspinal neoplasm:

A. X-ray may show calcification within the tumor. Atrophy of the vertebrae with dilatation of the canal may occur, increasing the size of the interpedicular spaces. Kyphoses may occur at the level of the tumor in children.

B. Lumbar puncture may show a partial or complete block in the vertebral canal (Queckenstedt's sign). The total protein of the CSF is

Ependymoma of Spinal Cord
With Massive Intraspinal Hemorrhage

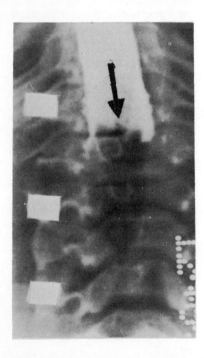
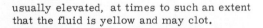

**Myelogram Showing Defect and Obstruction
of Iophendylate (Pantopaque®) Column
Produced by an Intraspinal Tumor**

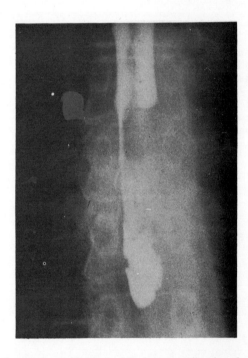

Spinal Cord Tumor. Myelogram showing defect and outline of spinal cord tumor (recurrent ependymoma).

usually elevated, at times to such an extent that the fluid is yellow and may clot.

C. Myelography may demonstrate the tumor. Iophendylate (Pantopaque®) is injected above or below the suspected site of the tumor and the outline of the tumor then visualized under fluoroscopy or x-ray.

D. Electromyography has been used to localize tumors. This test is based on the assumption that normal myograms are apt to be present above the upper level of the lesion and that abnormally active myograms may be obtained at or below the upper level.

Treatment and Prognosis.

Treatment consists of surgical removal followed, in some cases, by x-ray irradiation. In general, tumors of the intradural extramedullary group, e.g., neurinomas and meningiomas, are readily removed by operation. Intramedullary tumors offer a less favorable prognosis, but some improvement may occur after operative removal and subsequent radiation treatment.

28 . . .

Degenerative Diseases
of the Central Nervous System

MULTIPLE SCLEROSIS

Multiple sclerosis is usually a diffuse, chronic, slowly progressive neurologic disorder which has its onset in early adult life and is characterized by irregular, fluctuating periods of exacerbation and remission. It is now recognized with greater frequency than formerly. At one time or another, multiple sclerosis has been considered to be the result of infections, intoxications, nutritional deficiency states, lead poisoning, thrombophlebitis, and other causes. The presence of lipolytic enzyme in circulating blood and a disturbance in CNS lipid metabolism has been reported. There is a greater incidence in the northern latitudes of North America and Europe; the disease is comparatively rare in the Orient. The incidence of the disease has allegedly increased in the United States.

An acute form with a sudden onset may also occur.

Pathology.

Grossly, there are multiple irregular areas of degeneration which appear to have a predilection for the white matter as opposed to the gray matter of the brain and spinal cord. The lesions may vary in extent from the size of a pin-point to more than 1 cm. in diameter. Microscopically, the areas of degeneration show early demyelinization of the axon sheaths. Later there is breakdown and disappearance of axons and subsequent glial scar formation.

Clinical Findings.

The symptoms and signs frequently regress following their initial appearance. However, exacerbations usually occur and the disease almost always becomes more severe with the passage of time. The patient usually becomes progressively more disabled and cachectic, and is apt to develop some infection which will prove fatal. Involvement of the medullary or hypothalamic areas by plaques usually hastens death.

Multiple sclerosis characteristically affects persons between the ages of 20 and 40; onset is rare before age 12 or after age 50. Involvement of the visual system often occurs early and may be evident by impaired visual acuity, ocular motility, or both. A sudden onset of severe visual impairment, usually unilateral, with pain in or behind the globe, is often an early manifestation.

Signs of multiple involvement of the spinal cord or brain may be present; nystagmus, slurred speech, intention tremor, spastic paralysis, and retrobulbar neuritis are common. The usual symptoms at onset are weakness, visual disturbances, tremor, ataxia, and paresthesias.

It is not uncommon to find the patient euphoric. Hyperexcitability and even maniacal reactions have been observed.

Diagnosis.

The diagnosis depends on a characteristic history of relapse and remission and findings referable to multiple lesions. Occasionally multiple sclerosis is confined to a single area, in which case an inaccurate diagnosis may cause the patient to be erroneously operated upon for tumor.

The CSF usually shows a first or second zone or normal colloidal gold curve, but the presence or absence of this reaction does not establish or disprove the diagnosis. Gamma globulin often is increased. Skull and spine x-rays, electroencephalograms, cerebral angiography, pneumoencephalography, and iophendylate (Pantopaque®) or air myelography may be necessary in some cases to rule out neoplasms, herniated intervertebral disks, or other disorders which may mimic multiple sclerosis.

Treatment and Prognosis.

Various treatments based upon the etiologic and pathologic theories currently in vogue have been tried with disappointing results. Among the more common treatment methods which have been employed are fever therapy, antisyphilitic therapy, anticoagulant therapy, protein shock, and histamine desensitization. Therapeutic claims have also been made for tolbutamide, isoniazid, vitamin B_{12}, procaine, blood transfusions, fat-free diets, steroids, vasodilators (5-10% CO_2), and histamine infusions, but their value has not been established.

Physical therapy and symptomatic and supportive measures may prove helpful. Particular attention must be paid to prevention of bed sores, prompt treatment of respiratory infections, and avoidance of urinary tract infections. Adequate sleep at night and rest in the afternoon have been found to make patients more comfortable. Sudden changes in temperature (external or internal) should be avoided to reduce vascular spastic phenomena although the role of such spasm has been questioned. Heat makes these patients much worse, while cold often improves them temporarily. Rehabilitation, physical therapy, and psychotherapy are indicated to encourage the patient to live with his disability and make most of whatever assets he retains.

Multiple sclerosis is a chronic disease. Because of its progressive nature, the hazards of chronic invalidism usually increase the longer the patient survives. Intercurrent infections of the respiratory and urinary tracts are common. Although the prospects for cure are dim, relatively long quiescent phases are not uncommon. The course is varied and unpredictable. In almost all cases there is a remission of the initial symptoms, but with each recurrence of a symptom the chances of remission decrease. Early remissions may be remarkably complete; later in the course of the disease remissions tend to be partial. Remissions may last several months to 2 years. A clinical course of 10-20 years is not uncommon. In a large series, the average survival after onset of symptoms was estimated at 27 years.

PRESENILE DEMENTIA
(Pick's Disease and Alzheimer's Disease)

These relatively rare disorders are characterized by progressive dementia and dysphasia. In most cases age at onset is 40-60 years of age. Two clinical types have been described: one characterized by mutism, immobility, and loss of spontaneity, the other by restlessness and hyperactivity. Severe atrophy of the cerebral cortex is found in both diseases; atrophy is usually restricted to the frontotemporal lobes in Pick's disease and is more dif-

fuse in Alzheimer's disease. The course is progressive, and incapacity is complete by the time death occurs.

SENILE DEGENERATION

Changes within the brain as a result of the aging process may occur independently of changes in the cerebrovascular and other tissues.

Gross examination may show diffuse or focal changes. The brain may be small and the cortex relatively thin, with wide, deep sulci. The ventricles are apt to be dilated. The basal ganglia may be small and on cut section usually contain grossly visible small cystic spaces. Microscopically, the neuronal cells show atrophy, increased yellow pigment, nuclear degeneration, and degeneration of neurofibrils. Senile plaques, composed of an amorphous, granular argentophilic substance from which fibrils radiate, are apt to be found in the lower cortical layers. Increased gliosis and decrease in nerve fibers are also apparent.

Mental changes may be profound. Memory may be poor, especially for recent events. Impaired judgment, imagination, concentration, and attention are commonly present, as well as episodic excitement, delirium, depression, delusions, and hallucinations.

Physical stamina is diminished. Tremor, physical and mental sluggishness, and rigidity are commonly seen when the basal ganglia are significantly affected. Parkinsonian gait, posture, and facies may be apparent. Generalized epileptic seizures may occur. The Lhermitte and McAlpine syndrome refers to combined pyramidal-extrapyramidal disease due to encephalomalacia or encephalitis in the neighborhood of the internal capsule and adjacent extrapyramidal motor nuclei.

In presenile dementia (see above), the onset of symptoms is earlier (40-60 years of age), with slow progression thereafter. Pathologically, a great number of senile plaques are found.

PARALYSIS AGITANS
(Parkinson's Syndrome)

This disorder was originally described by James Parkinson, who noted "involuntary tremulous motion, with lessened motor power, in parts not in action and even when supported;

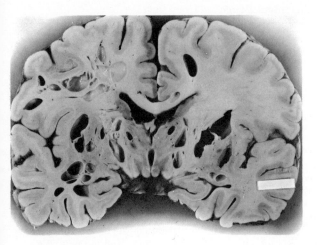

"Swiss Cheese Brain." Usually due to postmortem changes produced by an-aerobic gas-forming bacteria.

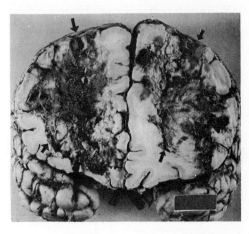

Cystic Degeneration Following Bilateral Frontal Leukotomy

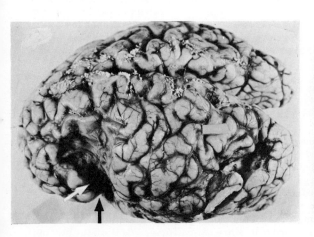

Cerebral Arteriosclerosis With Left Cerebral Cortical Atrophy

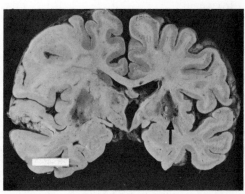

Lacunar Cystic Degeneration Involving Principally Left Caudate and Lenticular Nuclei

with a propensity to bend the trunk forwards and to pass from a walking to a running pace, the senses and intellect being unimpaired.''

Parkinsonism occurs most often in persons in their 50's and 60's. It may follow an attack of epidemic encephalitis or may be due to cerebral arteriosclerosis, carbon dioxide or manganese poisoning, trauma to the head, neurosyphilis, or cerebrovascular accidents. The precipitating cause is often unknown; in these cases the disease is ascribed to degeneration of cells and tracts of the striate bodies and substantia nigra, with loss of cells and alteration of the remaining cells.

Disturbed metabolism of brain amines has been recently proposed as the basis for the development of parkinsonism. Abnormally low concentrations of dopamine, norepinephrine, and serotonin in the basal ganglia and hypothalamus and their abnormal excretion in the urine have been reported, suggesting a defect in normal binding of amines.

Clinical Findings.

Onset is usually insidious and gradual, and progression is slow. The patient may complain of increasing rigidity and tremor, immobility of facial expression, slowness of

Antiparkinsonism Drugs

Drug	Tremor	Rigidity and Spasms	Akinesia (Weakness)	Oculogyric Crisis	Dosage	Precautions and Remarks
Atropine sulfate, 0.5% solution		×			3 drops t.i.d. in a glass of water, increasing by 1 drop every 3 days to 10 drops t.i.d. or toxicity.	May precipitate acute glaucoma in elderly persons and contraindicated in patients with glaucoma. Blurred vision, dryness of mouth, vertigo, and tachycardia are early toxic symptoms; late symptoms are vomiting, dizziness, mental confusion, and hallucinations. The synthetic drugs are apt to cause more dizziness than the natural alkaloids and are somewhat less potent parasympatholytics.
Belladonna tincture		×			15 drops t.i.d. in a glass of water, increasing by 1 drop every day to 30 drops t.i.d. or toxicity.	
Scopolamine hydrobromide	×			×	Elderly, 0.3 mg. ($^1/_2$00 gr.), b.i.d.; young, up to 0.6 mg. ($^1/_1$00 gr.), b.i.d. or t.i.d.	
Stramonium tincture	×				Start 15 drops t.i.d. and increase slowly until a therapeutic response is obtained, 60 drops t.i.d. are being given, or toxicity occurs.	
Rabellon®*		×	×		0.5 mg. tablets: $^1/4$, $^1/2$ or 1 tablet, 2-4 times daily.	
Trihexyphenidyl HCl (Artane®)		×	×	×	1-5 mg. t.i.d., starting at low dosage and slowly increasing. For oculogyric crisis use 10 mg. t.i.d.	
Biperiden HCl (Akineton®)	×			×	2 mg. 3-4 times daily.	
Procyclidine HCl (Kemadrin®)		×			2.5-5 mg. t.i.d. after meals.	
Caramiphen HCl (Panparnit®)		×			50-100 mg. q.i.d. Start with 12.5 mg. q.i.d. and gradually increase to optimal dosage.	Administer on a full stomach or with 1 or more full glasses of water. Other remarks as for atropine.
Cycrimine (Pagitane®)		×	×	×	1.25-5 mg. 3-4 times daily. Dosage may be gradually increased up to the limits of tolerance.	Useful when effects of trihexyphenidyl wear off. Other remarks as for atropine.
Benztropine methanesulfonate (Cogentin®)	×	×	—		0.5 mg. 1-2 times daily, increasing by 0.5 mg. at intervals of several days to 5 mg. daily or toxicity. Often most effective as single dose at bedtime.	Side effects similar to atropine. Best effect by combining with trihexyphenidyl or dextro amphetamine.
Diphenhydramine HCl (Benadryl®)	×				50 mg. 2-4 times daily.	Reduce dosage if transient drowsiness occurs.
Orphenadrine HCl (Disipal®)	×	×			50 mg. 3-5 times daily.	
Chlorphenoxamine ether HCl (Phenoxene®)		×			50 mg. 3-4 times daily.	Valuable adjunct to other drugs.
Ethopropazine HCl (Parsidol®, Lysovane®)	×	×			25-30 mg. q.i.d.	May be used in conjunction with other antispasmodic drugs. Drug is related to chlorpromazine; precautions as for this class of drugs.
Dextro amphetamine sulfate (Dexedrine®)			×		5 mg. morning or noon.	CNS stimulant to be used with caution in cardiac patients.

*Rabellon® is a mixture of hyoscine, atropine, and scopolamine.

movements, and diminished swinging of the arms and heaviness in the limbs when walking. Posture is commonly stooped, with the arms at the sides, elbows slightly flexed, and fingers adducted. Tremors of fingers, hands, and wrists usually occur, sometimes in association with a to-and-fro tremor of the head. The voice tends to become weak, low in volume, and monotonous. Motor power diminishes gradually throughout the body, so that movements of all kinds are carried out slowly. Patients sometimes have a tendency to break into a trot when standing or walking.

Intermittent tremor (about 2-6/second) occurs, which is worse when the limb is at rest. Tremors frequently are of the pill-rolling type, involving the thumb, index finger, or wrist, and are sometimes associated with a to-and-fro tremor of the head. Emotional disturbances and fatigue are apt to aggravate the tremor.

The limb muscles on passive motion are rigid (lead-pipe or cogwheel). There may be difficulty in getting out of a chair, so that several attempts to rise are made. Turning is difficult, even when standing or in bed. Movements such as adjusting a tie, buttoning the coat, and brushing the hair may ultimately become difficult without assistance. Some patients have a tendency to break into a run or trot (festination gait). The voice tends to become weak, low in volume, and monotonous. Oculogyric crises may occur.

Treatment and Prognosis.

The response to medical treatment is variable, but therapy usually brings some symptomatic relief. The drugs most successfully used include derivatives of belladonna root, synthetic compounds with atropine-like action [trihexyphenidyl (Artane®), cycrimine (Pagitane®), etc.], and the antihistamines. The disease is slowly progressive, and the patient may live for years. As disability increases, depression, anxiety, and emotional disturbances often occur.

In carefully selected patients, surgical destruction of portions of the globus pallidus or the ventrolateral nucleus of the thalamus has proved highly beneficial.

Physical therapy should include massage, stretching of muscles, and active exercise when possible. The patient should be taught to exercise daily the muscles most severely affected, especially those of the hands, fingers, wrists, elbows, knees, and neck.

Reassurance and psychologic support are of decided value, stressing the positive aspects of the disease: (1) symptomatic relief with drugs, (2) no impairment of mental faculties, (3) slow progression over many years, and (4) active research and the hope of therapeutic break-throughs.

Barbiturates should be avoided. Moderate use of alcohol to relax tension may be permitted. Nonbarbiturate sedatives (e.g., meprobamate, rather than phenothiazines) may be of value. Treatment with drugs, especially early in the disease, may produce temporary amelioration of complaints. Although significant improvement of tremor and rigidity may follow operative treatment (pallidotomy, thalamotomy) in some cases, patients selected for surgery should be free of generalized brain disease and have little pseudobulbar involvement such as loss of speech, and little akinesia; surgery may make these patients worse.

Treatment is mainly symptomatic. A number of drugs have been found effective in alleviating symptoms of parkinsonism. To obtain optimum therapeutic results, drugs are usually used in combinations. Combinations such as trihexyphenidyl (Artane®) and diphenhydramine (Benadryl®) t.i.d. may be used initially. Drugs should not be stopped abruptly when changing to new medications. The dosage of the new drug should be increased as the previously used drug is gradually withdrawn.

CHRONIC PROGRESSIVE CHOREA
(Huntington's Chorea, Adult Chorea)

Huntington's chorea is a hereditary disease of the basal ganglia and cortex, characterized by the onset in adult life of choreiform movements and mental deterioration. Many cases in America have been traced to 2 brothers who emigrated to Long Island from England. The movements are abrupt and jerky, though less rapid and lightning-like than those of Sydenham's chorea. Any somatic musculature may be involved. The disease is chronically progressive and usually leads to death in about 15 years.

Treatment is symptomatic. Large doses of tranquilizers, such as reserpine are helpful in management of the motor manifestations.

HEPATOLENTICULAR DEGENERATION
(Wilson's Disease)

This familial disease, with signs and symptoms of injury to the basal ganglia, is accompanied by cirrhosis of the liver and, in most cases, greenish-brown pigmentation of the cornea near the scleral junction (Kayser-Fleischer ring), best seen by slit lamp examination. Changes in the cerebellum, cerebral cortex, and other parts of the nervous system may be present to a lesser degree. An increase in the excretion of copper and amino acids in the urine and a decrease in the caeruloplasmin content of blood serum suggest that damage to the liver and brain may be due to familial metabolic disturbance. A normal adult usually excretes less than 50 μg. of copper in the urine in 24 hours; values above 100 μg. are considered abnormal.

Onset of symptoms is usually between the ages of 11 and 25 years. Clinical features are those of liver and nervous system disorders. Evidence of liver disease, ascites, or jaundice may occur at any stage of the disease. Tremors and rigidity are the commonest early symptoms. Tremors may be of the intention type or may be alternating like the tremors observed in Parkinson's disease. Commonly they are of the bizarre "wing-beating" type, confined to and accentuated by extension of the upper extremities.

Wilson's disease is insidious in onset and progresses slowly. Partial remissions and exacerbations commonly occur, but the outcome is usually fatal within 10 years. Treatment with dimercaprol (BAL) injections twice daily for ten-day periods every 2 months has been recommended. The clinically useful dose of BAL is 2.5 mg./Kg. weight intramuscularly. D,L-Penicillamine (250 mg. t.i.d.) is an effective chelating agent suitable for oral administration and may far surpass the effect of BAL in increasing excretion of copper. Some of the specific manifestations may be ameliorated by symptomatic therapy. The full effect of dimercaprol or penicillamine therapy on the course or longevity has not as yet been determined.

FRIEDREICH'S ATAXIA

Friedreich's ataxia is a familial and hereditary disease characterized pathologically by degenerative changes principally of the cerebellum and dorsal half of the spinal cord, and clinically by onset, in the first or second decades, of ataxia, absent deep reflexes, impaired proprioception of lower extremities, and extensor plantar responses. Scoliosis and clubbing of the feet are commonly associated, and there may be optic nerve degeneration and muscle atrophies. The disease is slowly progressive, but incapacity is complete by 30 years of age. Degeneration of the posterior columns and the lateral corticospinal and spinocerebellar tracts of the spinal cord, with extensive gliosis of the posterior columns, is the rule. Sometimes there is also loss of cells of Clarke's column and atrophy of dentate nuclei and Purkinje's cells of cerebellum.

FAMILIAL SPASTIC PARAPLEGIA

This relatively rare familial or hereditary disease is characterized by the development in the first years of life of spasticity and weakness of the lower extremities. Progression is the rule, and patients are apt to become paraplegic or chair-ridden before the age of 15-20 years. Weakness of extremities becomes severe, and the gait becomes spastic and scissors-like. There are usually no cerebellar or sensory findings.

OLIVOCEREBELLAR AND OLIVOPONTOCEREBELLAR ATROPHY

This disorder is characterized by progressive cerebellar ataxia of middle or adult life, with degeneration of the cerebellum, olives, and pons. In cases described by Holmes, degeneration of olives and cerebellum was noted; in those of Dejerine and Thomas, degeneration of olives, pontine nuclei, and cerebellum occurred. Clinically, this disease is similar to Marie's ataxia, in which optic atrophy and oculomotor palsies are apt to occur. Progressive cerebellar ataxia, impaired gait and equilibrium, scanning speech, and nystagmoid eye movements may be noted.

HEREDITARY CEREBELLAR ATAXIA WITH SPASTICITY
(Sanger Brown and Marie)

This hereditary disorder is characterized by onset late in life of ataxia and exaggerated tendon reflexes; optic atrophy and oculomotor palsies are often associated. The first symptoms may not begin until the fourth or sixth decades, with ataxia of gait and incoordination in use of the upper extremities. Mental deterioration may occur as a late manifestation.

PARENCHYMATOUS CEREBELLAR DEGENERATION

This disorder is characterized by development in middle life of cerebellar symptoms affecting predominantly the lower extremities. The course is slowly progressive and may extend over decades. The etiology is not known; men are more commonly affected than women. Initially there is difficulty with walking; the gait soon becomes wide-based, ataxic, and sometimes spastic. Nystagmus usually is not present but may occur. In the later stages, the upper extremities may also be involved.

HEREDITARY ATAXIA WITH MUSCULAR ATROPHY
(Levy-Roussy Syndrome)

This disorder may be a variant of Friedreich's ataxia in which there is a great deal of muscular wasting and relatively few symptoms. Symptoms develop early in childhood and include impairment of equilibrium in walking and standing, loss of knee and ankle jerks, atrophy of muscles of the lower extremities and sometimes of hands, occasional extensor plantar responses, and kyphoscoliosis. Symptoms progress slowly, and in a large percentage of cases seem to stop before disability becomes severe.

ATAXIA TELANGIECTASIA

A familial disease characterized by onset in early childhood of progressive cerebellar ataxia, oculocutaneous telangiectasis, and severe sino-pulmonary infections. Ocular dyspraxia, choreoathetosis, hyporeflexia, drooling speech, and nystagmus may also occur. In a few cases, hypogammaglobulinemia has been noted.

ACUTE CEREBELLAR ATAXIA OF CHILDREN

Children may show severe gait ataxia, usually of sudden onset and often shortly after a nonspecific infectious disease, with complete recovery possible within a few months. Affected patients, however, do not always recover and severe initial manifestations are as-

sociated with slow recovery. CSF and other laboratory data obtained on initial examination have been found to be normal. Persistent neurologic defects which may occur include gait disturbance, truncal tremor, ataxia of extremity movement, abnormal eye movement, delayed and impaired speech, and signs of mental retardation.

SCHILDER'S DISEASE
(Encephalitis Periaxialis Diffusa)

Schilder's disease is rapidly progressive, characterized by widespread demyelinization of the cerebral hemispheres, with convulsions, loss of vision, mental symptoms, and motor and sensory disturbances. The demyelinization usually occurs in the white matter of one or both cerebral hemispheres. Death usually occurs within 3 years after onset. Complete dementia, quadriplegia, and decerebrate rigidity may occur in the terminal stages.

NEUROMYELITIS OPTICA
(Devic's Disease)

This clinical syndrome is characterized by the acute occurrence of optic neuritis and transverse myelitis. It is believed by many to be a variant or acute form of multiple sclerosis or Schilder's disease. Demyelinating lesions are found in the optic nerves, brain, and spinal cord. Devic's disease usually either terminates fatally soon after onset or improves without subsequent development of new symptoms.

LEUKODYSTROPHY

The term leukodystrophy was originally proposed to designate disorders characterized by inheritable progressive degeneration of cerebral white matter. In these disorders there is an implied failure of glial cells to maintain nutrition of myelinated axons and to carry out effectively the degradation of myelin breakdown products to their final sudanophil stage of neutral fat and esterified cholesterol. While a broad distinction has often been made between a lipidosis, with its accumulation of lipid material within the bodies of nerve cells, and leukodystrophy, with a major pathologic process in the axons, neurochemical research is currently modifying these views and is increasingly concerned with the presumed enzymatic defects of the various disorders.

DIFFUSE SCLEROSIS
(Merzbacher-Pelizaeus Type)

Diffuse sclerosis is a slowly progressive heredofamilial disorder of the CNS which begins in the first months of life. It is characterized by diffuse degeneration of white matter, with nystagmus, intention tremor, ataxia, spasticity, dysarthria, and trophic changes.

METACHROMATIC LEUKOENCEPHALOPATHY
(Greenfield's Disease)

This form of diffuse sclerosis usually affects children or young adults; it is slowly progressive with quadriparesis, bulbar signs, and dementia. Optic atrophy and incoordination may be superimposed. Metachromatic material is deposited within the nervous system and the kidney, where it may be found by biopsy. This abnormal material, which may be found in centrifuged urine sediment, stains a golden brown metachromatic color with toluidine blue and is soluble in certain organic solvents. Increased amounts of hexosamine are found in the white matter. Sulfatide is found in excessive amounts in brain and kidney, and is responsible for the metachromatic staining of the lipid in the degenerating white matter. Pathologically, diffuse demyelination is prominent with accumulation of metachromatic material either free in tissue or within cytoplasm of proliferated glial cells. It is also found in nerve cells, especially of the midbrain, medulla and spinal cord, as well as in other organs such as kidney and liver.

MULTIFOCAL LEUKOENCEPHALOPATHY

This unusual disease may occur late in the course of chronic illness such as malignant lymphoma, leukemia, sarcoidosis, carcinomatosis, or miliary tuberculosis. Rapid progressive focal or asymmetric brain disorder may be noted with mental changes, impaired visual acuity, hemianopsia or blindness, apha-

sia, hemisensory impairment, ataxia, vertigo, nystagmus and choreiform movements possible. CSF examination is usually unremarkable. Skull x-rays, pneumograms, and cerebral angiograms are normal. EEG may show diffuse slow-wave activity. Pathologically, multifocal demyelinative lesions of varying size and evolution are found throughout the brain, especially in the brain stem and cerebellum, although the spinal cord is usually normal. The cause is not known, but decreased resistance to infections may be involved since this disorder is associated with diseases in which immunologic hyporeactivity has been found.

PROGRESSIVE SUBCORTICAL ENCEPHALOPATHY
(Binswanger's Disease)

This rare disorder is characterized by demyelinization of the white matter of the cerebral hemispheres associated with arteriosclerosis. The onset is usually between the ages of 40 and 50 years, and the course is progressive over the next year or 2. Seizures and focal neurologic signs develop. Diagnosis is usually made at necropsy.

MARCHIAFAVA-BIGNAMI DISEASE
(Primary Degeneration of Corpus Callosum)

This slowly progressive, usually fatal disease is characterized by mental symptoms with signs of focal or general brain disorder. It occurs usually in middle-aged or elderly Italian males and is associated with the finding of primary degeneration of the corpus callosum. Ingestion of crude Italian wine ("dago red") has been implicated as an etiologic factor in some cases.

HEREDITARY OPTIC ATROPHY
(Leber's Disease)

This disease of the optic nerve is characterized by loss of central vision with relatively normal peripheral fields of vision. It occurs usually in males but is transmitted solely by females; onset is between 12 and 25 years of age. The disease ordinarily progresses rapidly and commonly reaches its maximum extent within a few weeks. It rarely progresses to complete blindness.

STATUS MARMORATUS
(Vogt's Disease)

This disorder is characterized by the appearance in the first year of life of athetosis, dystonia, rigidity of muscles, and dysarthria. Mental deficiency is also sometimes noted. "Marble appearance" (status marmoratus) of the basal ganglia, particularly of the caudate and lenticular nuclei, is due to large bundles of abnormally situated myelin sheaths and may be related to excess formation by overgrowth of glia resulting from fetal anoxia or encephalitis.

STATUS DYSMYELINATUS

A disorder characterized by the development, in the first year of life, of athetoid movements which are gradually replaced by rigidity and death in the second decade. There is shrinkage of the caudate nucleus, globus pallidus, and subthalamic nucleus, with failure of staining or lack of development of myelin sheaths in affected zones.

SPASTIC PSEUDOSCLEROSIS
(Creutzfeldt and Jakob Syndrome)

A familial progressive disease of cortex, basal ganglia, and spinal cord, developing in the middle or late years. Onset is gradual, with pyramidal and extrapyramidal signs. Psychoses and mental deterioration are common. It is usually fatal within a few months to years.

HALLERVORDEN-SPATZ DISEASE
(Pigmentary Degeneration of Globus Pallidus)

This is a rare familial disease of the basal ganglia in which there is deposition of iron-containing pigment (green, blue, or brown) in ganglion cells and interstitial tissue. It is characterized clinically by the onset at about 10 years of gradually increasing stiffness of limbs, club-foot deformity, dysarthria, and dementia, with progression to death usually within 20 years.

DYSTONIA MUSCULORUM DEFORMANS
(Torsion Spasm)

The characteristic movements of torsion spasm involve the muscles particularly of the trunk and girdle and are similar to those of athetosis but more sustained in contraction. Pathologic changes include degenerative changes in the cells of the basal ganglia, cerebral cortex, and olivary nuclei. Onset is usually gradual and the course slightly progressive. Symptoms include gait abnormalities, twisting of the pelvis, dysarthria, facial grimacing, and torticollis.

SPASMODIC TORTICOLLIS
(Wryneck)

Intermittent spasmodic movements of muscles of the neck are characteristic of this disorder. The head may be turned to one side, rotate and bend in another, and may be forcibly flexed or extended. The most commonly affected muscle is the sternocleidomastoid of the side opposite deviation of the chin. Movements may spread to the facial and brachial muscles of both sides. The movements are adversely affected by emotional tension and may be influenced by postural changes or external stimuli. Medical treatment has proved unsatisfactory; some relief may be afforded by psychotherapy or surgery (section of spinal accessory nerve; section of anterior and posterior divisions of first 3 cervical motor roots).

•   •   •

29...

Metabolic and Toxic Disorders of the Nervous System

BLOOD DISEASES

POSTEROLATERAL SCLEROSIS
(Subacute Combined System Disease)

Posterolateral sclerosis is characterized by a progressive degeneration of the posterior and lateral columns of the spinal cord, sometimes with degeneration of the peripheral nerves. It is usually associated with and most often described as a complication of **pernicious anemia.** Nutritional deficiency states and other forms of anemia are also commonly cited as possible causes.

The severity of the disease when associated with pernicious anemia does not necessarily parallel the blood status, which suggests that the etiologic factors responsible for the neural and blood changes are not identical. Degeneration of the spinal cord may develop before other clinical manifestations of pernicious anemia and may occur early in pernicisious anemia rather than in the later phases.

Pathology.

Although posterolateral sclerosis is usually considered to be predominantly a disease of the spinal cord, pathologic changes may also be found in the brain. The posterior and lateral columns of the spinal cord undergo the most profound pathologic changes. Degenerated demyelinized areas give the appearance of a "spongy state" under the microscope. These areas are vacuolated and areolar in appearance, and there is little evidence of glial tissue or scar formation. Degeneration of cerebral white matter and peripheral neuropathies may be associated.

Clinical Findings.

The onset is characterized by tingling, numbness, and "pins and needles" sensations in the toes and feet, later in the fingers. Mental symptoms are not infrequent, and hallucinations, disorientation, memory defects, and personality changes are apt to occur. With pronounced peripheral nerve involvement there may also be tenderness of the calf and sole muscles, stocking distribution of impaired touch sensibility up to the level of the knees, weakness of the lower extremities (particularly in the distal segments), and depressed or absent knee and ankle jerks.

Posterior column disease may be evidenced by loss of position sense in the extremities, a positive Romberg's test, an ataxic, broad-based gait, loss of the faculty of two-point discrimination, and loss of vibratory sensation. **Lateral column** disease may be evidenced by voluntary muscle weakness, hyperactive deep muscle reflexes, spasticity of the extremities, and a positive Babinski's sign.

Diagnosis.

Posterolateral sclerosis should be suspected in any instance of obscure neurologic symptomatology in association with pernicious anemia or other macrocytic anemias. The diagnosis sometimes rests on a study of the factors associated with pernicious anemia or other anemias. The following studies are frequently made: (1) Gastric analysis for free hydrochloric acid with a histamine stimulation test if necessary. (2) Bone marrow and blood smear studies. (3) Stool examination for ova and parasites.

The Schilling test is useful in diagnosing defective vitamin B_{12} absorption in patients with combined system disease before the onset of anemia and in differentiating pernicious anemia from megaloblastic anemias due to folic acid deficiency.

Treatment and Prognosis.

Vitamin B_{12} therapy is specific, and there is usually no necessity for treatment with hydrochloric acid, liver, special diets or folic acid. Monthly vitamin B_{12} injections may be required for the rest of life. Purified and crude liver extract are not believed to have advantages over vitamin B_{12}. Give vitamin B_{12} (cyanocobalamin), 30 mcg. I.M. 2-3 times per week until blood values return to normal, and then 30 mcg. once a month; larger quantities are usually given in the presence of neurologic involvement. CNS symptoms are reversible if they are of relatively short duration, but may be permanent if present longer than 6 months. Despite treatment with vitamin B_{12}, achlorhydria and an abnormal Schilling test usually persist.

The individual well-developed syndrome will usually not progress if anti—pernicious anemia therapy is adequate. It is highly doubtful that the disease will occur at all if pernicious anemia is appropriately treated before neurologic symptoms appear. Once the disease is well established, the pathologic changes may be considered irreversible and full clinical recovery cannot be expected. Improvement of the peripheral nerve component is more likely to occur with adequate treatment. The prognosis is less favorable in patients over 60 years of age.

NEUROLOGIC COMPLICATIONS OF OTHER BLOOD DISEASES

Pernicious Anemia.

The neurologic complications of pernicious anemia are discussed under Posterolateral Sclerosis.

Polycythemia Vera (Osler-Vaquez Disease, Erythremia).

Thrombosis or rupture of intracranial vessels may occur. Papilledema may result from retinal circulatory changes or as a result of increased intracranial pressure. Lassitude, vertigo, tinnitus, visual disturbances, and paresthesias are commonly present. Hemiplegia, aphasia, or other focal neurologic signs usually follow cerebrovascular accident.

Sickle Cell Anemia.

The neurologic features are usually those of acute cerebrovascular lesion, i.e., infarct or hemorrhage. Thrombosis of the dural sinuses, subdural or subarachnoid hemorrhage, and hemorrhage (or thrombosis) of smaller vessels may occur.

Leukemia.

Petechial or gross brain hemorrhages may occur, particularly in acute types. Spotty leptomeningeal hemorrhages are common. Involvement of facial or optic nerves has been noted.

Kernicterus.

Erythroblastosis fetalis, associated with Rh incompatibility of the parents, may result in severe jaundice with staining of the brain, especially the basal ganglia, by pigment. Mortality is high. Survival may in some cases be associated with chorea and mental retardation.

Thrombocytopenic Purpura.

Because of the thromboses of small blood vessels, hemolytic anemia, and purpura which may occur in this disorder, a variety of neurologic manifestations are possible. The common neurologic findings are seizures, aphasia, cortical blindness, and organic mental syndrome.

Hodgkin's Disease; Lymphomas.

Hodgkin's disease and other lymphomas are often associated with significant neurologic complications. Herpes zoster, spinal cord compression by epidural tumor extensions, cranial nerve palsies, peripheral neuropathies, encephalitic syndromes, epilepsy, and CNS infections with fungi or yeasts may occur.

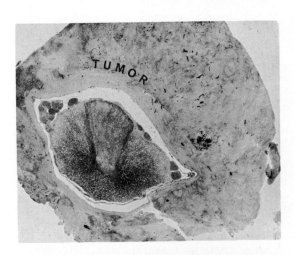

Epidural Tumor in Hodgkin's Disease With Compression of Thoracic Spinal Cord (Weil Stain)

DISORDERS OF LIPOID METABOLISM (LIPOIDOSES)

In certain diseases altered lipoid metabolism is reflected in or associated with CNS changes.

Cerebromacular Degeneration (Tay-Sachs Disease; Amaurotic Familial Idiocy).

This is a familial disease characterized by progressive loss of vision, dementia, and paralysis, usually with a fatal outcome. The onset in infants is within the first 6 months of life. Optic atrophy and macular degeneration (cherry-red spot in center of degenerated retinal area) are characteristic. The lipoids involved are believed to be lecithin and sphingomyelin; recent studies have shown increased gangliosides and neuraminic acid in affected cerebrocortical ganglion cells. Increased excretion of imidazole amino acids (carnosine, anserine, histidine, and 1-methyl-histidine) has been noted. Absence of fructose-L-phosphate aldolase has also been reported.

Niemann-Pick Disease.

This familial disease may occur in infants. It is characterized by enlargement of the spleen and liver, brownish skin discoloration, progressive blindness, and mental deterioration. The disease is considered to be due to a disturbance in phospholipid metabolism, especially sphingomyelin; it develops rapidly and leads to death in 2 years.

Gargoylism (Hurler's Disease).

This rare disorder is usually manifest in the early months of life. The child may resemble an achondroplastic dwarf. Mental and physical retardation, mental deficiency, hepatosplenomegaly, and optic atrophy may occur. The disease is believed to be due to a disorder of phospholipid metabolism, with combinations between polysaccharides and phosphatides or cerebrosides occurring in neurons and other tissues. The clinical syndrome is marked by dwarfism, infantilism, mental retardation, coarse facial features, large tongue, pot-belly, kyphosis, corneal clouding, and characteristic skeletal dystrophy.

Cranial Xanthomatosis (Hand-Schüller-Christian Disease).

This disease, believed to be due to a cholesterol metabolism defect, is characterized by defects in membranous bones, exophthalmos, and diabetes insipidus. Onset is in early childhood. Multiple small cutaneous skin plaques may occur, resembling seborrheic dermatitis. Lymphadenopathy, hepatosplenomegaly, and anemia are often present. Reticuloendothelial system pathology consists of lipoid cell hyperplasia and histiocyte proliferation. Characteristic x-ray defects of the skull and flat bones may be noted. The course is chronic and usually relatively benign. X-ray therapy of specific local lesions may be helpful.

Gaucher's Disease.

This chronic disease is characterized by the deposition of kerasin in the reticuloendothelial cells of the liver and spleen. It is manifested by listlessness and apathy, with head retraction. The onset is usually between 6 and 12 months in female infants. Infants are hypertonic, and show bulbar symptoms. The course of the disease is variable. In children, rapid progression may occur with early death. Supportive treatment and splenectomy for hypersplenism may be indicated.

Plasma Lipid Disturbance of Bigler.

Physical and mental retardation and hepatomegaly may occur in this rare hereditary lipid disorder with an increased plasma level of phospholipids and triglycerides. Treatment is symptomatic.

Bassen-Kornzweig Syndrome.

A rare neuromuscular disease usually associated with ataxia, proprioceptive sensory loss, and areflexia. Weakness, corticospinal signs, peripheral nerve sensory loss, ophthalmoparesis, and kyphosis may also occur. Characteristically there is also associated retinitis pigmentosa, abnormal erythrocytes (acanthocytes), and a complex lipid disorder. Impaired absorption of fat and fatty acids, deficiency of β-lipoprotein in serum, and reduced total lipids, triglycerides, cholesterol, and phospholipids in serum occur.

DISORDERS OF AMINO ACID METABOLISM

Phenylpyruvic Oligophrenia.

Phenylpyruvic oligophrenia (phenylketonuria) is a disorder in which large amounts of phenylpyruvic acid are present in the urine and blood (because of faulty metabolism of phenylalanine). It is associated with mental deficiency and occurs predominantly in fair-skinned, blue-eyed blonds of tainted families. Acidified urine of affected subjects turns green when tested with ferric chloride.

This disorder is inherited as a recessive trait and is due to absence of an enzyme, phenylalanine hydroxylase, which is capable of converting phenylalanine to tyrosine. Phenylalanine accumulates in blood, and its deamination product, phenylpyruvic acid, is excreted in urine. Mental retardation and schizoid changes usually occur if this disease is untreated, and tremor, ataxia, and hypertonicity have been occasionally noted. Serum phenylalanine levels are elevated. A diet low in phenylalanine started in the first few weeks of life in such patients may prevent mental retardation or arrest the condition in recently established cases.

A proposed screening program includes testing of blood on the day before discharge of newborn infants from the hospital nursery. The Guthrie inhibition assay test measures the presence of phenylalanine by the effect of a phenylalanine antagonist as inhibitor of Bacillus subtilis.

Maple Syrup Disease.

A familial cerebral degenerative disease may occur during the first week of life with rapid progression to a decerebrate phase and excretion of urine with maple syrup—like odor. The clinical course is characterized by decerebrate rigidity, respiratory irregularities, and occasional generalized seizures. Death has occurred in most cases before 20 months of age. A polymer of alpha-hydroxybutyric acid is believed responsible for the maple syrup odor.

The amino acid pattern of the urine may be normal at birth, but an increased excretion of leucine, isoleucine, and valine may occur during the later stages of the illness. A block in oxidative decarboxylation of alpha-keto acids has been inferred from the accumulation of these 3 keto-acids together with the absence of other metabolites along the degradation pathway of leucine. Pathologically there is a defect in myelin formation of white matter, with foci of increased severity, areas of spongy change, associated astrocytosis, and decrease in oligodendroglia.

Hartnup's Disease (H Disease).

This rare genetic defect in the renal transport mechanism for tryptophan is characterized by cerebellar ataxia, mental retardation, aminoacidemia, dermatitis, and increased excretion of indole and indican compounds. Treatment is by hydration to prevent renal calculus formation. Protein-restricted diets and niacinamide are of dubious value.

Leucine Sensitivity Disease.

A genetic metabolic disorder characterized by abnormal hypoglycemia and due to leucine sensitivity has been noted. Clinical features include hypoglycemia, flushing, sweating, and convulsions. Specific treatment is not available.

Albinism.

A congenital disorder in which tyrosinase is absent from melanocytes is featured clinically by absence of pigment in the skin, eyes, and hair. Photophobia, nystagmus, and defective vision may occur. The skin and hair are white; the irides and pupils are red.

Cystathioninuria.

This rare disorder of amino acid metabolism, believed related to a deficiency of cystathionine enzyme, is associated with mental retardation. No known treatment has been effective.

Citrullinuria.

Mental retardation may be associated with this rare aminoaciduria of undetermined origin. Increased levels of citrulline may be demonstrated in blood, CSF, and urine. No other amino acid abnormality nor renal tubular defect has been noted.

Familial Hyperprolinemia.

Nerve deafness, convulsions, mental retardation, and congenital renal hypoplasia may occur in this rare hereditary disorder. Increased levels of proline (8-10 mg./100 ml.), characteristic aminoaciduria (proline, hydroxyproline, and glycine only), and hematuria may occur. EEG abnormalities are also associated. The pathogenesis is not known, and no treatment is available.

Hydroxyprolinemia.

Mental retardation and abnormal urinary excretion of red and white cells are associated in this rare disorder with increased blood and urine levels of hydroxyproline. A low hydroxyproline diet does not affect the plasma hydroxyproline level.

Idiopathic Hyperglycinemia and Hyperglycinuria.

Mental and developmental retardation, protein intolerance, osteoporosis, neutropenia, and thrombocytopenia may occur in this rare disorder of amino acid metabolism characterized by abnormal glycinemia and glycinuria. Plasma concentration of other amino acids (leucine, glutamine) is increased without a corresponding increase in urine. Reduction of dietary protein reduces the frequency and severity of acute episodes.

Homocystinuria.

This is a recently described hereditary disorder, characterized clinically by mental retardation and dislocation of lenses, which occurs in children with sparse blond hair and genu valgum. The plasma homocystine and methionine levels are elevated. Urinary excretion of homocystine is increased, and the nitroprusside test of urine is positive (a magenta color develops). Absence (or lack of activity) of the enzyme cystathionine synthetase in liver is believed to cause the disease. A child born with homocystinuria may suffer from a cysteine deficiency immediately after birth, when the need for this particular amino acid is great.

DISORDERS OF CARBOHYDRATE METABOLISM

Galactosemia.

This disorder may become evident soon after birth by feeding problems, vomiting, diarrhea, abdominal distention, mental retardation, cataracts, hepatomegaly, and elevated blood and urine galactose levels. An enzyme (galactose-1-phosphate uridyl transferase) necessary for conversion of galactose to glucose is deficient in these children. Treatment consists of excluding galactose and lactose from the diet for the first 3 years of life. If instituted before the fourth month, clinical manifestations can be prevented.

Von Gierke's Disease.

This rare hereditary disorder may become evident in early life by easy fatigability, hepatomegaly, and hypoglycemia and ketosis with resulting shock and convulsions. Serum glucose does not respond to the epinephrine test. Excessive glycogen deposits in the liver and kidneys is caused by deficiency of the enzyme glucose-6-phosphatase, which is required for degradation of glycogen to glucose. Treatment is aimed at nutritional improvement and correction of hypoglycemia by frequent feedings. Death usually occurs in infancy or childhood, although if the patient survives symptoms improve as the child gets older.

McArdle's Syndrome.
See p. 371.

NEUROENDOCRINE DISORDERS

PITUITARY SYNDROMES

Simmonds' Disease (Pituitary Cachexia).

Simmonds' disease may be caused by total destruction of the anterior lobe of the pituitary by trauma, hemorrhage, tumor, etc. It produces severe asthenia, emaciation, and reduced metabolism, temperature, and blood pressure. Psychotic symptoms may occur. The disease resembles anorexia nervosa, a psychogenic disorder of young females who voluntarily refrain from eating. In severe cases, death may ensue. The cortisones or corticotropin are helpful in medical treatment.

Diabetes Insipidus.

This clinical syndrome is characterized by excessive urinary excretion and fluid intake. It is associated with a deficiency of antidiuretic hormone of the posterior pituitary, sometimes with lesions of the hypothalamus.

Adiposogenital Dystrophy (Fröhlich's Syndrome).

Fröhlich's syndrome occurs in children, usually boys, and is characterized by obesity and retarded development of secondary sex characteristics. Developmental abnormalities may correct themselves at puberty. The disease is sometimes noted with tumors of the suprasellar region.

Pituitary Dwarfism.

This disorder may occur in children with tumors of the suprasellar region. It is attributed to deficiency of anterior pituitary hormones. Dwarfism of various grades, retarded primary and secondary sexual development, and altered skin appearance may occur.

Cushing's Syndrome.

Cushing's syndrome was attributed at one time (by Cushing) to basophilic adenomas of the pituitary gland. It is now known to occur more commonly with tumor or hyperplasia of the adrenal cortex. Cushing's syndrome is characterized by obesity, osteoporosis with a tendency to kyphosis, sexual dystrophy, hypertension, acrocyanosis, somnolence, backache, easy fatigability, and ultimately, weakness.

Acromegaly.

Overgrowth of the skeleton occurs with hyperfunction of the pituitary gland and may be caused by an eosinophilic tumor of the pituitary gland. Gradual and progressive enlargement of the hands, feet, skull, and lower jaw is characteristic. The features coarsen, and there is overgrowth of facial hair. The activity of the gonads is decreased, with amenorrhea and loss of libido. A similar disorder in childhood, occurring before closure of the epiphyseal lines, results in generalized increase in size, particularly of long bones (gigantism).

ADRENAL SYNDROMES

Addison's Disease.

Chronic insufficiency of the adrenal cortex may result in weakness, fatigability, hyperpigmentation, hypotension, nausea, vomiting, diarrhea, irritability, and periodic hypoglycemia. The gland may be destroyed by tuberculosis, hemorrhage, or tumor. Crises may be precipitated by stress, overexertion, or infections. Relief may follow adequate hormone therapy (adrenocortical hormones) and a high-sodium, high-caloric diet.

Primary Aldosteronism.

Periodic episodes of severe muscle weakness, intermittent tetany, paresthesias, hypertension, polyuria, and polydipsia are believed to occur as a result of a tumor of the adrenal cortex which secretes aldosterone in pathologically large amounts. Laboratory findings include low serum potassium, elevated serum sodium, alkalosis, low urinary specific gravity, and an increase in the urinary excretion of sodium-retaining corticoids.

Cushing's Syndrome.

Hyperfunction of the adrenal cortex (by tumor or hyperplasia) may produce obesity, hypertrichosis, purplish abdominal striae, hypertension, polycythemia, hyperglycemia, amenorrhea, impotence, and osteomalacia. Mental symptoms may occur. This syndrome may be reproduced by administration of cortisone or corticotropin. It is more common in females than in males.

Waterhouse-Friderichsen Syndrome.

Sudden collapse, pallor, and purpura caused by adrenal hemorrhages, usually in conjunction with a fulminating septicemic form of cerebrospinal fever.

Pheochromocytoma.

Hyperfunction of the adrenal medulla as a result of a tumor of the chromaffin cells of that area may give rise to constant or intermittent hypertension of moderate to severe grade. Periodic attacks of hypertension with associated palpitation, precordial distress, headache, dizziness, perspiration, and anxiety may follow massaging of the abdomen in the region of the adrenals or intravenous injection of histamine. Death may result from cerebral hemorrhage, cardiac failure, or pulmonary edema. The phentolamine (Regitine®) test is used for diagnosis: 5 mg. injected rapidly intravenously will produce a prompt drop in blood pressure.

In normotensive intervals, the I.V. injection of 25-50 mcg. of histamine base may cause a blood pressure rise of 50 mm. Hg systolic and 25 mm. Hg diastolic within 3 minutes. Increased 24 hour urine excretion of catecholamines occurs in most patients with pheochromocytoma.

THYROID SYNDROMES

Cretinism.

This follows severe thyroid deficiency of early life and is characterized by retarded physical and mental development. In untreated children, dwarfism and a severe grade of mental deficiency may result.

Myxedema.

Myxedema in adults is characterized by nonpitting edema of subcutaneous tissue, weakness, lethargy, decreased sweating, sensitivity to cold, and enlargement of the tongue. Diagnosis may be aided by low BMR, elevated serum cholesterol level, and decreased uptake of radioiodine. The disease responds well to treatment with thyroid extract. Patients with myxedema may complain of pains or paresthesias in the hands which may be due, in some cases, to a carpal tunnel syndrome resulting from nerve compression by edematous tissue.

Graves' Disease.

The common neurologic alterations which may be associated with Graves' disease are tremors of the hands, exophthalmos, lid lag, convergence weakness, and weakness of muscles associated with an elevated BMR, increased concentration of serum protein-bound iodine, and an increased uptake of radioactive iodine by the thyroid gland. **Thyrotoxic myopathy** is apt to occur in males with thyrotoxicosis. It is manifested by weakness and wasting of the pelvic girdle and shoulder girdle muscles and may superficially resemble myasthenia gravis. **Exophthalmic ophthalmoplegia** (rare) may develop in association with or independent of hyperthyroidism. It is characterized by exophthalmos and paralysis of the extraocular muscles. Edema of lids, chemosis, and papilledema may occur.

OTHER NEUROENDOCRINE DISORDERS

Parathyroid Tetany.

The most common cause of parathyroid tetany is operative removal or destruction of the parathyroid glands. The disease may be associated with carpopedal spasm, convulsions, and numbness and cramps of the extremities. Decrease in serum calcium level varies with degree of hypofunction (values as low as 4.5 mg./100 ml. have been observed). Serum phosphorus is elevated. Relief may follow treatment with parathormone, dihydrotachysterol (Hytakerol®, A.T. 10), or high-calcium, low-phosphorus diet.

Manifestations of hyperirritability of nerves occur when the blood calcium falls below normal. These may include the following:

A. Chvostek's Facial Sign of Tetany: Tapping over the parotid gland results in spasmodic contraction of the ipsilateral facial muscles (hyperexcitability of the facial nerve).

B. Trousseau's Sign of Tetany: A typical spasm of the hand and forearm (accoucheur's hand) occurs after compression of the brachial artery for 1-5 minutes.

C. Erb's Sign of Tetany: Hyperexcitability of the peripheral motor nerve to galvanic current; in tetany the cathodal opening contraction current is commonly less than 5 milliamperes.

D. Hoffmann's Sign of Tetany: Tetanic muscular spasms produced by electric or mechanical stimulation of a sensory nerve. The ulnar nerve is usually selected for the test.

E. Kashida's Thermic Sign of Tetany: Development of hyperesthesias and spasms after application of hot or cold irritants.

F. Pool's Arm and Leg Signs of Tetany: (1) Tension on the brachial plexus by forcible abduction of the arm causes spasms of the muscles of the hand and arm. (2) Tension on the sciatic nerve by forcible flexion of the thigh on the trunk with the leg extended causes spasms of the muscles of the leg and foot.

G. Schlesinger's Leg Sign of Tetany: If the hip joint is flexed and the leg extended at the knee, painful spasm of the extremity occurs in a few seconds to 3 minutes.

H. Schultze's Tongue Dimpling Sign of Tetany: Tapping the protruded tongue with a percussion hammer causes dimpling at the point of mechanical stimulus.

Osteitis Fibrosa Cystica.

Muscular weakness, thinning of the bones, and formation of renal calculi may result from excess parathyroid hormone activity. It is usually caused by adenoma or diffuse enlargement of the parathyroid glands. Serum calcium is usually elevated, serum phosphorus decreased, and serum alkaline phosphatase increased.

Hypoinsulinism (Diabetes Mellitus).

Diabetes mellitus may be accompanied by polyneuritis, mononeuritis, diabetic coma, or cerebrovascular degenerative lesions similar to those of cerebral arteriosclerosis. In most cases the diabetes mellitus has been known to the patient for years. However, neurologic involvement occasionally provokes a medical examination and diabetes is discovered.

Hyperinsulinism.

The paroxysmal occurrence of nervousness anxiety, tremors, automatism, convulsions, and coma may be related to lowering of blood glucose level and tends to occur at times when blood glucose may be expected to be low. Symptoms are of variable intensity and are usually relieved promptly by the administration of glucose.

DISEASES OF COLLAGEN TISSUES

Periarteritis Nodosa.

The CNS is involved in about 30% of cases of periarteritis nodosa. Multiple peripheral neuritis is the most common neurologic finding. Damage to cerebral arteries may lead to thrombosis of small vessels, with convulsions and focal neurologic signs. In cases with exclusive or predominant localization of disease in the brain, the clinical picture may simulate encephalitis or brain tumor.

Lupus Erythematosus.

Involvement of the nervous system may occur in the late stages of the disease and may be associated with thrombosis of small vessels or multiple petechial hemorrhages. Convulsions, mental symptoms, polyneuritis, hemiplegia, and cranial nerve palsies may occur.

Dermatomyositis.

Painful erythema of the skin, tenderness, weakness, and loss of reflexes of affected muscles may occur. The muscles affected may be those of the face, extremities, jaw, or pharynx; the proximal portions of the pelvic and shoulder girdle muscles and the pharyngeal muscles are most often affected.

Temporal Arteritis.

This disorder, which occurs most often in elderly women, is characterized by headache and nodular, tender, prominent, tortuous temporal artery. Blindness sometimes occurs and is usually attributed to thrombosis of the central retinal artery.

Serum Reactions.

Most cases of nervous system complications following prophylactic administration of serum occur 1-2 days after the appearance of somatic evidence of serum sickness and about 1 week after the serum injection. Similar neurologic complications may appear, however, in the absence of any constitutional symptoms. Radiculitis, especially of the cervical roots, is the most common complaint; less often there may be polyradiculitis and polyneuritis, myelitis, or encephalomyelitis. The vast majority recover with little or no residual disability.

MISCELLANEOUS METABOLIC DISORDERS

Amyloidosis.

In amyloidosis, polyneuropathy may be associated with hepatosplenomegaly, heart failure, and macroglossia, alone or in combination. The Congo red test for amyloidosis may be positive, and amyloid may be demonstrable in a biopsied nerve. Preexisting longstanding infection or debilitating illness may precede amyloidosis. There is no effective treatment for systemic amyloidosis, and death may occur within a few years. Local amyloid "tumors" may be excised surgically, and secondary amyloidosis may presumably be prevented by early and adequate treatment of infections.

Porphyria.

Porphyria is a metabolic defect associated with the excretion of porphyrins in the urine. It may be associated with polyneuritis, convulsions, abdominal pains, and mental symptoms. **Acute porphyria** (the most common type) is inherited as a mendelian-dominant trait and believed to be due primarily to a hepatic defect. Excretion of burgundy-red urine, pigmentation of the skin, colicky abdominal pains, convulsions, mental symptoms, and polyneuritis may develop. Acute porphyria occurs most often in females. Symptoms are apt to appear in the third decade. The mortality rate in reported cases is about 50%. **Congenital porphyria** (relatively rare) is more common in males and transmitted as a mendelian-recessive trait. Manifestations become evident early in life and consist of sensitivity to light, anemia, and hepatosplenomegaly. The

bone marrow appears to be the site of the metabolic error.

Liver Disorders.

Confusion, delirium, stupor, or coma may occur with liver failure. Sometimes there are associated tremors and rigidity of the limbs, and extensor plantar responses. Deeper grades of "hepatic coma" usually are associated with an increased degree of slowing of frequencies in EEG. Reduction of cerebral oxygen consumption occurs gradually in hepatic insufficiency, and a severe depression of cerebral oxygen utilization appears necessary for the development of clinical manifestations of even moderate cerebral dysfunction. No constant relationship between the severity of hepatic disorder, the state of consciousness, and the blood ammonia level has been reported. No single pathogenic mechanism at present can account for the onset or perpetuation of hepatic coma. Among the various mechanisms alleged to affect the state of consciousness in liver dysfunction are increased blood and cerebral uptake of ammonia, slowing of the Krebs cycle with decreased oxygen consumption, liberation of alpha-ketoglutarate, pyruvate, and lactate; a possible disturbance of metabolism of indolic or phenolic compounds, or both; and liberation of toxic substances into the blood as a result of liver damage, which produces neuronal disturbances in brain.

Uremia.

Acute uremia may produce confusion, agitation, apathy, depression, stupor, and coma. Nystagmus, facial paralysis, and lower cranial nerve dysfunction are common. Muscle wasting, myalgia, tremor, fasciculations, myoclonus, and transient paresis are frequent. Convulsions are also frequent, but sensory phenomena are rare. No correlations with routine blood chemistries are noted, although rapid shifts are more likely to cause symptoms. The twitchings and convulsions observed in uremia are likely to be due to a generalized metabolic lesion and not just to hypocalcemia; many symptoms may be due to hypoxia. Polyneuropathy, with greatest involvement of most distal portions of nerves, may also occur in uremia.

Osteitis Deformans (Paget's Disease).

The neurologic complications of Paget's disease are those resulting from pressure on the CNS or the nerve roots by overgrowth of bone. Deafness, facial paralysis, visual changes, and compression of the spinal cord may occur. Secondary platybasia may take place in advanced cases.

Morgagni-Morel-Stewart Syndrome.

Hyperostosis of the internal table of the frontal bones in obese, hirsute women with complaints of headaches and mental disorders.

Vitamin B Complex Deficiencies.

Since members of the vitamin B complex are closely associated in function and occurrence, deficiency of more than one member often occurs. It is usually advisable to provide adequate dietary or parenteral sources for all members of the B complex.

A. Thiamine (Vitamin B_1): This is the coenzyme for decarboxylation of alpha-keto acids (pyruvic and alpha-ketoglutaric acid) and is important in normal carbohydrate metabolism. Beriberi (avitaminosis B_1) results from an inadequate intake due to diet, excessive cooking of foods, etc. Early or mild manifestations include anorexia, muscle cramps and tenderness, paresthesias, and depressed reflexes. Severe or late manifestations (beriberi) include anorexia, polyneuritis, paralysis of extremities, serous effusions, subcutaneous edema, and cardiac insufficiency. Treatment with thiamine chloride, 20-50 mg. orally, I.V., or I.M. daily in divided doses for 2 weeks and then 10-20 mg. orally daily, is usually adequate.

B. Niacin: Pellagra may result from deficiency of components of vitamin B complex. Niacin deficiency is the principal but not the only dietary deficit in pellagra; the low tryptophan content of some foods plays a role. Mild or early manifestations include skin redness and roughness and tongue redness. Severe or late changes include marked skin roughening after exposure to light and friction, diarrhea, scarlet red atrophic tongue, stomatitis, depression, mental dullness, rigidity, and peculiar sucking reactions. Nicotinamide, 50-500 mg. I.V., I.M., or orally daily, is given until symptoms subside, along with therapeutic doses of thiamine, riboflavin, and pyridoxine.

C. Pyridoxine (Vitamin B_6): Pyridoxine may be important in transamination and decarboxylation of proteins. Severe generalized convulsions occur in newborn infants and animals with pyridoxine dietary deficiencies. Neuropathies and convulsions secondary to drug effects produced by hydrazides may be prevented or alleviated with pyridoxine. In deficiency states, treatment with 10-50 mg. parenterally or orally daily is usually adequate.

D. Vitamin B_{12}: Vitamin B_{12} is believed to be the extrinsic factor or effective principle lacking in pernicious anemia. Posterolateral sclerosis (see p. 332) may be associated with deficiency of vitamin B_{12}.

NEUROLOGIC COMPLICATIONS OF DRUG AND CHEMICAL INTOXICATIONS

Heavy Metals.

A. Arsenic: The use of various arsenicals may be associated with polyneuritis, acute hemorrhagic encephalitis, or optic neuritis. Treatment with dimercaprol (BAL) may be helpful.

B. Lead: Neurologic complications of lead intoxication may take 2 forms. In adults there is usually a chronic polyneuritis with pain, paresthesia, weakness, and stocking and glove anesthesia of extremities. Lead encephalopathy, characterized by generalized or focal convulsions with subsequent paralysis, occurs in infants. Hemiplegia, papilledema, lethargy, and coma may occur. Treatment with chelating agents (calcium-disodium edathamil [Versenate®, EDTA]) may be helpful. Urinary lead excretion of less than 0.15 mg./liter is of doubtful diagnostic significance.

C. Manganese: Parkinsonism has been alleged to follow excessive exposure to manganese-containing dusts, which gain entrance to the body via the respiratory tract.

D. Thallium: Serious nervous system complications may occur. There may be associated optic neuritis or generalized polyneuritis. Acute severe poisoning may be associated with blindness, delirium, convulsions, and death.

E. Mercury: Organic mercurial poisoning was believed to account for the neurologic manifestations of Minamata disease. This disorder was noted among inhabitants of Minamata Bay in Japan who consumed contaminated fish and shellfish caught in the bay and developed constricted visual fields, ataxia, dysarthria, tremors, mental changes, salivation, sweating, and various extrapyramidal signs. Treatment with BAL and EDTA produced some improvement clinically.

Alcohols and Morphine.

A. Ethyl Alcohol: Acute ethyl alcohol intoxication may be associated with ataxia, mental confusion, psychosis, and coma. Chronic intoxication may be associated with delirium tremens, convulsions, polyneuritis, Korsakoff's psychosis, cerebellar degeneration, mental deterioration, or Wernicke's polioencephalitis. The onset of coma is believed to indicate a blood alcohol level of 250 mg./100 ml. Intoxication may be characterized by drunkenness, aggressiveness, or coma, and depression of some neurons of the brain may be the cause of neurologic disorders.

Withdrawal of alcohol after heavy drinking may induce, in sequence, tremulousness and nausea, seizure and hallucinosis, and delirium tremens. Vitamin supplements and a nutritious diet will not greatly speed recovery from the preceding clinical syndromes. However, dietary deficiencies associated with alcoholism may cause the syndromes of Wernicke's disease, Korsakoff's psychosis, polyneuropathy, amblyopia, and pellagra. Administration of thiamine to patients with Wernicke's disease reverses the ophthalmoplegia, ataxia, and nystagmus, and relieves apathy and drowsiness even if the patient continues to take alcohol. Alcoholic polyneuropathy and amblyopia may also be thus successfully treated. The psychic features of Wernicke's disease, the amnestic portion of Korsakoff's psychosis, and alcoholic dementia respond slowly and incompletely to thiamine therapy.

Korsakoff's syndrome consists of polyneuritis associated with loss of memory for recent events, confabulation, disorientation, and confusion. In **Wernicke's syndrome** the oculomotor palsies are due to involvement of nuclei of the third or fourth cranial nerve. Ptosis and pupillary changes are seen, and a tremor due to involvement of the red nucleus. There may also be optic neuritis, retinal hemorrhages, ataxic gait, and muscular weakness. Progression from drowsiness, stupor, and delirium to death usually occurs within 2 weeks. Quinquaud's sign or toxic tremor may occur in chronic alcoholism. When the patient spreads his fingers and presses their tips against the examiner's hand held vertically, a series of slight shocks are felt after a few seconds, as if the phalanges of each finger were knocking together.

B. Methyl Alcohol: Acute methyl alcohol intoxication may be characterized by lethargy, headache, impaired vision, delirium, and coma. Impaired vision may persist after acute intoxication; visual acuity may be greatly reduced, and central scotomas and contracted peripheral visual fields may occur.

C. Morphine and Related Alkaloids: Acute poisoning is manifested by stupor, coma, respiratory depression, pinpoint pupils, cyanosis, and shock. Death due to respiratory failure may occur. Oxygen, artificial respiration, and nalorphine (Nalline®) may be required. The suggested dose of Nalline® is 8 mg. intravenously every 20 minutes for a total of 3 doses.

Carbon Monoxide.
Acute serious carbon monoxide intoxications usually terminate in coma and death. In those few who recover, hemiparesis, impaired memory, aphasia, hyperkinesia, and parkinsonism may develop.

Anticonvulsant Drugs.
A. Hydantoins: Diphenylhydantoin (Dilantin®) may produce ataxia, nystagmus, hypertrophy of the gums, and morbilliform rash, which may be eliminated by discontinuing or reducing the drug.

B. Barbiturates: In therapeutic dosages, the barbiturate group may cause ataxia, thickness of speech, lethargy, and drowsiness. These usually disappear on reducing the dosage or withdrawing the drug. With acute overdoses, coma, respiratory depression, cyanosis, loss of reflexes, and pupillary reactions may occur. Chronic barbiturate poisoning is evidenced by mental changes, defective memory, emotional lability, nystagmus, ataxia, and tremor or weakness.

C. Bromides: Chronic bromidism may give rise to lethargy, ataxia, confusion, disorientation, delirium, and stupor. Chronic bromide poisoning is usually associated with an increased blood bromide level (above 150 mg./100 ml.).

Chemotherapeutic Drugs.
A. Streptomycin: Following high or prolonged dosage of streptomycin, vestibular and auditory nerve damage may occur, manifested by tinnitus, vertigo, and ataxia.

B. Quinine: Repeated use of quinine in large doses may be associated with visual loss (quinine amblyopia), pallor of optic disks, and papilledema.

C. Isoniazid: Excessive use of isoniazid in high dosage may cause polyneuritis, dizziness, headache, and convulsions in susceptible individuals.

Antihistaminic Drugs.
Diphenhydramine (Benadryl®), tripelennamine (Pyribenzamine®), and related compounds may cause drowsiness, headache, tremors, nervousness, excitement, and convulsions when excessive amounts are used.

Chlorinated Insecticides.
Acute poisoning with chlorophenothane (DDT), chlordane, and related compounds produces symptoms of hyperexcitability, tremors, ataxia, and convulsions.

Stimulant Drugs.

A. Strychnine is a component of various tonics and is commonly used in rodenticides. It may cause greatly increased reflex excitability, especially of the spinal cord. Spasms of muscles, particularly extensor spasms of extremities, of increasing severity and frequency, opisthotonos, and death from respiratory failure occur in acute intoxications.

B. Picrotoxin, pentylenetetrazol (Metrazol®), and nikethamide (Coramine®) stimulate the spinal cord, medulla, and cerebral cortex. The principal effect of intoxication with these drugs is convulsions.

C. Caffeine in large doses stimulates the CNS and may cause convulsions

Hemlock.

The principal evidences of hemlock poisoning are convulsions and respiratory failure. Following ingestion of water hemlock (Cicuta species), abdominal pain, nausea, vomiting, diarrhea, cyanosis, convulsions, and respiratory failure may occur. Following ingestion of poison hemlock (Conium maculatum), gradually-increasing muscle weakness and respiratory failure may occur.

Lathyrism.

A toxic agent found in the pea Lathyrus sativus is believed responsible for the selective pyramidal tract damage which occurs in lathyrism. This disorder, found in India and less often in Europe, is considered to be due to a variety of nitril compounds containing cyanide radicles which have been isolated from these legumes.

Snake Venoms.

Snake venoms may produce pronounced neurotoxic effects. Victims generally die through paralysis of respiratory muscles. Venoms may have a pronounced curarizing effect on muscles; weakness of limbs, oculomotor palsies, and ataxic gait appear first. Central effects, including analgesia, may also occur.

Hallucinogens.

The "hallucinogens" are drugs which can produce transient schizophrenic-like "experimental" psychoses in man. This group of drugs, most of which contain an indole ring in their chemical structure, includes lysergic acid diethylamide (LSD 25), yohimbine, harmine, ibogaine, mescaline, bufotenine, cannabis derivatives, tryptamine, and epinephrine breakdown products.

Different chemicals have been used to induce "model psychoses." These include the following: (1) Group composed of mescaline, DMT (NN-dimethyltryptamine) and DET (diethyltryptamine), psilocybin, LSD, and close derivatives. (2) Analogues of atropine. (3) Sernyl. (4) N-Allylnormorphine.

Studies on the mode of action of hallucinogenic drugs may help ultimately in uncovering some of the biochemical features of disorders which may produce psychoses in man.

Electrolytes.

Depletion of electrolytes by vomiting, intestinal drainage, diet, etc., may affect the sensorium and may induce mental changes, muscular weakness, and seizures. Excessive intake of fluids may cause water intoxication and convulsions. Extremely high levels of blood sodium may cause malaise, restlessness, confusion, hallucinations, and convulsions, and induce histologic changes in cerebral and renal tissues. Fluids in the form of 5% dextrose in water should be infused as needed once hypernatremia has been diagnosed.

Fatal or near fatal acidosis may follow ingestion of large doses of ammonium chloride. The associated low serum potassium has a neuromuscular depressant tendency.

Tranquilizers.

Many tranquilizers, especially the phenothiazines and reserpine, frequently produce reversible neurologic side effects of an extrapyramidal type. These effects include parkinsonism, dystonia or dyskinesia, and motor restlessness.

NEUROPATHIES

Polyneuritis (Multiple Neuritis, Peripheral Neuropathy).

Polyneuritis is a syndrome characterized by widespread sensory and motor disturbances of the peripheral nerves. It may appear at any age, although it is most common in young or middle-aged adults, especially in men. In most cases a noninflammatory degeneration of the peripheral nerves is present.

Polyneuritis may be caused by (1) chronic intoxications (e.g., alcohol, carbon disulfide, benzene, phosphorus, sulfonamides); (2) infections (e.g., meningitis, diphtheria, syphilis, tuberculosis, pneumonia, Guillain-Barré syndrome, mumps); (3) metabolic causes (e.g., diabetes mellitus, gout, pregnancy, rheumatism, porphyria, periarteritis nodosa, lupus erythematosus); and (4) nutritional causes (e.g., beriberi, vitamin deficiencies, cachectic states).

Symptoms usually develop slowly over a period of weeks. Notable exceptions with rapid onset may occur in infections plus alcoholic polyneuritis. Pains, tenderness, paresthesias, weakness and fatigability, and sensory impairment may be present. The pains may be mild or, occasionally, burning and sharp. Muscular weakness is usually greatest in the distal portions of the extremities. Impaired sensory perception, especially of vibration, is frequent; in alcoholic and arsenical polyneuritis, severe and extensive sensory defects may occur. The cutaneous sensory defect may consist of hypesthesia or anesthesia in an irregular stocking or glove distribution.

Tendon reflexes are usually depressed or absent. With paralyzed toes, the plantar response may be absent; with weak abdominal muscles, abdominal skin reflexes may be diminished or absent. Flaccid weakness and muscular atrophy of affected parts may occur, especially in the distal portions of the extremities. Foot drop with associated steppage gait may result.

Trophic changes of the skin of the extremities are manifested by a glossy red skin and impairment of the sweating mechanism. Muscles and nerves may be tender and hypersensitive to pressure and palpation.

Remove the patient from exposure to toxic agents (e.g., alcohol, lead). In lead polyneuritis, calcium disodium edathamil (Versenate®) may be beneficial. In arsenical polyneuritis, give dimercaprol (BAL).

Attempt to obtain optimal metabolism of nerve tissue by giving a high caloric diet and liberal use of vitamins, especially B complex. The entire B complex can be administered with thiamine hydrochloride, 15 mg. ($1/4$ gr.) 3-4 times daily orally or parenterally, and dried yeast (brewer's yeast), 10-30 Gm. ($1/3$-1 oz.) daily.

Place the patient at bed rest and forbid use of the affected limb. If a lower extremity is affected, keep a cradle over the foot of the bed to prevent pressure of bed covers. Give analgesics as necessary to control pain. After pain has subsided, massage and passive motion may be of value. Encourage active motion at the same time. Prevent contractures by means of splints and passive stretching.

In most forms of polyneuritis, recovery may occur once the cause has been corrected. In some cases the disorder progresses for weeks, remains stationary for a time, and goes on to slow recovery in 6-12 months. Objective sensory changes usually disappear first, and paralyses later; dysesthesias may persist during recovery.

Refsum's Syndrome.

A hereditary neuropathy (recessive) with atypical retinitis pigmentosa, night blindness and concentric constriction of visual fields, chronic polyneuritis, progressive nerve deafness, and elevated CSF protein.

Déjerine-Sottas Syndrome (Hypertrophic Interstitial Neuritis).

A rare heredofamilial disease characterized by chronic progressive polyneuritis associated with collagenous degeneration of the endoneurium or sheath of Schwann, with degeneration of myelin sheath and nerve fibers. Thickened peripheral nerves may be palpable and visible.

Macroglobulinemia (Waldenström's Primary Macroglobulinemia).

This disorder, characterized by excess of abnormal macroglobulin in blood, may be associated with severe polyneuropathy, generalized exhaustion, loss of weight, bleeding diathesis (with normal clotting factors), and Raynaud's syndrome.

Neuritis.

Inflammation or degeneration of the peripheral nerves may be local or widespread. **Mononeuritis** (localized neuritis) affects a small group of nerves or a single nerve trunk. Etiologic factors include trauma (contusion, tearing, compression, or stretching of the nerve), chronic intoxications (by alcohol or metallic poisons), and infections (local or generalized, or by extension from adjacent infected parts). The inflammatory reaction may be of one of 3 types: In perineuritis (limited to the perineurium) and interstitial neuritis (affecting the interstices) the nerves are swollen and red. Parenchymatous neuritis affects the nerve fibers themselves (myelin sheath, axis cylinders, and neurilemma), causing a shrunken, pale, translucent appearance. Symptoms include irritative phenomena (pain, tenderness, paresthesias), motor loss (flaccid paralysis with muscle atrophy and reaction of degeneration), sensory loss, and, at times, trophic and vasomotor changes. Prognosis depends upon the extent and character of the injury. Treatment is directed toward removal of the cause, relief of pain, and prevention of contractures.

Neuralgia.

Neuralgia is a syndrome affecting various sensory nerves and characterized by sudden paroxysmal attacks of pain, usually of short duration, occurring in the distribution of the nerve fibers and not associated with pathologic changes in the nerve. An attack may be brought on by various causes, e.g., local pressure, cold, movement, pressure on the nerve trunk, or stimulation of a "trigger zone." Vasomotor symptoms may accompany an attack, e.g., reddening of the skin, sweating, edema, tearing, and excessive salivation. The various types of neuralgia include the following: trigeminal, sphenopalatine, glossopharyngeal, superior laryngeal, cervico-occipital, brachial, intercostal, phrenic, visceral, lumbar, sciatic, and coccygeal.

Trigeminal (Trifacial) Neuralgia (Tic Douloureux).

Trigeminal neuralgia is characterized by a sudden attack of excruciating pain of short duration along the distribution of the fifth cranial nerve. The attack is normally precipitated by stimulation (usually mild) of a "trigger zone" in the area of the pain, and is characterized by recurrent paroxysms of sharp, stabbing pains in the distribution of one or more branches of the nerve. The onset is usually in middle or late life, and the incidence is higher in women. The pain may be described as searing or burning, occurring in lightning-like jabs, lasting only 1-2 minutes or as long as 15 minutes. The frequency of attacks varies from many times daily to several times a month or a year. The patient often tries to immobilize his face during conversation, or attempts to swallow food without chewing in order not to irritate the trigger zone.

Medical treatment is generally unsatisfactory, but the following have often been tried before resorting to surgery:

(1) Trichloroethylene (Trilene®), 15-20 drops a day by inhalation from a handkerchief, in a single dose or in divided doses one-half hour before meals.

(2) Massive doses of vitamin B_{12} (1 mg. I.M. daily for 10 days) have been reported to relieve the severe pain.

(3) Stilbamidine isethionate has been shown to produce a chemical neuropathy affecting the facial and cervical skin areas. Give a series of 10 daily I.V. injections of 0.15 Gm. freshly dissolved in 150 ml. of 5% glucose in distilled water over a period of one-half hour. Relief of pain may be delayed 1-5 months until the chemical neuropathy occurs. In a small percentage of cases treated with stilbamidine, unpredictable and troublesome formication and paresthesias of the face occur.

(4) Anticonvulsants, e.g., diphenylhydantoin sodium (Dilantin®), 0.1 Gm. q.i.d.; or vasodilators, e.g., tolazoline hydrochloride (Priscoline®), 50 mg. q.i.d., have been reported to be beneficial in some cases.

(5) Alcohol injection of the ganglion or the branches of the trigeminal nerve may produce analgesia and relief from pain for several months or years. Repeated injections may be required at later intervals.

Surgery may be required if there is no relief from medical treatment.

In most cases the paroxysms of pain are present for several weeks or months. Remissions may last from a few days to as long as several months or years. As patients become older, remissions tend to become shorter

•   •   •

30...

Epilepsy

Epilepsy is characterized by sudden, transient alterations of brain function, usually with motor, sensory, autonomic, or psychic symptoms and often accompanied by alterations in consciousness. Coincidental pronounced brain wave alterations in the electroencephalogram (EEG) may be detected during these episodes.

Etiology.

Epilepsy was formerly classified as "idiopathic" or jacksonian. With the development of more precise diagnostic tests and instruments, idiopathic epilepsy has been found in many cases to be the result of abnormally active brain tissue caused by injury, infection, or unknown agents. Idiopathic epilepsy tends to run in families.

Seizures indistinguishable from idiopathic epilepsy may occur in organic brain disease such as brain tumor, cerebral vascular accident, post-traumatic cerebral scar, and intracranial infection. Metabolic disorders, such as uremia, hypoglycemia, hypocalcemia, and excessive hydration may also give rise to seizures.

In children, the most common causes of symptomatic epilepsy are birth injury and anoxia, inflammatory brain lesions, cerebrovascular accidents, head injuries, and congenital brain malformations.

In susceptible individuals, physical stimuli (e.g., light, sound, touch) may precipitate seizures. In some epileptics, seizures characteristically occur during sleep. Other factors may indirectly affect the susceptibility of a particular patient to seizures, e.g., excessive alcohol intake, emotional tension, fatigue, and lack of food and sleep.

Seizures may occur in groups over a period of hours or days. In individual patients, the pattern of seizures is apt to be stereotyped. The patient himself may not be aware of the nature of his attacks, so that verification by a witness is desirable. Temporary postseizure paresis (Todd's paralysis) may occur, particularly with seizures arising in the motor cortex.

Pathology.

Since epilepsy is a syndrome rather than a specific disease entity, it is not surprising that in most cases of idiopathic epilepsy histologic examination fails to show specific pathologic tissue alterations. Despite many biochemical and physiologic studies in patients with convulsions, the pathophysiology of convulsive seizures remains obscure. Seizures are more apt to occur in patients with organic brain lesions than in those with a normal CNS.

Pathologic Physiology.

The metabolic activity of the brain varies somewhat with the state of functional activity. When there is a general increase in neuronal activity, as in convulsive states and in states of diffuse neuromuscular activity, metabolic activity is increased. However, there is no significant change in over-all metabolic activity in highly localized types of cerebral function. The decrease in oxygen consumption of brain and of activity of enzymes associated with glucose utilization in the older age groups may be due to progressive decrease in the ratio of neurons to glial cells.

Acetylcholine and cholinesterase activity have been demonstrated in every cortical layer of the normal brain and are roughly proportionate to neuron density and size. Epileptic cortical foci are reported to have elevated cholinesterase activity, and changes in the bound acetylcholine of the brain may be demonstrated before and during experimentally induced seizures in animals. These findings have been interpreted to indicate that alteration in acetylcholine metabolism occurs in conjunction with epileptic brain abnormalities.

However, other neurochemical mechanisms unrelated to acetylcholine metabolism may also be important in the production of convulsive seizures. Increased production of ammonia may immediately precede the onset of experimental seizures, and abnormalities of potassium distribution have been found in convulsed brain segments. Toxic epileptogenic

Classification of the Epilepsies*

Group	Attack Pattern	Electrographic Findings	Radiographic Findings	Clinical and Pathologic Findings
Focal epilepsy (cortical or sub-cortical)	Focal attack pattern depends on site or origin in brain. This includes focal temporal seizures with automatism. Attacks major or minor in degree.	Focal spikes, sharp waves, etc.	Cranial growth asymmetry, intra-cranial calcification, etc., may be present; pneumogram may show focal change, depending on type of lesion.	Clinical examination may show focal neurologic signs. Attacks secondary to a variety of lesions: agenesis and other congenital abnormalities, birth injury, focal vascular lesions and anomalies, syphilis, lead, parasites, encephalitis, degenerative diseases, diffuse vascular diseases, scar, neoplasm, abscess; or no lesion may be found.
Central or "centrencephalic" epilepsy	Attacks major or minor (true "petit mal"); little or no warning; movements symmetrical. Focal attack patterns unusual. Myoclonic jerks common. Automatism may occur.	3-per-second wave and spike, bilaterally synchronous. Bitemporal 4- to 6-per-second waves.	Cranium usually normal. Pneumogram normal or may show symmetrical enlargement of ventricles.	Examination usually normal. Cause usually unknown. Birth trauma and anoxia possible etiologic factors.
Epilepsy, unlocalized (of known cause)	Focal attack pattern unusual or varied. Attacks major or minor in degree.	Generalized multiforme (including slow spike and wave), or may be normal.	Pneumogram normal or shows diffuse changes. Usually atrophic.	Findings vary with cause: (1) diffuse cerebral lesions, as listed under focal epilepsy; (2) extracerebral causes, e.g., fever, hypoglycemia, cerebral anemia, anoxia.
Epilepsy, unlocalized (of unknown cause)	Focal attack pattern unusual. Attacks major or minor in degree.	Normal or indefinite.	Normal or indefinite.	Unknown or indefinite. Many patients fall first into this category. Further study may reclassify under one of the above groups.

*Modified by F. L. McNaughton and reproduced, with permission, from F. L. McNaughton, The Classification of the Epilepsies. Epilepsia (Third Series), Vol. I, November, 1952.

Penfield and Erickson attempt to relate type of seizure and anatomic localization, as follows:

	Clinical Type	Localization
Somatic motor	Generalized (grand mal)	Complete motor
	Jacksonian (local motor)	Pre-rolandic gyrus
	Masticatory	Lower rolandic
	Simple adversive	Frontal
	Tonic postural (decerebrate, opisthotonic)	Brain stem
Somatic sensory (auras)	Somatosensory	Post-rolandic gyrus
	Visual	Occipital
	Auditory	Temporal
	Vertiginous	Temporal
	Olfactory	Infratemporal
Visceral	Autonomic	Diencephalic
Psychical	Dreamy state	Temporal
	Petit mal	
	Automatism (ictal and post-ictal)	
	Psychotic states (secondary)	

Penfield and Erickson also relate age at onset of seizures to the presumptive cause, as follows:

Age at Onset	Presumptive Cause
Infancy (0-2)	Birth injury, degeneration, congenital
Childhood (2-10)	Birth injury, febrile thrombosis, trauma, cryptogenic
Adolescence (10-20)	Trauma, obscure causes
Youth (20-35)	Trauma, neoplasm
Middle age (35-55)	Neoplasm, trauma, arteriosclerosis
Senescence (55-70)	Arteriosclerosis, neoplasm

agents (e.g., fluoroacetate) block the citric acid cycle while producing convulsions. Inhibition of glutamine synthesis in the brain occurs after treatment with methionine sulfoxime, the toxic convulsant agent of nitrogen trichloride (agene). A deficiency of pyridoxine causes seizures in infants and animals, and certain convulsant drugs such as the carbazide series act by inducing pyridoxine deficiency. Glutamine and asparagine can reverse the defective glutamic acid metabolism of certain types of epileptogenic cortex, thus inhibiting seizures. Chronic experimental epilepsy is readily induced in monkeys by treatment of cerebral cortex with aluminum hydroxide; other metals may also be effective. In guinea pigs with allergic encephalomyelitis, convulsive seizures have been noted to be correlated directly with marked increase of intracellular sodium, and unrelated to water increase or potassium depletion. Hamsters develop convulsive seizures after large cream meals or meals of saturated fatty acids; however, after vegetable and fish oil meals of the same size, only occasional or no seizures occur. Reduction in available oxygen in brain occurred after cream meals and varied directly with the amount of cream feedings.

Classification.*

In general, an attempt should be made to determine the anatomic site of onset and the pathologic etiology. On the basis of clinical findings, the seizures may be classified as follows:

A. **Grand Mal:** A typical aura may signal to the patient that an attack is impending. This aura is usually specific for the individual patient and may consist of a sensation of nausea or numbness, an odor, a visual image, or a flash of memory. Loss of consciousness usually ensues, and the patient falls to the floor. In the fall, he may emit a cry and frequently incurs some bodily injury. Convulsions usually follow; the patient lies stiff and mildly rigid for as long as 1-2 minutes, and the muscles of the body are in a state of mild tonic contraction. A clonic stage follows in which rhythmic, severe, synchronous, convulsive movements of the body occur. Control of the bowels and bladder is frequently lost, and biting injuries to the tongue are common. More rarely, fractures of bones may occur. A variable period of sleep and stupor, lasting usually 1-4 hours, follows this phase. The patient is not his normal self if awake and has little recollection of events during this period.

*McNaughton's proposed classification of the epilepsies is given in the chart on p. 346.

Upon full recovery from the attack, he frequently is aware of painful muscles.

B. **Petit Mal:** Seizures may occur in which the patient has a minor or abortive attack not associated with falling or convulsive movements of the body. Instead there is a momentary or transient loss of consciousness, so fleeting or camouflaged in ordinary activity that neither the patient nor his associates may be entirely aware of it. The "petit mal triad," according to Lennox, includes myoclonic jerks, akinetic seizures, and brief absences, all of which usually are accompanied by the specific three-per-second spike and wave EEG pattern. In classic petit mal there is sudden vacant expression, cessation of motor activity generally, and sometimes loss of muscle tone. Abrupt return of consciousness with resumption of mental and physical activity occurs. Many attacks, sometimes as many as 100/day, may be noted.

Myoclonic jerks of limbs or muscles may occur without evident alteration of consciousness or in association with a typical absence. Myoclonic jerks tend to occur more frequently in the morning and on going to sleep; normal individuals may have rare myoclonic jerks in drowsiness or light sleep.

Akinetic attacks are seizures of sudden, brief loss of postural tone, the subject slumping a little before catching himself or recovering just after the knees or body touch the ground.

Myoclonus epilepsy (Unverricht's familial myoclonic epilepsy) is a familial convulsive disorder manifested by generalized seizures. It occurs usually in prepuberal girls. After several years, myoclonia (irregular, lightning-like, arrhythmic jerks of muscle groups, unaccompanied by movements of the extremities) becomes progressively more intense and widespread and is associated with gradual dementia and perhaps signs of a bulbar disorder.

C. **Psychomotor Seizures:** This category now includes practically all types of attacks which do not conform to the classical descriptions of grand mal, focal jacksonian seizure, or petit mal. Automatisms, patterned movements, apparently purposeful movements, incoherent speech, turnings of the head and eyes, smacking of the lips, twisting and writhing movements of the extremities, clouding of consciousness, and amnesia commonly occur. It has been postulated that "equivalent states" exist in which the patient exhibits a behavior disturbance rather than the classical convulsion. Temporal lobe foci (spikes, sharp waves, or combinations) are frequently associated with this type of epilepsy. Accentuation of EEG abnormalities during light phases of sleep is sometimes striking.

D. Jacksonian Epilepsy: Seizures due to focal irritation of a portion of the motor cortex may be confined to the appropriate peripheral area. Consciousness may be retained, and the seizure may spread over the rest of the adjacent motor cortex to involve adjacent peripheral parts. This type of seizure is most commonly associated with organic lesions such as brain tumor or scar.

E. Status Epilepticus: This serious disorder consists of a train of severe seizures with relatively short intervals or no intervals between. The patient becomes exhausted and frequently hyperthermic. Death not uncommonly occurs during attacks.

F. Epilepsia Partialis Continua (Kojevnikoff's Epilepsy): Characterized by convulsive activity of one part of the body which may continue steadily (or with brief interruptions) over long periods of time. Localized, continuing, myoclonic seizures or focal motor seizures, usually without spread, may occur.

G. Reflex Epilepsy: Focal or generalized convulsive seizures associated with concomitant alterations in the EEG can be evoked in some epileptic patients following sensory stimulation of a somatic trigger zone.

H. Febrile Convulsions: Fever and convulsions are commonly encountered in the very young. A febrile convulsion is apt to be the first convulsion of an epileptic child, and febrile convulsions are said to be about twice as common among children with a family history of epilepsy. Various explanations of this relationship have been offered, including the following: (1) Fever results from the liberation of heat and energy which occurs during muscular contractions caused by the seizure. (2) Fever results from hypothalamic seizure discharge. (3) Fever and convulsions both are caused by an infectious organism. (4) Excessive hydration and drugs to combat infection may cause convulsions. (5) Convulsions may result from a pathologic brain reaction induced by an infection. (6) The immature brain may respond to high fever and an infectious agent with a convulsion.

The prognosis of febrile convulsions varies. Many children subsequently develop psychomotor seizures. Nonfebrile convulsions also occur in a majority of patients with a history of febrile convulsions. Most children with a history of febrile convulsions have had only 1-2 such febrile seizures.

I. Massive Spasms: This type of seizure is fairly common in the first 2 years of life.

It is characterized by sudden strong contraction of most of the body musculature, often resulting in transient doubling up of the body and flexion-adduction of the limbs. Attacks may occur singly or in a series beginning with strong, prolonged contractions which become progressively weaker at progressively longer intervals. Attacks are apt to occur in children with evidence of motor and mental retardation and may disappear after the age of 3 years. Electroencephalography frequently shows a pattern of hypsarrhythmia; a favorable response to treatment with corticotropin has been noted in some cases.

Diagnosis.

The diagnosis of epilepsy may be made on the basis of a history of recurrent seizures and the observation of a typical seizure. Physical and neurologic examination, skull x-rays, CSF manometrics, cell and protein studies, cerebral angiography, and air studies may be helpful and are usually made. Electroencephalography (see p. 223) has become a most objective tool in the diagnosis of epilepsy. With the use of provocative measures such as intravenous pentylenetetrazol (Metrazol®) and barbiturates, sleep, hyperventilation, and postural changes, accurate diagnoses of epilepsy can be made with a fair degree of certainty.

Behavioral or emotional components may be so pronounced as to mask the underlying convulsive disorder. Following a grand mal episode or a series of brief seizures, patients may remain confused for minutes to hours. Disorientation, anxiety, hallucinations, paranoid delusions, excitement, and aggressive activity may be overwhelming.

Patients with petit mal, especially when attacks are frequent, may appear to be daydreaming; staring and blank spells often occur without the patient's knowledge. Impaired learning ability, short attention span, and restlessness are often associated. Petit mal status may be diagnosed as aimless wandering, erratic behavior, or incoherent speech.

Automatisms may occur, particularly with seizures of temporal lobe origin. Complex acts, movements, walking, lip-smacking, chewing movements, etc. may occur for periods of seconds to 10 minutes. An abnormal feeling of familiarity, called déjà vu, wherein the patient has the feeling he has lived through the present situation before, including what he sees, hears, thinks, or experiences, may be present. Depersonalization, in which familiar things, faces, etc. become strange, may also appear occasionally as part of a seizure syndrome. Fear or depression at the beginning of a convulsion, and automatic thinking of a stereotyped nature, may prevail. Increased irritability, especially before grand mal episodes, and variable grades of mental dullness may be manifested. Episodic psychoses in epileptic patients may be part of the epileptic disorder.

Children with epilepsy often appear to be restless, hyperactive, aggressive, and irritable. These traits as well as learning difficulties and apparent mental retardation sometimes may be improved by adequate anticonvulsant therapy.

Complications.

Fractures and soft tissue injuries may occur during seizures. Mental and emotional changes, particularly in poorly controlled epileptics, sometimes occur. Behavioral or emotional components may mask an underlying convulsive disorder. Examples are disorientation, hallucinations, excitement, incoherent speech, erratic behavior, automatisms, mental dullness, and irritability.

Treatment.

The objective of therapy is complete suppression of symptoms, though in many cases this is not possible. Most epileptics must continue to receive anticonvulsant therapy throughout life. However, if seizures are entirely controlled for 3-5 years, the dosage may be slowly reduced (over a period of 1-2 years) and finally withdrawn to ascertain if seizures will recur.

The patient must be acquainted with his disease and encouraged to become a member of local branches of groups interested in the welfare of epileptics, such as the American Epilepsy Society, the United Epilepsy Association, and the National Epilepsy League. Patients may receive information regarding research and treatment from these organizations.

Excellent books about epilepsy are W.G. Lennox: Science and Seizures, Harper, 1941; T.J. Putnam: On Convulsive Seizures, A Manual for Patients, Lippincott, 1945; and F.A. Gibbs and F.W. Stamps: Epilepsy Handbook, Thomas, 1958.

Epileptic patients should avoid hazardous occupations and driving. It is important to maintain a regular program of activity to keep the patient in optimal physical condition but avoiding excessive fatigue. Forbid all alcohol. Treat emotional factors as indicated. Impress upon the patient the absolute necessity of faithful adherence to the drug regimen. An epilepsy identification card should be carried at all times.

Except in status epilepticus, no specific treatment is usually given during an attack except to protect the patient from injury. Anticonvulsant measures (see also p. 350) in the 4 principal types of epilepsy are as follows:

A. Grand Mal: **Caution:** Never withdraw anticonvulsant drugs suddenly.

1. Diphenylhydantoin sodium (Dilantin®) is the drug of choice. Give 0.1 Gm. after the evening meal for 3-7 days, increasing dosage by 0.1 Gm. daily every week until seizures are brought under control. If attacks are severe and frequent, it may be necessary to begin with 0.3 Gm. daily on the first visit. The average dose is 0.4-0.6 Gm. daily. After convulsive seizures are controlled, the dosage may be reduced if desired, but the dosage should immediately be raised again if symptoms return.

2. Phenobarbital - If the patient is on maximum dosage of diphenylhydantoin and there is inadequate response, give phenobarbital in addition to diphenylhydantoin, increasing dosage as with diphenylhydantoin, while maintaining full dosage of diphenylhydantoin. Some clinicians prefer to begin with phenobarbital and maintain without diphenylhydantoin if possible. In many cases the 2 drugs used in combination are more effective than either drug used alone.

3. Methylphenylethylhydantoin (Mesantoin®) - If excessive gum hypertrophy results from the use of diphenylhydantoin, methylphenylethylhydantoin may be tried in its place. The dosage is the same. This drug may be effective where grand mal and petit mal coexist. Do not change suddenly to methylphenylethylhydantoin, but gradually substitute for diphenylhydantoin. Combinations of both may prove more useful than the individual drugs.

4. Bromides, primidone (Mysoline®), mephobarbital (Mebaral®), or ethotoin (Peganone®) may be tried (see p. 350).

B. Petit Mal: In very mild petit mal, if attacks are rare, treat only with phenobarbital. Mild attacks can often be treated successfully with amphetamine sulfate (Benzedrine®), 5-10 mg. 2-3 times daily. Do not use amphetamine if the patient also has grand mal, because this drug may precipitate grand mal attacks. Glutamic acid, 8-10 Gm. daily, may decrease the number of attacks.

For moderate and severe petit mal, trimethadione (Tridione®), is the drug of choice. Unfortunately it is not an entirely safe drug since it causes bone marrow depression in some patients. **Caution:** Whenever this drug is used, perform CBC once or twice a week for the first month, then every 2 weeks for 2-3 months, and monthly thereafter. Begin with

Drugs Used in Epilepsy

Drug	Indications	Average Daily Dose	Toxicity and Precautions	Remarks
Diphenylhydantoin sodium (Dilantin®)	Grand mal, some cases of psychomotor epilepsy.	0.4-0.6 Gm. in divided doses.	Gum hypertrophy (dental hygiene); nervousness, rash, ataxia, drowsiness, nystagmus (reduce dosage).	Safest for grand mal and psychomotor epilepsy. May accentuate petit mal.
Methylphenylethylhydantoin (Mesantoin®)	Grand mal, some cases of psychomotor epilepsy. Effective when grand mal and petit mal coexist.	0.3-0.5 Gm. in divided doses.	Nervousness, ataxia, nystagmus (reduce dose); pancytopenia (frequent blood counts); exfoliative dermatitis (stop drug if severe skin eruption develops).	Does not cause gum hypertrophy.
Trimethadione (Tridione®)	Drug of choice in petit mal.	0.3-2 Gm. in divided doses.	Bone marrow depression, pancytopenia, exfoliative dermatitis (as above); photophobia (usually disappears; dark glasses); nephrosis (frequent urinalysis; discontinue if renal lesion develops).	Do not use alone for grand mal; may aggravate this condition.
Paramethadione (Paradione®)	Petit mal.	0.3-2 Gm. in divided doses.	As for trimethadione.	Toxic reactions stated to be less than with trimethadione. Other remarks as for trimethadione.
Phenacemide (Phenurone®)	Psychomotor epilepsy.	0.5-5 Gm. in divided doses.	Hepatitis (liver function tests at onset; follow urinary urobilinogen at regular intervals); benign proteinuria (stop drug; may continue if patient is having marked relief); dermatitis (stop drug); headache and personality changes (stop drug if severe).	
Phenobarbital	All epilepsies, especially as adjunct.	0.1-0.4 Gm. in divided doses.	Drowsiness (decrease dose); dermatitis (stop drug and resume later; if dermatitis recurs, stop drug entirely).	One of safest drugs. May sometimes aggravate psychomotor seizures. Toxic reactions rare.
Mephobarbital (Mebaral®)	As phenobarbital.	0.2-0.9 Gm. in divided doses.	As for phenobarbital. Usually has no advantage over phenobarbital and must be used in twice dosage.	
Bromides (potassium bromide or sodium bromide)	All epilepsies, especially as adjuncts.	3-6 Gm. in divided doses.	Psychoses, mental dullness, acneiform rash (stop drug; may resume at lower dose).	Rarely used now. Effective at times when all else fails.
Metharbital (Gemonil®)	Grand mal.	0.1-0.8 Gm. in divided doses.	Drowsiness (decrease dose).	Especially effective in seizures associated with organic brain damage and infantile myoclonic epilepsy.
Primidone (Mysoline®)	Grand mal.	0.5-2 Gm. in divided doses.	Drowsiness (decrease dose); ataxia (decrease dose or stop drug).	Useful in conjunction with other anticonvulsants.
Phensuximide (Milontin®)	Petit mal.	0.5-2.5 Gm. in divided doses.	Nausea, ataxia, dizziness (reduce dose or discontinue); hematuria (discontinue).	
Methsuximide (Celontin®)	Petit mal, psychomotor epilepsy.	1.2 Gm. in divided doses.	Ataxia, drowsiness (decrease dose or discontinue).	

[Cont'd. on next page.]

Drugs Used in Epilepsy (Cont'd.)

Drug	Indications	Average Daily Dose	Toxicity and Precautions	Remarks
Acetazolamide (Diamox®)	Grand mal.	1-3 Gm. in divided doses (0.25 Gm. t.i.d. initially). Drowsiness and paresthesias may occur. (Reduce dose.)		
Ethotoin (Peganone®)	Grand mal.	2-3 Gm. in divided doses.	Dizziness, fatigue, skin rash (decrease dose or discontinue).	
Amino-glutethimide (Elipten®)	As phenobarbital.	0.75-1.5 Gm.	Frequent skin rash.	Doriden® analogue. Usefulness not yet established.

0.3 Gm. daily and increase the daily dose by 0.3 Gm. every 7 days until attacks are controlled. Do not give more than 2 Gm. daily.

If grand mal seizures occur also, trimethadione may aggravate this tendency; it may therefore be necessary to administer medication for grand mal seizures simultaneously, and in some cases to stop the trimethadione. Paramethadione (Paradione®) is said to be less toxic than trimethadione. It is almost equally effective in petit mal attacks, and may be effective where other drugs fail. Observe precautions as for trimethadione.

Phensuximide (Milontin®), phenobarbital, methsuximide (Celontin®), acetazolamide (Diamox®), or mephobarbital (Mebaral®) may prove useful (see table).

C. Status Epilepticus: Amobarbital sodium (Amytal Sodium®), 0.5-1 Gm. I.V., may be given. Intravenous phenobarbital sodium, 0.4-0.8 Gm., injected slowly may be used. Paraldehyde, 1-2 ml. diluted in a triple volume of saline I.V. slowly, is an effective alternative. If the convulsion continues, repeat the I.V. dose **very slowly and cautiously**, or give 8-12 ml. I.M. Diphenylhydantoin sodium (Dilantin Sodium®) may be injected I.V. at a rate not exceeding 50 mg./minute. A total dosage of 150-250 mg. may be required. General anesthesia may be used if all measures fail. Diphenylhydantoin sodium (Dilantin Sodium®), 250-500 mg. I.M. daily, or phenobarbital sodium, 30-60 mg. I.M. q.i.d. **(or both)**, may be required until the patient is able to take medication orally.

D. Psychomotor Epilepsy: Patients must be watched and guarded to prevent injury to themselves or others. Diphenylhydantoin sodium (Dilantin®), with or without phenobarbital, as for grand mal epilepsy, is the treatment of choice. Phenacemide (Phenurone®) is also effective. Give initially 0.5 Gm. t.i.d. and increase (until symptoms are controlled) up to 5 Gm. daily in 3-5 equal doses. Methylphenylethylhydantoin (Mesantoin®), mephobarbital (Mebaral®), primidone (Mysoline®),

acetazolamide (Diamox®), and methsuximide (Celontin®), alone or in combination with other drugs, are frequently useful.

E. Massive Spasms: Treatment is difficult, and the spasms are usually quite resistant to therapy. Metharbital (Gemonil®), mephobarbital (Mebaral®), methsuximide (Celontin®), and meprobamate (Equanil®, Miltown®) may be helpful; corticotropin (ACTH) or cortisone is also reported to be effective.

Prognosis.

In epilepsy due to identifiable lesions, the outcome varies with the underlying disease. In idiopathic epilepsy, skillful use of anticonvulsant drugs causes significant improvement in the great majority of cases.

NARCOLEPSY

Narcolepsy is a clinical syndrome characterized by intermittent episodes of uncontrollable sleep. Sudden transient loss of muscle tone in the extremities or trunk (cataplexy) and pathologic muscle weakness during emotional reactions may also occur. Attacks of sleep may occur several times daily and last from minutes to hours. Sleep attacks may occur under appropriate or inappropriate circumstances, with or without forewarning. The nocturnal sleep of narcoleptics is usually unremarkable. Narcolepsy may be associated with moderate to severe obesity. Cataplectic attacks, with loss of muscle tone and weakness, may occur under acute emotional stimulation, particularly with surprise. The Kleine-Levin syndrome (of hypersomnia and bulimia, believed to be related to narcolepsy) usually occurs in young males and is characterized by episodes of excessive hunger (bulimia) and somnolence. Clouding of the sensorium and amnesia for portions of the attacks may occur.

Treatment.

Treatment with stimulant drugs in sufficient dosage at proper intervals often gives satisfactory results.

A. Amphetamine Sulfate (Benzedrine®): The average dose is 10-20 mg. t.i.d., but up to 175 mg. daily may be required for some patients. The optimal dosage may be determined by starting with 10 mg. each morning and increasing the dosage as necessary to control symptoms.

B. Dextro Amphetamine Sulfate (Dexedrine®): Give 5 mg. each morning initially and increase as necessary. Long-acting capsules (Dexedrine Spansules®) are available in 5, 10, and 15 mg. doses.

C. Ephedrine Sulfate: Ephedrine is not as satisfactory as amphetamine but is helpful in many cases. The average dose is 25-50 mg. 2-4 times daily.

D. Methylphenidate Hydrochloride (Ritalin®): Used in doses of 5-10 mg. 3-4 times daily (or more if necessary).

Prognosis.

Narcolepsy usually persists throughout life. Although the attacks of somolence and sleep may be relieved by medical treatment, the cataplexy and attacks of muscular weakness which accompany emotional reactions (laughing, crying) are usually not affected by drug therapy.

BREATH-HOLDING ATTACKS

These attacks, which occur in infants and children, are usually precipitated by emotional distress, e.g., fright, pain, frustration, or anxiety. The child begins to cry, suddenly holds his breath, becomes limp or stiff, and loses consciousness. The episode usually lasts briefly and is associated with cyanosis; recovery from the episode is usually rapid and complete. In some cases, however, the rigid phase may be followed by a series of jerks or tonic-clonic generalized seizures, after which the infant may appear sleepy or fall asleep. These attacks are benign and generally cease by the time the child is 3 years old; they are not considered to be epileptic in origin, although there may be improvement under treatment with anticonvulsant drugs such as dipheny-hydantoin or phenobarbital.

31 . . .

Syncope and Coma

Syncope, or fainting, is a symptom complex in which there is a sudden, brief loss of consciousness and decreased muscle tone. Sensations of lightheadedness, dizziness, weakness, giddiness, and decreased motor power may precede the full episode. Some episodes of syncope may be aborted or prevented by lying down.

Syncopal attacks usually involve one or more of the following pathophysiologic mechanisms: (1) impaired cerebral circulation, (2) impaired cerebral metabolism, and (3) psychosomatic alterations.

Differential Diagnosis of Syncope.

Some clinical conditions are characterized by episodic disturbances which superficially resemble and must be differentiated from syncopal attacks.

A. Epilepsy: Those varieties not associated with pronounced motor convulsive manifestations, such as petit mal and some psychomotor types, are frequently considered as fainting by the patient and his family. Careful history and EEG studies will usually assist in differentiation (see Chapter 30).

B. Narcolepsy: This disorder is characterized by a propensity to sleep, even when the patient is well rested. It is sometimes associated with **cataplexy**, a symptom in which there is sudden loss of muscular tone without loss of consciousness, usually precipitated by acute emotional stimuli (e.g., fright, laughter).

C. Labyrinthitis: Disturbances of the vestibular mechanism may be associated with episodic dizziness and exacerbated by certain postures and motions. Attacks are often associated with nausea, vomiting, tinnitus, deafness, or nystagmus. Loss of consciousness does not usually occur.

VASODEPRESSOR SYNCOPE

The commonest variety of syncope is vasodepressor syncope. It may be precipitated by fear, anxiety, or pain (e.g., pre-

ceding or during surgical procedures), or psychic shock (e.g., the sight of blood). It is more apt to occur with the patient in the standing position.

Among the possible basic reactions contributing to syncopal episodes are the following: physiologic effects of the fear reaction; tissue damage; reaction to pain, especially from deep structures; reflex reactions to injury of certain areas (e.g., testicles, blood vessels, alimentary tract); impaired cerebral circulation (arteriosclerosis), reduced blood volume, and peripheral vasodilatation.

In the early phase there may be motor weakness, epigastric distress, perspiration, restlessness, yawning, and sighing respirations. The subject may appear anxious and may have a pale face and cold, moist extremities. After several minutes lightheadedness, blurring of vision, and sudden loss of consciousness with decreased muscle tone may appear. If the patient remains erect, a brief but mild convulsion may follow. The syncope is associated with a rapid drop in arterial blood pressure and a slowing of the heart rate. Loss of consciousness may occur at about 75 mm. Hg systolic blood pressure. The recumbent position usually aids in retarding further progression or in preventing recurrence of symptoms. In severe syncopal episodes, signs and symptoms similar to those of primary shock may occur, i.e., extreme pallor, weak pulse, shallow respirations, and flaccid muscles.

Electroencephalographic changes occur after the onset of unconsciousness. These consist of the abrupt appearance of diffuse, high amplitude, very slow wave activity.

Treatment of the individual episode consists of maintaining the patient in the recumbent position until fully recovered. When the patient resumes the erect position, he should move about actively. In individuals with frequent recurrences of syncopal attacks, psychologic evaluation and treatment may be indicated.

CAROTID SINUS SYNCOPE

Three types of carotid sinus syncope have been described. This classification is based

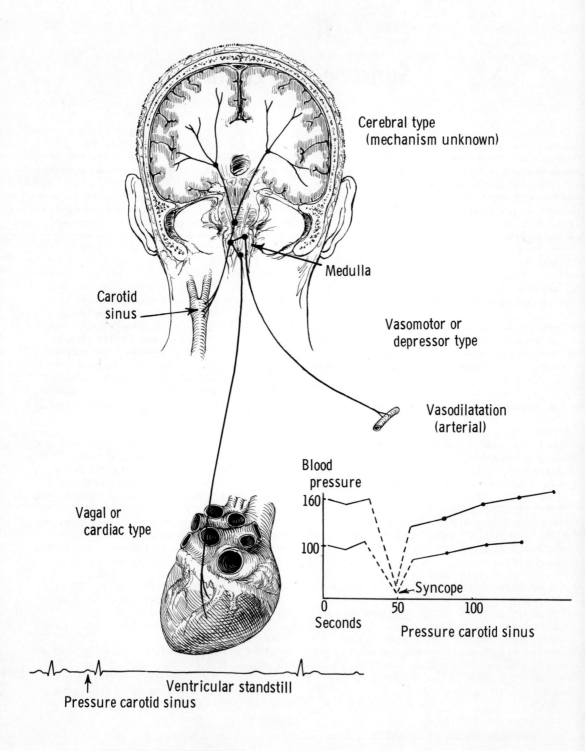

Cerebral type
(mechanism unknown)

Medulla

Carotid
sinus

Vasomotor or
depressor type

Vasodilatation
(arterial)

Blood
pressure

Vagal or
cardiac type

Syncope

Seconds

Pressure carotid sinus

Ventricular standstill

Pressure carotid sinus

The Mechanisms of Syncope in Carotid Sinus Hypersensitivity

on the pathophysiologic mechanisms involved: (1) Cardiodepressor (vagal), in which pressure on the carotid sinus causes slowing of the heart rate and consequent severe fall in blood pressure. (2) Vasodilator (vasomotor), in which critical fall in blood pressure occurs without significant decrease in heart rate after pressure on the carotid sinus. (3) Central (cerebral), in which the loss of consciousness following pressure on the carotid sinus is not associated with fall in blood pressure.

Dizziness or loss of consciousness associated with wearing of tight collars or abrupt turning of the neck suggests the possibility of a hypersensitive carotid sinus. Focal seizures occasionally follow the syncopal episode.

Simultaneous blood pressure, electrocardiographic, and electroencephalographic studies are of value in the analysis of individual cases. In elderly or debilitated individuals, there is a great risk of accidentally precipitating a cerebrovascular accident by stimulation of a hypersensitive carotid sinus, so that it is best not done on such patients.

The central type of carotid sinus syncope may be confused with cerebral ischemia due to cerebral artery occlusion in patients with cerebrovascular disease and with hysterical syncope. Occlusion of the common carotid artery below the carotid sinus will not affect patients with the cerebral type of carotid sinus syncope, while patients with inadequate collateral circulation (thrombosis of the opposite internal carotid artery, etc.) may show syncope, etc. In hysterical syncope, massage of some portion of the neck other than the carotid sinus may induce syncope in the recumbent patient.

Treatment.

Conservative medical management requires the education of the patient in regard to the influence of turning, tight collars, etc., and the use of drugs such as atropine and ephedrine. In selected intractable cases, surgical denervation of the carotid sinus may be performed with satisfactory results.

Correct all abnormalities whenever possible. Eliminate emotional problems and forbid use of tight collars. In severe cases, denervation of the sinuses may be necessary. Local anesthesia of the carotid sinuses abolishes all types of carotid sinus syncope.

A. Vagal Type: Atropine sulfate, 0.4-0.6 mg. 3-4 times daily (or more, if needed), will usually abolish attacks. Ephedrine sulfate or hydrochloride, 25 mg., with phenobarbital, 15 mg. 3-4 times daily, or amphetamine sulfate, 5-10 mg., may be used.

B. Vasomotor Type: Ephedrine and phenobarbital as above will usually prevent attacks.

C. Cerebral Type: Drugs are of no value

ORTHOSTATIC HYPOTENSION

This type of syncope is characterized by repeated fainting episodes associated with a sudden drop in arterial blood pressure whenever the patient assumes the erect position. Recognized contributing factors leading to the occurrence of orthostatic hypotension are prolonged convalescence and recumbency, faulty reflex postural adaptation, sympathectomy, peripheral venous stasis, chronic anxiety, and use of antihypertensive drugs. When vasodepressor syncope was induced in healthy young normals by head-up tilt and administration of sodium nitrite, loss of consciousness and severe EEG changes did not appear until the blood pressure fell to approximately 25 mm. Hg. This degree of hypotension was associated with marked increase in cerebral arteriovenous oxygen difference, indicating considerable reduction in cerebral circulation. Slowing of heart rate or cardiac arrhythmia usually preceded loss of consciousness, and relative bradycardia persisted for 2-4 minutes after return of consciousness and restoration of blood pressure.

Treatment is directed toward the underlying cause when possible. Withdraw or reduce the dosage of hypotensive drugs. Caution the patient against rising too rapidly from the sitting or lying position. If abdominal ptosis is present, an abdominal belt may help. Elastic stockings may be of value. Vasoconstrictor drugs may be tried but usually do not help.

Ephedrine sulfate, up to 75 mg. daily, may be useful. Fludrocortisone acetate has also been reported to be effective in daily doses of 0.1 mg. or more.

CARDIAC FUNCTIONAL CHANGE

Syncopal attacks may occur as a consequence of sudden cardiac functional change. In the **Stokes-Adams syndrome**, syncope occurs with evidence of a slow pulse and ECG changes indicative of a high grade of atrioventricular block. Attacks of syncope in this syndrome may vary greatly in frequency and may occur in both sleeping and waking states. In intervals between episodes, the patient may be quite comfortable. If the period of unconsciousness is prolonged, convulsions are apt to occur. Patients may expire during an attack of this syndrome. The treatment of choice is the energetic use of ephedrine hydrochloride or epinephrine.

Reflex heart block may contribute to some types of syncopal episodes. It may be a consequence of hypersensitivity of the carotid sinus, in which the syncope follows physical stimulation of the carotid sinus; viscerovagal reflexes, such as may occur following distention or irritation of a viscus producing syncope; oculovagal reflexes, such as occur after pressure on the eyeball; or postural changes.

Syncope may also be associated with other varieties of cardiac disorders, as follows: (1) Coronary and myocardial insufficiency. Syncopal episodes may occur with angina pectoris attacks; sometimes convulsions and sudden death may occur thereafter. (2) Paroxysmal tachycardia. Sudden impaired cardiac output may lead to syncope. (3) Aortic stenosis. Precipitation of syncope by exertion occurs in this condition. (4) Congenital heart disease. Syncope associated with sudden intense exertional efforts is well recognized in this group.

IMPAIRED BRAIN METABOLISM

Impaired cerebral metabolism may be the most significant factor in the production of some types of syncope. Examples of such varieties of syncope are those associated with the following: (1) anoxemia, as in patients with congenital heart disease; (2) severe chronic debilitating anemias; (3) hypoglycemia, as in "labile diabetics" after over-exertion or failure to eat after taking insulin; (4) acidosis, as in some patients with uncontrolled diabetes mellitus; (5) drug intoxication, as with barbiturates; and (6) acute alcoholism.

IMPAIRED BRAIN CIRCULATION

Impairment of the cerebral circulation may also lead to syncopal attacks. Syncope associated with transient focal neurologic findings is relatively common among elderly patients with arteriosclerotic cerebrovascular disease. Dizziness, followed by syncope, can occur following abrupt head movements in patients with head injuries. Transient episodes of lightheadedness or unconsciousness are commonly encountered in hypertensive encephalopathy, where it may be secondary to local impaired blood flow associated with narrowing of vessels. Lightheadedness and, more rarely, syncope, may be present as manifestations of migraine, a disorder which in its initial phase is associated with diminished cerebrocranial arterial blood flow. One of

the varieties of syncope in people with hypersensitivity of the carotid sinus is associated with profound abrupt fall in blood pressure and consequent impaired cerebral circulation (see above). In patients with intracerebral neoplasms or vascular malformations, displacement, engorgement or occlusion of intracranial blood vessels may be related to the syncopal episodes sometimes encountered.

Sudden syncope during the terminal phase of micturition may occur in young males shortly after assuming the upright posture following a period of recumbency and sleep; sudden decrease of reflex vasoconstriction on emptying a full bladder during motionless standing may be important. Syncope after coughing ("cough syncope") may be related to sudden increase in venous pressure, rise in CSF pressure, or concussion-like effect produced by the coughing; loss of consciousness may precede fall in peripheral arterial blood pressure.

Treat the specific cause whenever possible. Consciousness may be restored by rebreathing into a paper bag, breath-holding, or administration of 5-10% carbon dioxide with oxygen by mask. Recurrent attacks of hyperventilation syndrome suggest that psychiatric consultation should be considered.

SYNCOPE IN HYSTERIA

Syncope may occur as a hysterical feature. Psychologic evaluation may indicate that in such individuals the syncopal episode symbolizes an expression of a repressed drive. The syncopal episode in hysteria is usually not associated with evidences of anxiety. Women are especially apt to have this type of episode, especially during adolescence. Other features of hysterical personality may be prominent. In hysterical fainting, the EEG usually shows no significant changes during the period of unconsciousness.

COMA

Whereas the loss of consciousness in syncope is usually brief in duration and sudden in onset, more prolonged and profound loss of consciousness is described as coma. In this condition, a patient may show no reaction to painful stimuli or may react only with a primitive defense movement such as corneal reflex or limb withdrawal. Milder grades are referred to as semicoma; the patient may attempt to push away an offending stimulus. Still lesser grades are referred to as stupor or confusion, and are characterized by variable grades of impaired reactivity and disorientation.

Coma may be of intracranial or extracranial origin. Examples are given below:

A. Intracranial: Head injuries, cerebrovascular accidents, CNS infections, tumors, convulsive disorders, degenerative diseases, increased intracranial pressure, psychiatric disorders.

B. Extracranial: Vascular (shock or hypotension, as with severe hemorrhage, myocardial infarction, arterial hypertension); metabolic (diabetic acidosis, hypoglycemia, uremia, hepatic coma, addisonian crisis, electrolyte imbalance); intoxications (alcohol, barbiturates, narcotics, bromides, analgesics, ataractics, carbon monoxide, heavy metals); miscellaneous (hyperthermia, hypothermia, electric shock, anaphylaxis, severe systemic infections).

Clinical Findings.
A. History: Interrogate the patient during lucid intervals. Valuable information may also be obtained from the patient's friends, relatives, and attendants. Inquire specifically about the patient's occupation; previous physical, mental, or emotional illness; trauma, the use of alcohol and drugs, epilepsy, and hypertension.

B. Physical Examination: Place particular emphasis on vital signs, evidence of injury or intoxication, and neurologic abnormalities. Do not assume that sensory disturbances are due to alcoholic intoxication merely because an alcoholic breath is detected. Inspect the head and body carefully for evidence of injury. Discoloration of the skin behind the ear often is associated with skull fracture (Battle's sign).

Observe respiration, which may be deep and labored (suggesting diabetic acidosis) or of the Cheyne-Stokes type. Puffing out of one cheek with each expiration indicates paralysis of that side of the face.

Spontaneous movements may indicate which areas are normal parts or may represent the onset of focal motor convulsions.

Paralysis of extremities may be determined by lifting each extremity and allowing it to fall. In light coma the paralyzed limb will fall heavily, whereas a normal limb will gradually sink to the bed. Vigorous stimulation of the feet may cause a normal leg to react, whereas a paralyzed leg will not. Passive motion may disclose diminished tone of affected limbs in acute or recent flaccid hemiplegia.

Decerebrate rigidity or the presence of tonic neck reflexes suggests dysfunction at a brain stem level.

Check the eyes carefully. Hemianopsia may be demonstrable in light coma by failure of flinching on threatening hand gestures initiated from the hemianopsic side. Pupillary differences may be of vital diagnostic importance; enlarged pupils are often present with ipsilateral subdural hematoma. Papilledema indicates elevated intracranial pressure and is a grave prognostic sign.

Oculomotor paralysis of one eye is often associated with a ruptured aneurysm of the anterior portion of the circle of Willis.

Pronounced nuchal rigidity usually signifies meningeal irritation (meningitis, subarachnoid bleeding) or herniation of the cerebellar tonsils due to intracranial tumor or vascular accident.

C. Laboratory Findings: Catheterize the patient if necessary and examine the urine especially for protein, blood, glucose, and acetone. Take hemoglobin, WBC, differential count, and hematocrit. Draw blood for NPN, glucose, and blood ammonia when indicated (for diagnosis of uremia, diabetic coma, or hepatic coma). Lumbar puncture should be considered for all comatose patients unless there are specific contraindications (e.g., suspected posterior fossa lesions). CSF examination and culture may be helpful. Special studies may be indicated, e.g., blood cultures and analysis of body fluids for evidence of toxins. Skull x-rays, EEG, cerebral angiography, and pneumography are valuable aids in brain tumor and subdural hematoma suspects. Order chest x-ray and other x-rays as indicated.

Treatment.
A. Emergency Measures: The immediate objective is to maintain life until a specific diagnosis has been made and appropriate treatment can be started.
1. Maintain adequate ventilation - First determine the cause of any respiratory difficulty (e.g., obstruction, pulmonary disease, depression of respiratory center, vascular collapse).

Keep airways open. Place the patient on his side or abdomen with his face to the side and his head well extended (**never** on his back or with the head flexed). If necessary, pull the tongue forward with fingers or forceps and maintain in an extended position (e.g., by pharyngeal airways). Aspirate mucus, blood, and saliva from the mouth and nose with a lubricated soft rubber catheter. If no suction apparatus is available, use a 25-50 ml. syringe. Endotracheal catheterization or tracheostomy may be necessary. **(Caution:** If the endotracheal tube remains in place for more than 2 hours, there is danger of laryngeal edema and further obstruction upon its removal.) The services of a trained anesthetist or otolaryngologist are desirable.

Artificial respiration may be administered if respirations have ceased or are failing. Closed cardiac massage may be necessary.

Oxygen may be administered by mask, catheter, or tent as indicated.

2. Shock - Institute immediate treatment if patient is in shock or if shock is threatened.

B. General Measures: The patient must be observed constantly. Place him in the "shock" position (unless contraindicated), and change body positions every 30-60 minutes to prevent hypostatic pneumonia and skin ulcerations. Catheterize the patient if coma persists for longer than 8-12 hours and the patient fails to void. If necessary, insert an indwelling catheter (with appropriate aseptic technic).

Provide proper fluid and nutrition with I.V. glucose, amino acids, and saline solutions for the first few days until the patient is able to take fluids by mouth. If the patient is comatose for more than 2-3 days, tube feedings should be employed.

Whenever possible, avoid sedation or other depressant medications until a specific diagnosis has been made. Sedation with paraldehyde or barbiturates may be necessary for mild restlessness in coma which is not due to barbiturate or other drug toxicity.

I.V. urea: Increased intracranial pressure (e.g., in brain tumor, head injury, brain swelling) may be reduced for 3-10 hours by I.V. administration of urea. Give urea as 30% sterile solution (in 10% invert sugar) in a dosage of about 1 Gm./Kg. at a rate of about 60 drops/minute. Poor renal function or active intracranial bleeding are contraindications.

C. Specific Measures: Treat specific causes, such as fevers, infections, and poisonings.

MÉNIÈRE'S SYNDROME
(Paroxysmal Labyrinthine Vertigo)

Ménière's syndrome is characterized by recurrent episodes of severe vertigo associated with deafness and tinnitus. It is encountered most often in men in the age group from 40 to 60. The cause is not known, but "endolymphatic hydrops" with marked dilatation of the cochlear duct is suspected. Ménière's syndrome may follow head trauma or middle ear infection, but many cases develop without apparent damage to the nervous system or ear.

Intermittent severe vertigo, which may appear to throw the subject to the ground, is the principal symptom. Brief loss of consciousness occasionally occurs in an attack. "Spinning" of surrounding objects is often noted. Nausea, vomiting, and profuse perspiration are often associated. The attacks may last from a few minutes to several hours. The frequency of attacks varies considerably even in the same patient. Headache, nerve type hearing loss, and tinnitus occur during and persist between attacks. Hearing loss is apt to be progressive, and is unilateral in 90% of cases. Nystagmus may occur during attacks of vertigo. An altered labyrinthine response is often demonstrated by means of the caloric or Bárány test. There is increased sensitivity to loud sounds. Audiometric tests show recruitment, decreased speech discrimination, and a nerve type hearing loss.

Treatment.

Reassurance is important, since many of these patients have a marked psychic overlay. A salt-free diet and ammonium chloride, 1-2 Gm. q.i.d., may be helpful. Diuretics such as acetazolamide (Diamox®) and chlorothiazide (Diuril®) may also be used. Nicotinic acid, 50-100 mg. I.V. 2-3 times daily, or 100 mg. orally 5-6 times daily, has been found useful. The antihistamines, especially diphenhydramine hydrochloride (Benadryl®) and dimenhydrinate (Dramamine®), in doses of 50-100 mg. 3-4 times daily, appear to be of benefit to some patients. Parenteral diphenhydramine or dimenhydrinate - or atropine sulfate, 0.6 mg. - may stop the acute attack.

Destructive surgery on the labyrinth or vestibular nerve may be necessary in a few severe cases which do not respond to medical measures.

Prognosis.

Ménière's syndrome is a chronic recurrent disease which persists for several years. Remission or improvement of vertigo after treatment is often noted; however, tinnitus and deafness usually are unaffected and permanent. Progression is slow and sometimes stops before complete deafness occurs.

Cessation of attacks of vertigo may follow complete loss of hearing.

Procedures which destroy or interrupt an affected vestibular portion of acoustic nerve (such as destruction of the labyrinth or section of the acoustic nerve) may prevent further attacks of vertigo.

32 . . .

Headache

Headache is a common symptom which may be due to a wide variety of causes, including emotional disorders, head injuries, migraine, fever, intracranial vascular disorders, dental disease, diseases of the eyes, ears, or nose, or intracranial masses.

Clinical Disorders Associated With Headache.

Certain types of headache are frequently observed to be associated with specific clinical entities. Throbbing, pulsating headache is more likely to be encountered in vascular diseases such as migraine, arterial hypertension, and intracranial vascular malformations. Pressure headache, a sensation of tightness with a constricting, band-like feeling about the head, is often due to emotional disorders. A steady, dull headache is often encountered in patients with intracranial masses or head injuries.

The most severe headaches are believed to be those associated with migraine, meningitis, high degrees of fever, and ruptured intracranial aneurysms. A relatively prolonged, minor grade of headache may occur with such serious disorders as intracranial hematoma, brain tumor, or abscess.

Since headache may occur as a symptom of many clinical disorders, it may not always be possible to determine the etiology in a given case despite elaborate diagnostic procedures. The choice of a particular study frequently reflects the tentative diagnosis and, indirectly, the physician's clinical orientation. Thus the internist may feel that no patient with headache has been adequately studied without allergy tests; the psychiatrist may consider an elaborate psychometric assay essential; and the neurosurgeon may not feel satisfied until pneumoencephalographic, angiographic, and cervical myelographic studies have been exhausted. In some clinics, routine skull x-rays and electroencephalograms are made as initial "screening" tests in all patients with headaches, and further specific test procedures are then adapted to the particular diagnostic needs as necessary. Among the clinical types are the following:

(1) Traumatic headache: Following head injury, with or without obvious evidence of injury to the skull and adjacent soft tissues; following injury to the upper cervical spine or its associated soft parts (ligaments, muscles, fascia, and intervertebral disks).

(2) Inflammatory headache: Associated with paranasal sinusitis, mastoiditis, meningitis; febrile systemic illnesses, especially those with acute onset of high fever or fluctuations in temperature; myositis or arthritis involving tissues of the head or neck; or angiitis, as in temporal arteritis.

(3) Tumor headache: Associated with primary or metastatic tumors of the head and neck or intracranial hematoma (e.g., subdural, intracerebral).

(4) Vascular headache: Migraine, histaminic cephalalgia, intracranial aneurysms and vascular malformations, essential hypertension, and syncope (recovery phase).

(5) Metabolic headache: Hypothyroidism, ovarian dysfunction, anemias and blood dyscrasias, and drug intoxications (e.g., alcohol, carbon monoxide).

(6) Emotional headache: Anxiety or pain, conversion neuroses.

(7) Miscellaneous: Neuralgias (occipital, trigeminal), ocular disorders (refractive errors, glaucoma), or following lumbar puncture.

Pathogenesis.

According to H.G. Wolff, the following 6 basic mechanisms are commonly involved in the production of headaches from an intracranial source: (1) Traction on veins that pass to the venous sinuses from the brain surface and displacement of the major venous sinuses. (2) Traction on the middle meningeal arteries. (3) Traction on the large arteries at the base of the brain and their main branches. (4) Distention and dilatation of intracranial arteries. (5) Inflammation in or about any of the pain-sensitive structures of the head. (6) Direct pressure on the cranial and cervical nerves containing many afferent pain fibers from the head.

A. Areas of Pain: Whereas the skull, the brain parenchyma, the choroid plexuses, and most of the dura mater and pia-arachnoid are not sensitive to pain, the tissues covering the cranium, especially the arteries, are sensitive to pain.

B. Modification by Physical Measures: Under some conditions, the characteristics of headaches may be modified by physical measures. Abrupt increase in intracranial pressure, as is produced by coughing, sneezing, or straining, will usually exaggerate most headaches associated with intracranial masses or bleeding. Headache following lumbar puncture is usually made more severe by elevation of the head and improved by lowering the position of the head relative to the rest of the body. Manual compression of the common carotid artery in the neck or the major cranial branches of the external carotid artery may relieve the headache of migraine. Headaches following head injuries are frequently made worse by abrupt alteration in position of the head. Pressure headaches associated with emotional disorders may be greatly relieved by local gentle massage of the affected region. Nocturnal headaches of the migraine type sometimes are exaggerated by the recumbent position and relieved when the patient stands erect.

Classification of Headache.*
A. Vascular Headaches of Migraine Type: Recurrent attacks of headache, widely varied in intensity, frequency, and duration. The attacks are commonly unilateral in onset; are usually associated with anorexia and, sometimes, with nausea and vomiting; some are preceded by, or associated with, conspicuous sensory, motor, and mood disturbances; and are often familial.

Evidence supports the view that cranial arterial distention and dilatation are importantly implicated in the painful phase but cause no permanent changes in the involved vessel. Listed below are particular varieties of headache,· each sharing some, but not necessarily all, of the above-mentioned features:
1. "Classic" migraine - Vascular headache with sharply defined, transient visual, and other sensory or motor prodromes or both.
2. "Common" migraine - Vascular headache without striking prodromes and less often unilateral than classic and cluster migraine. Synonyms are "atypical migraine" or "sick" headache. Calling attention to certain re-

*Reproduced, with permission, from A.P. Friedman & others, J.A.M.A. **179**:717, 1962.

lationships of this type of headache to environmental, occupational, menstrual, or other variables are such terms as "summer," "Monday," "weekend," "relaxation," "premenstrual," and "menstrual" headache.
3. "Cluster" headache - Vascular headache, predominantly unilateral on the same side, usually associated with flushing, sweating, rhinorrhea, and increased lacrimation; brief in duration and usually occurring in closely packed groups separated by long remissions. Identical or closely allied are erythroprosopalgia (Bing); ciliary or migrainous neuralgia (Harris); erythromelalgia of the head or histaminic cephalalgia (Horton); and petrosal neuralgia (Gardner & others).
4. "Hemiplegic" migraine and "ophthalmoplegic" migraine - Vascular headache featured by sensory and motor phenomena which persist during and after the headache.
5. "Lower-half" headache - Headache of possibly vascular mechanism, centered primarily in the lower face. In this group there may be some instances of "atypical facial" neuralgia, sphenopalatine ganglion neuralgia (Sluder), and vidian neuralgia (Vail).

B. Muscle-Contraction Headache: Ache or sensations of tightness, pressure, or constriction, widely varied in intensity, frequency, and duration, sometimes long-lasting, and commonly suboccipital. It is associated with sustained contraction of skeletal muscles in the absence of permanent structural change, usually as part of the individual's reaction during life stress. The ambiguous and unsatisfactory terms "tension," "psychogenic," and "nervous" headache refer largely to this group.

C. Combined Headache, Vascular and Muscle-Contraction: Combinations of vascular headache of the migraine type and muscle-contraction headache prominently coexisting in an attack.

D. Headache of Nasal Vasomotor Reaction: Headaches and nasal discomfort (nasal obstruction, rhinorrhea, tightness, or burning), recurrent and resulting from congestion and edema of nasal and paranasal mucous membranes, and not proved to be due to allergens, infectious agents, or local gross anatomic defects. The headache is predominantly anterior in location, and mild or moderate in intensity. The illness is usually part of the individual's reaction during stress. This is often called "vasomotor rhinitis."

E. Headache of Delusional, Conversion, or Hypochondriacal States: Headaches of illnesses in which the prevailing clinical disorder is a delusional or a conversion reaction and a peripheral pain mechanism is nonexistent. Closely allied are the hypochondriacal reactions in which the peripheral disturbances relevant to headache are minimal. These also have been called "psychogenic" headaches.

Note: The foregoing represent the major clinical disorders dominated by headache - those which are particularly common, and in which headache is frequently recurrent and disabling.

F. Nonmigrainous Vascular Headaches Associated With Generally Nonrecurrent Dilatation of Cranial Arteries:
    1. Systemic infections, usually with fever.
    2. Miscellaneous disorders, including hypoxic states, carbon monoxide poisoning, effects of nitrites, nitrates, and other chemical agents with vasodilator properties, caffeine-withdrawal reactions, circulatory insufficiency in the brain (in certain circumstances), postconcussion reactions, postconvulsive states, "hangover" reactions, foreign-protein reactions, hypoglycemia, hypercapnia, acute pressor reactions (abrupt elevation of blood pressure as with paraplegia or pheochromocytoma), and certain instances of essential arterial hypertension (e. g., those with early morning headache).

G. Traction Headache: Headaches resulting from traction on intracranial structures, mainly vascular, by masses:
    1. Primary or metastatic tumors of meninges, vessels, or brain.
    2. Hematomas (epidural, subdural, or parenchymal).
    3. Abscesses (epidural, subdural, or parenchymal).
    4. Post-lumbar-puncture headache ("leakage" headache).
    5. Pseudotumor cerebri and various causes of brain swelling.

H. Headache Due to Overt Cranial Inflammation: Headaches due to readily recognized inflammation of cranial structures, resulting from usually nonrecurrent inflammation, sterile or infectious.
    1. Intracranial disorders - Infectious, chemical, or allergic meningitis, subarachnoid hemorrhage, postpneumoencephalographic reaction, arteritis, and phlebitis.
    2. Extracranial disorders - Arteritis and cellulitis.

I-M. Headaches Due to Disease of Ocular, Aural, Nasal and Sinusal, Dental, or Other Cranial or Neck Structures:

I. Headache due to spread of effects of noxious stimulation of ocular structures (as contraction of ocular muscles, trauma, new growth, or inflammation).

J. Headache due to spread of effects of noxious stimulation of aural structure (as by trauma, new growth, or inflammation).

K. Headache due to spread of effects of noxious stimulation of nasal and sinusal structures (as by trauma, new growth, inflammation, or allergens).

L. Headache due to spread of effects of noxious stimulation of dental structures (as by trauma, new growth, or inflammation).

M. Headache due to spread of pain from noxious stimulation of other structures of the cranium and neck (periosteum, joint, ligaments, muscles, or cervical roots).

N. Cranial Neuritides: Caused by trauma, new growth, or inflammation.

O. Cranial Neuralgias: Trigeminal (tic douloureux) and glossopharyngeal. The pains are lancinating ("jabbing"), usually in rapid succession for several minutes or longer; are limited to a portion or all of the domain of the affected nerve; and are often triggered by end-organ stimulation. Trigeminal neuralgia must be distinguished, in particular, from cluster headache (A3), with which it is often confused.

Note: So-called chronic post-traumatic headache may arise from any one of several mechanisms. Such headache may represent sustained muscle contraction (B), recurrent vascular dilatation (A2), or, rarely, local scalp or nuchal injury (M). In some patients, the post-traumatic pain is part of a clinical disorder characterized by delusional, conversion, or hypochondriacal reactions (E).

Clinical Findings.
    Headaches are of variable duration; in the same patient, different periods of distress may occur. Pressure headaches, commonly present in tension states of emotional origin, may persist for days or weeks. Brief, paroxysmal, prostrating headache of less than 30 minutes' duration may occur in migraine.
    Periodic recurrence of headache is a recognized phenomenon. In women with migraine,

intracranial vascular malformations or aneurysms, headaches are prone to occur at the time of the menstrual period. Seasonal variations in the incidence of headaches are sometimes related to the coincidental increase of emotional tension in migraine patients. Headaches associated with paranasal sinus or nasal disorders are more frequent when upper respiratory infections are most common.

Associated local tenderness at the site of a headache sometimes occurs with head injury, migraine, osteitis, or myositis.

The location of a headache may provide a clue to its origin. Headaches of the pressure type due to emotional disorders may start in the occiput and upper neck and then radiate frontally. Unilateral, recurrent headache suggests migraine, intracranial vascular malformation, or aneurysm of that side. Headache associated with dental, paranasal, or eye disease is apt to be frontal in location at the onset.

Increasingly severe headache suggests the possibility of an enlarging intracranial mass (brain tumor, aneurysm, subdural hematoma).

General Nonspecific Treatment Measures.

These include physical and mental rest, sedatives, and analgesics. Sedatives should be used only as a temporary measure and should not be used as a substitute for a complete work-up and specific therapy. Narcotics are generally contraindicated except in terminal disease. Analgesics constitute specific therapy in febrile headaches due to their antipyretic activity. They should not be administered for prolonged periods indiscriminately; their routine use often obscures important pathology.

MIGRAINE

Migraine is characterized by paroxysmal attacks of headache which is usually localized to one side of the head. The headache may be preceded by psychologic or visual disturbances and sometimes is followed by drowsiness. It is said to affect about 8% of the population. It is more frequent among women than men and occurs more commonly among persons with a background of inflexibility and shyness in childhood and with perfectionistic, rigid, resentful, and ambitious character traits in adult life. There is commonly a history of similar headaches in blood relations.

The headache of migraine is believed to result from vascular changes. An initial episode of cerebral, meningeal, and extracranial arterial vasoconstriction is believed to occur (accounting for the visual and other prodromal phenomena), followed by dilatation and distention of cranial vessels, especially of the external carotid artery. Increased amplitude of pulsation is said to determine the throbbing nature of the headache. Rigid, pipe-like vessels result from persistent dilatation, and the headache becomes a steady ache. A phase of muscle contraction, with pain, is believed to follow. During severe and long-lasting headaches of the migraine type, neurokinin, an extremely powerful vasodilator, may be found in body fluids. An enzyme capable of forming neurokinin and called neurokinin-forming enzyme (NFE) is contained in body fluids. Intradermally injected tissue fluids containing mixtures of neurokinin and NFE induce pain, lower the pain threshold, increase capillary permeability, and heighten vulnerability to injury. The release or activation of NFE and subsequent formation of neurokinin has been observed in man during neuronal excitation, suggesting that they are useful in local vasomotor control of the nervous system and linked to migraine headache attacks.

Migraine often begins in childhood; about one-half of migraine patients report their initial attack before the age of 15 years. Characteristically, the headache occurs in episodes associated with gastrointestinal or visual symptoms (nausea, vomiting; scintillating scotomas, photophobia, hemianopsia, blurred vision). UML-491 (L-methyl-D-lysergic acid butanolamide bimaleate) may be effective in reducing the number and severity of migraine attacks, although it lacks the capacity to terminate an existing headache. The recurrent increased reactivity of cranial blood vessels is reduced, thus preventing the crises of vasoconstriction and vasodilatation that characterize the migraine attack.

Ophthalmoplegic Migraine: The association of migraine and ophthalmoplegia may in some cases be due to aneurysm or tumor, but in others no apparent cause can be shown by cerebral angiograms, surgical exploration, or postmortem study. The paralyses usually occur after many years of simple migraine and, in the attack, paralysis occurs several hours or days after the headache phase.

Onset of paralysis is sudden and subsidence gradual. The oculomotor, trochlear, or abducens nerves may be involved singly or in combination. Occasionally vasoconstrictor drugs relieve the ophthalmoplegia. Edema of cranial vessels at the end stage of migraine with direct pressure of the edematous arteries on adjacent cranial nerves, or interference with vasa vasorum to cranial nerves peripherally, has been considered the likely cause.

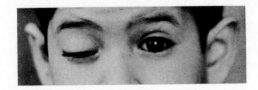

Ophthalmoplegic Migraine. Severe recurrent right oculomotor paralysis in a child with associated migraine headaches. Carotid angiogram normal. Prostigmin® and Tensilon® tests negative for myasthenia gravis.

Treatment.

In most cases treatment with ergotamine or similar drugs is effective. Psychotherapy is useful in reducing the frequency of attacks.

A. Treatment of Acute Attack:

1. Ergotamine tartrate (Gynergen®) I.M. is the treatment of choice; 0.25-0.5 mg. will relieve headache within an hour in most cases. Administer the drug as early in the attack as possible. Do not repeat more often than once weekly. Oral or sublingual administration is not generally advised because ergotamine is less effective by these routes and because of the possibility of overdosage, since if the patient vomits it is impossible to know how much of the drug he has absorbed. The dosage is 4-5 mg. sublingually or orally; continue with 2 mg. every hour until headache has disappeared or until a total of 11 mg. has been administered.

Toxicity: Do not administer ergotamine to patients in septic or infectious states or who have peripheral vascular or arteriosclerotic heart disease, or to pregnant women. A few patients complain of numbness and tingling of extremities and some muscle pains and tension.

2. Dihydroergotamine (D.H.E. 45®), in doses of 1 mg. I.M. or I.V., may be substituted for ergotamine tartrate. Repeat in 1 hour if necessary.

3. Ergotamine with caffeine (Cafergot®) or atropine is sometimes more effective by the oral route alone and requires a smaller total dose. It is available as suppositories for rectal use if vomiting prevents oral administration.

4. Pressure on the external carotid artery or one of its branches early in the attack may abolish pain. Oxygen, 100%, by nasal mask may relieve the acute attack.

B. General Measures: Until the drug begins to relieve headache, have the patient at rest in a chair. After headache has been relieved, he should rest in bed for at least 2 hours in a quiet, darkened room without food or drink. This will promote relaxation and is necessary to prevent another attack from occurring immediately.

C. Aborting an Attack: When the patient feels an attack of migraine coming on he should seek relaxation in a warm bath and then rest in bed in a quiet, darkened room. The following drugs may help: Pentobarbital, 0.1 Gm. orally; ergotamine tartrate (Gynergen®), 3-4 mg. sublingually; or even acetysalicylic acid, with or without codeine.

D. Prevention: Methysergide maleate (Sansert®) may be effective in preventing vascular headaches. The average daily dose is 2-4 tablets (2 mg. each), preferably one tablet with each meal. This drug is contraindicated in pregnancy, peripheral vascular disease, and severe arteriosclerosis.

HISTAMINIC CEPHALALGIA
(Horton's Syndrome)

Histaminic cephalalgia is characterized by a sudden onset of severe unilateral pain. The pain is of short duration and subsides abruptly. Associated signs include redness of the eye, lacrimation, rhinorrhea or stuffiness of the nostril, swelling of the temporal vessels on the affected side, and dilatation of the vessels of the pain area. The headache involves the orbital area, frequently radiating to the temple, nose, upper jaw, and neck. Typical attacks can be induced by injections of small quantities of histamine diphosphate. Attacks occur most frequently during sleep. Pain does not appear to follow distribution of a particular cranial nerve, and no trigger areas are noted. Attacks tend to develop in clusters ("cluster headache"), while remissions and exacerbations occur spontaneously. More males than females (6:1) are affected. This type of headache is considered to be identical or closely allied with erythroprosopalgia of Bing, ciliary neuralgia of Harris, and petrosal neuralgia of Gardner.

Diagnosis may be aided by a positive **histamine test:** 0.35 ml. of concentrated solution of histamine diphosphate (2.75 mg./ml.) injected subcutaneously usually brings on a typical headache in 20-40 minutes in susceptible persons.

Methysergide maleate (Sansert®), 2 mg. 2-3 times daily with meals, is highly effective in treatment. Histamine desensitization by means of frequent subcutaneous injections of increasing doses of histamine diphosphate over a period of several weeks has also been advocated as an effective type of treatment. Management of the acute phase is similar to that for migraine. Ergotamine derivatives, bed rest, inhalations of oxygen, and cold compresses may be necessary. Long-range management usually requires adequate psychologic evaluation and treatment.

TENSION HEADACHES

Tension headaches are by far the most commonly encountered of all types of headache. However, since emotionally disturbed patients may have headaches due to other causes, a complete and adequate history and examination is always necessary.

Tension headaches seem to have no precise localization and usually do not conform to the distribution of cranial or peripheral nerves of roots. Patients characterize the headache as being dull, drawing, pressing, burning or vague in character. Medications, including potent analgesics, may not give complete relief. Exacerbation of complaints and association with anxiety, worry, or other emotional upsets is not always obvious to the patient.

Mild sedatives and analgesics are usually required, as well as psychiatric evaluation and treatment. Recognition and alleviation of fundamental emotional causes may require extensive and painstaking efforts on the part of the physician.

HEADACHES DUE TO MENINGEAL INVOLVEMENT

These headaches are the most severe, but they usually respond to analgesics. Manifestations and specific treatment depend upon the type and site of underlying disease.

Analgesics should be given as needed if pain is not too severe. Narcotics may be necessary. Lumbar puncture, performed very cautiously, may sometimes be used to relieve headache associated with increased intracranial pressure (e. g., subarachnoid hemorrhage, hypertension, nephritis; not in posterior fossa tumors).

Lumbar puncture headaches are believed to be due to leakage of the CSF from the puncture site. If headache is mild upon arising, analgesics such as acetylsalicylic acid, 0.3 Gm. every 2-3 hours, may suffice. Codeine may be necessary. If lumbar puncture headache is very severe, it can be alleviated by lying down. Intrathecal injection of small quantities of sterile normal saline may afford relief in severe cases.

SOME DIFFERENTIAL DIAGNOSTIC FEATURES *of various types of* HEADACHES

Characteristics	Migraine — Typical	Migraine — Atypical · Hybrid	Histaminic Cephalgia	Hypertensive Headache	Tension Headache	Muscle Tension Headache	Myofibrositic Headache	Rheumatic Headache	Temporal Arteritis	Arteriosclerotic Headache	"Allergic" Headache	Headache with Brain Tumor	Psychogenic Headache
Age of onset	Childhood, adolescence, early adult	Adolescence, early adult	Early or middle adult	Any	Any	Any	Usually adult	Adult	55 years or older	Late adult	Any	Any	Adult
Periodicity	+ + Often with menses or ovulation		+ Often seasonal	—	—	—	—	—	—	—	May be seasonal	—	—
Location	Quadrantic, hemicranial, or whole head	Quadrantic, hemicranial	Quadrantic, hemicranial	Occipital, frontal, rarely vertex	Frontal, generalized	Occipital, nuchal, shoulders	Occipital, nuchal, shoulders	Occipital, nuchal, shoulders	Distribution of temporal artery	Temporal artery or deep	Vertex, band	Any	"All over"
Severity, I-IV	II-IV	I-IV	IV	I-IV	I-III	I-II	I-III	II-IV	IV	I-III	I-III	I-IV	0-I
G.I. disturbance	+ -	+ -	—	—	—	—	—	—	—	—	—	—	—
Cortical disturbance	+ -	+ -	—	— (unless encephalopathy)	—	—	—	—	—	—	—	+ -	—
F.H. migraine	+ -.	+ -	—	Often	—	—	—	—	—	—	—	—	—
Nasal stuffiness and rhinorrhea	+ - Uni-or bilateral	+ - Unilateral	+ Unilateral	—	—	—	—	—	—	—	+ - Bilateral	—	—
Conjunctivitis and lacrimation	+ - Uni-or bilateral	+ - Unilateral	+ Unilateral	—	—	—	—	—	—	—	+ - Bilateral	—	—
Character of pain	Throbbing, bursting, vise-like	Stabbing, waxes and wanes	Knifelike, shooting, throbbing	Throbbing or steady, dull	Constant, may throb	Stiff, sore, with superficial tenderness	Superficial, with superficial tenderness	Exquisite superficial tenderness	Knifelike, shooting, stabbing, throbbing, with marked superficial tenderness	Dull, steady, or may-be tic-like	Tight band, weight, or bursting	Any	Constant, invariable ache
Duration of pain	Hours to days	2-12 hours	Minutes to 2 hours	2-3 hours usually	4-16 hours	2-3 hours	Days to weeks	Months	2-6 months	Minutes to weeks	2-3 hours usually	Any	"All the time"
Night pain	Rarely wakens unless associated with hypertension	Often wakens from sleep	Always wakens from sleep	Wakens 4-6 A.M.	—	—	May prevent sleep, does not waken	Prevents sleep	Prevents sleep	Does not waken unless associated with hypertension	—	+ -	—
Other features	Often an unconscious but marked hostility toward an individual or situation. Ambitious, perfectionist, inflexible, meticulous, restrained, "time-bound"		Ulcer not infrequent. Ulcer and cephalgia exacerbate and remit simultaneously	Hypertension or vascular hyper-reactor	Follows stress	Often associated with arthritis of cervical spine	Normal sedimentation rate. No fever, no nodules	Elevated sedimentation rate, globulin ± Low grade fever ± Lymphocytosis ± Muscle nodules	Malaise, weakness, fever, night sweats, weight loss, leucocytosis, anemia, elevated sedimentation rate, loss of vision	Other evidence of arteriosclerosis	Other stigmata of allergy	Other findings of brain tumor	Other features of psychiatric illness
Precipitants	Fatigue — physical, mental, emotional. Vasodilators		Vasodilators, Histamine	Widened pulse pressure	Fatigue, stress	Muscle tension	Dampness, cold	Dampness, cold	—	—	Allergen	Sudden change CSF or blood pressure, body position	—
Relief of acute attack	Gynergen, Dihydroergotamine, Catergot		Dihydroergotamine	Upright posture. Thiocyanates	Rest	Change of posture, heat, massage	Heat, massage vasodilators, salicylates	Heat, massage, vasodilators, salicylates	Opiates	Salicylates, vasodilators, histamine subcutaneously	Nasal vasoconstrictors, antihistaminics	Acetylsalicylic acid, opiates	Psychotherapy

*Reproduced, with permission, from Macy, J.A.M.M.Women's A.5:352, 1950.

33...

Neuromuscular Disorders

Clinical Features of Neuromuscular Disorders.
Characteristic clinical features may be associated with neuromuscular disorders, so that a careful history and examination often provide highly informative leads and are essential for intelligent and accurate diagnosis and treatment. Patients with neuromuscular disease may describe specific functional motor impairment resulting from difficulty in contracting or sustaining contraction of particular muscle groups. A patient may have trouble lifting his head from the pillow or rolling over in bed, and in arising from a low chair he may have to push himself up with his hands. He may be unable to cross his knees without using his hands to flex the thigh. Walking may be difficult because his ankles tend to turn or his feet to "flop." Ascending or descending stairs, squatting and arising, or lifting a leg into a car may be difficult. Upper extremity weakness may result in inability to lift heavy objects, turn doorknobs, or hold the arms overhead. Extraocular muscle weakness may produce diplopia and drooping of eyelids. Lip muscle weakness may interfere with clear enunciation, whistling, sucking with a straw, or expanding a balloon. A changed facial expression or a "frozen," fixed expression may be noted. Jaw muscle weakness may lead to tiring of jaws or inability to bite hard. Regurgitation, nasal speech, dysphagia, and dysarthria may be caused by weakness of the muscles of the pharynx, palate, and tongue. Food may be trapped between the teeth and the cheeks in the presence of facial and tongue weakness. It should be noted that impaired motor performance resulting from spasticity, rigidity, stiffness, pain, and functional or psychiatric disorders may be readily confused - by the patient as well as by the unwary examiner - with true or primary muscle weakness.

Inspection, palpation, and percussion of peripheral nerves and muscles and tests of muscle strength and muscle stretch reflexes may yield valuable diagnostic information. Several peripheral nerves are susceptible to direct palpation and percussion. Palpation of nerves in the axillas, the radial nerve above the lateral humerus, the ulnar nerve at the elbow, or the peroneal nerve just below the head of the fibula may disclose tenderness, abnormal thickening, or masses. Muscle size and bulk vary greatly depending upon age, sex, body habitus, occupation, nutritional status, physical training, etc. Atrophy of a muscle usually means that the muscle was once longer and is now shorter. Inspection and palpation of the muscle, comparison with neighboring muscles and with homologous muscles of the opposite side, and observation of general muscular development should be carried out. Altered contour and shape of a muscle often confirms a suspicion of atrophy. Repeated examination at intervals may be necessary to determine the true status of a muscle or group of muscles. Muscle atrophy caused by muscle or lower motor neuron disease is usually associated with significant muscle weakness, but muscles atrophied from disuse, systemic disease, or senility may still show vigorous contraction. Hypertrophy of muscle may be obvious in the increased size of that muscle, although in the presence of atrophied neighboring muscles a normal muscle may appear hypertrophied by contrast.

The term "fibrillation" is reserved for spontaneous independent contractions of individual muscle fibers. These are so minute that they cannot be observed through the intact skin. Denervated muscle may show electromyographic evidence of fibrillations 1-3 weeks after the muscle has lost its nerve supply, and these usually persist for a year or so. Fasciculation twitches may be seen, palpated, and even heard with the aid of a stethoscope. Fasciculations are usually seen better in oblique lighting in a well-lighted room. Light percussion of affected muscle activates fasciculations, and administration of neostigmine to susceptible persons greatly increases their twitches. Spontaneous fasciculations may vary because of the length and number of muscle fibers involved. They can result from any disease producing degeneration or irritation of the lower motor neuron and may be seen in poliomyelitis, spinal cord disease, motor root and peripheral nerve disease, and amyotrophic lateral sclerosis. Spontaneous fasciculations are occasionally noted in persons without recognizable neurologic or muscular disease and are referred to as benign fasciculations. Fasciculations present for several months unassociated with other clinical or electrical signs of denervation usually turn out to be benign.

Contraction fasciculations disappear upon relaxation of muscle, and are thus differentiated from spontaneous fasciculations, which persist in resting, relaxed muscle. Contraction fasciculations may occur during weak muscular contractions and usually are seen in tense persons who cannot relax and also in poliomyelitis and amyotrophic lateral sclerosis.

Twitches of normal muscle may result from shivering as a result of cold. Patients therefore should be kept warm when being observed for spontaneous fasciculation. Tremors may resemble fasciculations, and the tongue is best observed for fasciculation while it lies at rest in the mouth to avoid confusion with the increased tremors associated with tongue protrusion.

Myokymia is a benign form of muscle twitching which usually occurs without apparent cause but sometimes is associated with infection or metabolic disorders. Spontaneous, brief, tetanic contractions of motor units or groups of muscle fibers occur, sometimes producing a continual undulation of muscle surface. The movements of myokymia are slower and more prolonged than the brief twitchings of fasciculation with which they may be confused.

Sharp percussion of normal muscle usually causes it to contract. The muscle fibers that have been directly percussed contract, causing a brief longitudinal depression in the muscle. This muscular excitability may persist even in the absence of the stretch reflex, so that direct percussion of the muscle should be avoided in the study of stretch reflexes. Persistence of a strong muscular contraction after stimulation has ceased is typical of myotonia and is usually referred to as the myotonic reaction. It may also occur when myotonic muscle contraction is produced voluntarily, mechanically, or electrically. When myotonia is suspected, it may be demonstrated after the patient has strongly grasped the examiner's hand for about 5 seconds, after which contraction persists when the patient tries to release his grasp quickly on command. Percussion myotonia may be demonstrated by sharp percussion (with the tip of a reflex hammer) of the thenar eminence, tongue, deltoid, etc.; the portion of the muscle struck contracts, producing a visible crease or depression in the percussed muscle which persists for several seconds. Normal muscles, in contrast, produce a much briefer and less pronounced contraction. Myo-edema, which occurs occasionally in normal persons and

more often in debilitated states and myxedema, is characterized by the formation of a small elevation or hillock at the site of the percussed muscle and is unaccompanied by electrical activity of underlying muscle.

Palpation of muscle may disclose muscular tenderness which may be distinguished from tenderness of superficial skin and subcutaneous tissue by the response to gentle touching, pressing, and squeezing of the overlying skin. Local phlebitis, with associated findings such as linear tenderness, local warmth, and a firm, tender vessel, must also be differentiated. The consistency of muscle tends to vary greatly among different individuals. The atonic muscle resulting from acute denervation is flabby upon palpation. Increased consistency, ranging from rubberiness to woodenness, may occur with muscular dystrophy, polymyositis, and muscular contractures. Some muscles may be found upon palpation to be diffusely affected, whereas in others increased consistency may be localized and patchy. Spastic, rigid, and tender muscles are generally of increased consistency.

Contractures of muscles may be detected by passive motion of joints because there is usually a limited range of motion of the joint due to tightening of the affected muscle tendon. True contracture, usually considered to be due to changes in the fibrous and elastic supporting tissue of muscle, must be distinguished from muscle spasm or structural joint changes. Contractures of muscles occur most often in the back extensors, shoulder adductors and internal rotators, hip flexors, extensors, and adductors, and forearm flexors and pronators as well as in other extremity flexors.

Evaluation of individual muscle strength is an important but difficult part of the muscle examination (see Chapter 8). The degree to which the patient cooperates must be gauged in assessing psychogenic factors and elements. Apparent improvement or progression of a motor disorder depends upon adequate and accurate motor testing. In some disorders such as muscular dystrophy, the localization and pattern of weakness - and in other disorders such as myasthenia gravis, the character of the muscle weakness - provide important clues about the nature of the neuromuscular disorder.

Muscle stretch reflexes may be useful in distinguishing primary muscle diseases from those secondary to peripheral nerve disorders. In primary muscle disease, the stretch reflex usually remains intact until profound muscular wasting and weakness occur, whereas in peripheral nerve or anterior horn cell disorders diminished stretch reflex often occurs very early. The amplitude of response, the rapidity with which it occurs, and its duration should be noted. In myxedema, the reflex duration time is lengthened. Clinical evaluation of a stretch reflex depends upon comparison with reflexes from other muscles and the opposite side.

Classification.

The neuromuscular disorders include a number of chronic diseases which are characterized by a progressive weakness and atrophy of certain groups of muscles. It is customary to differentiate atrophies from dystrophies: muscular **atrophies** result from a neural lesion, involving either the cell body or axon of the lower motor neuron. Muscular **dystrophies** result from primary disease of the muscle itself. Muscular weakness and atrophy and loss of tendon reflexes may occur, however, in many dissimilar diseases.

logic disorders following intrathecal injection in cats. One or 2 days after injection, spontaneous contractions of muscle fibers, myoclonic jerks, and augmented muscle tone and reflexes occurred; in severe cases flaccid paralysis with loss of reflexes and severe muscle atrophy occurred. Impaired biosynthesis of nucleic acid in nerve cells with formation of defective co-enzymes and abnormal RNA molecules, is believed related to the neurologic disorder. Spongy disorders of spinal cord white matter and more severe neurologic changes occurred after the second week.

Spinal Types. (Sometimes erroneously called chronic poliomyelitis.)

Aran-Duchenne atrophy (myelopathic muscular atrophy) is the adult form of progressive spinal muscular atrophy. It is a rare disorder

Differential Diagnosis of Atrophies and Dystrophies

Atrophies	Dystrophies
Generally occur late in life.	Occur in childhood.
Affect distal muscle groups, e.g., the small muscles of the hand.	Affect the proximal muscle groups, e.g., the hip and shoulder girdle.
Show fasciculations.	No fasciculations.
May show spastic phenomena.	No spastic phenomena.
No familial incidence.	Generally familial.

PROGRESSIVE MUSCULAR (OR NUCLEAR) ATROPHIES

The progressive muscular atrophies are due to nuclear involvement of the lower motor neuron by progressive lesions. Since the causative agent is usually unknown, the classification has been based upon the level of involvement rather than upon etiology. Diet, deficiency states, inflammatory conditions, vascular disorders, and toxic processes have been implicated in some cases. The term "motor system disease" has also been used to refer to this group of diseases.

Syndromes similar to those occurring naturally have been associated with specific pathogenic etiologies. A group of cases has recently been found secondary to chronic mercury poisoning, and in some of these the lesions appeared limited to the lower motor neuron, thus resembling the clinical features of progressive muscular atrophy. A familial syndrome with clinical and pathologic features of amyotrophic lateral sclerosis, Parkinson's disease, and Alzheimer's disease in natives in Guam has been extensively studied.

A pyrimidine analog, 5-fluoroorotic acid, which was found to interfere with production of nucleic acid in nerve fibers, produced neuro-

of middle age, starting in the small hand muscles with atrophy and fibrillations and slowly extending to involve the arms, shoulders, and trunk muscles. A degenerative lesion is found in the cervical gray matter of the cord. It may occur as the first stage of an amyotrophic lateral sclerosis (see below).

Werdnig-Hoffmann paralysis is a hereditary form of progressive spinal muscular atrophy occurring in children, starting in the pelvic girdle and thighs and spreading to the extremities. Associated adiposity may produce a pseudohypertrophy.

Oppenheim's disease (amyotonia congenita) is considered by some to be a fetal form of spinal muscular atrophy due to growth abnormalities (see p. 374).

Bulbar Types.

True bulbar palsy is caused by a nuclear involvement of the last 4 or 5 cranial nerves and characterized by twitchings and atrophy of the tongue, palate, and larynx, drooling, dysarthria, dysphagia, and finally respiratory paralysis. True bulbar palsy is usually a manifestation of amyotrophic lateral sclerosis.

Fazio-Londe atrophy is a bulbofacial type of progressive muscular atrophy occurring in childhood.

Pontile Type.

Pontile atrophies produce a chronic progressive ophthalmoplegia (Von Graefe's disease) due to involvement of the nuclei of the eye muscles. Some of these cases are readily confused with progressive muscular dystrophy of the external ocular muscles.

Spastic Type.

Amyotrophic lateral sclerosis is a combined upper and lower motor neuron lesion which may involve either the spinal or bulbar levels, or both. It is a chronic progressive disease of unknown etiology associated with fibrillation and atrophy of the somatic musculature. It is predominantly a disease of middle life, with onset usually between the ages of 40 and 60 years. Amyotrophic lateral sclerosis occurs in all races and in all parts of the world. A high incidence has been noted among natives of Guam and the Mariana and Caroline Islands. The possibility of a dominant inheritance was suggested by the marked familial aggregation of cases. Degeneration of the motor cells of the spinal cord and brain stem and, to a lesser extent, of the motor cortex may occur, with secondary degeneration of the lateral and ventral portions of the spinal cord. There may be spastic weakness of the trunk and extremities, with associated hyperactive deep reflexes and extensor plantar responses. If the fibers of the bulbar nuclei become involved, pseudobulbar or bulbar paralysis may appear. The initial symptom is often weakness and wasting of the extremities (usually the upper extremities). The course is progressively downhill without remission. The average duration of life from the appearance of the first symptom is about 3 years.

Neural Form or Peroneal Muscular Atrophy (Charcot-Marie-Tooth Disease).

This relatively rare disease is characterized by clubbing of the feet and muscular wasting which begins in the legs and later involves the muscles of the distal portion of the thigh and upper extremities. Atrophy of the leg muscles gives a characteristic "stork-leg" appearance; atrophy usually starts in the intrinsic muscles of the feet and in the peroneal muscles. The onset of symptoms is usually before 20 years of age, but is sometimes delayed until 40 or 50 years. Objective loss of sensation occasionally occurs.

PROGRESSIVE MUSCULAR DYSTROPHY

This disease of unknown cause shows a strong hereditary trend and may occur in several members of a family. It is characterized by a chronic progressive disturbance of the skeletal musculature. There are several variants, depending upon the site of initial muscular involvement and the distribution of apparent hypertrophy and atrophy. A defect in creatine metabolism, possibly due to muscle wasting, is usually present. Striated muscle is chiefly affected. On cut section the muscle fibers may appear swollen, indistinct, and homogeneous, with disturbed striations; some fibers may be hypertrophic and others atrophic. The late stages are characterized by fibrosis and fatty infiltration of muscles.

Elevation of various serum enzymes may be noted in muscular dystrophy patients. Two serum transaminases, aldolase, and 2 types of dehydrogenase occur in highest levels early in childhood muscular dystrophy and taper toward normal several years later. Serum creatine phosphokinase has also been reported to be greatly increased in patients with progressive muscular dystrophy. The possibility that some forms of muscular dystrophy may be "molecular diseases" similar in pathogenesis to the abnormal hemoglobin diseases has been inferred from abnormal spectrophotometric absorption spectra of the myoglobin in 2 forms of muscular dystrophy.

A general metabolic dysfunction may produce a neuromuscular disorder resembling one of the typical clinical types. Proximal myopathy may occur in late middle life in association with malignancy.

Pseudohypertrophic Type (Duchenne).

This type occurs in early youth and is characterized by bulky calf and forearm muscles, which, however, are quite soft as a result of infiltration by fat and fibrous tissue; and progressive atrophy and weakness of the thigh, hip, and back muscles and shoulder girdle. It usually occurs in males and rarely in females, with onset in the first 3 years of life. It is considered to be sex-linked and recessive, with a high mutation rate (rarely, autosomal recessive). Symmetric early involvement of the pelvic girdle muscles and, later, of the shoulder girdle muscles occurs. In about 80% of cases there is pseudohypertrophy, particularly of the calf muscles but sometimes of the quadriceps and deltoids. Steady and rapid progression usually leads to inability to walk within 10 years. The gait becomes waddling, and there is difficulty in going up or down stairs. In rising from a recumbent position the patient does so laboriously by "climbing up upon himself." When an effort is made to lift the patient by his armpits, the loose shoulder girdle permits his head to slip through the examiner's hands. Lordosis frequently develops from the weakness of the

**Familial
Myelopathic**

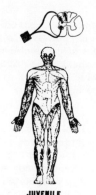
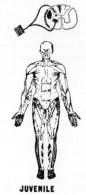

INFANTILE   **ADULT**   **JUVENILE**   **JUVENILE**

Infantile Muscular
Atrophy (Werdnig-
Hoffman)

Hyperneuritis
(Déjerine-
Sottas)

Peroneal Muscular
Atrophy (Charcot-
Marie-Tooth)

Familial
Ataxia
(Friedreich)

**Familial
Myopathic**

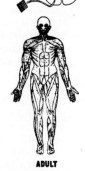

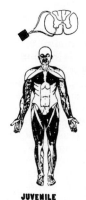

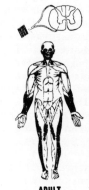

ADULT   **JUVENILE**   **JUVENILE**   **JUVENILE**   **ADULT**

Myasthenia
Gravis
(Wilks, Erb)

Familial Peri-
odic Paralysis)
(Cavare)

Progressive Mus-
cular Dystrophy
(Erb-Landouzy)

Myotonia
(Thomsen)

Myotonic
Dystrophy
(Deleage)

**Sporadic
Myelopathic**

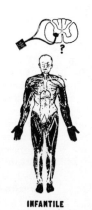
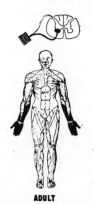
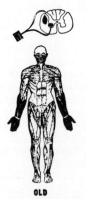

The mannikin representative
of each disease shows the
distribution of atrophy, which
is quite varied and yet characteristic of each disease.
Muscles most affected are
shown solid black; those not
regularly affected are cross-
hatched.

INFANTILE   **ADULT**   **OLD**

Amyotonia Congen-
ita (Oppenheim)
(Myopathic?)

Progressive Mus-
cular Atrophy
(Aran-Duchenne)

Amyotrophic Lat-
eral Sclerosis
(Charcot)

Classification of Muscular Atrophies. (Modified and reproduced, with permission, from Aring
and Cobb: The muscular atrophies and allied disorders. Medicine **14**:77, 1935.)

trunk muscles. Late in the disease the patient becomes too weak to move or support himself. Progressive deformity with muscular contractures, skeletal distortion, and atrophy results. Death from inanition, respiratory infection, or cardiac failure usually occurred in the second decade of life in the past; but with current antibiotic, supportive, and intensive care, patients often reach the middle years of life.

Facioscapulohumeral Type (Landouzy-Déjerine).

Atrophy begins early in life and affects the muscles of the face, shoulder girdle, and upper arms; the muscles of the forearms are not involved. It occurs in either sex, with onset at any age from childhood until late adult life. It is transmitted usually as an autosomal dominant, occasionally with sex limitation. Abortive cases are common. Initially, the face and shoulder girdle muscles are involved and later the pelvic girdle muscles. Muscular pseudohypertrophy, contractions, and skeletal deformity are the rule. The characteristic facial involvement, with drooping of the eyelids, is known as "myopathic facies" and the thickened overhanging lip as "tapir lip." The weakened shoulder girdle causes "winging" of the scapula. The absence of forearm involvement gives a "Popeye the sailor" appearance. The disease progresses insidiously with prolonged periods of apparent arrest, and most patients survive and remain active to a normal age.

Limb-girdle Type (Erb).

This form of muscular dystrophy involves the shoulder and pelvic girdles. The face is not affected. It occurs in either sex, with onset usually in the second or third decade but occasionally late in the first decade or in middle life. It is usually transmitted as an autosomal recessive characteristic. Primary involvement of either shoulder girdle or pelvic girdle muscle is noted, with spread to the other after a variable period. Muscular pseudohypertrophy occurs uncommonly. Abortive or static cases are uncommon. Variable severity and rate of progression may occur, but severe disability usually is present 20 years after onset. Muscular contractions and skeletal deformity come on late in the course of the disease. Most patients become severely disabled in middle life and the span is shortened.

Distal Myopathy.

This is a form of benign muscular dystrophy described first by Gowers which occurs rarely in both sexes. The disease begins in the small muscles of the hands and in the feet and legs, starting between the ages of 40 and 60 years. It appears to be inherited as an autosomal dominant.

Ocular Myopathy.

Muscular dystrophy may affect external ocular muscles, producing ptosis, diplopia, and possibly complete external ophthalmoplegia. Although formerly most such patients were considered to have progressive nuclear ophthalmoplegia, tissue examination of involved muscles in recent cases has indicated that some of these were examples of muscular dystrophy of the extraocular muscles. In some cases of muscular dystrophy of the external ocular muscles, there has been associated upper facial muscle weakness, dysphagia, and atrophy and weakness of neck, trunk, and limb muscles.

McARDLE'S SYNDROME

A myopathy characterized by weakness, stiffness, pain, and prolonged contracture of the skeletal muscles with moderate exercise results from the hereditary absence of muscle phosphorylase, leading to an inability to convert glycogen to glucose in muscle. A transient myoglobinuria is noted. The myopathy may not be noted in resting muscles. Treatment includes limitation of physical exercise and adequate diet. Glucagon intramuscularly 3 times daily has been reported helpful.

FAMILIAL PERIODIC PARALYSIS

This is a rare disorder in which the victim is seized by periodic attacks of flaccid paralysis lasting from a few minutes to several hours. Between attacks he is apparently normal. A severe attack may cause death from respiratory paralysis. A "cadaveric" electric reaction accompanies the attack. Decrease in serum potassium and serum phosphate is associated. Treatment includes oral administration of potassium salts. Attacks in susceptible individuals may be produced by injection of hypertonic glucose, insulin, desoxycorticosterone, or epinephrine, or by water diuresis or excess sodium intake.

During attacks the muscle potassium and sodium are not significantly elevated and the muscle becomes electrically unexcitable. Membrane potentials recorded by microelectrodes within the muscle cell do not disclose hyperpolarization. During attacks increased fluid may be noted in large vacuoles within the endoplasmic reticulum of muscle cells. Accumulation of abnormal glycogen breakdown products in these vacuoles may cause the influx of electrolytes and water into muscle cells to preserve ion balance.

Treatment is with potassium chloride, 5-10 Gm. (75-150 gr.) orally when diagnosis has been made and then 5 Gm. (75 gr.) 2-4 times daily during acute episodes as needed to prevent weakness or paralysis. In respiratory paralysis, give a prepared solution containing 1 Gm. (15 gr.) potassium chloride in 50-60 ml. distilled water very slowly I.V. **Caution:** This is a dangerous procedure.

Patients with this disease should avoid high-carbohydrate foods. Routine administration of potassium chloride enteric-coated tablets, 8-12 Gm. (120-180 gr.) t.i.d. prevents attacks.

With adequate treatment, the prognosis is excellent. Death may result from respiratory paralysis, but this is rare.

Adynamia episodica hereditaria, described recently by Gamstorp, is a disorder in which an increase in serum potassium accompanies paralytic attacks. Muscle weakness may be provoked in these patients by administration of potassium chloride or by rest after physical exertion. Onset is usually in the first decade. Attacks occur during rest after physical exertion. Mild paresthesias of the limbs usually precede attacks, and if exercise is begun at this stage paralysis may be aborted.

CENTRAL CORE DISEASE

A newly recognized congenital myopathy with onset probably before the first month of life has recently been described. Proximal muscle weakness, most severe in the lower extremities, results in delayed walking. The disability tends to remain stationary after the patient learns to walk. Hypotonia occurs, but deep tendon reflexes are normal and muscle wasting is not extensive. The principal histologic change is in the anatomic arrangement and histochemical characteristics of aberrant, fibrillary bundles found in the center of muscle fibers; frequent large fibers and central nuclei are also noted. The primary biochemical abnormality causing central core disease has not yet been identified. This disorder is one of many disorders of infancy associated with hypotonia, so that it too must be considered in the differential diagnosis of such children ("floppy infant").

POLYMYOSITIS

Muscular atrophy and weakness may be secondary to widespread local inflammatory changes. In children this disorder may be confused with progressive muscular dystrophy, although its course is apt to be more rapid. Muscles are sometimes tender and indurated. Muscle biopsy discloses variations in muscle fiber size with necrosis, active phagocytosis, and cellular infiltration. **ACTH** or steroid medications may be helpful. Regeneration of muscles may occur, and spontaneous recovery is frequent.

Polymyositis and dermatomyositis occur most commonly in middle age, affecting women more than men, and are characterized by proximal limb and girdle muscular weakness and, to a lesser extent, distal and neck muscular weakness. Associated features may include dysphagia, muscular stiffness, pain, induration, and atrophy.

MYOHEMOGLOBINURIA

Myohemoglobin may be found in the urine in idiopathic spontaneous hemoglobinuria, crush injuries of muscle, following extreme muscular exertion, or following ingestion of certain toxic agents. Myohemoglobinuria is suspected when a dark urine gives a positive reaction for occult blood in the absence of red blood cells in a person without evidence of hemolytic disease. The idiopathic type may be familial, associated with paroxysmal muscle pains and weakness, and may prove fatal. The term "paroxysmal paralytic myoglobinuria" has been suggested for the group in which the disease is precipitated by exertion, starts in young adult life, has a high familial incidence with many repeated attacks, and is frequently complicated by weakness and atrophy. Absolute identification is made by spectrometric studies of the abnormal urine.

MYASTHENIA GRAVIS

This disorder, characterized by marked weakness and fatigability of muscles, is believed to affect the motor apparatus at the myoneural junction. Although almost any muscle in the body may be affected, the disease shows a special affinity for muscles innervated by the bulbar nuclei (face, lips, eyes, tongue, throat, and neck). The etiology is essentially unknown, although some investigators consider myasthenia gravis to be a metabolic disorder. Dysfunction at the myoneural junction, with unusually rapid splitting and inactivation of acetylcholine, has been inferred from chemical and biologic studies.

Pathologic examination has failed to demonstrate consistent specific changes in the CNS, peripheral nerves, or muscles. Abnormalities of the thymus gland, including enlargement and tumor formation, have been described in some patients. It has been suggested that myasthenia gravis is an auto-immune disease since multiple auto-antibodies (including anti-skeletal muscle antibody) have been found in the sera of patients with this disorder.

Clinical Findings.

There is usually pronounced fatigability of muscles, with consequent weakness and paralysis. The muscles innervated by the bulbar nuclei are especially susceptible. Weakness of the extraocular muscles results in diplopia and strabismus. Ptosis of the eyelids may become most apparent late in the day. Speech and swallowing difficulties may be recognized after prolonged exercise of these functions. Difficulty in the use of the tongue and a high-pitched, nasal voice may be present. A snarling, nasal ("myasthenic") smile may be evident.

Women are more often affected than men, and the disease appears most commonly between 20 and 30 years of age.

Other somatic musculature may also be affected, resulting in generalized weakness. Fatigability of the deep tendon reflexes, with increasing diminution in response on repeated tendon tapping, is sometimes demonstrable. After a short rest, a single stimulus may then produce a strong muscle contraction. The Jolly reaction refers to the unusual fatigability of muscle upon repeated electric response, with pronounced capacity to recover after a short rest.

Diagnosis.

A. Neostigmine (Prostigmin®) Test: Prompt relief of symptoms (appearing within 10-15 minutes and lasting up to 4 hours) follows the subcutaneous injection of neostigmine methylsulfate, 1.5 mg., in most cases of myasthenia gravis. Atropine sulfate, 0.6 mg., is administered simultaneously to counteract side reactions. Observations are made 30 minutes later. If dysphagia is present, the response to neostigmine may be readily observed fluoroscopically as the patient swallows a thin barium paste.

B. Edrophonium (Tensilon®): Edrophonium is a quaternary ammonium salt which exerts a direct stimulant effect on the neuromuscular junction. Intravenous injection of 10 mg. edrophonium may relieve weakness within 20-30 seconds. Intramuscular injection of 25-50 mg. may produce improvement lasting for several hours. Intravenous injection of 2-3 mg. may be used as a test dose to distinguish myasthenic crisis (which improves) from overtreatment intoxication (no change) in myasthenic patients under treatment.

Treatment.

A. Emergency Treatment: Sudden inability to swallow or respiratory crises may occur at any time. The patient should always carry 2 ampules of 0.5 mg. (^{1}/120 gr.) of neostigmine methylsulfate (Prostigmin®), to be given immediately subcut. or I.M. if severe symptoms develop. He should be placed under medical care at once; if additional neostigmine is needed, 1 mg. (^{1}/60 gr.) may be given parenterally 2-3 times in one hour until an adequate response is obtained.

Progressively and potentially fatal weakness of the muscles of respiration may occur in spite of the administration of increasingly large amounts of neostigmine. A tracheostomy set, oxygen equipment, suction apparatus, and respirator should be available. After tracheostomy is performed, place the patient in a respirator and give oxygen as needed. Withhold neostigmine. Maintain fluid and electrolyte balance during the period of artificial respiration. After a few days, it is usually possible to gradually decrease the time spent in the respirator. In patients who survive the crisis remissions may occur, in some instances lasting for several years.

B. General Measures: Acquaint the patient with his disease, using simple lay terms. Maintain good nutrition and health.

C. Specific Measures:

1. Neostigmine bromide, 15 mg. (^{1}/4 gr.) orally 4 times a day and increase (up to 180 mg./day) as required to give relief.

2. Pyridostigmine bromide (Mestinon®), an analog of neostigmine, is at times more effective in treatment of bulbar muscle weakness. Give 0.6-1.5 Gm. daily at intervals spaced to provide maximal relief. Long-acting tablets (Mestinon Timespan®), 180 mg. each, are especially useful at bedtime.

3. Ambenonium chloride (Mytelase®) may act twice as long as neostigmine and has fewer side effects. Start with 5 mg. t.i.d. and increase as necessary to give relief. The average dose is 5-25 mg. q.i.d.

4. Edrophonium chloride (Tensilon®) may relieve myasthenic weakness. Ten mg. I.V. gives relief in 20-30 seconds; 25-50 mg. I.M.

gives improvement lasting for hours. Two to 3 mg. I.V. may be used as a test dose for patients under treatment to distinguish between myasthenic crisis (improves) and overtreatment (no change).

5. Ephedrine sulfate, 12 mg. ($1/5$ gr.) with each dose of neostigmine often enhances the action of neostigmine.

6. Potassium has also been found to be of value to supplement neostigmine, but it must be given in nearly toxic doses: 4-6 Gm. potassium chloride.

7. Side effects of treatment with anticholinesterase drugs (e.g., abdominal cramps, nausea and vomiting) may be ameliorated or prevented by adding atropine or atropine-like drugs to the therapeutic regimen as necessary.

8. Galanthamine and lycoramine compounds increase muscle contraction and inhibit cholinesterase. They are now under study and show promise as effective agents for the treatment of myasthenia gravis.

D. X-ray Therapy: Patients who do not respond satisfactorily to oral medications may be given x-ray therapy (3000 r) to the thymus in 10-12 divided doses. Partial remission occurs in about half of patients so treated.

E. Surgical Measures: Thymectomy has been recommended for women under 40 years of age who have responded poorly. Complete remissions occur in about one-third and partial remission in another third. The results in men are uncertain.

F. For thymoma the recommended treatment is thymectomy following a 3000 r course of x-ray therapy to the thymus over a period of 3-6 weeks.

Management of Newborn Infants of Myasthenic Mothers.

Immediately after delivery, children of patients with myasthenia gravis may have severe signs of the disease. Immediate treatment with neostigmine is necessary to preserve life. After a few days the symptoms may disappear, and the child thereafter usually does not suffer from myasthenia.

Prognosis.

Spontaneous remissions occur frequently, but relapse is the rule. Pregnancy usually produces amelioration, although exacerbations may also occur at this time.

Myasthenic crisis, with sudden death from apparent respiratory failure, may occur. Survival of crisis may be followed by a remission. Overtreatment with neostigmine may produce muscle weakness simulating myasthenic crisis.

In myasthenic crisis the mortality may be reduced by withdrawing anticholinesterase medications for about 72 hours after onset of respiratory difficulty or arrest and instituting early tracheostomy with positive pressure respiration using a cuffed tracheostomy tube.

According to some studies, the most critical period is the 2 years following onset.

AMYOTONIA CONGENITA
(Oppenheim's Disease)

Amyotonia congenita is a rare congenital disorder of children characterized by a marked atony of the muscles. It is not progressive. Oppenheim thought it represented a delay in muscular development. Others claim it to be due to agenesis of the lower motor neurons and classify it as a fetal form of spinal muscular atrophy of the Werdnig-Hoffmann type. Numerical deficiency of the anterior horn cells has been observed on pathologic examination.

Oppenheim felt that in his infants the generalized hypotonia, muscle weakness, and areflexia affecting infants from birth had as its most characteristic feature a tendency to recover with the passage of time. This, he felt, distinguished this disorder from the spinal muscular atrophy of Werdnig and Hoffman. Muscle biopsy and electrodiagnostic studies may be of value in diagnosis.

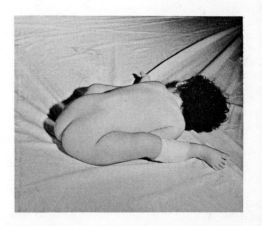

Amyotonia Congenita. Child with hypotonia, hyporeflexia, and muscle weakness.

MYOTONIA CONGENITA
(Thomsen's Disease)

Myotonia congenita is a rare heredofamilial disorder characterized by localized or generalized myotonia. Hypertrophy and hypertonicity of the muscles may occur, rendering them rigid and unyielding. The disease has occurred in 5 successive generations in the family of Dr. Thomsen, who first described it. Although it usually is not serious, the increased muscle stiffness makes it difficult for its victims to enjoy physical activity. Some have periodic attacks of generalized muscular spasm. Typically the disorder is present from birth and there is stiffness and difficulty in relaxation of the entire voluntary musculature. Stiffness is usually accentuated by cold and relieved by exercise, and generalized muscular hypertrophy is common. It is inherited usually as an autosomal dominant characteristic. Quinine has been used successfully in relieving hypertonicity. Myotonia acquisita is a form of Thomsen's disease which has its onset late in life.

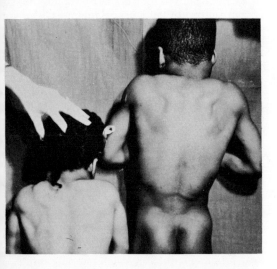

Myotonia Congenita. Hypertrophied myotonic shoulder muscles of young brother and sister.

MYOTONIA ATROPHICA
(Dystrophia Myotonica)

Myotonia atrophica is a rare heredodegenerative disease of adult life which appears to be a mixture of Thomsen's disease and muscular dystrophy. There is hypertonicity of some muscles, usually of the tongue and the fist-making muscles of the hand, together with atrophy and weakness of the face, jaw muscles, peronei, and others. In both myotonia congenita and myotonia atrophica the patient characteristically grasps an object and then is unable to release his grip immediately. Myotonia, muscle atrophy (especially of face and neck), cataracts, early baldness, testicular atrophy, and evidence of dysfunction of other endocrine glands usually occur.

Paramyotonia congenita is a relatively rare disorder characterized by myotonia which increases in the presence of cold, intermittent flaccid paresis which is not necessarily dependent upon cold or myotonia, and a hereditary pattern dependent upon a single autosomal dominant gene.

"STIFF MAN" SYNDROME
(Progressive Fluctuating Muscular Rigidity and Spasm)

This is a disorder of unknown etiology and pathogenesis characterized by stiffness, tightness, or rigidity of the muscles, and painful spasms of the muscles of the limbs and back. Board-like rigidity of back and abdominal muscles, stiff gait, and a tendency to fall like a "wooden man" may be noted intermittently.

Diazepam (Valium®), a benzdiazepine derivative of chlordiazepoxide, has been reported to produce dramatic improvement in patients in doses of 10-15 mg. 4 times daily.

GENERALIZED MYOSITIS OSSIFICANS

This progressive familial disease begins in early childhood and is often accompanied by congenital anomalies of the digits. Interstitial tissue shows the earliest changes; swellings in muscles are noted which gradually are transformed into bony-hard lumps. Respiratory muscles may be affected, and progressive respiratory embarrassment is prone to occur in some patients.

CONGENITAL NEUROMUSCULAR DISORDERS

Some congenital disorders of muscle or of the lower motor neurons are essentially non-progressive. The following classification has been found useful:

Congenital Absence of Muscle.

This relatively common defect appears to affect certain muscles more than others. The pectoralis major, trapezius, serratus anterior, and quadratus femoris muscles are reported to be most commonly absent. The defect may be asymptomatic or may be associated with other developmental defects.

Congenital Neuromuscular Disease With Localized or Restricted Weakness.

A. Congenital Facial Diplegia, External Ophthalmoplegia, and Related Abnormalities: Congenital weakness of the facial muscles, the external rectus muscles (Moebius syndrome), and other muscles supplied by the cranial nerves may coexist with other congenital defects. Although the site of primary pathology is generally considered to be at the levels of the cranial nerve nuclei, not many confirmatory pathologic studies have been reported.

B. Congenital Ptosis: Isolated weakness of the levator palpebrae muscle may be unilateral or bilateral. Affected individuals go about frequently with neck extended and the brow furrowed in attempts to compensate for ptosis. Congenital Horner's syndrome may also occur with slight ptosis, defective iris pigmentation, and miosis.

C. Congenital Neuropathies and Radiculopathies: Unilateral facial weakness related somehow to pregnancy or the birth process is common, and the prognosis for recovery from this and similar cranial nerve palsies in the first year of life is excellent. Traction palsies (Erb and Klumpke; see p.   ) are usually attributed to brachial plexus injuries but may result from injury at the spinal root level instead. The congenital and birth palsies must be distinguished from those acquired in the few days after birth from injections, trauma, infection, etc.

Congenital Neuromuscular Disorders Associated With Contracture and Deformity About Joints.

At birth, infants with neuromuscular disease may have contractures and fixed deformities about one or more joints. Associated local weakness, atrophy, or absence of muscle or other congenital disorders such as myelomeningocele, spina bifida, etc. may also occur.

A. Congenital Club Foot: This is considered to be one of the most common congenital musculoskeletal deformities, and the term club foot is applied to any fixed, abnormal posture of one or both feet. Plantar flexion and inversion of the foot is the most common position, and more than one member of a family, usually male, may be affected. In a few instances, abnormalities of the spinal cord and peripheral nervous system have been described, but in most cases no pathologic changes in the nervous system can be established.

B. Congenital High Shoulder (Sprengel's Deformity): The scapula is broader and shorter than usual. It is usually rotated and elevated, so that the lower angle lies closer to the spine than normally. Extensive fibrosis in the upper portion of the trapezius muscle, and absence or replacement by fat and connective tissue of the lower portion of the trepezius have been noted.

C. Congenital Torticollis: Typically there is contracture of the sternocleidomastoid muscle, with the occiput inclined toward that side and the chin deviated up and toward the opposite side. The head may be bent laterally, the face broadened, the frontal prominences minimized, and the occiput exaggerated on the affected side. The involved sternocleidomastoid muscle is often firmer than normal to touch. Extensive fibrosis occurs within the residual fibers of the affected sternocleidomastoid muscle. The cause is not known, but presumably antedates birth. Spontaneous recovery may occur, or may be aided by physiotherapy, cast, or collar. Surgical measures directed at the muscle or its nerve supply, when necessary, may be therapeutically effective.

D. Deformity About Several Joints (Arthrogryposis Multiplex Congenita): This syndrome refers to a condition in which multiple joints are deformed or bent in association with contracture of muscle. An imbalance of muscle strength about the joints resulting from neural or myopathic disease usually occurs without primary disorders of the joints. In disorders of neuropathic origin, the lower limbs are usually abducted, flexed, or extended at the hips, extended at the knees, and plantar flexed at the ankles. In those of myopathic origin the hips are adducted and the knees and ankles flexed. Associated anomalies such as absence of the lower limbs, hemivertebrae, fusion and deformity of the ribs, scoliosis, meningomyelocele, and genitourinary disorders may occur.

Congenital Neuromuscular Disorders With Nonprogressive Generalized Weakness and Hypotonia.

Many disorders may present as nonprogressive congenital conditions with generalized hypotonia, including amyotonia congenita, mongolism, cretinism, arachnodactyly, Turner's syndrome, etc. Some CNS diseases may present with mental retardation and generalized hypotonia, although weakness may not be the most prominent feature. Congenital myasthenia gravis, polyneuritis of infancy, progressive muscular dystrophy, and polymyositis may sometimes be mistaken for amyotonia congenita. The syndrome of the "floppy infant" - the flaccid, limp, slack, hypotonic child - usually presents a diagnostic challenge because of the many clinical entities with which it may be associated.

. . .

34...

Psychiatric Disorders

Neurologic disorders are frequently associated with psychiatric symptoms, either as a result of primary involvement of the cerebral cortex or because of psychic reactions to unpleasant or progressive chronic disability. Conversely, psychiatric disorders may mimic neurologic disorders (e.g., conversion reaction and psychophysiologic disturbances), and the differentiation may at times be exceedingly difficult. Any type of psychiatric disturbance may occur in neurologic disease.

Neurologic diseases of insidious onset (e.g., multiple sclerosis, brain tumor, paresis) are often considered to be of psychogenic origin during their early phases. It is important to diagnose neurologic disorders when present, and one should not be misled even when there is overwhelming evidence of psychiatric disturbance. This is especially true for those neurologic disorders which may be amenable to therapy (e.g., infections, toxins, injury).

ACUTE BRAIN SYNDROME

The acute brain syndromes are a group of disorders of perception and interpretation, usually associated with delirium. They are often reversible, and may result from temporary impairment of brain function secondary to a variety of causes including systemic or CNS infection, exogenous or endogenous intoxication, trauma, cerebrovascular disease, convulsive disorders, intracranial tumors, and metabolic disorders such as anoxia and dehydration.

The onset may be abrupt or gradual. Acute brain syndromes are most common in old age and childhood and are more apt to occur among dependent personalities with little sophistication from lower economic and social groups. The clinical course may be benign, ending in complete remission, or the disorder may progress to irreversible brain damage or death.

The clinical features (often reversible) may include the following: (1) disorientation, particularly with respect to time; (2) memory impairment, especially for recent events; (3) impaired intellectual function, especially in comprehension, learning, calculation, and knowledge, with poor concrete ideation, per-

severation, and confabulation; (4) impairment of judgment and planning ability; and (5) labile or shallow emotional responses. Great alterations in mental function may occur within brief periods. Delirium, usually associated with impaired perceptions, visual hallucinations and illusions, and increased psychomotor activity, may occur; or there may be stupor, with apathy and mental retardation.

An organic cause must be sought even in patients with a past history of social maladjustment and psychic stress and numerous emotional upsets. Clinical features related to headache, vomiting, impaired vision, convulsions, paralyses, incoordination, and paresthesias should be carefully investigated. Psychologic testing may disclose patterns suggestive of organic intellectual and memory impairment. Physical and neurologic examination and appropriate laboratory studies (blood, x-rays, CSF, EEG, etc.) should be carried out.

Whenever possible, treatment should be specifically directed against an established cause. Supportive measures are usually of great importance. The patient is best kept in a cool, quiet room with subdued lighting. Supervision is essential to protect the patient and others from injury. Sedatives and tranquilizers may be required for excessive agitation or aggression. Additional nursing and supportive measures required may include maintenance of hydration and electrolyte balance, reduction of fever, vitamin supplements, attention to bladder and bowel function, and skin care.

CHRONIC BRAIN SYNDROME

Chronic brain syndromes consist of usually permanent, often diffuse impairment of cerebral function which may be almost imperceptible clinically. Although the manifestations may ultimately become milder, some degree of impaired judgment, memory, orientation, comprehension, and affect usually persists. This is apt to be the case even if the underlying pathologic process subsides or responds to specific treatment.

Chronic brain syndrome may be due to man of the same underlying disorders which cause acute brain syndromes, and the differentiation may sometimes be based upon the demonstration of permanent impairment of brain function in the chronic group. The most common causes of chronic brain syndrome are chronic alcoholism, cerebrovascular disease, senility, presenility, multiple sclerosis, head trauma, convulsive disorders, brain tumors, and neurosyphilis.

The usual clinical picture is one of slow deterioration in memory, confusion, irritability, stereotyped behavior, and delusional somatic complaints. Disorientation for time, place, and person is often present. Confabulation - to fill the gaps of memory deficit - is encountered in Korsakoff's psychosis. The patient often becomes untidy, mentally dull, rigid, and self-centered. Evidence of associated or underlying organic brain disease such as that associated with cerebrovascular disease or brain tumors may be apparent on examination. Laboratory studies and special tests may provide significant clues to the underlying brain changes and etiology.

In addition to treatment of the underlying disease (when feasible), symptomatic and supportive treatment, supervision, nursing care, sedation, and the use of tranquilizers are frequently necessary. Since the underlying disease may be untreatable, custodial care in a suitable environment or institution is often required.

THE PSYCHOSES

Psychoses may occur without known or recognizable physical cause or structural brain changes. Characteristic features are personality disintegration of variable degree with failure to properly evaluate external reality. The ability to work and to relate adequately to other people is impaired. The psychoses are characterized by withdrawal, bizarre or asocial behavior, and outbursts of antisocial, dangerous, or self-destructive behavior are likely to occur. Borderline and ambulatory psychotic states may also occur, and in these cases the individual may make a marginal type of adjustment without the necessity of hospitalization.

The great majority of patients in mental institutions have psychotic disorders. The onset is commonly during adolescence although it may be at any time from infancy to old age. Psychotic breaks frequently occur in persons whose behavior and thinking have always been different from others. The psychoses may last from a few hours to years or even most of a lifetime.

AFFECTIVE REACTIONS

The affective reactions are those psychotic disorders in which mood change is the principal symptom.

Manic-Depressive Reactions.

The manic-depressive state is characterized by abnormal mood swings with increased or decreased psychomotor activity. Over a period of many years the same patient may have isolated attacks of mania and depression, although in some patients one type of reaction tends to recur. This disorder is most common in young adults, and occurs more frequently in women than in men. A familial tendency has been noted, and relatively minor events may trigger an acute episode.

The patient in the manic phase demonstrates flight of ideas, increased psychomotor activity, and emotional excitement. Other features include bizarre dress, hallucinations, hypersexuality, grandiose delusions, and even delirium.

The depressed phase is characterized by difficulty in thinking, psychomotor retardation, and depression. In severe cases, hallucinations and self-accusatory delusions may occur; suicidal tendencies are often prominent. Clouding of consciousness or stupor may occur.

Mixed types also occur in which the cardinal symptoms of both phases are present, such as in agitated depression or maniacal stupor. This is most apt to occur when a patient in the depressed or manic phase is undergoing a shift to the opposite mood.

During acute episodes hospitalization is usually required. Electroshock therapy may be effective in shortening the depressive phase as well as the acute manic phase. Antidepressant drugs may also prove effective. In the manic phase, continuous tub baths (sedative hydrotherapy), sedative-hypnotics, and phenothiazine tranquilizers may be useful. Psychiatric care after the acute episode is usually desirable. Recovery from a single episode usually occurs, although recurrences are frequent.

The acute phase may last from a few days to many years. Onset in early life usually implies a life-long history of recurrence of hyper- and hypoactive moods and behavior.

Psychotic Depressive Reaction.

These patients are severely depressed and have difficulty in relating to reality. Delusions and hallucinations may be present. There usually is no history of recurrent depressive episodes or mood swings, but a history of an external precipitating factor directly related to the onset of the depression can often be elicited. The prognosis is usually good, and treatment, consisting of psychotherapy, drugs, or electroshock therapy, is usually effective.

Involutional Psychotic Reaction.

Psychotic disturbances characterized by depression may occur during the involutional period of life, particularly in women in association with the menopause. Insomnia, increasing agitation, somatic delusions, and feelings of unreality may gradually appear. Marked depression, with agitation, may become so profound that precautions against suicide must be instituted. These disorders usually respond favorably to electroshock and drug therapy, especially if instituted early. Supportive psychotherapy and psychiatric supervision are advisable.

SCHIZOPHRENIC REACTIONS

The schizophrenic reactions are characterized by progressive withdrawal from the environment as manifested by specific alterations of the ability to think, feel, and relate to the external world. The schizophrenias are the largest group of severe behavioral disorders and account for one of every 4 hospital beds in the U.S.A. Although schizophrenia occurs most often in adolescents and young adults, it may occur at any age from childhood to middle age. The schizophrenic reaction may be of brief duration or may be protracted over many years or throughout the entire lifetime of the patient.

Patients with schizophrenia have deficits in awareness of social or interpersonal realities. Defects in associative function, changes in affect, and ambivalence are noted. Auditory hallucinations with persecutory meaning frequently occur. Delusions are usually persecutory in type, although delusions of grandeur and imaginary diseases also are noted. Memory disturbances, including amnesias, are common. Speech and writing may show blocking, poverty of ideas, incoherence, and delusional content. The speech may be characterized by affected mannerisms, substitutions, and accidental associations. Catatonic symptoms, including catalepsy, stupor, hyperkinesis, and stereotyped speech, movement, expression, and mannerisms, may also occur.

The physical examination is usually not remarkable although schizophrenics tend to have an asthenic habitus, autonomic instability, weight loss, poor motor coordination, and an awkward gait.

Treatment usually includes psychotherapy, the use of psychopharmacologic agents, and electroshock therapy in selected patients. The prognosis is variable, although an acute onset, catatonic symptoms, and a marked degree of affective disturbance are usually associated with a better prognosis; whereas onset at a young age, slow progress, and the absence of overt anxiety indicate a poor prognosis.

A variety of clinical types have been distinguished on the basis of the predominance of some of the symptoms.

Paranoid Schizophrenia.

Patients become suspicious and interpret even indifferent events and objects as threats to themselves. They feel that others are conspiring against them, and hear voices that talk about and to them. This may lead to violent action, as in fleeing from or turning against a supposed tormentor. As the disorder becomes more chronic, ideas of omnipotence and delusions of grandeur may appear.

Catatonic Schizophrenia.

The principal signs are stupor, mutism, negativism, and peculiarities of gait. Periods of catatonic excitement may occur with impulsive activity, self-disregard, sleeplessness, and repetitious overactivity. In the akinetic phase, the patient may show waxy flexibility, refusal to swallow, and automatic responses to commands. The onset is often acute, and the patient's mood may alternate between mania and melancholia.

Hebephrenic Schizophrenia.

This is an acute psychosis followed by deterioration but without paranoid or catatonic features. The onset is usually between 12 and 25 years of age. Pronounced feelings of mental and physical incapacity, pathologic sensations, emotional dulling, grotesque silliness, and sexual preoccupation are the principal features. Hebephrenic schizophrenia includes acute noncatatonic forms characterized by melancholia, mania, amentia, and twilight states.

Simple Schizophrenia.

Patients become intellectually and affectively impoverished, with diminishing ability to make competent judgments and to work and care for themselves. They appear stupid and finally show a picture of severe dementia. Simple schizophrenia is slowly progressive over a period of many years. Institutional care is usually required.

THE NEUROSES

The neuroses are personality disturbances in which there is no gross impairment of perception or ability to interpret reality and no severely antisocial behavior. They are frequently precipitated by environmental factors. The cause appears to lie in early life conditioning, although the patient's current life situation triggers the actual neurotic symptoms. The major types of neurotic reactions are classified according to the predominant reaction.

ANXIETY REACTION

The anxiety reaction is characterized by feelings of apprehension or tension when faced with real or symbolic danger. In some patients, continuous or recurrent symptoms result from "free-floating" anxiety; this syndrome is seen in young adults and is known as anxiety neurosis. Complaints include palpitations, tremors, headache, dizziness, chest pains, choking, faintness, and dyspnea. Attacks are precipitated by emotional or physical stress. Crowded areas (e. g., public gatherings) often form the setting of attacks. Increased irritability and intolerance for mild annoyances may make hospitalization necessary. The patient may have a sensation of impending disaster. Attacks may last from a few minutes to hours, and may assume panic proportions.

Physical examination may reveal excessive perspiration of hands, tremors, mild tachycardia, or flushed face and neck.

Anxiety may be of brief duration or may last many years, with exacerbations and remissions. Treatment includes a complete medical work-up to reassure the patient, the use of sedatives and tranquilizers, and psychotherapy.

PHOBIC REACTION

In some cases anxiety is precipitated only by a particular object or situation which symbolically represents a neurotic conflict. Neurotic reactions in children are frequently of this kind. Elaborate efforts to avoid the phobia-inducing object cause the patient's life to become increasingly isolated.

Treatment consists of psychotherapy directed toward achieving insight so that the patient can overcome his phobia and what it represents to him.

CONVERSION REACTION
(Conversion Hysteria)

Insupportable anxiety may be converted into impairment of motor or sensory function. The resulting handicap is often dramatic and bizarre, but despite apparent paralysis, blindness, paresthesias, etc. the patient seems remarkably undisturbed. Patients with immature, unsophisticated backgrounds are most susceptible. Amnesia and dissociation of ideas may occur and represent avoidance mechanisms. In peacetime this syndrome is most apt to occur in women.

Conversion symptoms may at times be difficult to distinguish from organic symptoms, but in general the patient's apparent illness will have atypical features. For example, anesthetic areas are frequently of the "stocking and glove" type rather than corresponding to anatomic nerve distribution; paralyses vary in degree and distribution from time to time; visual fields in hysterical blindness may be the same at varying distances from the eyes, and the patient appears able to avoid obstacles. Hysterical attacks of variable types occur, and may be difficult to distinguish from epileptic seizures. However, patients with hysterical seizures usually do not become unconscious, do not hurt themselves, and do not lose bladder or bowel control.

Treatment by suggestion, persuasion, hypnotism, and sedation may be effective. In resistant or severely disabled patients, psychotherapy is usually required. Removing the patient from a threatening situation often has a beneficial effect on symptoms.

OBSESSIVE-COMPULSIVE REACTION

In this type of neurosis obsessive thoughts or compulsive acts dominate the patient's behavior. Obsessive thoughts tend to persevere and usually cannot be put out of consciousness; compulsions are repetitious acts, usually of a ritualistic, stereotyped character. The typical patient is clean and neat, polite, perfectionistic, indecisive, and unimaginative, but with superior intellectual capacity. Anxiety and depression occur if the ritual is interrupted. Rituals include repetitive hand washing, object touching, and prolonged dressing. Obsessive thoughts may relate to death, sex, or other subjects disturbing to the patient.

Psychiatric treatment is often difficult, and may be of little help in severe cases.

PERSONALITY DISORDERS

A person's character structure is reflected in the habitual attitudes and reaction patterns he displays in human relationships. Personality or character disorders consist of inappropriate exaggeration of one or more aspects of behavior. Lifelong patterns of action and behavior rather than specifically identifiable mental or emotional symptoms characterize the personality disorders.

Except for some cases of alcohol or drug addiction, treatment is usually limited to social measures for the protection of the patient and the community.

PERSONALITY TRAIT DISTURBANCES

Patients with these disorders are unable to maintain their emotional equilibrium and independence under stress because of emotional maldevelopment.   There are 3 types.

Emotionally Unstable Personalities.
These persons show poor judgment under stress and their relationships with other people are characterized by fluctuating emotional attitudes with poorly controlled hostility, guilt, and anxiety.

Passive-Aggressive Personalities.
These persons tend to be helpless and indecisive or react to frustration by irritability, temper tantrums, and destructive behavior. They tend to establish relationships of the child-parent type, showing either excessive dependency upon or control over others.

Compulsive Personalities.
Compulsive personalities display chronic excessive or obsessive concern, with strict adherence to high standards of conscience and conformity. They are usually rigid, overly conscientious, and hard-working, and are unable to feel free of tension.

PERSONALITY PATTERN DISTURBANCES

These disorders are more deeply seated than the personality trait disturbances and are usually even more refractory to therapy.

Inadequate Personalities.
These persons show poor judgment, inadaptability, ineptness, and social incompatibility. Although they have no gross physical or mental deficit, they respond inadequately to intellectual, emotional, social, and physical demands.

Schizoid Personalities.
Schizoid personalities avoid close interpersonal relationships, lack aggressiveness, and are unable to display hostility. Their thinking is autistic, and they are usually described as quiet, shy, obedient, sensitive, and retiring individuals. Peculiar or "off-beat" ideas and behavior are frequently present.

Cyclothymic Personalities.
Individuals in this group fluctuate between elation and sadness without obvious relation to external events.

Paranoid Personalities.
These persons are similar to the schizoid types, but they also show suspiciousness, envy, extreme jealousy, and stubbornness.

SOCIOPATHIC PERSONALITY DISTURBANCES

The sociopathic personality usually has a lifelong history of conflict with the customs and laws of society. This group of disorders must be differentiated from other severe personality disorders, neuroses, psychoses, and organic brain disease, which may also be characterized by failure to conform to prevailing cultural and legal norms.

Antisocial Reaction.
Individuals in this group are chronically in trouble with society and do not benefit from punishment or experience. They are often chronic liars and emotionally immature, with poor judgment and no sense of responsibility. They may present a likable, pleasant appearance, and tend to rationalize their behavior. Former terms for these individuals are "psychopaths, " "psychopathic personalities, " and "constitutional psychopathic inferiors. "

Dyssocial Reaction.
Persons in this group, because of prolonged life in an abnormal environment, disregard the usual social codes. They may, however, show strong loyalties among themselves.

Sexual Deviation.
The sexual deviates exhibit sexual behavior contrary to accepted cultural codes and customs. Similar symptoms may occur with schizophrenia, the psychoneuroses, or senile psychosis, so that these disorders must be ruled out. Some of the more common deviations are the following: (Combinations of these sexual deviations may occur.)
1. Homosexuality - Attraction to or sexual relations with persons of the same sex.
2. Fetishism - Substitution of some object (e. g., shoe, garment) for the genitals.
3. Transvestism - Sexual pleasure obtained from wearing the clothing of the opposite sex.
4. Voyeurism - Sexual pleasure obtained from observation of exposed genitals or the sexual activity of others.
5. Bestiality - Sexual relations with animals.

6. Pederasty - Anal intercourse with boys.

7. Sadism - Sexual pleasure derived from acts of cruelty to others. Sexual activity may occur concurrently.

8. Masochism - Sexual pleasure derived from experiencing pain.

Addiction.

Alcohol addiction is common among people with personality or character disorders, and may also occur in many types of psychosis and neurosis. During periods of intoxication the patient may have increased feelings of importance. Following an acute alcoholic bout, however, he usually feels considerable self-blame and self-contempt.

Narcotics addicts generally show neurotic or psychopathic backgrounds with excessive emotional dependence upon others. Addicts are apt to use any means, legal or illegal, to obtain the funds necessary to secure their addicting drug.

GLOSSARY OF PSYCHOLOGIC TERMS

Abreaction: Emotional discharge resulting from conscious recall of repressed intolerable experience.

Acting out: Expression by actions of unconscious emotional feelings or conflicts.

Acute stress or situational reaction: Acute emotional reaction related to extreme emotional stress.

Adjustment: Adaptation of individual to his environment.

Affect: Emotional feeling tone. Emotion and affect are synonyms.

Affective reaction: Severe disorder of mood; manic depressive psychosis.

Aggression: Physical, verbal, or symbolic forceful attacking action.

Agitation: Chronic restlessness; often an expression of emotional tension.

Ambivalence: Coexistence of opposing drives or emotions toward a person, object, or goal.

Amnesia: Pathologic loss of memory; may be organic or emotional (or both) in origin.

Anal eroticism: Pleasurable experience of anal function. Common in childhood; in later life, may appear in disguised and sublimated forms.

Autism (autistic or dereistic thinking): Thinking which gratifies unfulfilled desires unrealistically; not in accord with reality, logic, or experience.

Blocking: Impaired recall or interruption of thought or speech, usually due to emotional factors.

Compensation: Attempt to make up for real or fancied deficiencies.

Complex: Group of related ideas with strong common emotional tone.

Compulsion: Irresistible drive to do something often contrary to best judgment or desire.

Confabulation: Imaginary filling-in of memory gaps, usually unconsciously.

Conflict: A conscious or unconscious clash between opposing emotional forces.

Confusion: Lack of orientation with respect to persons, place, and time.

Conversion: Transformation of emotions into physical manifestations.

Delirium: Mental disorder characterized by disorientation and confusion.

Delusion: False belief which cannot be corrected by reason.

Dementia praecox: Obsolete term for schizophrenia.

Denial: Denying existence of important elements that would otherwise cause anxiety and conflicts.

Dependency needs: Infantile needs for love, protection, and nutrition; may continue beyond infancy in overt or hidden forms.

Depersonalization: Feelings of unreality regarding self or environment.

Depression: Profound, unrealistic morbid sadness.

Disorientation: Impaired awareness of self in relation to space, time, and person.

Displacement: An unconscious mental mechanism in which emotion is transferred from its original object to a more acceptable substitute object.

Dissociation: An unconscious defense mechanism; a splitting off of emotion from idea, object, or situation.

Drive: A basic urge; motivation.

Echolalia: Automatic repetition of phrases and words; frequent in schizophrenic patients.

Ego: Part of the personality which possesses consciousness, deals with reality and the outside world; the conscious self.

Emotion: Subjective feeling such as fear, grief, anger, joy, or love.

Empathy: Awareness of meaning and significance of emotions and behavior of other persons.

Euphoria: Feeling of physical and emotional well-being.

Fantasy: An imaginary sequence of events or mental images.

Flight of ideas: Skipping from one idea to another. Ideas are apt to be fragmentary and related only by chance association.

Free association: Unselective verbalization of whatever comes to mind.

Fugue: Amnesia and physical flight from a particular environment.

Hallucination: False sensory perception of external object in the absence of the object.

Hysteria: Disorder arising from emotional conflicts, usually with dramatic physical clinical features characterized by immaturity, dependency, and use of defense mechanisms of conversion and dissociation.

Id: Part of the personality which contains instinctive and unconscious drives.

Identification: Attempt of an individual to pattern himself after another.

Illusion: Misinterpretation of a real, external experience.

Inhibition: Unconscious interference with, or restriction of, instinctual drives.

Insight: Self-understanding; one's understanding of the origin and nature of his behavior and attitudes.

Intelligence: Potential capacity to understand, recall, and integrate previous experience and learning to meet new situations.

Introjection: Unconscious symbolic taking within the self of loved or hated external objects; the converse of projection.

Libido: Psychic drive or energy, usually associated with the sexual instinct.

Mania: Mental illness with increased excitability, acceleration of thought, speech, and motor activity, and a grandiose, elated mood.

Melancholia: Pathologic dejection, often with psychosis.

Narcissism: Self-love and interest. Normal in early childhood.

Negativism: Resistance and opposition to advice or suggestions; normal in late infancy.

Neologism: New word or combination of words coined by the patient; common in schizophrenia.

Neurosis: Emotional disorder due to unresolved unconscious conflicts with minimal loss of contact with reality. Types include anxiety reaction, phobic reaction, conversion reaction, and obsessive-compulsive reaction.

Nihilism: Delusion of nonexistence of self or part of self.

Obsession: Persistent intrusive unwanted impulse or idea that cannot be eliminated by reasoning.

Organic psychosis: Mental syndrome found with organic brain disease and usually associated with disorientation, impaired memory and judgment, intellectual deficiency, and behavioral changes.

Paranoia: A rare, slowly developing chronic psychotic disorder characterized by persecutory or grandiose delusions with the rest of the personality essentially normal.

Phobia: Persistent unrealistic fear of external objects or situations such as heights, open spaces, dirt, etc.

Psychopath: Person whose behavior is highly amoral or antisocial with little anxiety or guilt.

Psychosis: Severe emotional illness characterized by abnormal patterns of feeling, thinking, and acting and loss of contact with - or serious distortion of - reality.

Rationalization: Making motives, feelings, behavior more acceptable by ascribing acceptable or worthwhile motives to such as might otherwise be intolerable or unacceptable.

Reaction formation: Development of behavior and attitudes based on the opposite of unacceptable impulses.

Regression: Return to more infantile modes of gratification.

Repression: Purposeful but unconscious forgetting.

Resistance: Psychic defenses against bringing repressed thoughts or impulses into awareness, thus avoiding anxiety.

Restitution: Attempt to assuage unconscious guilt feelings by making reparation.

Schizoid: Refers usually to traits of shyness, introspection, and introversion.

Schizophrenia: Severe psychosis usually with retreat from reality, delusions, hallucinations, and regressive behavior. Types: (1) **Paranoid**, characterized by delusions of persecution and megalomania. (2) **Catatonic**, characterized by marked immobility. (3) **Hebephrenic**, characterized by shallow, inappropriate emotions and unpredictable, childish behavior. (4) **Simple**, characterized by withdrawal, apathy, inability to relate effectively to others.

Secondary gain: External gain derived from illness (disability payments, attention, etc.).

Sensorium: State of mental clarity and consciousness at a given time.

Sublimation: Diversion of unacceptable, instinctual drives into acceptable channels.

Substitution: Replacement of an unattainable goal, emotion, or object by one more acceptable or attainable.

Superego: Censoring force of the personality, conscience; contains morals and ethics of the individual; in our culture, derived largely from parents.

Suppression: Conscious efforts to overcome unacceptable thoughts or desires.

Symbolization: An abstract representation of a particular object, idea, or constellation.

Undoing: Symbolically acting out in reverse, usually repetitiously, an unacceptable prior action.

Verbigeration: Stereotyped, apparently meaningless, irrelevant verbal responses to questions.

Appendix

THE NEUROLOGIC EXAMINATION

HISTORY

A complete history of the nature, onset, extent, and duration of the presenting complaint and associated complaints must be taken. Previous diseases, personal and family history, occupational data, and social history should be recorded. It may be desirable or necessary to interview relatives and friends. Occasionally it is advisable to record portions of the history verbatim.

Detailed information is especially sought in regard to the following: (1) **Headache:** Duration, time of onset, location, frequency, severity, progression, precipitating circumstances, associated symptoms, and response to analgesics. (2) **Seizures and episodic loss of consciousness:** Character of the individual episode, age at onset, frequency, duration, mental status during and after episodes, associated signs and symptoms, aura, type and effectiveness of previous treatment. (3) **Pain:** Onset, progression, frequency, characteristics, effect of physical measures, associated complaints, type and effectiveness of previous treatment. (4) **Visual disturbances:** Previous similar or related changes, progression or remissions, scotomas, acuity changes, diplopia, field changes, associated phenomena.

PHYSICAL EXAMINATION

A thorough general physical examination should always be made. In particular, the circulatory, respiratory, genitourinary, gastrointestinal, and skeletal systems should be studied. A record of the temperature, pulse rate, respiratory rate, and blood pressure is routinely made. Note especially deformity or limitation of the head, neck, vertebral column, and joints. The scalp and skull are inspected and carefully palpated for localized thickening of the skull, clusters of abnormal scalp vessels, depressions of skull, abnormal contours and asymmetry of skull, craniotomy and other operative scars. Percussion may disclose local scalp or skull tenderness over diseased areas and, in hydrocephalic children, a tympanitic "cracked pot" sound. Auscultation of the skull and neck for bruits is carried out; if bruits are present, the effect of separate carotid artery compression is also noted.

NEUROLOGIC EXAMINATION

Mental Examination.

Mental changes are frequently encountered in clinical neurology, and an understanding of them is helpful for diagnosis and treatment. Mental deterioration, confusion, excitement, mania, lethargy, apathy, anxiety, depression, neurotic behavior, psychotic reactions, personality disturbances, and character disorders may be associated with neurologic disease. The type of mental disturbance is not specific for any given neurologic disorder, although impaired intellectual functioning is very common in cerebral disease. The insidious onset of certain neurologic disorders (e. g., brain tumor, multiple sclerosis, paralysis agitans), with remissions and exacerbations, frequently results in the faulty diagnosis of psychogenic illness. Early neurologic disease may occur without significant physical, laboratory, x-ray, or other special diagnostic findings. Drugs used in treatment may further complicate the clinical picture.

A. General Behavior: Speech, appearance, cooperation, posture, general attitude, characteristic mannerisms, motor behavior. The patient's appearance, including condition of clothes and hair, facial expressions, attitude, peculiarities, rapport with environment; and his conduct, including activity, postures, gestures, and changeability are evaluated during the interview as well as from information and observations of his family, friends, and others. Speech and stream of thought are examined, with special attention to its spontaneity, relevance, and coherence. Distractibility, flights of ideas, blocking, punning, rhyming, neologizing, and stereotypy are noted, and verbatim examples recorded.

B. Mood: Anxiety, depression, apathy, fear, suspicion, irritability, elation, aggression, etc. Note the general emotional state of the patient as judged by his appearance and conduct. Obtain patient's own statement of his mood and make an objective estimate of mood. Check for suicidal ruminations.

C. Sensorium: Orientation, retention, alertness, stupor, coma. When possible, check orientation for time, place, person, situation, and self.

D. Level of Intelligence: Vocabulary, judgment, cultural outlook, general information, etc. Intellectual performance tests, including calculation, judgment, retention, similarities and differences, etc., should be evaluated.

Evidence of an organic brain disorder may be disclosed by tests of intellectual performance. The subject's ability to abstract, use symbols, and evaluate new experiences on the basis of past experience may be judged with the aid of the following tests:

1. Memory - Details and dates of recent and remote events should be elicited, including items such as birth date, marriage date, names and ages of children and relatives, specific details of past few days, orientation as to time, place, and person, educational history with dates and names.

2. General information - Should be adapted to patient's background. Usually include names of President and Vice-President, Governor of state, capitols of European countries and American states; current events in politics, sports world, etc.; identification of world figures and leaders.

3. Similarities and differences - Compare wood and coal; iron and silver; book, teacher, and newspaper; president and king; dwarf and child; lie and mistake.

4. Calculation - Subtract 7's from 100 ($100 - 7 = 93$; $93 - 7 = 86$; $86 - 7 = 79$, etc.); add, multiply, or divide single numbers and make them more difficult depending upon patient's background, e.g., 3×5, 4×3, 16×3, etc. Count from one to 20 and backward from 20 to one. Calculate interest at 6% for 18 months.

5. Retention - Repeat digits in natural or reverse order. (Normally, an adult can retain 7 forward and 5 backward.) After instruction, ask the subject to repeat a list of 3 cities and 3 two-digit numbers after a pause of 3 minutes.

6. Judgment - Ask patient for symbolic or specific meaning of simple proverbs, e.g.: "A stitch in times saves nine." "The rolling stone gathers no moss." "People who live in glass houses should not throw stones." The content of a simple story or paragraph from a newspaper, magazine, etc., may be read and the patient's retention, comprehension, and formulation observed.

7. Memory and comprehension - The patient may be asked to reproduce a story in his own words and to explain its meaning. Two commonly employed stories are the "Cowboy" and "Gilded Boy" stories:

Cowboy Story: A cowboy went to San Francisco with his dog, which he left at a friend's while he went to buy a new suit of clothes. Dressed in his brand new suit of clothes, he came back to the dog, whistled to it, called it by name, and patted it. But the dog would have nothing to do with him in his new coat and hat, and gave a mournful howl. Coaxing was of no avail, so the cowboy went away and put on his old suit and the dog immediately showed its wild joy on seeing its master as it thought he ought to be.

Gilded Boy Story: At the coronation of one of the popes, about 300 years ago, a little boy was chosen to play the part of an angel. In order that his appearance might be as magnificient as possible, he was covered from head to foot with a coating of gold foil. The little boy fell ill, and although everything possible was done for his recovery except the removal of the fatal golden covering, he died within a few hours.

E. Content of Thought: Obsessions, phobias, delusions, compulsions, recurrent dreams or nightmares, depersonalization, hallucinations. Special preoccupations and disorders of content are checked with attention to special topics of concern to the patient and the form they take.

F. Language: Comprehension of spoken language; ability to read and write. Recognition and ability to name familiar objects; capacity for verbal and nonverbal means of expression; ability to recognize errors; spontaneous or automatic speech.

G. Insight: Patient's evaluation and explanation of his illness.

Coordination, Gait, and Equilibrium.
A. Simple Walking Test: While the patient walks, his posture, gait, coordinated automatic movements (swinging of arms), and ability to walk a straight line and to make rapid turning movements are observed. A detailed and full description of the gait should be recorded. Certain abnormal gaits are highly characteristic of some clinical disorders. (See p. 164.)

B. Romberg Test: The patient stands with his heels and toes together and his eyes closed. Increased swaying commonly occurs in patients with dysfunction of cerebellar or vestibular mechanisms. A patient with disease of the posterior columns of the spinal cord may fall when his eyes are closed although he is able to maintain his position well with the eyes open.

C. Finger-to-Nose and Finger-to-Finger Tests: The finger-to-nose test, in which patient places the tip of a finger on his nose, and finger-to-finger test, in which he attempts to approximate the tips of the index fingers after the arms have been extended at the side, are performed. Dysmetria, with overshooting of the mark, is often observed in cerebellar disorders. (See p. 164.)

D. Toe-Finger Test: The supine patient touches the examiner's finger with his great toe and holds it there until the examiner moves his finger to a new position 6-18 inches away, the patient then following the examiner's finger with his toe.

E. Heel-to-Shin Test: The patient places one heel on the opposite knee and then moves the heel along the shin.

F. Rapidly alternating movements of fingers are tested by having the patient rapidly flex and extend the fingers or tap the table rapidly with extended fingers. Good rhythm cannot usually be maintained in cerebellar disease.

G. Supination and pronation of the forearm are tested in continuous rapid alternation. The inability to perform these movements speedily and smoothly is a feature of adiadokokinesia (see p. 164).

H. Rebound Phenomenon: The inability to stop a strong active movement to avoid striking an obstacle is known as the "rebound phenomenon." Its presence in the upper extremity may be demonstrated by the sudden release by the examiner of the strongly flexed upper extremity, whereupon the hand of the flexed extremity may strike the patient's shoulder, neck, or face.

Sensation.

Sensory examination is a difficult and wearing procedure for both the patient and the physician. The patient should be well rested and must be reassured and in a cooperative frame of mind before a sensory examination is attempted. Abnormalities, especially of minor degree, should be checked by frequent reexamination and charted. The following modalities are tested:

A. Pain: The ability to perceive pinprick or deep pressure.

B. Temperature: The ability to detect and distinguish between warm and cold. (Use a test tube of warm water and one of cold water.)

C. Touch: Ability to perceive light stroking of the skin with cotton.

D. Vibration: The ability to feel the "buzz" of a tuning fork (C 128) applied to the bony prominences. After the tuning fork has been set into maximum vibration, the duration of the perception of the tuning fork is timed with the base of the fork applied to the malleoli, patellas, iliac crests, vertebral spinous processes, and ulnar prominences.

E. Sense of Position: This is tested by determining the position of the digits of the toes and fingers. The digit is grasped on the sides and the patient, with eyes closed, attempts to determine whether the digit is moved upward or downward. The larger joints of the extremities are tested if impairment is demonstrated in the digits.

F. Passive Motion: Ability to perceive passive movements of the extremities, especially the distal portions.

G. Stereognosis: The capacity to recognize the forms, sizes, and weights of objects is tested. Familiar objects such as a coin, key, or knife are placed in the patient's hand and he is asked to identify the object without looking at it.

H. Two-Point Discrimination: The shortest distance between the 2 separated points of a compass or calipers at which the patient perceives 2 stimuli is compared for homologous areas of the body. (Normal: finger tips, 0.3-0.6 cm.; palms of hands and soles of feet, 1.5-2 cm.; dorsum of hands, 3 cm.; shin, 4 cm.)

I. Topognosis: The ability of the patient to localize a spot on his body where he has been touched is tested by having the patient point to the spot after he has been touched while his eyes were closed. Similar areas of both sides of the body are compared.

J. Double Stimulation: Two stimulations are presented together to both sides of the body in homologous areas (simultaneous homologous) or to nonhomologous areas (simultaneous nonhomologous). Two stimulations are similarly carried out on the same side of the body.

Reflexes.

The following reflexes are routinely tested and the response elicited is graded from 0 to 4+ (see p. 204).

A. Deep Reflexes:

1. Biceps reflex - The examiner strikes his thumb which has been placed on the patient's biceps tendon (elbow flexed at right angles) and produces, normally, a slight contraction of the biceps muscle.

2. Triceps reflex - With the patient's elbow supported in the examiner's hand, the triceps is sharply percussed just above the olecranon. Contraction of the triceps with extension of the forearm usually results.

3. Knee reflex - The patellar tendon, after being located by palpation, is tapped lightly with a percussion hammer with increasing force until contraction of the quadriceps muscle can be elicited. The patient may be seated on the edge of a table or bed with his legs hanging loosely. In bed patients, the subject's knees are flexed over the supporting arm of the examiner with the heels resting lightly on the bed.

4. Ankle reflex - This is best elicited by having the patient kneel on a chair with his ankles and feet projecting over edge of chair; the Achilles tendon is then struck with a percussion hammer. It is frequently obtained with difficulty in bed patients, where the optimum position is one in which the thigh is externally rotated and the knee flexed at about a 45° angle.

B. Superficial Reflexes:

1. Abdominal reflex - With the patient lying supine with relaxed abdominal muscles, the skin of each quadrant of the abdomen is briskly stroked with a pin from the periphery toward the umbilicus. Normally the local abdominal muscles contract, causing the umbilicus to move toward the quadrant stimulated.

2. Cremasteric reflex - In men, stroking the skin of the inner side of the proximal third of the thigh causes retraction of the ipsilateral testicle.

3. Plantar response - With the thigh in slight external rotation, the outer surface of the sole of the foot is stroked lightly with a large pin or wooden applicator from the heel toward the base of the little toe and thence inward across the ball of the foot. Normal plantar response usually consists of plantar flexion of all toes with slight inversion and flexion of the distal portion of foot. In abnormal responses, there may be extension of the great toe with fanning and flexion of the other toes (Babinski).

C. Clonus: In patients with exaggerated reflexes, clonus (repeated reflex muscular movements) may be elicited. In the wrist, clonus is sometimes elicited by forcible flexion of the wrist. Patellar clonus may be elicited by a sudden downward movement of the patella with consequent clonic contraction of the quadriceps muscle. Ankle clonus is tested by quickly dorsiflexing the foot, producing clonic contractions of the calf muscles.

Motor System.

The power of muscle groups of the extremities, neck, and trunk is tested. Where an indication of diminished strength is apparent, testing of smaller muscle groups and of individual muscles is performed. Care must be exercised so that apparent weakness is not confused with real weakness of muscles. Retesting or concealment from the patient of the object of a given test movement may sometimes indicate more power than on the patient's initial test. Atrophy or hypertrophy of muscles is judged by inspection and palpation and by measurement of the circumferences of the limbs in the case of the musculature of the extremities. The differences between the 2 sides may be related to the handedness or occupation of the subject. Abnormal movements are noted and the influence upon them of postural and emotional change. Intention and voluntary movements are recorded.

Muscle tone (tonus) is judged by palpation of the muscles of the extremities and passive movements of the joints by the examiner. Increased or decreased resistance to passive movement is carefully described. Tone alterations, including claspknife spasticity, plastic or cogwheel rigidity, spasms, contractures, and hypotonia are noted. Involuntary movements, including tremors, athetosis, chorea, tics, and myoclonus are described. Earliest upper motor neuron weakness is usually found in the dorsiflexors of the wrist and ankle. Fatigue usually increases all types of motor weakness, and in myasthenia gravis may induce actual paralysis. Barré's sign is failure to maintain the legs in vertical position with the patient lying face down and the legs flexed vertically at the knees. Mingazzini's sign is failure of the patient in the supine position to maintain the thighs vertically with the knees flexed at right angles and the legs parallel to the table.

Pendulousness, the motion of a passively displaced extremity when it is permitted to swing freely, is increased in hypotonia, markedly reduced in rigidity of extrapyramidal origin, and irregular in pattern - though normal or slightly diminished in duration - in spasticity.

The Cranial Nerves.

A. Olfactory Nerve (I): Use familiar odors such as peppermint, coffee, menthol, or vanilla, and avoid use of irritant substances such as ammonia and vinegar. With eyes shut and one nostril held closed, the patient is asked to identify a test substance passed rapidly toward him from a distance of about 3 feet. Obstruction of the nasal passages, as by a cold or septal deformity, should be excluded by having the patient sniff with each nostril alternately occluded. Complete or unilateral anosmia may be of significance in the absence of intranasal disorders.

B. Optic Nerve (II):

1. Visual acuity test - A Snellen chart may be used. Measure visual acuity as 20/ size read and determine whether improvement is obtained with correction. Jaeger or related test charts can be used at the bedside, where the patient (wearing his glasses if he ordinarily requires them) reads a series of sentences or figures in various sizes of type at a reading distance of about 30 cm. Cruder tests may be employed in individuals with severe defects, in whom the ability to count fingers, detect hand movements, and detect changes from dark to light is noted.

2. Ophthalmoscopic examination - Each optic fundus must be examined as part of the neurologic examination. If necessary the pupils may be dilated with eucatropine (Euphthalmine®) or homatropine (after the pupillary reflexes have been noted). Details of the ophthalmoscopic examination should include the color, size, and shape of the optic disk; the presence of a physiologic cup; the distinctness of the optic disk edges; the size, shape, and configuration of the vessels; and the presence of hemorrhage, exudate, or pigment.

3. Visual field test - The visual fields may be roughly tested by confrontation with the patient seated about 3 feet from the examiner. The patient looks at the examiner's left eye with his left eye covered. The examiner raises both hands from a position where he can barely see his own hands in the 2 lower quadrants, and the patient signifies when he sees the moving hands of the examiner rising in the lower quadrants. The upper quadrants are similarly tested with the examiner's hands moving downward. The left eye of the patient is then tested against the right eye of the examiner.

More accurate visual field determination requires the use of a perimeter or tangent screen. Visual fields are indicated in the evaluation of patients with known visual disturbances, abnormalities of the fundus, suspected supratentorial tumors, and disorders of the hypophysial area.

C. Oculomotor (III), Trochlear (IV), and Abducens (VI) Nerves: Strabismus, nystagmus, ptosis, exophthalmos, and pupillary abnormalities may be detected on initial examination. Ocular movements are tested by having the patient follow the movement of an object or light to the extremes of the lateral and vertical planes. A subject with defective vision is requested to look at his own hand, which is then appropriately moved. In patients with diplopia, the use of a red celluloid or glass placed over one eye will facilitate the examination. The area of the visual field where diplopia is noted and where the divergence between the 2 images is greatest is carefully noted.

The size and shape of each pupil are noted. The reactions of both pupils to a bright light flashed into one eye in a darkened room while the patient gazes in the distance are noted. The direct light reaction refers to the response of the pupil of the illuminated eye; the consensual light reaction refers to the reaction of the opposite pupil which is carefully shielded from the stimulating light.

The accommodation-convergence response may be demonstrated by having the subject alternately focus on a distant object and one held 6 inches in front of his face.

D. Trigeminal Nerve (V): The ability to perceive pin prick or the touch of a bit of cotton is tested over the face and anterior half of the scalp. The oronasal cavity sensation is tested by reaction to a pin prick. The corneal reflex is tested as the patient looks upward by approaching the cornea from the side and touching it with a strand of cotton. Care must be taken not to touch the eyelashes or conjunctiva. The motor function of the trigeminal nerve is tested by palpating the contraction of the masseter and temporalis muscles induced by a biting movement of the jaws. The ability of the subject to move his mandible from side to side is noted. His capacity to open his jaw, against resistance in the midline, is tested. With the opening of the mouth, deviation of the mandible to one side becomes more obvious.

E. Facial Nerve (VII): The facial expression and mobility and facial symmetry are noted. Voluntary movements of the lower facial musculature are tested by having the patient smile, whistle, show his teeth, or pucker his lips. The upper facial musculature is tested by having him close his eyes or wrinkle his forehead.

Taste sensation of the anterior two-thirds of the tongue is tested by application of small quantities of test solutions to the protruded tongue with cotton applicators. The test solutions used are sweet (sugar), bitter (quinine), salt (saline), and sour (vinegar). The subject indicates his reaction by pointing to a labeled card as he perceives the taste. Between tests, the tongue is irrigated with water.

F. Cochlear Nerve (VIII): The subject's ability to hear the examiner's voice in ordinary conversation is noted. The ability to hear the sound produced by rubbing the thumb and forefinger together is then tested for each ear at distances up to a few centimeters. The farthest distance from either ear at which the ticking of a loud watch or the spoken voice is heard may be measured.

With the aid of a tuning fork vibrating at 256 cycles per second, air and bone conduction are tested for each ear as follows: The vibrating tuning fork is placed on the mastoid process and then in front of the ear (Rinne's test). Normally the vibrating tuning fork is heard for several seconds longer when placed in front of the ear after it no longer can be heard on the mastoid. In injury to the auditory nerve ("nerve deafness") there may be complete or partial inability to hear the vibrating tuning fork. When partial hearing remains, air conduction exceeds bone conduction. In disease of the middle ear with impaired hearing ("conduction deafness"), the bone conduction of the tuning fork is better than the air conduction.

Where loss of hearing is unilateral, the sound of a vibrating tuning fork (256) placed on the bridge of the nose or over the midvertex of the scalp may be lateralized to one ear; in normal subjects, the sound is heard equally well in both ears (Weber's test). In deafness due to middle ear disease, the sound is heard in the affected ear.

G. Vestibular Nerve (VIII): The caloric test is frequently employed to evaluate vestibular function: The ear drum is first examined to make certain no perforations exist. Irrigation of the ear canal with ice water is performed on the suspected pathologic side first (the reaction on this side may be minimal). The patient is seated with head tilted slightly forward in order to test the vertical canals (or lies supine with his head tilted back at an angle of 60 degrees in order to test the horizontal canals), and a slow, steady irrigation of the external auditory canal is carried out with the reservoir about one foot above the level of the patient's head. Irrigation is continued until the patient complains of nausea or dizziness or until nystagmus is detected. This normally takes 20-30 seconds. If no reaction occurs after 3 minutes, the test is discontinued. The time of onset of initial symptoms, the time of onset and direction of nystagmus and past pointing, and the reaction to the Romberg test are noted immediately after the irrigation is completed.

Modifications of the galvanic test may be adapted for the purpose of judging vestibular function: The patient stands balanced astride a board about one foot square whose undersurface is divided in the middle by a projection 3 inches wide. An electrode is applied to the mastoid process and the other (indifferent) electrode is placed on the subject's back. Current from the battery is increased gradually (through a rheostat) and the amount of current in milliamperes necessary to make the patient lose his balance is noted. A response to galvanic stimulation may be present in the absence of a response to caloric stimulation, in which case the pathologic disorder is believed to be chiefly in the labyrinth.

H. Glossopharyngeal Nerve (IX): Taste over the posterior third of the tongue is tested (in a manner similar to that described under the facial nerve for the anterior two-thirds of the tongue). Sensation (usually touch) is tested on the soft palate and pharynx. The pharyngeal or gag reflex response is tested bilaterally.

I. Vagus Nerve (X): The swallowing function is tested by noting the patient's ability to drink water and eat solid food. The pharyngeal wall contraction is observed as part of the gag reflex. Movement of the median raphe of the palate and uvula when the patient says "ah" is recorded. In unilateral paralysis of the vagus, the raphe and uvula move toward the good side and the posterior pharyngeal wall of the paralyzed side moves like a curtain toward the good side. The character, volume, and sound of the patient's voice are recorded. With the aid of a dental mirror, the position of the vocal cords may be visualized by indirect laryngoscopy. The resting heart rate and the bradycardia produced by pressure on the eyeball (oculocardiac reflex) or pressure on the carotid sinus may be influenced by lesions involving the vagus nerve.

J. Accessory Nerve (XI): The subject is instructed to rotate his head against resistance applied to the side of the chin to test the function of the opposite sternocleidomastoid muscle. For testing both sternocleidomastoids together, the subject is instructed to flex his head forward against resistance placed under his chin. The trapezius muscle function is tested by having the patient shrug his shoulder against resistance.

K. Hypoglossal Nerve (XII): The tongue is examined for atrophy and for fasciculations or tremors when protruded and when lying at rest in the mouth. Deviation of the tongue on protrusion is tested. Deviation to the same side occurs with lesions of the hypoglossal nerve.

When the examination has been completed, a summary of the findings should be recorded and a tentative diagnosis made. Plans for further study and for treatment may then be made.

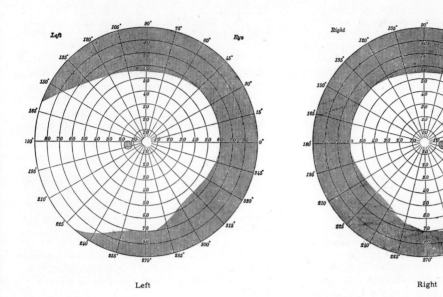

Left   Right

Visual Field Charts. In order to chart fields on the perimeter, small white objects subtending
1° or 0.5° are moved slowly. The smaller the object, the more sensitive the test. With gross
error of refraction, 1° is reliable. State the size of object used (in degrees or mm.) over
distance in mm. (e.g., 5/2000). Red has the smallest normal field and gives the most sensitive field test. Chart central field defects on a Bjerrum screen, moving an object from the
center outward until it can be seen. Make sure the patient's eye does not move or deviate
while the object is being moved.

NEONATAL NEUROLOGIC EXAMINATION

The neonatal neurologic examination is
usually performed between 36 and 60 hours
after birth. As much of the examination as
reasonably possible should be done, depending
upon the infant's condition. Repeat examinations at weekly intervals may be desirable. In
general, the examination should be planned and
carried out so that relatively little handling
or stimulation of the infant occurs initially.

General Status.
Observe motor pattern and supine and
prone body posture; evaluate reflexes throughout the examination.

A. In normal infants, the limbs are flexed,
the head may be turned to the side, and kicking
movements of the lower limbs may occur.
Extension of the limbs may occur with intracranial hemorrhage, opisthotonos with kernicterus, and asymmetry of the upper limbs
with brachial plexus palsy.

B. Paucity of movements may occur with
anoxia; reduced movement or paralyzed parts

may occur with brachial plexus palsy and meningomyelocele.

C. Infants normally become more re-
active during the examination and cry. In
anoxia or intracerebral hemorrhage, the infant
reacts very little.

Cranial Nerves.
A. Optic Nerve (II): Test blink response
to light. Ophthalmoscopic examination should
be made at the end of the examination.

B. Oculomotor, Trochlear, and Abducens Nerves (III, IV, VI): Size, shape, and
equality of the pupils and pupillary responses
to light are checked. Lateral rotation of the
head causes rotation of the eyes in the opposite direction ("doll's eye reflex").

C. Trigeminal and Facial (V, VII) Nerves:
A finger or nipple placed between the lips is
sucked (sucking reflex). A fingertip touching
the cheek causes the infant to open his mouth
and turn it toward the stimulus (rooting reflex).

D. Auditory Nerve (VIII): Blink response
or startle response occurs to loud noise. The

baby may be held up opposite the examiner, who then rotates his own body several turns to the right and then to the left. A normal baby will look ahead in the direction of rotation and, on stopping, look back in the opposite direction (labyrinthine reflex).

E. Glossopharyngeal and Vagus (IX, X) Nerves: The ability to swallow is noted.

Motor Systems.

Spontaneous and induced motor activity are noted. If the infant is inactive and quiet, the Moro reflex may be used to induce movement. The infant may be placed in the prone position to induce movement.

A. Incurvation reflex (Galant's reflex) will disclose movements of spine normally. With the infant prone, tactile stimulation of the thoracolumbar paravertebral zone with the finger produces contraction of the ipsilateral long muscles of the back so that the head and legs curve around the stimulated area and the trunk moves away from the stimulus.

B. Muscle tone is assessed by palpation of muscles during activity and relaxation. Resistance to passive extension of the elbows and knees is noted.

C. The infant's ability to change the position of his limb from a given position is checked.

D. The infant's hip and knee joints are flexed to check the pull of gravity when the infant is held head down in vertical suspension.

Reflexes.

Various reflex patterns may be useful in evaluation, especially of motor components.

A. Stimulation of ulnar palmar surfaces causes forceful grasp of hands (grasp reflex).

B. Contraction of shoulder and neck muscles occurs when normal infant is pulled from supine to sitting position (traction response).

C. The normal infant may make stepping movements when held upright with his foot just touching the table (stepping response).

D. When the dorsum of the foot is drawn across the lower edge of a moderately sharp surface, such as the edge of an examining table, this normally produces flexion at the knee and hip followed by extension at the hip (placing reaction).

E. If the plantar surface comes in contact with a flat surface, further extension of the knee and hip may occur (positive supporting reaction).

F. The Moro reflex is present in normal infants. A sudden stimulus (loud noise, sudden body displacement, blow to bed, etc.) causes abduction and extension of all extremities with extension and fanning of digits except for flexion of the index finger and thumb. This is followed by flexion and adduction of the extremities.

G. The knee jerk, plantar responses, and abdominal reflexes are tested with the infant quiet and relaxed. Ankle clonus should be tested.

Sensation.

Withdrawal of the stimulated limb and sometimes also the unstimulated limb may be caused by pin prick of the sole of the foot.

DEVELOPMENTAL SCREENING (DR. SALLY PROVENCE), FIRST YEAR
(Adapted From Gesell & Others)

AGE (Mo.)	POSTURE AND LOCOMOTION		HANDLING OF TOYS (Rattle and bell)	SOCIAL AND LANGUAGE	
Birth	Supine: Asymmetric posturing	Prone: Lifts head briefly	Focuses on rattle in line of vision	Reduces activity when talked to	
2		Prone: Lifts head halfway	Follows rattle with eyes briefly — Actively (not reflexly) holds rattle when placed in hand	Smiles socially when stimulated	
3	Supine: Symmetric posturing predom.	Prone: Lifts head high; chest up	Puts toys to mouth	Laughs aloud: "belly laugh"	
4					
5	No head lag when pulled to sit			Squeals	
	Rolls, supine to prone		Reaches out, grasps toy with 1 hand	"Talks" to toys (spontaneously)	
6			Transfers toy from hand to hand / Bangs table with toy		
7	Sits briefly when placed	Pivots in prone	Handles toy in each hand	Consonants (da, da, etc.)	
8	Sits alone (steady)		Grasps small toy with thumb and index finger	Imitates sounds: "razzing," etc.	
9	Creeps (hands and knees)	Pulls to standing	Bangs 2 toys together	Dada-Mama (specific) Extends toy to person without releasing it.	Waves "bye" or pat-a-cakes
10			Explores bell; pokes clapper		
11	Walks with 2 hands held	Cruises at rail			
12	Walks with 1 hand held		Finds toy behind screen	2 "words" besides Mama, Dada	Understands "Give it to me" (request and gesture)

[Charts on pp. 393 and 394 reproduced, with permission, from Silver & others: Handbook of Pediatrics, 5th Ed. (Lange, 1963.)]

AVERAGE DEVELOPMENT FROM ONE TO FOUR YEARS
(Adapted From Provence)

	MOTOR DEVELOPMENT	CRAYON AND PAPER	SELF HELP AND PLAY WITH TOYS	LANGUAGE
12 mos.	Walks alone.	Imitates scribbling.	Enjoys "putting in and taking out."	3-6 words, mostly names.
15 mos.	Creeps upstairs. Releases ball with slight toss toward examiner.		Shows or offers toy. Builds tower of 2 blocks.	Jargon. Names a few pictures.
18 mos.	Walks upstairs with 1 hand held. Climbs into adult chair. Walks fast, runs stiffly. Seats self in small chair. Hurls ball (overhand).	Scribbles spontaneously. Strokes imitatively (imitates examiner's motion).	Hugs a doll or teddy bear. Feeds self with some spilling. Builds tower of 3-4 blocks. Turns pages of book (2-3 at once).	Understands simple verbal directions.
21 mos.	Squats in play. Kicks ball on floor (imitatively). Walks upstairs, holding rail. Walks downstairs with 1 hand held.		Builds tower of 5-6 blocks. Handles cup well.	Combines 2-3 words spontaneously.
2 yrs.	Walks up and down stairs alone. Jumps from low object.	Imitates vertical and circular strokes when demonstrated.	Pulls on simple garment. Explores drawers, cupboards, etc. Plays alongside other children. Builds tower of 6-7 blocks. Turns page of book singly.	Begins to use pronouns. Uses 3-word sentences. Refers to self by name. Verbalizes immediate experiences.
2½ yrs.	Walks on tiptoe (after demonstration).	Holds crayon with fingers. Imitates vertical and horizontal strokes.	Can help put things away. Builds tower of 8 blocks.	Refers to self by pronoun. Gives full name.
3 yrs.	Alternates feet going upstairs. Pedals tricycle.	Imitates a cross (demonstrated). Copies a circle from picture.	Puts on shoes. Knows a few rhymes Can feed self with little spilling. Understands taking turns. Unbuttons clothes.	Tells sex. Uses plurals. Names 6-8 objects in picture book. Understands 2 prepositions.
3½ yrs.	Balances on 1 foot briefly.		Washes hands and face.	Repeats 3 numbers. Understands 3 prepositions.
4 yrs.	Skips with 1 foot. Throws ball well overhand.	Copies a cross from picture. Draws a "man" with 2 parts.	Plays with other children (real social interchange). Washes hands and face, brushes teeth. Laces shoes. Has dramatic play.	Understands 4 prepositions (on, under, behind, beside).

New York University - Bellevue Medical Center
Institute of Physical Medicine and Rehabilitation
400 East 34th Street
New York 16, N.Y.

PHYSICAL DEMANDS OF DAILY LIFE FROM BED TO JOB

NAME _____ WARD _____ AGE _____ SEX _____ DATE _____

ADDRESS _____ APPARATUS _____

CAUSE _____ DIAGNOSIS _____

DISABILITY _____ DATE ONSET _____ DATE REFERRED _____

METHOD OF RECORDING TEST

☐ 1. If at the time of the initial testing an activity cannot be performed independently, leave the block blank.

☐ 2. If the activity can be performed independently, fill in the block with Blue pencil.

☐ 3. If the activity is not essential for the person's physical demands, draw diagonal lines in the block.

METHOD OF RECORDING PROGRESS

☐ 1. When the activity can be performed independently, fill in the block in Red and indicate the date of accomplishment.

NON-WALKING ACTIVITIES

A. BED ACTIVITIES   DATE

1. Moving from place to place in bed
2. Roll to right and then to left side
3. Sitting erect in bed
4. Turn and lie on abdomen
5. Procure objects from night table

B. HYGIENE (TOILET ACTIVITIES)

1. Combing or brushing hair
2. Brushing teeth
3. Shaving or putting on cosmetics
4. Washing hands and face
5. Washing extremities
6. Manipulating bed-pan
7. Applying Urinal/Special Pants
8. Taking shower
9. Tub Bath
10. Ability to dry self after shower or bath
11. Adjusting clothing for toilet needs

C. EATING ACTIVITIES

1. Cutting meat
2. Buttering bread
3. Eating with fork
4. Eating with teaspoon, tablespoon
5. Drinking from glass
6. Drinking from cup
7. Stirring coffee, tea, etc.

D. DRESSING AND UNDRESSING ACTIVITIES   DATE

1. Put on underclothes
2. Removing underclothes
3. Put on buttoned shirt (zipper)
4. Remove buttoned shirt
5. Put on slip-over garment
6. Remove slip-over garment
7. Put on slacks
8. Remove slacks
9. Tying shoes (buckle, zipper)
10. Tying tie
11. Putting on hose
12. Removing hose
13. Put on braces or prosthesis
14. Remove braces or prosthesis

E. HAND ACTIVITIES

1. Write name and address
2. Fold letter, place in envelope and seal envelope
3. Open envelope, remove letter
4. Use dial telephone
5. Turn pages of book
6. Wind wrist watch
7. Open and close cylinder lock
8. Open and close ice box door
9. Open and close doorlock with key
10. Open and close drawers
11. Open and close door hooks
12. Open and close window
13. Pull window shade
14. Push door bell
15. Use workshop switch
16. Use work plug switch
17. Use work push button
18. Work key light switch
19. Work pull chain light
20. Ring door bell
21. Open and close cabinet lock
22. Turn 4-pronged faucet
23. Turn circular faucet
24. Open and close medicine chest
25. Open and close bottle
26. Open and close safety pin
27. Strike match

F. WHEELCHAIR ACTIVITIES

1. Bed to wheelchair
2. Wheelchair to bed
3. Raising and lowering foot rests
4. Propelling wheelchair forward 30 feet and stopping
5. Propelling wheelchair backward 30 feet and stopping
6. Locking and unlocking brakes on wheelchair
7. Opening and closing doors in wheelchair and return
8. Wheelchair to chair
9. Chair to wheelchair
10. Wheelchair to toilet

"Physical Demands of Daily Life From Bed to Job." (Courtesy of Institute of Physical Medicine and Rehabilitation, New York University–Bellevue Medical Center.)

WHEELCHAIR ACTIVITIES (CONTINUED)

11. Toilet to wheelchair
12. Wheelchair to tub and/or shower
13. Bathtub or shower to wheelchair
14. Wheelchair to automobile
15. Automobile to wheelchair
16. Wheelchair to floor
17. Floor to wheelchair

G. ELEVATION ACTIVITIES

1. Bed to erect position
2. Erect position to bed
3. Wheelchair to erect position
4. Erect position to wheelchair
5. Chair to erect position
6. Erect position to chair
7. Erect position to chair at table
8. Chair at table to erect position
9. Upholstered chair and/or sofa to erect position
10. Erect position to upholstered chair or sofa
11. Erect position to toilet
12. Toilet to erect position
13. Down to floor
14. Up on floor

II. WALKING ACTIVITIES

H. PROGRESSING ACTIVITIES

1. Walking forward 30 feet
2. Walking backward 30 feet
3. Opening and closing door, erect and return

I. GAIT (Underarm crutches . . . Lofstrand Crutches . . .
          Wooden canes . . . Other support . . .)

1. 4-point alternate
2. Swing-to
3. Swing-through
4. 2-point alternate

J. CLIMBING ACTIVITIES

1. Up 15 degree ramp, 3 feet
2. Down 15 degree ramp, 3 feet
3. Up 6 standard steps, one hand rail
4. Down 6 standard steps, one hand rail
5. Up 6 standard steps, no hand rail
6. Down 6 standard steps, no hand rail
7. Up and down one flight of stairs, one hand rail
8. Up and down one flight of stairs, no hand rail
9. Up curb
    a. 4 inch curb
    b. 6 inch curb
    c. 8 inch curb

CLIMBING ACTIVITIES (CONTINUED)

10. Down curb
    a. 4 inch curb
    b. 6 inch curb
    c. 8 inch curb
11. Up bus steps
12. Down bus steps

K. TRAVELLING ACTIVITIES

1. Cross standard street on green light
2. Get in bus, place coin in turnstile
3. Go through turnstile and stand holding on overhead strap
4. Sit down and get up from bus seat
5. Travel to middle door of bus
6. Descend from bus to street
7. Walk to taxi, 10 feet, open door and enter cab
8. Descend from taxi, close door and walk 10 feet
9. Walk forward 300 feet with package
10. Carry cafeteria tray with dishes

SUMMARY:

_____
          Examiner

"Physical Demands of Daily Life From Bed to Job." (Courtesy of Institute of Physical
Medicine and Rehabilitation, New York University-Bellevue Medical Center.)

Index*

Abadie's sign, 294
Abscess, brain, 290, 292
    spinal, 292
Accoucheur's hand, 165
Acetrizoate, 251
Acetylcholine, 71, 147
    esterase, 71
Acoustic meatus, internal, 79
    nerve, 76, 78, 95
Acromegaly, 336
Acroparesthesia, 149, 194
Actin, 151
Action potentials, 69, 152, 232, 234
Addiction, 383
Addison's disease, 336
Adenosinediphosphate, 71, 151
Adenosinetriphosphatase, 151
Adenosinetriphosphate, 71
Adiadokokinesia, 164
Adiposis dolorosa, 150
Adiposogenital dystrophy, 336
ADP, 71, 151
Adrenal syndromes, 336
Adynamia episodica hereditaria, 372
Affective reactions, 379
Afferent neuron, 204
After-discharge, 74
After-potentials, 71
Agnosia, 214
Agranular cortex, 9
    gigantopyramidal cortex, 9
Agraphia, 211
Akinetic attacks, 347
Albinism, 335
Alcohol addiction, 383
    intoxication, 340
    methyl, poisoning, 341
Aldosteronism, 337
Alexia, 211
Allesthesia, 193
Allochiria, 193
Allocortex, 5, 9
N-Allylnormorphine, 342
Alpha motor neurons, 159, 160
    rhythm, 226
Alzheimer's disease, 324
Amaurosis, 85
Amaurotic familial idiocy, 84, 334
Amblyopia, 85
Amino acid metabolism, disorders
    of, 334
    nitrogen, 59
Aminoglutethimide, 351
Amyloidosis, 339
Amyotonia congenita, 374
Analgesia, 193
Anemia, pernicious, 194, 332, 333
    sickle cell, 333
Anesthesia, 193
Aneurysm, intracranial, 283, 284,
    285, 287
Angiography, cerebral, 251
Angiomas, 313
Angioneurotic edema, 149
Ankle clonus, 207
Anosmia, 81

Anosognosia, 214
Ansa hypoglossi, 103, 110
    lenticularis, 15, 21, 162
Anticholinesterases, 73
Anticonvulsant drug(s), 350
    poisoning, 341
Antihistaminic drug poisoning, 341
Antiparkinsonism drugs, 326
Antisocial reaction, 382
Anton's syndrome, 214
Anxiety reaction, 381
Ape hand, 119, 120
Aphasia, 13, 210, 211, 212
Apraxia, 213
    motor, 213
Aqueduct of Sylvius (cerebral), 25,
    43, 219
Arachnoid, 62
Aran-Duchenne muscular atrophy, 368
Archicerebellum, 37, 39, 40
Arcuate fibers, 32, 40, 192
Argyll Robertson pupil, 84, 89, 293
Arms, motor innervation of, 166
    muscles of, 188
Arnold-Chiari malformation, 273
Arnold's bundle, 29
Arsenic poisoning, 340
Arteries of head and neck, 48
Arteriograms, 252, 255, 320
Arteriosclerosis of the brain, 275
Arteriovenous aneurysm, 287
Arteritis, temporal, 338
Arter(ies), angular, 255
    ascending frontoparietal, 255
    auditory, internal, 45
    basilar, 45, 256
    callosomarginal, 255
    carotid, 45, 48, 255, 257
        thrombosis of, 279
    cerebellar, 45
    cerebral, 45, 255, 256
        thrombosis of, 280
    choroidal, anterior, 45, 255
    communicating, 44, 45, 255
        aneurysm of, 287
    to face and neck, 48
    frontoparietal, ascending, 255
    frontopolar, 255
    lenticulostriate, 45
    maxillary, 48
    meningeal, 48
    ophthalmic, 79, 255
    parietal, posterior, 255
    pericallosal, 255
    pontine, 45
    radicular, 68
    spinal, 45, 67, 68
    temporal, posterior, 255
    vertebral, 45, 256
Arthrogryposis multiplex congenita,
    376
Arthropathy, neurogenic, 216
Association areas, 12, 13
Astasia-abasia, 165
Astereognosis, 193, 214
Astroblastoma, 315

Astrocytoma, 315
Ataxia, 164, 165, 294, 328, 329
Athetoid movements, 162
Atopognosis, 193
ATP, 71, 151
ATPase, 151
Atrophy of disuse, 215
    hereditary optic, 330
    muscular, 368, 370
    olivocerebellar, 328
    olivopontocerebellar, 328
    progressive muscular, 234, 368
Atropine analogues in "model"
    psychoses, 342
Audiograms, 263
Audiometry, 262
    speech, 263
Auditory cortex, primary, 12
    meatus, internal, 95
    receptive cortex, primary, 11, 21
Auriculotemporal nerve syndrome,
    92
Automatic bladder, 145
Autonomic nerve(s) to head, 141, 142
    impulses, responses of
        effector organs to, 148
    to urogenital organs and
        rectum, 143
    nervous system, 75, 138
        parasympathetic division, 140,
            141
        pharmacology of, 147
        physiology of, 146
        sympathetic division, 138, 139
Autosomes, 267
Autotopagnosia, 214
Avellis's syndrome, 104
Ayala's index, 221

Babinski-Nageotte bulbar syndrome,
    105
Babinski's platysma sign, 208
    pronation sign, 208
    sign, 74, 207
Back pain, low, 310
Baillarger, lines of, 6
Barbiturate poisoning, 341
Basilar impression, 274
Basket cells, 39
Bassen-Kornzweig syndrome, 334
Bechterew, nucleus of, 31
Bechterew's sign, 208
Beevor's sign, 74, 124
Bell-Magendie law, 106
Bell's palsy, 93
    phenomenon, 93
Bender Gestalt test, 265
Benedikt's syndrome, 28, 29
Beriberi, 340
Bestiality, 382
Beta rhythm, 226
Biceps reflex, 206
Biernacki's sign of tabes, 295
Bigler, plasma lipid disturbance of,
    334
Bikeles' sign, 114

*The following are indexed under the nouns: arter(ies), foramen(s), gangli(a), lobe(s), muscle(s), nerve(s), nucle(i), plexus(es), reflex(es), sinus(es), sulc(i), tract(s), vein(s), ventricle(s).

Binswanger's disease, 330
Birth injuries, 307
Bladder, automatic, 145
    cystometrogram, 259
    flaccid neurogenic, 261
    reflex(es), 145, 206, 207
    spastic, 260
    urinary, 143
        innervation of, 144
Blindness, 83, 85
    color, 85
Blood-brain barrier, 55
Bonnier's syndrome, 105
Botulism, 301
Brachium conjunctivum, 39, 192
        superior cerebellar peduncle,
            30
    pontis, 30, 39, 163
        middle cerebellar peduncle,
            30, 163
Brain, abscess of, 290
    adult, 58
    arteriosclerosis of, 275
    blood flow, 52
    circulation of, 43
        impaired, 356
    development of, 60
    embryonic, 57
    injuries, 307
    metabolism, 57
    monkey, 35
    sagittal section of, 25
    stem, 29, 30, 158
    syndromes, acute, 378
        chronic, 378
    tumor, syndromes, classic,
        316, 317
    venous drainage, 49
    visceral, 15
Breath-holding attacks, 352
Broca's area, 12, 214
Bromide poisoning, 341
Brown-Sequard syndrome, 194, 195
Brudzinski's sign, leg, 289
    neck, 289
Bulbar neuritis, 84
    palsy, 368
Bulb, olfactory, 82

Cacosmia, 82
Cadaveric reaction to electric
        stimulation, 239
Caffeine toxicity, 342
Calamus scriptorius, 43
Calcar avis, 41
Calcification, brain, 57
    intracranial, 241
    vascular, 246
Caloric test, 96, 390
Cannon's law of denervation, 147
Capsule, internal, 14, 15, 16,
        158, 162
Carbohydrate, brain, 58
    metabolism, disorders of, 336
Carbon monoxide poisoning, 341
Cardiac functional change, 355
Carotid body, 98
    occlusion of, 279
    sinus syncope, 353
Carpal tunnel constriction, 119
    syndrome, 121
CAT, 265
Cataplexy, 353
Catatonic schizophrenia, 380
Cauda equina, 67
Caudate nucleus, 15, 16, 162
Causalgia, 107, 150, 194, 216

Central canal, 62
    core disease, 372
    nervous system, congenital
        defects of, 266
        degenerative diseases of, 323
        disorders due to vascular
            disease of, 275
        infectious diseases of, 289
        trauma to, 302
        tumors of, 313
Cephalalgia, histaminic, 363
Cerebellar abscess, 291
    connections, 39
    convolution, 38
    degeneration, parenchymatous,
        329
    fit, 164
    peduncle, 30, 31, 32
Cerebellum, 36, 37
    cortex of, 39
        primary, 7, 10
        principal visual (striate), 12
    diseases of, 164
    internal structure of, 38
    microscopic appearance, 39
    white matter, 40
Cerebral aqueduct, 43
    artery, thrombosis of, 280
    circulation, 43
        impaired, 356
    concussion, 302
    cortex, 162
        arterial supply, 46
        sectoral map of, 9, 10, 11
        venous drainage of, 50
    edema, 303
    embolism, 278, 282
    hemispheres, 1, 3
    hemorrhage, 277, 282, 306
    metabolism, impaired, 356
    palsy, 269, 270
    peduncle, 26, 30, 78
    thrombosis, 276, 282
Cerebromacular degeneration, 333
Cerebrospinal fluid, 42, 219
    findings in disease, 222
Cerebrovascular accidents, 276
    disease, classification of, 288
        diagnosis of, 282
Cerebrum, 2, 12, 14
    arterial supply, 47
    main divisions of, 1
Cervical rib syndrome, 274
    spine, acute sprain of, 311
    spondylosis, 311
Cestan-Chenais syndrome, 31, 105
Chaddock's toe sign, 207
    wrist sign, 208
Chamberlain's line, 274
Charcot-Marie-Tooth disease, 369
Charcot's joint, 216
Charcot-Wilbrand syndrome, 214
Chemoreceptor trigger zone, 34
Chemotherapeutic drug poisoning,
        341
Children's apperception test, 265
Chlorinated insecticide poisoning,
        341
Cholinesterase, 71
Chorda tympani nerve, 92
Chorea, Huntington's, 327
    Sydenham's, 300
Choreiform movements, 162
Choriomeningitis, lymphocytic, 298
Chromosomes, sex, 266
Chronaxie, 69, 235, 238
Chvostek's facial sign of tetany, 338

Cingulum, 5
Circle of Willis, 43, 45
Cisterna superior, 219
Citrullinuria, 335
Clarke's column, 67
Claustrum, 14, 15
Clava, 30, 32
Claw hand deformity, 122
Climbing fibers, 39
Clonus, 388
    ankle, 207
    patellar, 207
Closure defects, 268
Clubfoot, 165, 376
Cluster headache, 360
Cogan's syndrome, 96
Collagen tissues, diseases of, 338
Collet's syndrome, 105
Colliculi, 24
Color blindness, 85
Column(s), anterior, 65
    ascending tracts, 66
    descending tracts, 65, 66
    or funiculi, 62
    gray, 63, 65
    lateral, 65, 66
    posterior, 62, 64, 192
Coma, 356
Combined system disease, 332
Commissure, anterior, 5, 14, 18, 22
        white, 63
    habenular, 30
    hippocampal, 5
    posterior, 18, 23
Compression of spinal cord, 308
Compulsive personalities, 382
Concussion, cerebral, 302
    of spinal cord, 308
Conduction deafness, 263, 390
Congenital absence of muscle, 376
    defects, 266
    facial diplegia, 376
    neuromuscular disorders, 376
    neuropathies, 376
    radiculopathies, 376
Conjugate ocular deviation, 88
Constriction, carpal tunnel, 119
Contusion of spinal cord, 308
Conus medullaris, 63
Conversion hysteria, 381
Convulsions, febrile, 348
Convulsive seizures, classification,
        346
    states, 345
Coramine toxicity, 342
Cordotomy, 196
Corpora quadrigemina, 24
Corpus callosum, 1, 3, 14, 22, 25
    luysi, 21
    striatum, 15
Costen's syndrome, 96
Cough syncope, 356
Cowboy story, 386
Coxsackie virus infection, 298
Craniopharyngioma, 313, 316
Craniostenosis, 272
Craniosynostosis, 272
Cranium bifidum, 269
Cretinism, 337
Creutzfeldt and Jakob syndrome, 331
Crocodile tears syndrome, 94
Crowe's sign, 292
Culmen, 37
Cuneate tubercle, 32
Cuneus, 3, 4
Cushing's syndrome, 336, 337
Cutaneous innervation, 197

Cycloplegics, 88
Cyclothymic personalities, 382
Cystathioninuria, 335
Cystometrogram, 259
Cystometry, 258
Cytomegalic inclusion body disease, 293

Dandy-Walker syndrome, 270
Deafness, 96, 262, 263, 390
Decomposition of movement, 164
Decussation of Forel, 26
    fountain, of Meynert, 26
    pyramidal, 32
Defecation, 145
Deformities and postures, 165
Déjerine-Roussy syndrome, 19
Déjerine's cortical sensory
    syndrome, 194
Déjerine-Sottas syndrome, 343
Delta rhythm, 225, 227
Dementia, presenile, 324
Denervation fibrillation potentials, 233
Deoxyribonucleic acid, 56, 266
Depolarization, 69, 152
Dercum's disease, 150
Dermatomes, 72, 202
Dermatomyositis, 338
Dermoid tumors, 313
DET, 342
Developmental screening, 393, 394
Devic's disease, 329
Diabetes insipidus, 23, 24, 336
    mellitus, 338
Diaschisis, 149
Diatrizoate, 251
Diazepam, 271, 375
Diencephalon, 17, 18, 60
Dilantin, 341
Diodrast, 251
Diphenylhydantoin, 341
Diphtheria, 301
Diplegia, 158
Diplopia, testing, 88, 91
Discrimination, two-point, 194, 387
Dizziness, 89
DMT, 342
DNA, 56, 266
Dorsal root fibers, 67
Double stimulation, 194, 387
Drug addiction, 383
Duane's retraction syndrome, 90
Dura mater, 42
Dwarfism, pituitary, 336
Dysarthria, 164
Dysautonomia, familial, 150
Dysgranular cortex, 9
Dysmetria, 164, 387
Dyssocial reaction, 382
Dystonia(s), 162
    musculorum deformans, 331
Dystroph(ies), adiposogenital, 336
    muscular, 233, 368, 369
        limb-girdle, 371
    progressive muscular, 369

Echoencephalography, 253
Echolalia, 211
Effector systems in the neuraxis, 157
Efferent (motor) neuron, 204
Ejaculation, 146
Electric stimulation of muscles and
    nerves, 235
    test of hearing, 96
Electrocorticogram, 225
Electrode placements, EEG, 224

Electrodiagnostic examination, 235, 320
Electroencephalography, 223
Electrolyte(s), depletion, 342
    nerve, 71
Electromyography, 232, 322
Elipten, 351
Embolism, cerebral, 278
Embryology of brain, 61
    of nervous system, 59
Embryonic brain, 57
Emetic center, 34
Emotionally unstable personalities, 382
Emotion, Papez' mechanism of, 24
Encephalitis, epidemic, 297, 298
    periaxialis diffusa, 329
Encephalograms, 248
Encephalography, fractional, 251
    radioisotopic, 253
    ultrasonic, 320
Encephalomyelitis, equine, 298
Encephalopathy, hypertensive, 276
    progressive subcortical, 330
Endarteritis, Heubner's, 293
End-plate, motor, 73
Enuresis, 145
Ependymoma, 318
Epidermoid tumors, 313
Epilepsia partialis continua, 348
Epilepsy, 345
    post-traumatic, 306
Epiloia, 272
Epithalamus, 21
Erb-Duchenne syndrome, 114
Erb's sign of tetany, 338
Erection, 146
Erythremia, 333
Erythromelalgia, 149
Exophthalmic ophthalmoplegia, 337
External capsule, 14
Exteroceptors, 189, 191
Extradural hemorrhage, 304
Extrafusal fibers, 154
Extramedullary tumors, 321
Extraocular movements, 87
Extrapyramidal system, 17
    diseases of, 161
Eye muscles, paralyses of, 87

F-ab-er-e sign, Patrick's, 132, 310
Facial diplegia, congenital, 376
    hemiatrophy, progressive, 149
    palsy, 94
    spasm, 94
Facilitation, 7
Facilitatory area, 160
    center, 33
    and suppressor systems, 163
Falx cerebri, 1
Familial dysautonomia, 150
Fasciculations, 366, 367
Fasciculus cuneatus, 30, 32, 62, 67
    gracilis, 30, 62, 67
    inferior longitudinal, 5
    lenticularis, 15, 21
    medial longitudinal, 25, 26, 29, 67
    proprius, 67
    superior longitudinal, 5
    uncinate, 40
Fazio-Londe muscular atrophy, 368
Febrile convulsions, 348
Fetishism, 382
Fibers, association, 5
    climbing, 39
    internal arcuate, 32
    nerve, classification of, 106

Fibrillation, 366
Fick principle, 51
Filum terminale, 62
Final common pathway, 74, 156
Finger-to-finger test, 387
Finger-to-nose test, 387
Fissura prima, 37
Fissure, anterior median, 62
    calcarine, 1, 4, 25
    collateral, 2
    hippocampal, 4
    lateral cerebral, 1, 3
    longitudinal cerebral, 1
    parieto-occipital, 1, 3
    primary, 37
    of Rolando, 1, 246
    superior orbital, 79
    of Sylvius, 1, 246
    ventral median, 63
Fit, cerebellar, 164
Floppy infant syndrome, 377
Focal epilepsy, 346
Focus, EEG, 227
Foot drop, 133
    motor innervation of, 167
Foramen(s), interventricular, 41
    jugular, 78, 79
    lacerum, 79
    of Luschka, 43, 219
        and Magendie, 220
    of Magendie, 43, 219
    magnum, 79
    of Monro, 219, 220
    optic, 79
    ovale, 79
    principal, 79
    rotundum, 79
    spinosum, 79
Forced grasping, 7
Forearm, motor innervation of, 166
Forel, decussation of, 26
    fields of, 21
Fornix, 3, 5, 18, 25
Fossa, rhomboid, 30, 41
Foster Kennedy syndrome, 84
Fourteen and six positive spikes, 225
Foville's syndrome, 31
Frequency analyzers, EEG, 225
Frey's syndrome, 92
Friedreich's ataxia, 328
Fröhlich's syndrome, 336
Froin's syndrome, 221
Froment's sign, 121
Frontal bone, 242
    lobe, 1, 10
Functional tests for muscles, 172
Funiculi, 32, 62, 63
Funiculus cuneatus, 32
    gracilis, 32

GABA, 59
GAD, 59
Gaits, 164
Galactosemia, 336
Galant's reflex, 392
Galvanic test of hearing, 96, 390
Galvanic-tetanus ratio, 239
Gamma-aminobutyric acid, 59
Gamma loop, 159, 160
    motor fibers, 159
Gangli(a), basal, 15
    celiac, 138
    cervical sympathetic, 110
    ciliary, 141, 142
    dorsal root, 67
    geniculate, 95
    mesenteric, 138

Gangli(a), Cont'd.
  otic, 98, 142, 143
  of Scarpa, 76
  semilunar, 78
  sphenopalatine, 82, 90, 142, 143
  spinal, 67
  submaxillary, 142, 143
  sympathetic, 138
Gargoylism, 334
Gaucher's disease, 334
Genetic diseases, 266
Geniculate body, 19, 20, 26
  neuralgia, 94
Gennari, line of, 5
Gerstmann's syndrome, 214
Gierke's disease, 336
Gilded boy story, 386
Glioblastoma multiforme, 315
Gliomas, 252, 315
Globulin X, 151
Globus pallidus, 14, 15, 16, 162
Glossopharyngeal neuralgia, 97
Glutamic acid decarboxylase, 59
Golgi tendon organs, 154, 155
Goodenough Draw-A-Man Test, 265
Gordon's leg sign, 207, 208, 209
Gradenigo's syndrome, 90
Graefe's disease, 89
Grand mal, 346
Granular layer of cerebellum, 39
Grasset and Gaussell sign, 207
Graves' disease, 337
Gray matter of spinal cord, 65
Greenfield's disease, 330
Guillain-Barré syndrome, 300
Guthrie inhibition assay test, 335
Gyrectomy, 196
Gyri, 2

Habenular trigone, 21
Hallervorden-Spatz disease, 331
Hallucinogens, 342
Hand, motor innervation of, 166
  muscles of, 188
Hand-Schüller-Christian disease,
  334
Hartnup's disease, 335
H disease, 335
Headache, 359
  classification of, 360
  differential diagnosis of, 365
Head injury, 302
  muscles, 186
  transillumination of, 270
Hearing loss, 96, 262, 263, 390
Heavy metal poisoning, 340
Hebephrenic schizophrenia, 380
Heel-to-shin test, 387
Heine-Medin disease, 299
Helwig's bundle, 67
Hemangioblastoma, 313
Hematoidin, 57
Hematoma(s), 252
  chronic subdural, 305
Hemeralopia, 85
Hemianopsia, 83
Hemiballism, 163
Hemiedema, 150
Hemiplegia, 158
  acute infantile, 293
  alternans, 159
  alternating abducent, 30
    hypoglossal, 33
    trigeminal, alternating, 31
Hemlock poisoning, 342
Hemofuscin, 57
Hemorrhage, brain, 277, 304, 305

Hemosiderin, 57
Hepatolenticular degeneration, 327
Herniation of intervertebral disk, 308
Herpes zoster, 195, 216
  thoracic, 124
Heubner's endarteritis, 293
Hindbrain, 60
Hip, motor innervation of, 167
Hippocampal commissure, 5
Hippocampus, 4
Hippus, 89
Hirschberg's sign, 207
Hirschsprung's disease, 149
Histamine test, 337, 363
Histaminic cephalalgia, 363
Hodgkin's disease, 333
Hoffmann's sign, 208, 338
Holmes-Adie syndrome, 84
Holmes's rebound phenomenon, 164
Homocystinuria, 335
Homosexuality, 382
Homotypical isocortex, 9
Hook bundle of Russell, 5, 39, 40
Hoover's sign, 207
Horn cell, anterior, 158
Horner's syndrome, 124, 147
Horton's syndrome, 363
Huntington's chorea, 327
  sign, 208
Hurler's disease, 334
Hydantoin poisoning, 341
Hydrocephalus, congenital, 269
Hydrophobia, 300
Hydroxyprolinemia, 335
Hypalgesia, 193
Hypaque, 251
Hyperesthesia, 193
Hyperglycinemia and hypergly-
  cinuria, idiopathic, 335
Hyperinsulinism, 338
Hyperkinesias, 161
Hyperosmia, 81
Hyperostosis, 247
Hyperpolarization, 69
Hyperprolinemia, familial, 335
Hypertension, benign intracranial,
  321
Hypertensive encephalopathy, 276
Hypesthesia, 193
Hypoglossal canal, 79
  hemiplegia alternans, 33, 105
Hypoinsulinism, 338
Hypophysectomy, 196
Hypotension, orthostatic, 355
Hypothalamic connections and
  nuclei, 22
Hypothalamus, 14, 18, 23
  of cat, diagram, 24
Hypotonia, 164
Hypsarrhythmia, 225
Hysteria, syncope in, 356

Idiocy, mongolism, 272
Idiomuscular activity, 161
Inadequate personalities, 382
Incontinence of urine, 259
Indusium griseum, 4
Infarct, pale, 277
  red, 277
Infections, pyogenic, 292
Infundibulum, 23
Inhibition, 73
Inhibitory area, 163
  center, 33
Inion, 243
Innervation, muscle, 166, 168
  ratio, 73

Innervation, Cont'd.
  segmental, extremities, 200, 201
  of skin, 190
Innominate canal, 79
Insula, 4, 14
Intelligence quotient, 271
Intercalated neuron, 204
Interoceptors, 189, 191
Intervertebral disk, herniation of,
  308
Intracranial aneurysm, 283
  pneumography, 247
  tumors, 313
Intrafusal fibers, 154
Involutional psychotic reaction, 379
Iodopyracet, 251
I.Q., 271
Ischemia, cerebral, 278
Island of Reil, 4, 14
Isocortex, 5
Isoniazid toxicity, 341

Jacksonian epilepsy, 348
Jackson's syndrome, 104
Jendrassik method of reinforce-
  ment, 205
Jolly's myasthenic reaction, 239
  position, 165
Juxtallocortex, 9

Kashida's thermic sign of tetany,
  338
Kernicterus, 333
Kernig's sign, 74, 289, 310
Kleine-Levin syndrome, 351
Klinefelter's syndrome, 267
Klippel-Feil syndrome, 272
  thumb sign, 208
Klumpke's paralysis, 114
Kojevnikoff's epilepsy, 348
Koniocortex, 9
Korsakoff's psychosis, 379
  syndrome, 341

Labyrinthitis, 353
Landry's paralysis, 300
Lasègue's sign, 132, 310
Lathyrism, 342
Laurence-Moon-Biedl syndrome,
  272
Lead poisoning, 340
Leber's disease, 330
Leg, motor innervation of, 167
  muscles of, 188
Lemniscus, medial, 25, 26, 29, 192
Lentiform nucleus, 15
Leptomeningitis, 289
Leri's sign, 208
Lermoyez's syndrome, 95
Leucine sensitivity disease, 335
Leukemia, 333
Leukodystrophy, 329
Leukoencephalopathy, meta-
  chromatic, 329
  multifocal, 330
Leukotomy, 13
Levy-Roussy syndrome, 329
Lid drop, 88
Lindau-Von Hippel syndrome, 272
Lipids, 56
Lipodystrophy, 149
Lipoidoses, 333
Little's disease, 270
Liver disorders, 339
Lobe(s), ansiformis, 39
  of cerebellum, 34
  flocculonodular, 39

Lobe(s), Cont'd.
  frontal, 1, 2, 3, 6, 10
  median, cerebellum, 37
  occipital, 2, 3, 6
  parietal, 2, 3, 6
  temporal, 2, 3, 4, 6
Lobotomy, 13, 196
Lobule, central, cerebellum, 37
  paracentral, 3
  posteromedian, 37
Lockjaw, 92
Locomotor ataxia, 294
Low back pain, 310
LSD, 342
Lumbar puncture, 221
Lupus erythematosus, 338
Luys, body of, 21
Lymphocytic choriomeningitis, 298
Lymphomas, 333

Macewen's sign, 270
Macroglobulinemia, 343
Make-A-Picture-Story-Test, 265
Mammillary bodies, 2, 22, 23, 25
Mandible, 244
Manganese poisoning, 340
Manic-depressive reaction, 379
Maple syrup disease, 335
MAPS, 265
Marchiafava-Bignami disease, 330
Marcus-Gunn syndrome, 94
Marie and Foix retraction sign, 208
Marin-Amat syndrome, 94
Masochism, 383
Massa intermedia, 19, 25, 41
Massive spasms, 348
Masticator root of trigeminal
  nerve, 76
Maxilla, 244
Mayer's sign, 208
McArdle's syndrome, 371
McCarthy's sign, 208
Meatus, internal acoustic, 79
Medulla oblongata, 27, 29, 31, 32, 78
Medullary lesions, 32
  syndromes, 32
Medulloblastoma, 315
Melanin, 56
Mendel-Bechterew sign, 207
Ménière's syndrome, 358
Meningeal headaches, 364
Meningioma, 252, 313, 316, 317
Meningitis, 289, 290, 293, 295, 297
Meningocele, 268
Meningomyelocele, 268
Mental retardation, 271
Meralgia paresthetica of Roth, 127
Mercury poisoning, 340
Mescaline, 342
Mesencephalon, 24, 59
Mesocortex, 9
Metencephalon, 60
Metrazol toxicity, 342
Meyer's loop, 82
Meynert, fountain decussation of, 26
Microelectrode recordings, EEG,
  225
Midbrain, 24, 25, 26, 59
  syndromes of, 28
Migraine, 360, 362
  ophthalmoplegic, 362
Millard-Gubler syndrome, 31
Milroy's disease, 149
Minamata disease, 340
Minnesota Multiphasic Personality
  Index, 265
Minor's sweat test, 217

Miotics, 88
Model psychoses, 342
Moebius' syndrome, 94, 376
Mongolism, 272
Monoplegia, 158
Morgagni-Morel-Stewart syndrome,
  340
Morphine poisoning, 341
Morquio's syndrome, 272
Morvan's syndrome, 150, 274
Motion, 156
  range of, 185
Motor area, 12
  supplementary, 214
  cortex, 158
  end plate, 70
  fibers, 106, 159
  function chart, 169
  innervation, 166, 167
  levels of the spinal cord, 108
  loss, 75
  or masticator portion of
    trigeminal nerve, 76
  neuron, lesions of, 156
    upper, 207
  points for electric stimulation,
    236
  power, disturbances in, 156
  projection cortex, primary, 7
  and sensory areas, supplemental,
    15
  speech (Broca's) area, 12
  system disease, 368
    examination of, 388
  units, 73, 232, 233
Multiple sclerosis, 194, 323
Muscle(s), 151
  of arm, 188
  congenital, absence of, 376
  contractures of, 367
  examination, charts, 184
  extractives, 151
  fast and slow, 152
  free nerve endings in, 155
  function of, 153
  functional tests of, 172
  of hand, 188
  of head and neck, 186
  innervation and testing, 166
  inorganic constituents of, 151
  of leg, 188
  metabolism of, 153
  neck, 186
  nerve fibers, 70
  ocular action of, 87
  proteins, 151
  receptors, 154
  red and white, 152
  smooth, 152
  spindles, 154
  strength, evaluation of, 367
  striated, 151
  structure of, 151
  superficial, of right extremities,
    188
  tests, 166
  tonus, 159
  of trunk, 187
  twitch, 367
Musculospiral nerve, 117, 118
Myasthenia gravis, 372
Myasthenic states, 89
Mydriatics, 88
Myelencephalon, 60
Myelogram, 322
Myelography, 254
Myelotomy, 196

Myoclonic jerks, 347
Myoclonus, 162
  epilepsy, 347
Myogen, 151
Myoglobin, 151
Myohemoglobinuria, 372
Myokymia, 367
Myopathies, 233, 370, 371
Myosin, 151
Myositis ossificans, 375
Myotonias, 233, 367, 374, 375
Myotonic reaction to electric
  stimulation, 239
Myxedema, 337

Naffziger's syndrome, 274
Narcolepsy, 351
Nasion, 242
Neocerebellum, 37, 39, 40
Neocortex, 5
Neonatal neurologic examination, 391
Neri's sign, 208
Nerve(s), abducens, 29, 76, 77,
    78, 86, 389
  nucleus of, 29
  accessory, 77, 78, 101, 390
  acoustic, 76, 78, 95
  action potentials, 69
  alveolar, 90
  anococcygeal, 137
  antebrachial cutaneous, 112,
    116, 117, 118
  auditory, 79
  auricular, great, 109, 110, 197,
    199
  auriculotemporal, 90, 142
  autonomic, 138
  axillary, 111, 116, 117, 169,
    174, 198, 199
  brachial cutaneous, lateral, 116
    medial, 112
  cardiac, 100, 138
  cervical, 109, 169
    cutaneous, 110
  cervicofacial, 92
  chorda tympani, 92, 142, 143
  circumflex, 116, 117
  clunical, 131
  cochlear, 31, 77, 95, 389
  complete section, 233
  cranial, 76, 77
    I, 76, 77, 81 | VII, 76, 77, 93
    II, 76, 77, 82 | VIII, 76, 77, 95
    III, 76, 77, 85 | IX, 76, 77, 97
    IV, 76, 77, 85 | X, 77, 78, 99
    V, 76, 77, 91 | XI, 77, 78, 101
    VI, 76, 77, 85 | XII, 77, 78, 102
    and arteries, 44
    components of, 77
    nuclei, 78
    paralysis, 306
  crural, anterior, 127
  cutaneous, 112
  deafness, 263, 390
  deep peroneal, 171
  descendens cervicalis, 103, 110
    hypoglossi, 103, 110
  dorsal, of penis, 137
    scapular, 169
  electrolytes, 71
  facial, 29, 76, 77, 78, 79, 93, 389
    lesions, 75, 107
    peripheral injuries, com-
      plete, 195
  femoral, 126, 127, 129, 168,
    171, 180
    cutaneous, anterior, 127, 131,
      199

Nerve(s), Cont'd.
  fiber(s), in muscle, 70
    structure of, 75
    types of, 68
      in mammalian nerve, 69
  frontal, 90
  function, 71
  gases, 72
  geniculotympanic, 142
  genitofemoral, 125, 127
  glossopalatinus, 93, 142
  glossopharyngeal, 76, 77, 78,
    79, 97, 98, 390
  gluteal, 129, 131, 175, 181, 182
  hemorrhoidal, inferior, 137
  hypoglossal, 42, 77, 78, 79, 102,
    103, 390
    paralysis, 103
  iliohypogastric, 125, 198, 199
  ilioinguinal, 125, 198
  infraorbital, 90
  infratrochlear, 90
  intercostobrachial cutaneous, 198
  of Jacobson, 97
  laryngeal, 100
  lingual, 90
  long thoracic, 114
  lumbar, 124
  lumboinguinal, 198
  mandibular, 90
  maxillary, 90
  median, 111, 112, 119, 120, 170,
    177, 178, 198, 199
    lesions, 123
  musculocutaneous, 111, 112, 115,
    116, 169, 175
  musculospiral, 117, 118
  mylohyoid, 90
  obturator, 125, 126, 128, 171,
    181, 198, 199
  occipital, 109, 110, 197
  oculomotor, 25, 76, 78, 86, 389
  olfactory, 76, 77, 78, 79, 81, 388
  ophthalmic, 90
  optic, 26, 76, 77, 78, 79, 82, 389
  palatine, 82
  parasympathetic, 140, 141
  pelvic, 140, 141
  perineal, 137
  peripheral, 106
  peroneal, 136, 168
    common, 129, 130, 133, 134,
      136, 198, 199
    deep, 133, 134, 168
    superficial, 133, 168, 171
  petrosal, 79, 92, 142
  phrenic, 110, 169
  plantar, 135, 136, 199, 388
  popliteal, 135
  pudendal, 137, 171
  radial, 111, 117, 118, 170, 175,
    176, 198
  rami, communicating, 138
  recurrent laryngeal, 99
  sacral, 128
  saphenous, 126, 198, 199
  scapular, dorsal, 112, 114, 173
  sciatic, 129, 130, 131, 171, 182
  sinus, carotid, 97
  spinal, 106
    accessory, 79, 172
    roots and, 67
  splanchnic, 138
  suboccipital, 109
  subscapular, 111, 169, 174
  supraclavicular, 110, 198, 199
  supraorbital, 90

Nerve(s), Cont'd.
  suprascapular, 112, 114, 169, 173
  supratrochlear, 90
  sural, 133, 134
  sympathetic, 138
  temporofacial, 92
  thoracic, 112, 114, 115, 123,
    169, 173
  thoracodorsal, 111, 115
  tibial, 129, 130, 135, 136, 171,
    182, 199
  trigeminal, 27, 76, 77, 78, 79,
    90, 91, 197, 389
  trochlear, 30, 76, 77, 78, 80,
    88, 389
  trunk(s), electric stimulation of,
    239
    peripheral, components of, 75
  tympanic, of Jacobson, 98, 142
  ulnar, 111, 112, 121, 122, 169,
    170, 178, 179, 199
    lesions of, 123
  vagus, 32, 77, 78, 79, 99, 140, 390
  vestibular, 77, 95, 390
  vidian, 82, 92, 142
  of Wrisberg, 93
Nervus erigens, 140
  intermedius, 92, 95
Neural crest, 60
  tissue composition, 55
Neuralgia, 195, 343
  glossopharyngeal, 97
  trifacial, 344
  trigeminal, 344
Neuraxes, effector systems in, 157
Neurectomy, 196
Neurinoma, 313
  acoustic, 317
Neuritis, 195, 342, 343
  bulbar, 84
  optic, 84
  retrobulbar, 84
Neurochemistry, cellular, 5, 6
Neurodiagnosis, principles of, 156
Neuroendocrine disorders, 336
Neurofibromatosis, 272
Neurogenic arthropathy, 216
  bladder, 258
Neurohypophysis, 23
Neurologic examination, 385
  neonatal, 391
Neuromas, 313
Neuromuscular disorders, 366
  clinical features of, 366
  congenital, 376
  transmission, 153
Neuromyelitis optica, 329
Neurons, fine chemical anatomy
  of, 57
  types of, 204
Neuropath(ies), 342
  congenital, 376
  in uremia, 339
Neuroses, 380
Neurosyphilis, 293
Neurotoxins, bacterial, 301
NFR, 235
Niacin deficiency, 340
Niemann-Pick disease, 334
Night blindness, 85
Nikethamide toxicity, 342
Nissl bodies, 56
Nitrous oxide study of brain
  circulation, 51
Normal formula of response, 235
Nucle(i) of abducens nerve, 29, 80
  of accessory nerve, 80

Nucle(i), Cont'd.
  of acoustic nerve, 80
  ambiguus, 32, 80, 98, 100
  amygdaloid, 14, 15, 16, 41
  caudate, 14, 16
  of cerebellum, 38
  of cochlear nerve, 31
  of cranial nerves, 78, 80
    in the pons, 29
  cuneatus, 32
  of Darkschewitsch, 28
  Deiters', 39
  dentate, 38, 39
  dorsalis, 65
    accessory olivary, 32
  Edinger-Westphal, 80
  emboliform, 38, 39
  facial nerve, 29, 80
  fastigial, 38, 39
  globose, 38, 39
  gracilis, 32
  habenular, 21
  hypoglossal, 32, 80, 103
  hypothalamic, 23
  inferior olivary, 32
  interpeduncular, 18
  interpositus, 38
  lentiform, 16
  medial accessory olivary, 32
  of mesencephalic root of
    trigeminal nerve, 26
  of oculomotor nerve, 26, 80
  paraventricular, 23
  pontine, 29
  pulposus, herniation of, 308
  red, 21, 25, 26, 28, 39, 164
  salivatorius, 32, 80, 92
  of spinal tract of trigeminal
    nerve, 32
  subthalamic, 21
  supraoptic, 23
  thalamic, 18
  of tractus solitarius, 32, 80, 92,
    98
  of trigeminal nerve, 29, 80, 90
  of trochlear nerve, 26, 80
  of vagus nerve, 32, 80
  of vestibular nerve, 31
Nyctalopia, 85
Nystagmus, 88, 89, 96, 164

Obex, 30
Objective psychometric tests, 264
Obsessive-compulsive reaction, 381
Occipital bone, 243
Occlusion, arterial, 276, 277
  phenomenon, 73
Oculogyric spasm, 162
Olfactory bulb, 4, 81
  receptive area, 13
  trigone, 4, 81
Oligodendroglioma, 315
Olivocerebellar atrophy, 328
Olivopontocerebellar atrophy, 328
Opercula of insula, 4
Ophthalmodynamometry, 53
Ophthalmoplegia(s), 89
  external, congenital, 376
Ophthalmoplegic migraine, 362
Opisthotonos, 165
Oppenheim's disease, 368, 374
  sign, 207
Optic atrophy, 84
  chiasm, 2, 14, 23, 25, 81
  neuritis, 84
Orgasm, 146
Orthostatic hypotension, 355

Osler-Vasquez disease, 333
Osteitis deformans, 339
    fibrosa cystica, 338
Otorrhea, 306

Paget's disease, 339
Pain, 191, 193, 387
    back, low, 310
    deep, segmental areas of, 203
Pale infarct, 277
Paleocerebellum, 37, 39, 40
Palsy, Bell's, 93
    bulbar, 158, 368
    cerebral, 269
    facial, 94
    infantile cerebral, 270
        pseudobulbar, 279
PAM, 72
Papilledema, 84
Paracentral lobule, 3
Parakoniocortex, 9
Paralysis agitans, 324
    of eye muscles, individual, 87
    family periodic, 371
    flaccid, 7
    types of, 158
Paramyotonia congenita, 375
Paranoid personalities, 382
    schizophrenia, 380
Paraphasia, 213
Paraplegia, 159
    familial spastic, 328
Parathyroid tetany, 337
Paratrigeminal syndrome, 91
Paresis, general, 294
Paresthesia, 193
Parietal bone, 242
Parinaud's syndrome, 28, 29
Parkinsonism, 161
Parkinson's syndrome, 324
Parosmia, 81
Paroxysmal labyrinthine vertigo, 358
Passive-aggressive personalities,
    382
Passive motion, 387
Pathway, final common, 156
Patrick's f-ab-er-e sign, 132, 310
Pederasty, 383
Peduncle(s), cerebellar, 29, 163
    cerebral, 25, 26, 30
Pellagra, 340
Pelvic nerve, 140
Pentylenetetrazol toxicity, 342
Perforated substance, anterior, 4
Periaqueductal gray matter, 25
Periarteritis nodosa, 338
Perimetry, 85
Periosteo-radial reflex, 206
Peripheral facial paralysis, 93
Personalit(ies), compulsive, 382
    cyclothymic, 382
    disorders, 381
    disturbances, sociopathic, 382
    emotionally unstable, 382
    inadequate, 382
    paranoid, 382
    passive-aggressive, 382
    schizoid, 382
    trait disturbances, 382
Petit mal, 347
Phase reversal, 227
Phenylpyruvic oligophrenia, 334
Pheochromocytoma, 337
Phobic reaction, 381
Phosphocreatine, 153
Photic driving, 223
Pia mater, 62

Pick's disease, 324
Picrotoxin toxicity, 342
Pineal body, 23, 25, 30
    recess, 23
Pinealoma, 317
Pituitary adenoma, 316
    cachexia, 336
    dwarfism, 336
    syndromes, 336
    tumors of, 318
Plasma lipid disturbance of Bigler,
    334
Plasticity, 34
Plate, neural, 59
Platybasia, 274
Plexus(es), basilar, 49
    brachial, 111, 112, 113
        injuries, 114
    cardiac, 100, 140, 141
    celiac, 140, 141
    cervical, 109, 110
    choroid, 14
        of fourth ventricle, 43, 219
        of third ventricle, 219
    coccygeal, 135, 137
    esophageal, 140
    great prevertebral, of
        autonomics, 141
    hypogastric, 139, 140, 141
    lumbar, 125
    pudendal, 135
    pulmonary, 100, 140, 141
    sacral, 129
    solar, 141
Plurosthotonus, 164
Pneumococcic meningitis, 289
Pneumoencephalography, 247
Pneumography, intracranial, 247
Poliomyelitis, acute anterior, 299
Polycythemia vera, 333
Polymyositis, 372
Polyneuritis, 342
Polyneuropathy in uremia, 339
Pons, 25, 27, 29
    syndromes of, 31
Pontine hemorrhage, 286
    syndromes, 30
Pontocerebellar angle tumor
        syndrome, 30, 31
Pool's arm and leg signs of tetany,
    338
Popliteal nerve, 135
Porphyria, 339
Porteus maze test, 265
Position, sense of, 194, 387
Posterolateral sclerosis, 195, 332,
    340
Post-traumatic syndrome, 306
Postural reactions, 34
Postures, 165
Potentials, action, 69, 70
    denervation fibrillation, 233
    nerve fiber, 69
Precuneus, 3
Pressure, sensation of, 192
Projective tests, 265
Proprioception, 191, 192
Proprioceptors, 189
Propulsion, 165
Prosencephalon, 59
Proteins of nervous tissue, 56
Pseudobulbar palsy, 279
Pseudosclerosis, spastic, 331
Pseudotumor cerebri, 321
Psilocybin, 342
Psychiatric disorders, 378
Psychic blindness, 85

Psychologic terms, 383, 384
Psychometric tests, 264
Psychomotor seizures, 347
Psychoses, 379
    "model," 342
Psychotic-depressive reaction, 379
Ptosis, 88, 89
    congenital, 376
Pulseless disease, 278
Pulvinar, 19
Pure tone threshold, 263
Purkinje cells of cerebellum, 39
Purpura, thrombocytopenic, 333
Putamen, 14, 15, 16, 162
Pyridine-2-aldoxime methiodide, 72
Pyridoxine deficiency, 340

Quadrantanopsia, 83
Quadriplegia, 159
Queckenstedt's test, 221
Quincke's disease, 149
Quinine toxicity, 341
Quinquaud's sign, 341

Rabies, 300
Radiculopathies, congenital, 376
Radioactive isotope studies, 320
Radioisotopic encephalography, 253
Radiologic examination, 241
Raeder's syndrome, 91
Raimiste's leg sign, 208
Rami communicantes, 107
Ramsay Hunt syndrome, 94
Raymond-Cestan syndrome, 31
Raynaud's disease, 149
R. D. (reaction of degeneration), 238
Rebound phenomenon, 387
    of Holmes, 164
Recess, optic, 41
    pineal, 41
Recklinghausen's disease, 272
Red infarct, 277
    nucleus, 164
Reflex(es), 204, 387
    abdominal, 205, 206, 388
    Achilles tendon, 205, 206
    accommodation, 206, 207
    allied, 74
    anal, 205, 206
    anatomy of, 204
    ankle, 388
    antagonistic, 74
    arc, 204
    Babinski, 209
    biceps, 205, 206, 388
    bladder, 145, 206, 207
    bulbocavernosus, 206, 207
    carotid sinus, 97, 206, 207
    Chaddock, 209
    ciliospinal, 206, 207
    conjunctival, 205
    consensual light, 207
    corneal, 205, 206
    cremasteric, 205, 206, 388
    deep, 205, 206, 388
    epilepsy, 348
    extensor, 74, 209
    flexion, 73
    flexor, 74
    gag, 205
    gluteal, 205
    Gonda, 209
    Gordon, 209
    heart block, 356
    integration of, 34
    interscapular, 205
    jaw jerk, 205, 206

Reflex(es), Cont'd.
  Jendrassik method of rein-
      forcement, 205
  knee jerk, 205, 388
  light, 90, 205, 206
  Magnus-de Kleijn tonic neck, 34
  mass, 74, 207
  maxillary, 205
  muscle stretch, 367
  nasal, 205, 206
  nociceptive, 74
  oculocardiac, 206, 207
  Oppenheim, 209
  patellar, 205, 206
  pathologic, 207
  periosteo-radial and -ulnar, 205,
      206
  pharyngeal, 205, 206
  plantar, 205, 206, 209, 388
  postural, 34
  pupillary, 205
  rectal, 206, 207
  righting, 34
  Schaefer, 207
  segmental spinal, 73
  sneeze, 205, 206
  Stransky, 207
  stretch, 74, 155
  summary of, 206
  superficial, 205, 206, 388
  tonic labyrinthine, 34
      neck, 34
  triceps, 205, 206, 388
  types of, 204
  uvular, 205, 206
  visceral, 205, 206
  Westphal's sign, 205
  wrist, 205, 206
Refsum's syndrome, 343
Rehabilitation charts, 395
Reichert's syndrome, 97
Reid's base line, skull, 241, 246
Reil, island of, 14
Respiratory center, 34
Restiform body, 39, 164
Restless legs syndrome, 195
Retardation, mental, 271
Reticular activating system, 34
  formation, 28, 35, 65
  substance, 25, 32
Rheobase, 69, 235
Rhinencephalon, 4, 13, 15
Rhinorrhea, 306
Rhizotomy, 196
Rhombencephalon, 60
Rhythms, EEG, 226, 227
Ribonucleic acid, 56
Rigidity, 160, 161
  decerebrate, 33
Riley-Day syndrome, 150
Rinne's test, 96, 262, 390
RNA, 56
Rods and cones of retina, 82
Roentgenography of the skull, 241
Rolando, fissure of, 1, 3
  substantia gelatinosa of, 65
Romberg's sign, 149, 295
  test, 386
Root(s), and nerves, spinal, 67
  pains, 195
Rorschach test, 265
Rossolimo's sign, 207
Russell, hook bundle of, 5, 39, 40

Sadism, 383
Salivatory nuclei, 92
Sardonic smile, 165

Scapula, winged, 114, 115
Schaefer's sign, 209
Schilder's disease, 329
Schizoid personalities, 382
Schizophrenia, 380
  childhood, 271
Schlesinger's leg sign of tetany, 338
Schmidt's syndrome, 104
Schultze's tongue dimpling sign of
      tetany, 338
Schwabach's test, 262
Scleroderma, 149
Sclerosis, amyotrophic lateral,
      234, 369
  diffuse, 330
  multiple, 194, 323
  posterolateral, 332
  tuberous, 272
Scotomas, 85
Seasickness, 95
Secondary motor and sensory
      areas, 13
Segmental innervation, 200
Semantic aphasia, 210
Senile degeneration, 324
  plaques, 324
Sensation, 189
Sensory areas, 13
  distribution, 199
  disturbances, 75, 193
  fibers, 106
  modalities and sense organs, 189
  projection cortex, primary, 7
Sentence completion test, 265
Septum, dorsal median, 63
  pellucidum, 14, 25
Sernyl, 342
Serotonin, 59
Serum reactions, 339
Sex chromosomes, 266
Sexual deviation, 382
  function, 146
Sham rage, 24
Shock, spinal, 74
Shoulder-hand syndrome, 311
Shoulder, high, congenital, 376
  motor innervation of, 166
Sicard's syndrome, 105
Sickle cell anemia, 333
Simmonds' disease, 336
Simple schizophrenia, 380
Sinus(es), cavernous, 43
  inferior petrosal, 43
  intercavernous, 43
  occipital, 49
  petrosal, 43
  right, 49
  sagittal, 42
  straight, 43, 256
  superior longitudinal, 43
  transverse, 43
  venous, 256
Skew deviation of the eyes, 164
Skin, innervation of, 190
Skull, anatomy of, 242, 243, 244,
      245
  fracture, 304, 306
  roentgenography of, 241
Sleep records, EEG, 225
Smell, disturbances of, 81, 82
Snake venoms, 342
Sociopathic personality disturb-
      ances, 382
Souques' sign, 208
Spasmodic torticollis, 331
Spasms, habit, 162
Spasticity, 160, 163

Spastic pseudosclerosis, 331
Speech areas of brain, 214
  audiometry, 263
Sphincterometry, 258
Spina bifida, 267
  occulta, 267, 268
Spinal canal, tumors within, 321
  cord, 60, 62, 63, 64, 66, 68, 158
    dorsal roots, 67
    injuries, 308
    motor and sensory levels of,
        108
    thoracic, levels, 124
  shock, 74, 149
Spine, cervical, sprain of, 311
  roentgenography of, 254
Spondylosis, cervical, 311
Spongioblastoma, 318
Sprengel's deformity, 376
Squint, 88
Stammering and stuttering, 313
Stanford-Binet Intelligence Test, 265
Status dysmyelinatus, 331
  epilepticus, 348
  marmoratus, 331
Stereognosis, 387
Sterling's sign, 208
Stewart-Holmes rebound phenom-
      enon, 164
Stiff man syndrome, 375
Stimulant, drug intoxication, 342
Stimulation, double, 194
Stokes-Adams syndrome, 355
Strabismus, 88, 89
Strength duration curves, 239
Streptomycin toxicity, 341
Stria lateralis, 81
Strokes, treatment of, 281, 283
Strümpell's pronation sign, 208
  tibialis anterior sign, 208
Strychnine poisoning, 342
Sturge-Weber syndrome, 246, 272
Stuttering and stammering, 213
Subarachnoid hemorrhage, 278,
      304, 308
  space, 42
Subdural hematoma, 305
  hemorrhage, 304
Substance, perforated, 81
Substantia alba, 65
  gelatinosa, or Rolando, 65
  grisea, 65
  nigra, 21, 25, 26
Subthalamus, 21
Sulc(i), central, 1
  cingulate, 1, 25
  dorsal (posterior) median, 63
  dorsolateral, 63
  lateral occipital, 2
  posterior median, 62
  posterolateral, 62
  ventrolateral, 63
Summation, spatial and temporal, 73
Superficial reflexes, 206
Suppression, 7
Suppressor and facilitatory
      systems, 163
Suture, coronal, 244
  lambdoid, 243
  sagittal, 244
Sweating, 26
  thermoregulatory, 218
Sylvius, aqueduct of, 25, 42, 43,
      219
  fissure of, 1, 3, 246, 248
Sympathectomy, 196
Sympathetic ganglion, 138

Sympathin, 147
Synapse, 73
Synaptic transmission, 72
Synchiria, 193
Syncope, 353
  cough, 356
Synergy, disturbances in, 163
Synesthesia, 193
Syringomyelia, 194, 195, 216, 273

Tabes dorsalis, 194, 216, 294
Takayasu's syndrome, 278
Tapia's syndrome, 33, 105
Taste area, cortical, 10
TAT, 265
Tay-Sachs disease, 84, 334
Tegmentum, of midbrain, 26
Tela choroidea, 41
Telangiectasia, ataxia, 329
Teleceptors, 189, 191
Telencephalon, 60
Temperature sense, 191, 387
Temporal arteritis, 338
Tension headaches, 364
Tentorium cerebelli, 37
Teratomas, 313
Tetanic reaction to electric
    stimulation, 239
Tetanus, 153, 301
Tetany, parathyroid, 337
  signs of, 338
Tetraplegia, 159
Thalamic apoplexy, 19
  radiation, 19
  syndrome, 19
Thalamocortical interrelations, 21
  projections, 20
Thalamotomy, 13, 196
Thalamus, 14, 16, 18, 19, 25, 30, 162
  lesions of, 194
  massa intermedia of, 32
Thallium poisoning, 340
Thematic Apperception Test, 265
Thermoregulatory sweating, 218
Theta rhythm, EEG, 227
Thiamine deficiency, 340
Thigh, motor innervation of, 167
Thomsen's disease, 375
Thoracic cord levels, 124
Thorium dioxide, 251
Thorotrast, 251
Thrombocytopenic purpura, 333
Thrombophlebitis, 292
Thrombosis, 276, 279, 280
Thymectomy, 374
Thymoma, 374
Thyroid syndromes, 337
Thyrotoxic myopathy, 337
Tic(s), 162
  douloureux, 91, 344
Tinnitus, 96
Toe-finger test, 387
Topectomy, 13
Topognosis, 387
Torcular Herophili, 49
Torsion spasm, 331
Torticollis, congenital, 376
  spasmodic, 331
Touch, sensation of, 192, 387
Toxoplasmic encephalitis, 298
Tract(s), ascending, spinal cord, 67
  of Burdach, 67
  comma, of Schultze, 67
  corticospinal, 29, 64
  descending, spinal cord, 67
  dorsal spinocerebellar, 32, 40, 67
  frontopontine, 26

Tract(s), Cont'd.
  of Goll, 67
  of Meynert, retroflex, 23
  olfactory, 4, 81
  olivocerebellar, 40, 192
  olivospinal, 64, 67
  optic, 78
  parietotemporopontine, 29
  reticulospinal, 66, 163
  retroflex, of Meynert, 23
  rubrospinal, 26, 64, 67, 164
  of Schultze, comma, 67
  septomarginal, 67
  spinocerebellar, 32, 37, 49, 64,
    192
  spino-olivary, 64, 66, 192
  spinotectal, 67
  spinothalamic, lateral, 25, 27,
    64, 66, 67, 191
    ventral, 64, 192
  tectospinal, 27, 64, 65
  temporopontine, 26
  of trigeminal nerve, spinal, 32
  ventral corticospinal, 65
    spinocerebellar, 29, 32, 40,
      67
    spinothalamic, 66
    vestibulospinal, 64
  vestibulocerebellar, 40
  vestibulospinal, 66
Tractotomy, 196
Tractus solitarius, 100
Tranquilizers, toxic reactions to,
  342
Transillumination of head, 270
Transverse (commissural) fibers, 5
  localization, in spinal cord, 64
Transvestism, 382
Trapezoid body, 27, 29
Tremors, 161
Trifacial neuralgia, 91, 344
Trigeminal angiomatosis, 246
  hemiplegia, alternating, 31
  neuralgia, 91, 344
Trismus, 92
Trisomy, 267
Trophedema, hereditary, 149
Trophic changes, 215
  disturbances, 75
Trophoneuroses, 149, 216
Trousseau's sign of tetany, 338
Tube, neural, 59
Tuber cinereum, 23, 81
Tuberculoma, 296
Tuberculous meningitis, 295
Tuberous sclerosis, 272
Tubular vision, 83
Tumors of central nervous system,
  313
  extramedullary, 321
Tuning fork tests of hearing, 262,
  263
Türck's bundle, 29
Turner's syndrome, 267
Two-point discrimination, 194, 387
Tympanic nerve of Jacobson, 98, 142

Ultrasonic electroencephalography,
  320
Uncinate fasciculus, 5, 39, 40
  gyrus fits, 82
Uncus, 3
Unverricht's familial myoclonic
  epilepsy, 347
Upper motor neuron, lesions of, 156
Urea, I.V., 358
Uremia, 339

Urinary bladder, 143, 144
Urine, incontinence of, 259
Urokon, 251

Vail's syndrome, 143
Valium, 271, 375
Vascular tumors, 313
Vein(s), anastomotic, small, 43
  basal, of Rosenthal, 43, 256
  cerebral, 42, 43, 256
  great anastomotic, 43
    cerebral, 42
    of Galen, 43, 256
  jugular, external, 43
  of Labbé, anastomotic, 43
  of Rosenthal, basal, 256
  of Trolard, great anastomotic, 43
Velum, anterior medullary, 43
Venograms, 256
Ventricle(s), 41
  fourth, 25, 36, 37, 41, 42, 43
  lateral, 14, 16, 41
  third, 14, 30, 41, 219
Ventricular system, 42, 250
Ventriculogram, 249
Ventriculography, 320
Vermis, 37, 39
Vernet's rideau phenomenon, 97
  syndrome, 105
Vertebral arteriogram, 256
Vertigo, 96, 164
  paroxysmal labyrinthine, 358
Vibration sense, 387
Villaret's syndrome, 105
Visceral brain, 15
Vision, macular, 10
Visual acuity, 85
  apparatus, lesions of, 84
  cortex (striate), principal, 12
  field charts, 391
    defects of, 83
  receptive cortex, primary, 10
Vitamin B complex deficiencies, 340
Vocalization, 212
Vogt's disease, 331
Voice tests of hearing, 262
Volkmann's ischemic contracture,
  216
Von Economo's disease, 297
Von Gierke's disease, 336
Von Graefe's disease, 89
Von Hippel-Lindau syndrome, 272
Von Recklinghausen's disease, 272
Voyeurism, 382

WAIS, 264
Waldenström's primary macro-
  globulinemia, 343
Walking test, 386
Wallenberg's syndrome, 33, 105
Watch tick tests of hearing, 262
Waterhouse-Friderichsen
  syndrome, 337
Wave-and-spike, EEG, 227
Weber's syndrome, 28, 29
  test, 96, 262, 390
Wechsler Adult Intelligence Scale,
  264
Wechsler-Bellevue Intelligence
  Test, 264
Wechsler Intelligence Test for
  Children, 264
Werdnig-Hoffmann atrophy, 368
  paralysis, 368
Wernicke's aphasia, 210
  area, 214
  syndrome, 341

Westphal's sign, 295
Whiplash injury, 311
White matter of spinal cord, 65
  substance, 5
Willis, circle of, 43, 45
Wilson's disease, 161, 327
WISC, 264

Witzelsucht, 13
Wrist drop, 118
Wryneck, 331

Xanthochromia, 221
Xanthomatosis, cranial, 334
X-rays of skull, plain, 241

Yeast meningitis, 297
Young-Helmholtz theory of light
  perception, 83

Zona incerta, 21

SELECTED REFERENCE TEXTBOOKS

Clinical Neurology.

Alpers, B. J.: Clinical Neurology, 5th Ed. Davis, 1963.

Baker, A. B.: Clinical Neurology, 2nd Ed. Hoeber, 1962.

Bing, R., and Haymaker, W.: Local Diagnosis in Neurological Disorders. Mosby, 1956.

Brain, R.: Clinical Neurology. Oxford, 1961

Brain, R.: Diseases of the Nervous System, 6th Ed. Oxford, 1962.

Brock, S., and Krieger, H. P.: The Basis of Clinical Neurology, 4th Ed. Williams & Wilkins, 1963.

DeJong, R. N.: Neurologic Examination, 2nd Ed. Hoeber, 1958.

Denny-Brown, D.: Handbook of Neurological Examination and Case Recording, 2nd Ed. Harvard, 1957.

Ford, F. R.: Diseases of the Nervous System in Infancy, Childhood and Adolescence, 4th Ed. Thomas, 1959.

Gardner, E.: Fundamentals of Neurology, 4th Ed. Saunders, 1963.

Goldstein, K.: Language and Language Disturbances. Grune & Stratton, 1948.

Grinker, R. C., Bucy, P. C., and Sahs, A. L. Neurology, 5th Ed. Thomas, 1960.

Holmes, G.: Introduction to Clinical Neurology, 2nd Ed. Williams & Wilkins, 1952.

Lamm, S. S.: Pediatric Neurology. Appleton, 1959.

Mayo Clinic: Clinical Examinations in Neurology, 2nd Ed. Saunders, 1963.

Merritt, H. H.: A Textbook of Neurology, 3rd Ed. Lea & Febiger, 1963.

Monrad-Krohn, G. H.: Clinical Examination of the Nervous System, 11th Ed. Hoeber, 1958.

Nielsen, J. M.: A Textbook of Clinical Neurology, 3rd Ed. Hoeber, 1951.

Penfield, W., and Jasper, H.: Epilepsy and Functional Anatomy of the Human Brain. Little, Brown, 1954.

Walshe, F. M. R.: Diseases of the Nervous System, 10th Ed. Williams & Wilkins, 1963.

Walton, J. N.: Essentials of Neurology. Lippincott, 1961.

Wartenberg, R.: Diagnostic Tests in Neurology. Year Book, 1953.

Wechsler, I. S.: A Textbook of Clinical Neurology, 9th Ed. Saunders, 1963.

Weisenberg, T. H., and McBride, K. E.: Aphasia. Oxford, 1935.

Wilson, S. A. K.: Neurology, 2nd Ed. Williams & Wilkins, 1955.

Neuroanatomy.

Bailey, P., and von Bonin, G.: The Isocortex of Man. Univ. Illinois, 1951.

Buchanan, A. R.: Functional Neuroanatomy, 4th Ed. Lea & Febiger, 1961.

Crosby, E., Humphrey, T., and Lauer, E.: Correlative Anatomy of the Nervous System. Macmillan, 1962.

Hausman, L.: Clinical Neuroanatomy, Neurophysiology, and Neurology. Thomas, 1958.

House, E. L., and Pansky, B.: A Functional Approach to Neuroanatomy. Blakiston-McGraw, 1960.

Krieg, W. J. S.: Functional Neuroanatomy, 2nd Ed. Blakiston-McGraw, 1953.

Krieg, W. J. S.: Brain Mechanisms in Diachrome, 2nd Ed. Brain Books, 1957.

Kuntz, A.: The Autonomic Nervous System, 4th Ed. Lea & Febiger, 1953.

Mettler, F. A.: Neuroanatomy, 2nd Ed. Mosby, 1948.

Papez, J. W.: Comparative Neurology. Hafner, 1961.

Peele, T. L.: The Neuroanatomical Basis for Clinical Neurology, 2nd Ed. Blakiston-McGraw, 1961.

Ranson, S. W., and Clark, S. L.: The Anatomy of the Nervous System, 10th Ed. Saunders, 1959.

Truex, R. C.: Strong and Elwyn's Human Neuroanatomy, 4th Ed. Williams & Wilkins, 1959.

White, J. C., Smithwick, R. H., and Simeone, F. A.: The Autonomic Nervous System, 3rd Ed. Macmillan, 1952.

Neuroradiology.

Davidoff, L. M., and Dyke, C.: The Normal Encephalogram, 3rd Ed. Lea & Febiger, 1951.

Davidoff, L. M., and Epstein, B. S.: The Abnormal Pneumoencephalogram, 2nd Ed. Lea & Febiger, 1955.

Davidoff, L. M., Jacobson, H. G., and Zimmermann, H. M.: Neuroradiology

Workshop, Vols. I and II. Grune & Stratton, 1961, 1963.

Di Chiro, G.: An Atlas of Detailed Normal Pneumoencephalographic Anatomy. Thomas, 1958.

Ecker, A.: The Normal Cerebral Angiogram. Thomas, 1951.

Epstein, B.S., and Davidoff, L.M.: An Atlas of Skull Roentgenograms. Lea & Febiger, 1953.

Orley, A.: Neuroradiology. Thomas, 1949.

Pendergrass, E.P., Schaeffer, J.P., and Hodes, P.J.: The Head and Neck in Roentgen Diagnosis, 2nd Ed. Thomas, 1956.

Ritvo, M.: Roentgen Diagnosis of Diseases of the Skull. Hoeber, 1949.

Robertson, E.G.: Pneumoencephalography. Thomas, 1957.

Wilson, M.C.: The Anatomical Foundation of Neuroradiology of the Brain. Little, Brown, 1963.

Neuropathology.

Adams, R.D., Denny-Brown, D., and Pearson, C.M.: Diseases of Muscle, 2nd Ed. Hoeber, 1962.

Bailey, P.: Intracranial Tumors, 2nd Ed. Thomas, 1948.

Bailey, P., and Cushing, H.: A Classification of Tumors of the Glioma Group. Lippincott, 1926.

Biggart, J.H.: Pathology of the Nervous System, 3rd Ed. Williams & Wilkins, 1961.

Courville, C.B.: Pathology of the Central Nervous System, 3rd Ed. San Lucas, 1950.

Dekaban, A.: Neurology of Infancy. Williams & Wilkins, 1959.

Greenfield, J.G.: Neuropathology. Williams & Wilkins, 1958.

Hassin, G.B.: Histopathology of the Peripheral and Central Nervous Systems. Wood, 1933.

Innes, J.R.M., and Saunders, L.Z.: Comparative Neuropathology. Academic, 1962.

Lichtenstein, B.: Neuropathology. Saunders, 1949.

Malamud, N.: Atlas of Neuropathology. Univ. California, 1957.

Merritt, H.H., and Fremont-Smith, F.: The Cerebrospinal Fluid. Saunders, 1937.

Russell, D.S., and Rubinstein, L.J.: Pathology of Tumours of the Nervous System. Williams & Wilkins, 1959.

Weil, A.: Textbook of Neuropathology, 2nd Ed. Grune & Stratton, 1945.

Zimmermann, H., Netsky, M., and

Davidoff, L.M.: Atlas of Tumors of the Nervous System. Lea & Febiger, 1956.

Zülch, K.: Brain Tumors. Springer, 1957.

Neurophysiology.

Bard, P.: Medical Physiology, 11th Ed. Mosby, 1961.

Brazier, M.A.B.: The Electrical Activity of the Nervous System, 2nd Ed. Macmillan, 1960.

Bucy, P.C.: The Precentral Motor Cortex. Univ. Illinois, 1944.

Chatfield, P.: Fundamentals of Clinical Neurophysiology. Thomas, 1956.

Eccles, J.C.: The Physiology of Nerve Cells. Johns Hopkins, 1957.

Fulton, J.F.: Physiology of the Nervous System, 3rd Ed. Oxford, 1949.

Fulton, J.F.: Textbook of Physiology, 17th Ed. Oxford, 1955.

Ganong, W.F.: Review of Medical Physiology. Lange, 1963.

Magoun, H.W.: Handbook of Physiology. Section I: Neurophysiology. Williams & Wilkins, 1959.

Ruch, T. et al.: Neurophysiology. Saunders, 1961.

Sherrington, Sir Charles: The Integrative Action of the Nervous System. Yale, 1906.

Walsh, F.B.: Physiology of the Nervous System. Little, Brown, 1958.

Neuro-ophthalmology.

Adler, F.H.: Physiology of the Eye, 3rd Ed. Mosby, 1959.

Bender, M., ed.: The Oculomotor System. Hoeber, 1963.

Cogan, D.C.: Neurology of the Ocular Muscles, 2nd Ed. Thomas, 1956.

Duke-Elder, W.S.: System of Ophthalmology, Vol. 2. Mosby, 1961.

Kestenbaum, A.: Methods of Neuro-ophthalmologic Examination. Grune & Stratton, 1961.

Lyle, D.J.: Neuro-ophthalmology, 2nd Ed. Thomas, 1954.

Spiegel, E.A., and Somner, I.: Neurology of the Eye, Ear, Nose and Throat. Grune & Stratton, 1944.

Walsh, F.B.: Clinical Neuro-ophthalmology, 2nd Ed. Williams & Wilkins, 1957.

Electroencephalography.

Cohn, R.: Clinical Electroencephalography. Blakiston-McGraw, 1949.

Fois, A.: The Electroencephalogram of the Normal Child. Thomas, 1961.